15.00

D1543279

中國森林植物學續篇
Forest Botany of China
Supplement

李 順 卿 著

by

Shun-ching Lee

中華民國六十二年十一月卅日

November 30, 1973

PREFACE

It has been popularily recognized that the flora of China is one of the richest countries of the world and the woody plants play an important part in its composition. Although in the plains and at the lower altitutes agriculture has destroyed most of the natural forests, there are still existing in the higher mountains extensive wooded areas. Forests, in China, as well as in any other country, form parts of the wealth of the country, not only by the supply of timber and other products, but also as an important climatic and edaphic factor in the regulation of humidity and precipitation and prevention of erosion and flood disastrocusness. China, owing to have too much negligences to these facts, her natural forests have been destroyed by ruthless cuttings, burning, and other thoughtless destructions. The people are suffering from the famines year after year, yet there are very few people ever realizing the real causes of these famines and nobody knows how much these forested areas now left, where and what kinds and how many these virgin forests with economic values there are, and where necessary afforestation and reforestation should take their place. The writer has been trying his best to set his task in solving the fundamental problems of Chinese forestry by studying the woody plants of China at the Arnold Arboretum of Harvard University, U.S.A., where the largest and most complete collection of specimens of Chinese plants, with detailed field notes, and a great number of Chinese living plants planted at the Arboreatum, and a supplement of these studies at the Royal Botanical Garden, Kew, London and other large botanical institutions of Europe during the period of 1932-1933. The work presents a systematic enumeration and detailed descriptions of the trees of China including the more inportant shrubs as complete as it could be made. In 1934 a volume of "Forest Botany of China" was published, which indicated the characters, economic values, uses, and the altitudinal and latitudinal distributions of 1500 species and varieties, belonging to 200 genera and 61 families of the most important Chinese forest trees and shrubs distributed over the entire country.

During the year 1961-1962 the writer had another opportunity to go back to the Arnold Arboretum of Harvard University and made a further study of the same project for one full year. As in a period of 28 years since the first print of this study there must be many new families, genera, species and varieties discovered, and a lots of field notes added, and many nomenclatures, and the natural sequence of systematic arrangement have been changed. This volume consists of 4073 species and varieties, belonging to 230 genera and 65 families and presents the results of the former and the recent studies and intending to foresters for reference in reforestation and afforestation of China, to botanists for checking up the changed nomenclatures and synonymies of the Chinese plants, and to students of Chinese dendrology for identifying the trees found in the field.

Finally but certainly not least, the author wishes to express his appreciation to his friend and collegue at Harvard, Dr. S. Y. Hu for her invaluable assistance during the preparation of the manuscript of this revised edition.

Department of Botany

National Taiwan University

Taipei, Taiwan, Dec. 1963

Shun Ching Lee

CONTENTS

Family 65. Rubiaceae Juss.

Class I. Gymnospermae Lindl.

Family 1. Cycadaceae Linn.
(See orig. text page 1)

Family 2. Ginkgoaceae Engl.
(See orig. text page 4)

Genus (1) Ginkgo L.

1. **Ginkgo biloba** Linn. (See orig. text page 5)

2. **Ginkgo biloba** varieties and forms:

    (1) **G. biloba** var. **fastigiata** (Henry) Rehder - Brs. ascending, forming a narrow pyramidal or columnar crown.

    (2) **G. biloba** f. **pendula** (Van Geertl.) Beissner-Brs. pendulous.

    (3) **G. biloba** f. **laciniata** (Carr.) Beissner - Lvs. larger deeply incised and divided.

    (4) **G. biloba** f. **variegata** (Carr.) Beissner (G. *biloba* var. *dissecta* Hochst.)-Lvs. yellowish-variegated.

    (5) **G. biloba** f. **aurea** (Nels.) Beissner-Lvs. bright yellow.

Family 3. Taxaceae Lindl.
(See orig. text page 10)

Genus (1) Taxus L.

1. **Taxus chinensis** Rehder (See orig. text page 11)

2. **Taxus cuspidata** Sieb. et Zucc.

      Taxus baccata Rupr. et Maxim.

      Taxus baccata spp. *cuspidata* (Sieb. et Zucc.) Pilger

      Taxus sieboldii Lot. ex Cheng

    This species originally described from Japan occurring also in Korea and the Amur Provinces. The range extending North of   the Tsing-ling Range; distinguished by its linear oblong leaves, obtuse and mucronate at the apex and not papillose on the midrib beneath and by its keeled persistent scales.

Distribution: Shensi, Kirin, Heilungkiang, the Northeastern Provinces.

3. **Taxus mairei** (Lemee et Level.) Shiu Ying Hu ex Liu

Cephalotaxus mannii Pritzel

Tsuga mairei Lemee et Level.

Taxus speciosa Florin.

This tree is distinguished from the *Taxus chinensis* Rehder by its broader leaves with the midrib beneath non-papillose. The type of *Tsuga mairei*, Lemee et Levl, and *Taxus speciosa* Florin are identical in the shape and size of the leaves and in all the other essential characters, which Florin used to distinguish his species. The earlier specific name has to be adopted.

Distribution: Taiwan, Fukien, Kwangtung, Kwangsi, Kiangsi, Anhwei. Hunan, Kweichow, Yunnan and Szechuan.

4. **Taxus wallichiana** Zucc.

Taxus baccata spp. *wallichiana* Pilger.

This species is distinguished by having falcate leaves with papillose midribs beneath, persistent bud scales and conspicuous stomatic apparatus.

Distribution: The range is from Philippine, Malaya, Burma and extending to Southwestern China occurring as a tree in northwestern Yunnan, Southwestern Sikong and Szechuan in mixed forests at altitude of 1000-3200 meters.

Genus (2) Torreya Arn.

1. **Torreya fargesii** Franchet

Torreya grandis Rehd. et Wilson

Tumion fargesii Franchet

A related species of *T. grandis* Fortune. Trees up to 25 m. in height. Leaves 1.5-2.5 cm. long, more graduate-pointed, dark green above with 2 more or less distinct grooves along the midrib, bands below slightly narrower than the green margin. Fruits globose-ellipsoid, 2-2.5 cm. long, deeply ruminate almost to the middle. It is distinguished by its stiff linear lanceolate acumulate leaves, obovoid-subglobose fruits and deeply ruminate albumen.

Distribution: Originally described from Northeastern Szechuan its range extending from Northwestern Hupei South westernward to Kiangsi and Yunnan. A common tree occurring in mixed forests at altitudes 1000-2800 meters.

Var. 1. **Torreya grandis** var. **chingii** Metcalf

A rare cultivated variety distinguished by its obovoid fruit with cylindric seed up to 4 cm. long.

Distribution: Chekiang.

Family 4. Podocarpaceae W. T. Saxton

(See orig. text page 18)

Genus (1) Podocarpus L'Her.

1. **Podocarpus brevifolius** (Staff) Foxw.

    Podocarpus neriifolius var. *brevifolia* Staff.

    A small tree distinguished by its short linear-elliptic leaves and solitary or 2-5 fasciculate staminate flowers.

    Distribution: High Mountains of tropical Asia from Borneo Northeastward to the Philippines, Hainan and Kwangsi.

2. **Podocarpus chingianus** Shiu-Ying Hu

    A small tree of 4-8 meters high at sea level up to 1000 meters altitude, rare; distinguished by its columnar habit, small oblanceolate leaves rarely up to 3 cm. long, and by its relatively large apiculum of the anthers.

    Distribution: Chekiang, Kiangsu, and Szechuan, occurring in woods or open thickets.

3. **Podocarpus costalis** Presl.

    A dwarf tree, distinguished by its oblanceoloate leaves rounded at the apex.

    Distribution: It is endemic to the Philippines, occurring also in Taiwan, Botel Tobago.

4. **Podocarpus forestii** Craib et W. W. Sm.

    Podocarpus macrophyllus Diels.

    A small tree closely related to *Podocarpus macrophyllus* var. *maki* Sieb., distinguished by its lower habit of growth, shorter and broader leaves 5-8 cm. long, 9-13 mm. wide, obtuse or rotundate at the apex.

    Distribution: Endemic to Tali Range of Western Yunnan.

5. **Podocarpus formosensis** Duemmer

    Podocarpus nageia Henry.

    P. nagi Sasaki

    P. nagi var. *angustifolia* Sasaki.

    P. formosensis var. *koshunensis* Merr. et Yamamoto

    P. koshunensis Kanehira

    A small tree endemic to Taiwan, restricted to the southern end of the island.

6. **Podocarpus imbricatus** Blume.

    Podocarpus cupressinus R. Br.

    P. horsfieldii Wall.

    P. javanicus Merr.

    P. kawai Hayata

    A large tree with a trunk of 1.5 meter in diameter, distinguished by its dimorphic leaves, some scaly and imbricated and others flat distichous; Fruits bright red.

Distribution: Old world tropics, occurring in forest ravinces in Hainan, Kwangtung, Kwangsi, and Southern Yunnan, at altitude of 700–1350
meters.

7. **Podocarpus macroyhyllus** (Thunb.) D. Don.

Taxus macrophylla Thunb.

Podocarpus longifolius Hort. ex Sieb.

Podocarpus makoya Hort. ex Endl.

Podocarpus miquelia Hort.

A small tree distinguished by having oblong–linear or lanceolate leaves of 5.5–9 cm.
long. 7–12 mm. wide, attenuate at both ends.

Distribution: Originally described from Japan, widely distributed in China,
occurring along streams or on open moist slopes, at altitude
of 200–1150 meters, often cultivated in temples in Chekiang,
Fukien, Kiangsi, Anhwei, Yunnan.

Var. 1. **Podocarpus macroyhyllus var. angustifolius** Blume.

Podocarpus macrophyllus f. *angustifolius* (Bume) Pilger.

P. chinensis var. *angustifolius* (Blume) Hay.

P. macrophyllus var. *acutifolius* Hao

A narrow leaved form cultivated in temples, with leaves of 5–9 cm
long and 4–5 mm. wide, cuneate at the base, acute at the apex.

Distribution: Kiangsi.

Var. 2. **Podocarpus macrophyllus f. argenteus** (Gordon) S.Y. Hu

Podocarpus chinensis var. *argentea* Gordon.

Podocarpus maki var. *albo-varigata* Regel.

Taxus chinensis Roxb.

juniperus chinensis Roxb.

Podocarpus chinensis Sweet.

Podocarpus japonicus Hort. et Sieb.

Podocarpus macrophyllius spp. *maki* Pilger.

Podocarpus chinensis var. *maki* (Sieb) Hao.

A cultivated form with white variegated leaves.

Distribution: Introduced to London by Robert Fortune in 1861.

8. **Podocarpus neriifolia** D. Don.

------------------ See orig. text book pages 19–20.

9. **Podocarpus wallichianus** Presel.

Podocarpus latifolia Wall.

Nageia latifolia Gordon.

Nageia wallichiana O. Ktze.

This tree is distinguished by its opposite large ovate–lanceolate leaves; staminate flowers branched; and well developed fleshy receptacles.

Distribution: Tropical Asia from the Himalayan region to Taiwan, Kwangtung, but very rare in China.

Family 5. Cephalotaxaceae F. W. Neger
(See orig. text page 20)

Genus (1) Cephalotaxus Sieb. et Zucc.

1. **Cephalotaxus fortuni** Hook. (See orig. text page 21)

Var. 1. **Cephalotaxus fortunei** Hook. var. **alpina** Li

A geographical race of Western China with the center of distribution in Yunnan hence Northward to Western Szechuan and Southwestern corner of Kansu; occurring in spruce forest at altitude of 1800–3300 meters.

A tree of 7–13 meters high, distinguished by its narrow long leaves with the margins recurved; the stomatic bands white and glaucose, and the stomas in 10–15 longitudinal rolls; Leaves resemble those of *Cephalotaxus sinensis* and acuminated and also resemble those of *Cephalotaxus mannii* Hook. f. 2–4.5 cm long and the peduncles of its staminate flowers like that of *Cephalotaxus drupacea*, very long and scaly. The Chinese specimen that Franchet interpreted as *Cephalotaxus mannii* should be belonged here.

Var. 2. **Cephalotaxus fortunei** var. **brevifolia** Dallimore et Jackson

A short leaved form, geographically sharing the same range as the typical *C. fortunei*; distinguished by its shorter leaves 2–5 cm. long and 2–3 mm wide, obtuse at the base, acuminate at the apex and by its oblong fruits. This variety differs from *C. mannii* only in its glacuose stomatic bands; the length of the leaves – aproches *C. harringtonia* but the bases of the leaves of the latter species are obliqusly cordate.

Distribution: Yunnan, Szechuan, Sheisi, Honan, Hupei.

Var. 3. **Cephalotaxus fortunei** var. **concolor** Franchet.

A broad–leaved form sharing the same geographical range as the typical *C. fortunei* and differing from it only in having pruinose stomatic bands; Leaves about 5 cm. long 4 mm. in wide, linear, acutely pointed with prominent midrib, upper surface pale green, glaucous beneath with stomatiferous bands.

Distribution: Fukien, Chekiang, Anhwei, Kiangsi, Hunan, Hupei, Kweichow, Yunnan, and Szechuan.

Var. 4. **Cephalotaxus fortunei** var. **globosa** Shiu-Ying Hu

A tall tree up to 27 meters high, occurring in mixed forests at altitude of 3500 meters; distinguished by its globose fruits and long linear leaves of 5–8.5 cm long, 3–4 mm wide, with obtuse base and acuminated apex; fruits 1.5 cm long and 1.3 cm. wide.

Distribution: Yunnan, Szechuan, Anhwei, and Honan.

2. **Cephalotaxus drupacea** Sieb. et Zucc.

Taxus baccata Thunb.

Taxus coriacea Hort. ex Knight et Perry

Cephalotaxus coriacea Hort. ex Knight et Perry

Podocarpus drupacea Hort. ex Knight et Perry

Cephalotaxus fortunei var. *foemina* Hort. ex Carr.

Taxus japonica Hook. ex Gordon

Cephalotaxus griffithii Oliver.

Cephalotaxus foemina Hort. ex Carr.

Cephalotaxus harringtonia var. *drupacea* (Sieb. et Zucc.) Koidzumi

Cephalotaxus kaempferi Anon.

Cephalotaxus filiformis Knight et Perry. ex Gordon.

Cephalotaxus drupacea Koch

Cephalotaxus mannsii Master

Cephalotaxus lanceolata Hort.

Cephalotaxus fortunei var. *longifolia* Hort. ex Dallimore

Distribution: Chekiang, North Kwangtung, Kwangsi, Fukien, Yunnan and northward to Yang-tze provinces; occurring in woods at altitude 330–1300 m; often used in grave yard.

3. **Cephalotaxus harringtonia** (Forbes) Koch

Taxus harringtonia Knight ex Forbes

Cephalotaxus pedunculata Sieb. et Zucc.

Taxus sinensis Knight et Gordon

Cephalotaxus drupacea var. *pedunculata* (Sieb. et Zucc.) Miq.

Cephalotaxus griffithii Hook. f.

Cephalotaxus drupacea var. *harringtonia* (Forbes) Pilger

Cephalotaxus drupacea var. *sinensis* Merrill

A tropical species found in Hainan Island in wooded ravine at altitude of 600 meters. It is distinguished by the squamose peduncles, falcate subsessile leaves, truncate or obliquely subcordate at the base. An isotype of C. *griffithii* matches Forbes plate very well.

Distribution: Indo-China eastward to Burma and Hainan.

4. **Cephalotaxus oliverii** Masters. (See orig. text pages 25–26)

5. **Cephalotaxus sinensis** Rehder et Wilson

Cephalotaxus drupacea var. *sinensis* Rehd. et Wils.

C. fortunei Franch.

C. pedunculata Franch.

C. griffithii Beissner

C. harringtonia var. *sinensis* (Rehd. et Wils.) Rehder

A small tree or bush up to 4 meters high; occurring in woodlands of altitude 1000–2000 meters. Rehder & Wilson interpreted it as a variety of *Cephalotaxus drupacea*. They overlooked the short peduncles of its staminate flowers, which are naked and not covered with scales. In this respect it differs from all other known Chinese *Cephalotaxus* as well as *C. drupacea*. Its relationship with *C. drupacea* is comparable to that of *C. fortunei*. It should not be treated as variety of neither of them.

Distribution: The type specimens collected from Tsing-Ling northeast Szechwan and northeastern Sikang, additional collections extended its range to Hupei, Hunan, Honan, Kiangsu, and Chekiang.

Var. 1. Cephalotaxus sinensis var. globosus (Rehd. et Wils.) Li

Cephalotaxus sinensis var. *drupacea* var. *sinensis* f. *globosus* Rehder et Wilson

It is distinguished by its short leaves 1.5–2.5 cm long, 2 mm wide, acuminate at the apex and by its subglobose fruits of 18 mm long 1.5 mm in diameter. The fruit of the typical *C. sinensis* is oblong-ellipsoid, 2.5 cm long.

Distribution: Western Hupei (Hsing-Shan Hsien).

6. **Cephalotaxus wilsoniana** Hayata

A small tree with leaves resembling those of *Cephalotaxus sinensis* Rehd. et Wils. in appearance and size. Material with staminate flowers not available for comparison.

Distribution: Endemic to Taiwan; localized in Mt. Arisan, occurring in mixed forest at altitude 1400–2955 meters.

Genus (2) Amentotaxus Pilger

1. **Amentotaxus argotaenia** (Hance) Pilger (See orig. text page 26)

2. **Amentotaxus formosana** Li

Podocarpus argotaenia sensu Matsum. et Hay, non Hance

Amentotaxus argotaenia sensu Yamamoto, non Pilger

An endemic species to Southern Taiwan, distinguished from *Amentaxus argotaenia* Pilger by the stomal bands being broader than the green marginal ones; Leaves 7–9.5 mm wide.

Distribution: Taiwan; occurring in the broad-leaved forests, at an altitude of 700–1300 meters.

3. **Amentotaxus yunnanensis** Li

An endemic species in Southeastern Yunnan; the outstanding characters being the large leaves of 10–15 mm wide, up to 10.5 cm long and with stomatic bands 3 or 4 times broader than the marginal ones; The nature fruits are red.,

Distribution: Yunnan, Ma-Li-Po. common in mixed forests at altitude of 1600–

1800 meters.

Family 6. Pinaceae Linn.
(See orig. text page 27)

Key to Chinese genera of Pinaceae (See orig. text page 28)

Sub family A.

Genus (1) Abies Miller (See orig. text page 29)

1. **Abies chensiensis** Van Tiegham (See orig. text page 31)
2. **Abies delavayii** (See orig. text page 31)
3. **Abies ernestii** Rehder

   Abies beisseriana Rehd. et Wilson

   A tree of 20-60 meters in height and 2-4 m. in diam. Bark grayish brown, shallowly fissured; Branchlets pale gray; Leaves 2-3.5 cm in length, ascending flat, some bluntely pointed, some with a notch at apex; midrib slightly depressed above, pale green and glaucose below; Staminate flowers scattered in small catkin-like pale yellow cones; Cone purplish when young, later truning to gray-brown, small 5-8 cm in length; Cone scales thin and broad. It is specially distinguished by resinous buds, non-recurved leaves with acute, rare emarginate leaves and very in conspicuously glaucose stomatic bands and by its completely concealed bracts.

   Distribution: Endemic to Western Szechwan and the adjacent Sikong, occurring in forests at altitude 2700-3300 meters. It is closely related to *Abies chensiensis* Van Tieghem.

4. **Abies fabri** (Masters) Craib

   Keteleeria fabri Masters

   Abies delavayi Masters

   A tree closely related to *Abies delavayi* Franch. apparently a northern form; distinguished by its glabrous branchlets, broader leaves with obtuse-mucronate or emarginate apex, white stomatic bands beneath and recurved margins, and by its large ovate cylindric cones with included bracts and the lower angles of the cone-scales auriculate.

   Distribution: Endemic to western Szechwan and adjacent area of Sikang.

5. **Abies fargesii** Franchet

   Abies veithii Beissner

   Abies fargesii var. *sutchuenensis* Franchet

   Abies sutchuenensis (Franchet) Rehder

   Abies kansouensis Borderes-Rey et Gaussen

7. **Abies firma** Sieb. et Zucc.

   Abies bifida Sieb. et Zucc.

Pinus firma(Sieb. et Zucc.) Antoine

Picea firma Gordon

Abies firma var. *bifida* (Sieb. et Zucc.) Masters

A large tree, native of Japan, intorduced into European gardens since 1861, cultivated in Shangtung Tsing-Tao and Kiangsi Lu-Shan;. distinguished by its slightly grooved branchlets, pilose in the grooves, by its rigid sharply-2-pointed leaves and by its yellowish green cones with straight exserted bracts.

8. **Abies georgei** Orr et Hand.-Mazz.

Abies forrestii C. C. Rogers var. *smithii* Viguie et Gaussen

Tree closely related to *Abies forrestii* C. C. Rogers and *Abies faxoniana* Rehd. et Wils., the former has glabrous or glabrescent branchlets and the later has smaller cones. Distinguished by its ferrogenously and densely pubescent branchlets, by its unusually large cones, the axis of which measuring 15 cm long, 1.5 cm wide, and by its much exserted oblong-cuneate bracts.

Distribution: Endemic to northwestern Yunnan and the adjacent areas of Szechwan and Sikang, occurring in forests, at altitude of 3200-4000 meters.

9. **Abies holophylla** Maixm.

Picea holopyhlla (Maxim) Gordon

Pinus holophylla (Maxim.) Parlatore

Abies firma Masters

Abies yoneyamae Sato

10. **Abies kawakami** (Hayata) Ito

Abies mariesii Matsumura et Hayata

Abies mariesii Masters var. *kawakamii* Hayata

This species is endemic to the high mountains of central Taiwan, occurring at altitude of 2800-3200 meters, forming pure forests; A very distinct species with pubescent or glabrescent branchlets, small and narrow leaves 7-22 mm long, 1.25-1.5 mm wide, stomatiferous on both surfaces; small cones and completely included bracts.

Distribution: Taiwan.

11. **Abies mayriana** (Miyabe et Kudo) Miyabe et Kudo

Abies sachalinensis Masters f. *typica* Mayr

Abies sachalinensis Fr. Schm. var. *mayriana* Miyabe et Kudo

Tree endemic to Northern Japan, according to Sata, it is cultivated in Liaoning. It is distinguished by having dark-brown pubescent branchlets; narrow emarginate leaves 5-10 cm long, 2.5-3.9 mm wide; Cones cylindric with exserted and reflexed bracts.

12. **Abies sibirica** Ledeb.

Pinus pichta Loddiges

Pinus sibirica (Ledeb.) Turcz.

Abies pichta Forbes

Abies semenovii Fedtschenko

This species is endemic to the Altai Mountains, its range extending Eastward to Western Kirin, southward to Tibet and Turkestan. It is distinguished by its pubescent branchlets, narrow leaves, 2-3.4 cm long, 1.5 mm wide, stomatiferous on both surfaces; and by its medium sized cylindric cones with obvate short bracts.

14. **Abies spectabilis** (D. Don) Spach

Pinus spectabilis D. Don

Pinus webbiana Wall.

Abies webbiana Lindl.

A large tree attaining a height of 70 m and a girth of 10 m distinguished by having a deeply grooved reddish-brown pubescent branchlets; Leaves very long; Cones large, 14-18 cm long with hidden bracts.

Distribution: A native of the Himalayan region, thence extending northward to Yunnan and Tibet.

Genus (2) Keteleeria Carr.

1. **Keteleeria chien-peii** Flous

Keteleeria davidiana Cheng

A large tree with reddish brown bark and densely pubescent branchlets; Leaves pointed mucronate; Cones ovoid-cylindric 8 cm lomg 3.5 cm in diameter; Distinguished from *K. fortunei* Carr. by its pointed mucronate leaves.

Distribution: Kwangsi and Kweichow at altitude 1200 meters.

2. **Keteleeria formosana** Hayata --- Taiwan Keteleeria

Keteleeria davidiana var. *formosana* Hayata

A large evergreen tree with brownish bark; young branchlet grayish and slender, tomentose, sometimes with stiff hairs; Leaves linear, alternate, in two vertical raws, with midrib, elevated on both sides round or slightly emarginated at tip, 2-4 cm long, and 3-4 mm broad, dark green above and light green beneath; Cone cylindrical or pyramidal, 10 cm long, 4.5 cm broad; scales ovate, about half as long as the seeds, 3-clefted on the top, the edge curved backward; seeds winged, the wings sltghtly longer than the sacles.

Distribution: Taiwan.

3. **Keteleeria davidiana** (Franch.) Beissner (See orig. text pages 39-41)

4. **Keteleeria fortunei** Carr. (See orig. text pages 41-43)

5. **Keteleeria eveleyniana** Masters (See orig. text pages 43-44)

Genus (3) Pseudotsuga Carr. (See orig. text pages 43-44)

1. **Pseudotsuga sinensis** Dode (See orig. text pages 44-45)

2. **Pseudotsuga wilsoniana** Hayata (See orig. text pages 45-46)

Genus (4) Tsuga Carr. (See orig. text page 46)

1. **Tsuga chinensis** (Franch.) Pritzel (See orig. text pages 46-48)

Abies chinensis Franch.

Abies dumosa var. *chinensis* Franch.

Tsuga brunoniana var. *chinensis* (Franch.) Masters

Tsuga yunnanensis Masters

Tsuga formosana Hayata

2. **Tsuga yunnanensis** (Franchet) Masters (See orig. text page 40)

Abies yunnanensis Franchet

Abies dumosa var. *chinensis* Franchet

Tsuga brunoniana var. *chinensis* (Franchet) Masters

3. **Tsuga longibracteata** (See orig. text page 49)

Genus (5) **Picea** A. Dietr. (See orig. text pages 49-52)

1. **Picea ascendens** Pat.

2. **Picea asperata** Masters (See orig. text page 52)

Var. 3. **Picea asperata** Masters var. **heterolepis** (Rehd. et Wils.) Cheng (See orig. text pages 52)

This variety is distinguished by its reddish or yellowish brown branchlets; Leaves bluish green, often glaucescent; cone scales rhombic-ovate, the lower ones deeply emarginate.

Distribution: West China; altitude 2200-3000 meters.

3. **Picea aurantiaca** Masters (See orig. text page 52)

4. **Picea balfouriana** Rehder et Wilson (See orig. text page 53)

5. **Picea brachytyla** (Franch.) Pritzel (See orig. text page 54)

Abies brachytyla Franch.

Picea ajaenensis Masters

Picea alcockiana Masters

Picea pachyclada Patschke

Picea sargentiana Rehd. et Wils.

Picea brachytyla f. *latisuama* Stapf

6. **Picea complanata** Masters

7. **Picea gemmata** Rehder et Wilson

8. **Picea heterolepis** Rehder et Wilson (See orig. text page 55)

9. **Picea hirtella** Rehder et Wilson (See orig. text page 56)

10. **Picea jezoensis** Carr.

11. **Picea likiangensis** (Fr.) Prity

Var. 1. **Picea likiangensis** Prity var. **purprea** Dall. et Jackson

Tree 10-12 m high, the trunk 30-40 cm in diameter; bark dark brownish gray, longitudinally fissured; branchlets brownish-yellow, pubescent, pendulous, with 2 white bands on lower leaf surface; male flowers in catkins and yellow; cone scales dark brown and purplish at base; seeds brownish-purple.

Distribution: In forests of Yunnan, Chungtien Tehgoh.

12. **Picea meyeri** Rehder et Wilson (See orig. text page 57)

13. **Picea montigena** Masters

14. **Picea morrisonicola** Hayata (See orig. text page 57)

Large tree up to 40 m high, the trunk 2 meters in diameter; bark gray, scaly, in circular pellet; leaves dark green.

Distribution: Mt. Morrison of Taiwan; altitude 2760-3000 m.

15. **Picea obovata** Ledeb. (See orig. text page 58)

16. **Picea purpurea** Msaters

17. **Picea retroflexa** Masters

18. **Picea sargentiana** Rehder et Wilson

19. **Picea schrenkiana** Fischer et Meyer

20. **Picea watsoniana** Masters

21. **Picea wilsonii** Masters

22. **Picea sikangensis** Cheng

Tree 5-10 m tall, trunk 0.3-0.4 m in diameter; bark gray, exfoliating in irrregular relatively thin flakes; branches spirally arranged, spreading or horizontally spreading, relatively long, rather slender and with ascending tips, branches yellow or pale brownish yellow, becoming gray in second year, with more or less glandular hairs; pulvini prominent, petioles more or less with glandular hairs, especially on lower side, about 1 mm long, spreading or ascending-spreading, slightly curved, dull dark in color, the upper side yellow, scars quadrangular or nearly triangular; buds ovoid, or acutish, very resinous, yellow-brown, the lower scales acuminate, keeled on back, bud-scales persistent, closely appressed at the base of the branchlets, lateral ones ovoid or subglobose, obtuse. Leaves spirally arranged, linear, slightly compressed, acute or acutish, keeled on both sides, more prominent beneath, 10-13 mm long, 2 mm broad, curved, dark green, with 2 white bands above, each with 4-7 rows of stomata, the bands inconspicuous beneath, with 2-4 rows of stomata each; Cones ovoid-oblong, resinous, 6-8 cm long, 2.6-3 cm broad, dark purplish-black or nearly black before maturity, glaucescent, persistent on the tree for a year after ripening, scales closely appressed or somewhat loosely appressed only at apex, rhombic-ovate, more or less woody, thickened at base, thinner on margin, 2.3-2.5 cm long, 1.8-2 cm. broad, rounded or slightly narrowed at apex; bracts spatulate, 3 mm lomg, rounded or slightly narrowed at apex; bracts spatulate 3 mm long, rounded and slightly erose at apex; seeds puberulous, with wing about 12-14 mm long, wing oblong-ovate, reddish-brown, rounded, slightly brown at apex.

Distribution: Sikang, Southwest of Tatsienlu, around hamlet of Muki, in forests, altitude 3700-3800 m. (Aug. 24 1930 W.C.Cheng, No. 1820 type)

This spruce, belonging to the section Casicta, is a very distinct species differing from all other Chinese spruces by its purplish-black cones with closely appressed, rhombic-ovate scales and spatulate bracts. It is a very interesting spruce, growing in the mixed forests of *Picea retroflexa* Mast., *Picea likiangensis*

Pritz., and *Larix potaninii* Batal. with *Picea likiangensis* Pritz. being the dominant-species. It occurs around hamlet of Muki, Southwest of Tatsienlu in Western China.

Genus (6) Pseudolarix Gord. (See orig. text pages 61-62)

1. Pseudolarix amabilis (Nelson) Rehder (See orig. text page 62)

Genus (7) Larix Mill. (See orig. text pages 62-64)

1. **Larix potaninii** Batalin
2. **Larix gmelinii** (Rupr.) Litvin
3. **Larix mastersiana** Rehder et Wilson
4. **Larix sibirica** Ledeb.
5. **Larix griffithiana** Carr.
6. **Larix merrilliana** C. L. Wu

Tree 10-20 m high; bark grayish brown and ridged in longitudinally narrow plates, branches dark gray, longitudinally furrowed; branchlets grayish - brown; leaves greenish, glaucescent; cones cylindric-oblong, 6-8 cm long, 3-5 cm wide, brownish-green when young and yellow when old; seeds brown and orbicular in shape.

Distribution: Yunnan Likiang Snow Range and East of Chung-Tien Chia-Tze on Yang-tze bank in forests ; At altitude up to 3700 meters.

Genus (8) Cedrus Link (See orig. text page 67)

1. **Cedrus deodara** (Roxb.) Loudon

A native of Western Himalayan Region, being the most important conifer at altitude of 1300-3300 meters, introduced to European gardens in 1822, cultivated in large cities of China such as Nanking, Peiping and Mukden; distinguished by its pendulous and pubescent branchlets, glaucous green leaves up to 4.5 cm long and large barrel-shaped cones, 7-10 cm long, round at the apex.

Var. 1. **Cedrus deodara** f. **argentea** (Nels.) Beissner

C. deodara var. *argentea* Hort. ex Rehd.--A cultivated form with bluish or slivery white leaves.

Var. 2. **C. deodara** var. **aurea** Tutenberg --- A cultivated form with yellowish leaves.

form.1. **C. deodara** f. **pendula** Beissner-- A garden form with the leading shoot and branchlets so pendent that to induce vertical growth and the leading shoots must be staked.

form.2. **C. deodara** f. **robusta** (Laus.) Beissner -- A garden form with stouter branchlets and more rigid leaves of about 5 cm long.

Subfamily B.

Genus (1) Pinus Linn. (See orig. text pages 67-68)

A. **Haploxylon** Koehne (See orig. text pages 68-71)

Leaves with one fibrovascular bundle, entire or serrulate, usually without stomata on back; bracts of leaf-fascicles not decurrent; sheaths deciduous; wood soft with little resin.

1. **Pinus armandi** Fr.

2. **Pinus bungeana** Zucc.

3. **Pinus excelsa** Wall.

Tree 10-20 m high; bark dark brown longitudinally scaly; leaves 5 in a fascicle, slender, pendulous, 15-25 cm long, with long brownish leaf-sheaths; cones cylindrical-ovoid, 10-20 cm long, bluish green when young to grayish brown at maturity.

Distribution: On sunny and open slopes and valley Kiangsi, Kwangsi and Yunnan; Altitude of 2400-2600 Meters.

4. **Pinus koraiensis** S. et Z. (See orig. text page 71)

5. **Pinus morrisonicola** Hayata

A tree up to 34 m high. Tips of branchlets often pendulous; bark grayish-brown, almost smooth when young; leaves in fascicles of 5, stiff, 6-8 cm long, sometimes twisted, acute, flattened beneath, keeled above, triangular in section, coarsely serrulate; cones erect, ovate-oblong, obutse at apex, 6-10 cm long, 4-6 cm wide, composed of about 40 scales; scales elliptic, cuneate at base, rounded at apex, slightly reflexed, 3 cm long, 1.3 cm wide, brown in color; seeds ovoid, obtuse at apex, 9-10 mm long, 6 mm wide, grayish-brown, smooth; wing membranous, hatched-shaped, 2 cm long, 8 mm wide.

Distribution: Kwangtung, Hainan, and Taiwan. Altitude: 1600 meters.

(Remarks: *Pinus morrisonicloa* Hayata is closely related to *P. parvifolia* S. et Z. with which it has been associated by some authors (Cheng) but the Chinese species, *P. morrisonicola* Hayata erect ovate-oblong cones with elliptic scales rounded at apex and hatched-shaped winged seeds. and (Shaw and Dallimore, and Jackson) unite this pine with *Pinus parvifolia* S. et Z. which is distinct, however, from the former by its horizontal or spreading cones with scales convex at apex, ovate in outline, and brown, broadly winged seeds.)

B. **Diploxylon** Koehne (See orig. text page 71)

Leaves with 2 vascular bundles, and with dorsal and ventral stomata, serrulate; bracts of leaf-fascicles decurrent; sheaths persistent, rarely deciduous; cones with dorsal umbo; wood hard, with dark resinous bands and clearly defined annual rings.

1. **Pinus insularis** Endl. (See orig. text page 70)

2. **Pinus massoniana** Lamb. (See orig. text page 71)

Pinus sinensis Lambert

Pinus canaliculata Miquel

Pinus argyi Lemee et Leveille

Pinus argyi var. *longivaginans* Leveille

Pinus cavaleriei Lemee et Leveille

3. **Pinus tabulaeformis** Carr. (See orig. text pages 71–73)

  Var. 1. Pinus **tabulaeformis** Carr. var. **densata** Rehd.(See orig. text pages 73–75)

  Var. 2. Pinus **tabulaeformis** Carr. var. **pseudo-sylvestris** C. L. Wu

   Tree, 6–8 m high, with oblong-ovoid cones, leaves 2 in a fascicle, bluish green, rigid. (See orig. text page 75)

Distribution: Mongolia, at altitude of 1750–2125 meters.

  Var. 3. Pinus **tabulaeformis** Carr. Var. **gacilifolis** C. L. Wu

   Tree 25–30 m high, 1 – 1.2 m in diameter; bark grayish-brown when old, smooth, longitudinally furrowed when old; leaves 2 in a fascicle, dark green to glaucous.

Distribution: Kansu Lien-Hwa-Shan, Shensi and Shansi; at altitude 1600–2000 meters.

  Var. 4. Pinus **tabulaeformis** Carr. var. **leucosperma** (Maxim.) C. L. Wu

     (Hwang–Sung)

   Tree up to 20 m high, trunk 1 meter in diameter; leaves dark green, thick, rigid and erect, sharp pointed, 4–12 cm long; branches dark gray to brown, rough and scaly; cones broadly ovoid, 6–8 cm long, brownish, glaucescent, pendulous.

Distribution: Wu-Chai Hsien, Ta Nan Kow, Southern Kansu; at altitude 2000 –3300 meters.

  Var. 5. Pinus **tabulaeformis** Carr. var. **leucosperma** (Max.) C. L. Wu

   f. **takunayagai** (Nakai) C. L. Wu

   Tree 10–12 meters high growing on lime-stone rocky slope; leaves longer and thicker than other forms and dark green in color; branchlets more rigid and thicker, light grayish-brown; cones larger and thicker, obovoid, 8–12 cm long.

Distribution: Ho Lan Shan, Shansi Wu Tai Shan and Northern Hopei; at altitude 1250–2650 meters.

  Var. 6. Pinus **tabulaeformis** Carr. var. **wilsonii** (Shaw) C. L. Wu

   Tree 10–12 m high; bark grayish – brown, longitudinally fissured; leaves 2 in a fasciele, deep green ; leaf-sheath long and yellow-gray; cone obovoid-oblong subsymmetrical, 3–6 cm long, 2–4 cm broad, the old cones grayish-brown to dark brown, 8–12 cm long; cone scales very thin.

Distribution: Western Hupei and Western Szechwan, at altitude 1550–2500 m.

4. **Pinus densiflora** Sieb. et Zucc.

  Pinus henryi Masters

  Pinus nana Faurie et Lemee

A Japanese red pine closely related *Pinus massoniana* Lamb. differing chiefly in the longer leaves, mucronate conelet, and the sublustrous nut-brown cone, often confuse with *P. massoniana* Lamb.; tree up to 35 m hight, with horizontal branches, forming an irregular, rather broad head; bark orange-red, thin, scaly; branches orange-yellow, bloomy; buds oblong-ovoid, chestnut-brown; leaves 2, slender, 8-12 cm long, bright bluish-green; conelets conspicuously mucronate; cones short stalked; conic-ovoid to oblong, symmetrical, 3-5 cm long, dull tawny-yellow; apopyhsis flattened, the small umbo with a short prickle or obtuse.

Distribution: West Hupei, Kiangsi, Honan, Kiangsu, Shantung, Yalu River Basin of Manchuria,   Altitude: 200-500 meters.

Var. 1. **Pinus densiflora** S. et Z. var. **aurea** Mayr. Leaves yellow.

Var. 2. **P. densiflora** S. et Z. var. **pendula** Mayr

With pendulous or prostrate branches.

Var. 3. **P. densiflora** S. et Z. var. **globosa** Mayr

Dwarf globose form with short leaves.

Var. 4. **P. densiflora** S. et Z. var. **umbraculifera** Mayr

Low form to 4 meters tall of spreading branches, forming an umbrella like head.

Var. 5. **P. densiflora** S. et Z. var. **funebris** (Komarov) C. L. Wu

A small tree with light gray bark and slender branchlets, leaves short green, 6-10 cm long, occurring in Manchuria.

5. Pinus luchuensis Mayr

Tree 15-25 m high; bark smooth when young and bluish scaly when old; leaves 2 in a fascicle, 10-15 cm long, grayish-green in color, staminate flowers purplish.

Distribution: Lilkiu to Taiwan, at altitude 100-200 m.

Var. 1. **Pinus luchuensis** Mayr var. **hwang-shanensis** (Hsia) C. L. Wu

Tree up to 30 m tall, trunk 60-80 cm in diameter; bark brownish-dark gray, very rough; leaves dark green, short, thick, stout, ascending; staminate flowers lemon yellow.

Distribution: Kiangsi, Anhwei Hwang Shan, Chekiang and Tien Mo Shan, at altitude 200-1500 m.

6. Pinus merkusi Jung et De Urier (See orig. text page 76)

7. Pinus sylvestris L. var. mongolica Li

Tree 25-40 m with spreading branches, pyramidal when young, round-topped and irregular when old; bark red or red-brown, rather thin and smooth on the upper part of trunk, darker and fissured below; branchlets dull grayish-yellow; bud oblong-ovate, brown, resinous; leaves 2 in a fasciale, rigid, usually twisted, 3-7 cm long, blusish green; conelet reflexed, minutely mucronate; cone short stalked, reflexed, conic oblong, 3-6 cm long, dull tawny-yellow; apophysis flat, sometime pyramidal; umbo small with a minute prickle or its remnant.

Distribution: This is an important European species; this variety occurring in Hailar, Manchuria and Mongolia.

8. **Pinus taiwanensis** Hayata

Large tree, 20–30 m high, trunk 1–2.5 m in diameter; bark grayish-brown, fissured into irregularly longitudinal plates; leaves 2 in a fascicle, 6–18 cm long; resin ducts medial, with an occasional external ducts; cones oblong, 4–6 cm long, 3–5 cm thick, dark brown in color; cone scales thin and flat; conelets mucronate; spines deciduous.

> Distribution: Endemic to Taiwan, not yet found in the mainland of China; In open coutnry, on mountains of Taiwan, in association with *Pinus armandi* Franchet, common in Nan-Tao and Arisan at altitude of 1500–2800m.

9. **Pinus yunnanensis** (Franch.) Shaw (See orig. text page 76)

Family 7. Metasequoiaceae Hu et Cheng

Tree with opposite branchlets, distichously arranged foliage shoots, deciduous in winter; Leaves deciduous, opposite, distichously arranged, linear, sessile or nearly sessile, with 4–6 rows of stomata on each side beneath; flower solitary, monoecious; staminate flowers axillary and terminal, opposits, on racemose or paniculate flowering branchlet-system, bracts decussate; androecium with about 20 stamens, filaments short, anthers 3–celled, pollen-grains not winged; pistillate flowers solitary bracts decussate, 14–16, peduncles leafy, with distichous opposite linear leaves; cones pendulous; scales woody, decussate, peltate; seeds 5–9 under each scale, compressed, winged all round; cotyledons 2.

This family has 10 fossil species widely distributed in Europe, Asia, and North America, from Cretaceous to Pliocene time. It has only one living species which occur in Central China.

Genus (1) Metasequoia Miki.

Characters of the genus as that of the family.

1. **Metasequoia glyptostroboides** Hu et Cheng

Tree to 35 m tall, the trunk to 2.3 m in diam. usually strongly buttressed at the base, pyramidal when young, in old age usually spreading with broadly rounded crown; bark dark gray, fissured, peeling off in long thread in old age, exfoliating in thin plates exposing the purplish brown inner bark beneath while young; barnchlets opposite, glabrous, smooth, green when young becoming brownish later and changing to brownish gray or gray in the second or the third year; lateral foliage shoot deciduous in winter, glabrous, opposite, up to 7 cm long, distichously arranged, with persistent bracts at the base, without both terminal and axillary buds, winter buds ovoid or ellipsoid, obtuse, 4 mm long, 3 mm across, glabrous bracts decussate, 12–16, broad-ovate, rounded or obtuse at apex, 2–2.5 mm long and broad, yellowish brown, paler and thinner on the margin, lustrous and longitudinally keeled on the back; leaves deciduous, opposite, distichously arranged, linear, 8–15 mm long, 1.2 mm broad at the middle, broader toward the base, sessile or nearly sessile, midrib elevated on both surfaces, bluish green above, light green and with 4-6 rows of stomata on each side beneath; flowers monoecious, solitary, glabrous; staminate flowers axillary and terminal, opposite, about 5 mm long, on racemose or paniculate flowered, branchlets, bracts, decussate, triangular-ovate or obovate, obtuse at the apex, the large ones 4 mm long, 3 mm broad at the base; pedicels 3 mm long; androecium subglobose, with about 20 stamens, filaments short, anthers 3-celled, orbicular-oblong or elliptic oblong, rounded at the apex, 1-1.2 mm long, 0.5-1 mm broad; pistillate flowers solitary, about 8 mm long, bracts 14-16, decussate, glabrous on both sides, the lower ones triangular-ovate, 2 mm broad, 1.5 mm high, keeled on the back, thinner and erose on the margin, obtuse at the apex, the middle ones 3 mm broad, 2.5 mm high, the upper ones elliptic-oblong, 3.5-4.5 mm long, 1.5-2 mm broad, pendulous, 3 mm long, leafy, bracts on peduncle decussate, linear-oblong or linear, 3.5 mm long, 1. mm broad, slightly broader above the middle, rounded at the apex; conelets oblong-ellipsoid, 3 mm long, 1.6-2 mm across; scales 22-26, rarely 28, decussate, ovate, 1-1.2 mm high, 0.8-1 mm broad, abruptly narrowed at the apex, ovules erect 5-9 to each scale, the lowest and the upper most scales sterile, the lower ones bearing 9 ovules, the middle ones 7 and the upper ones 5; cones ripening in the first year, pendulous, subquadrangular-globose, or shortly cylindric, 18-25 mm long, 16-23 mm across, dark brown, scales woody, decussate, mostly 22-24, sometimes 28, peltate, dilated from a wedge shaped base into a transver sely elliptic or triangular disk, seeds 5-9 under each scale, winged all around, compressed obovate notched at apex, 5 mm long, 4 mm broad, cotyledons 2.

Distribution: East Szechwan, Wan Hsien, Mo tao Hsi, and Western Hupei; at altitude 900-1350 m.

The fossil species: **Metasequoia disticha** (Heer) Miki and **M. japonica** (Endo) Miki from the Pliocene beds in Japan; **M. chinensis** (Endo) Hu from Eocene beds in Fu Shun coal mines in Southern Manchuria and in Kawakami coal mines in southern Saghalian.

Metasequoia macrolepis Chaney

Metasequoia heerii Chaney

Metasequoia fastigiata Chaney

Metasequoia concinna Chaney

Metasequoia langsdorffi Chaney

Metasequoia nordenskioldi Chaney

Metasequoia reichenbachii Chaney

Family 8. Taxodiaceae Pilger
(See orig. text pages 67-83)

Family 9. Cupressaceae W. T. Saxton
(See orig. text pages 67-83)

Subfamily 1. Thujoideae Pilger

Genus (1) Thujopsis S. et Z.

Genus (2) Thuja Linn.

Genus (3) Libocedrus Endl.

Genus (4) Cunninghamia R. et Br. (See orig. text page 82)

1. **Cunninghamia konishii** Hayata

Large tree up to 50 meters high, the trunk 2-2.5 meters in diameters, scattered in woods with *Chamaecyparis taiwaniana* and other broad-leaved species; bark light brown, with verticillate spreading branches, pendulous at the extermities; leaves linear, narrower and smaller than that of *Cunninghamia lanceolata*, rigid, but not very stiff, densely and spirally arranged but spreading in two ranks, with acute apex, 1.5-2 cm long; flowers monoecious, staminate flowers oblong in small terminal clusters; pistillate flowers globose, consisting of roundish-ovate pointed serrate scales; cones oviod or globose, 2-2.5 cm long.

Distribution: Fukien and Taiwan; at altitude of 1000-2600 meters.

2. **Cunninghamia lanceolata** Hooker (See orig. text page 83)

Genus (5) Calocedrus Kurz (See orig. text page 89)

Libocedurs subg. *Heyderia* Pilger

(Type species: *Heyderia decurrens* (Torr.) Koch)

1. **Calocedrus formosana** (Florin) Florin (See orig. text page 90)

Libocedrus formosana Florin

Heyderia formosana (Fl.) Li

Libocedrus macrolepis Benth. var. *formosana* (Fl.) Kudo

Tree, 12-23 meters high, trunk 0.4-1.2 meter in diameter; bark dark gray, rather smooth; the crown broad, more or less flattened, consisting of several branches and many thin branchlets of secondary order; branches horizantal or slightly ascending; wood very fragrant used for making incense sticks; distinguished by its strongly compressed smooth branchlets and by its larger elongate-ovoid cones, on very short stalk of 6-8 mm long. The vegetative characters of this species resemble that of *Fokienia*, except the leaves verticillate and the flatened branchlets green on both surfaces.

Distribution: On cliffs of ridges mixed with broad-leaved species in Urai, Taipei endemic to northern and central Taiwan; at altitude 300-1900 m.

Genus (6) Heyderia K. Koch

1. **Heyderia macrolepis** (Kurz) Li (See orig. text page 90)

Calocedrus macrolepis Kurz

Libocedrus macrolepis Benth. et Hook.

Thuja macrolepis Voss

Genus (7) Fokienia Henry et H. H. Thomas (See orig. text page 90)

Subfamily 2. Cupressoideae F. Vier

Genus (1) Cupressus Linn.

1. **Cupressus chengiana** S. Y. Hu

Tree of 20 m high and 1 m in diameter; bark brown to dark-brown, longitudinally splitting; its branchlets terate, closely related to *C. torulosa* distinguished by samll fruit with 6-8 rugose and papillose scales. In *C. torulosa* the cone scales are cutinized.

Distribution: Endemic to Northwestern Szechwan, occurring in the Ming River Valley at altitude of 1300-1660 m.

2. **Cupressus duclosiana** Hickel (See orig. text page 94)

3. **Cupressus funebris** Endl. (See orig. text pages 93-94)

4. **Cupressus torulosa** D. Don

> *Cupressus semipervirens* Lour. et Fl.
>
> *Juniperus nepalensis* Louden
>
> *Cupressus corneyana* Knight et Perry
>
> *Juniperus corneyana* Gordon

Tree, 10-30 m high, trunk 1.5-2 m in diameters; bark dark brownish-gray, longitudinally splitting; crown ascending; branchlets, terete, 1.25 mm in diameter; leaves 0.5-1 mm long, 1-1.25 mm wide; cones 1-2 cm in diameter, usually oblong in outline; seeds suborbicular with well developed wing.

Distribution: Kansu Kaichow and Ming-Chow; Szechuan Fu-pin Hsien; Sikang; at altitude 1800-3000 meters.

Genus (2) Chamaecyparis Spach

1. **Chamaecyparis formosensis** Matsum.

Large trees. The largest coniferous tree in Eastern Asia, attaining 53 meters high, the crown 22 meters in diameter, constituting one of the most important timber trees in Taiwan; distinguished by its leaves triangular with sharp apex, darked green, oblong cones, 6-7mm in diameter, with 10-13 peltate scales, each with 2-winged seeds; wood reddish-brown, fragrant, fine-textured, resistent to termites.

Distiribution: Endemic to Taiwan often forming pure stands, at altitude 1000-2200 meters.

2. **Chamaecyparis taiwanensis** Masamune et Suzuki

Differing from *C. formosensis* by leaves light been with obtuse apex; cone large; the wood brownish, good for buildings and boats.

Distribution: In pure stands, or mixed with *C. formosensis* and hemlock, Taiwan mountains, at altitude of 1200-2900 meters.

Subfamily 3. Juniperoideae Pilger

Genus (1) Juniperus Linn.

1. **Juniperus formosana** Hayata

> Var. 1. **Juniperus formosana** Hayata var. **concolor** Hayata
>
> Bush or samll tree. Bark grayish brown; branchlets brown and slender; Leaves dark green, 2-3 cm long, 2-3 mm wide, sharply-

pointed; fruit glabular, 1–1.5 cm long.

Distribution: Very common on limestone cliffs, occurring near the sea and very common on high mountains of Taiwan.

Var. 2. **Juniperus formosana** Hayata var. **tennella** Hand.–Mazz.

2. **Juniperus chinensis** Linn. (See orig. text page 98)

3. **Juniperus convallium** Rehd.et Wilson

4. **Juniperus distans** Florin

5. **Juniperus glaucescens** Florin

6. **Juniperus jarkendensis** Komarov

7. **Juniperus komarovii** Florin

8. **Juniperus mekongensis** Komarov (See orig. text page 103)

9. **Juniperus pingii** Cheng

A small tree of 5 meters high; bark reddish brown; leaves prickly pointed, dark green in color.

Distribution: Sikang; on high mountains at altitude of 2800 meters.

10. **Juniperus prczwalskii** Komarov (See orig. text page 103)

11. **Juniperus ramulosa** Florin

12. **Juniperus rigida** S. et Z.

13. **Juniperus saltuaria** Rehd. et Wilson

14 **Juniperus squamata** Lamb.

15. **Juniperus sphaeriça** Lindl.

Juniperus sheppardii (Veitch) Melle.

Juniperus sheppardii var. *torulosa* Melle.

Tree, 5–20 meters high, very variable in growth habit; bark gray-brown to reddish brown, fibrous peeling off in strips; leaves of two types yellowish green to deep green, linear, sharply pointed, spreading in with 2 white bands above, or scale like appressed, obtuse; fruit globular, brown–violet, with mealy bloom, 6–8 mm in diameter.

Distribution: Fukien, Chekiang, Kiangsi, Szechuan, Hunan and Hupei; at altitude 120–2000 meters.

Family 10. Ephedraceae V. Wettst.

Genus (1) Ephedra Linn. (See orig. text page 110)

Family 11. Gnetaceae Lindl.

Genus (1) Gnetum Linn. (See orig. text page 114)

1. **Gnetum scandens** Roxb.

2. **Gnetum indicum** (Lour.) Merr.

A woody climber, stem 20-30 meters long, 6-10 cm thick; semi-woody or strongly woody, bark dark gray; leaves opposite, dark green and shiny above, pale below; leathery, entire, ovate with blunte apex, 10-16 cm long, 6-8 cm wide, short petoiled; fruits in large clusters, oblong, drupaceous covered by silvery scales easily detached, nuts or fruits yellow or red, edible when baked.

Distribution: Kwangsi Hanning, Kwangtung, Hainan, Yunnan, at altitude 800-1800 meters.

Var. 1. Gnetum indicum (Lour.) Merr. f. megalocarpum F. Markgraf

A twining shrub of few meters long; bark brown with granulated scales; leaves large 15-25 cm long, 10-15 cm broad, pointed at apex, commonly with milky juice; fruits oblong-cylindric to ovoid, green, with whitish dots.

Distribution: Yunnan, at altitude 1800 m.

Var. 2. Gnetum indicum (Lour.) Merr. f. parvifolium (Warb.) Masam.

Gnetum scandens var. *parvifolium* Warb.

A semi-woody climber, sometimes erect growing in sandy soil thickets, 3-4 meters high or up to 20 m long; fruit red or yellow, edible.

Distribution: Kwangtung Hainan.

Class II. Angiospermae Brongn.

(See orig. text pages 115–116)

Division A. Monocotyledonae Juss.

Family 13. Graminae Juss.

(See orig. text page 117)

Subfamily Bambusae (See orig. text page 47)

The total number of bamboo of the world is about 200 species, out of which 160 species occurred in Asia. The total genera of bamboo is 23, out of which about 13 genera occurred in China.

Genera of bamboos in China:

1. *Arundinaria*
2. *Pleioblastus*
3. *Brachystachyum*
4. *Sinarundinaria*
5. *Semiarundinaria*
6. *Indocalamus*
7. *Indosasa*
8. *Bambusa*
9. *Phyllostachys*
10. *Dendrocalamus*
11. *Shibataea*
12. *Sasa*
13. *Lingnania*

Distribution of bamboos is from the sea – level to 3300 m at Himalayan regions and 5000 m at Andes The sizes of bamboos is from 33–40 m tall, 20–30 cm in diameter.

Genus (1) Arundinaria Michx. (See orig. text page 119)

1–15. (See orig. text pages 119–125)

Genus (2) Pleioblastus Nakai

Low or tall shrubs up to 10 m., with caespitose or creeping rootstock; stems upright or arching, each node with 3–7 branches, stem-sheaths persistent; leaf-sheaths with smooth flexuous bristles at apex; spikelets with articulate rachis; lemma falcate-convolute, ressellate palea 2-keeled; lodicules 3, one twice as large as the others; stamens 3; style with 3 stigmas (Greek pleio, several and blastos, bud; referring

24

to the several buds at each node) About 30 species in East Asia.

1. **Pleioblastus hindsii** (Munro) Nakai

Culm to 4 m tall, quite erect, to 2.5 cm thick, hollow, dark olive-green, bloomy at first, internode to 20 cm long; branches erect, in dense clusters; Leaves erect, 16-20 cm long, 1-2 cm broad, long-pointed, rapering at the base, denticulate, dark green above, glaucescent beneath, with 3-6 pairs of veins, tessellated.

Distribution: Fukien and Taiwan at low altitudes.

2. **Pleioblastus scabriformis** McClure

Shrub, 1 m tall, growing in thickets. Leaves lanceolated, sharply pointed, 5-8 cm long, 1-2 cm wide; flowers white.

Distribution: Aboundant on dry clay steep slopes of Kwangtung borders, Shap Man Taai Shan, Kwangsi at altitude up to 1000 m.

Genus (3) Brachystachyum Keng

This genus somewhat resembles *Fargesia* Franch. in the general appearance of its inflorescence, but it differs in that (1) the spikelets evenly arranged on the rachis, (2) the subtending scales or spathes equals or even exceeds the raceme in length. The spike-like racemes or spikelet-clusters are subtended by a series of successively scales. This character strongly recalls that of *Phyllostachys* Sieb. et Zucc., but the absence of the intermingling spathes between the spikelets marks it off sufficiently from the latter genus. Spikelets several flowered, the upper floret imperfect, sub-sessile, ususally a few to several arranged densely into a spikelike raceme, the latter subtended below with a series of closely set scales, the rachilla disarticulating above the glumes and between the florets; glumes 1-3, the first scarious and 1-nerved when 3, the others similar to the lemma but shorter; lemmas chataceous, acuminate-pungent, several-nerved: palea 2-keeled, 2-lobed or bidentate, equalling or slightly exceeding the lemma; lodicules 3, the posterior 1 narrower, the antherior 2 obovate-oblong, nervose below, ciliate above; stamens 3, the anthers linear, obtuse, terminally exserted at maturity; Ovary narrow, glabrous, subtriquetrous above; style 3, very short; stigima very slender, plumose; Rhizomes monopodial; culm fruticose or arborescent, terete or slightly flattened above the nodes bearing several branches; racemes usually few below each leafy branchlet, the upper subtending scales spathaceous but much shorter than the raceme. ---- Monotypic known only from Southeastern China.

1. **Brachystachyum densiflorum** (Rendle) Keng

Arundinaria densiflora Rendle

Fargesia densiflora (Rendle) Nakai

This species is characterized by the short crowded groups of spikelets, closely arranged on the slender flowering shoots, which are more or less densely associated and overtopped by leafy shoots.

Distribution: Kiangsu and Chekiang.

Genus (4) Sinarundinaria Nakai

Shrubs, caespitose 6 m tall, with creeping rootstock, Stem-sheaths with appendages, deciduous; each node with several branches; Leaves glabrous; leaf-sheaths with flexuous smooth bristles; inflorescence paniculate, on leafy branches; stamens 3; style short, with 3 stigmas. Three species in China and the Himalayan regions.

1. **Sinarundinaria nitida** (Mitf.) Nakai

Culms 6 m tall, hollow, erect and leafless the first year, branching and arching the second year; stem-sheaths purplish, pubescent; leaves 5-8 cm long, 0.6-1.2 cm broad, slender-pointed and rounded at the base, denticulate, bright green above, glaucescent beneath, with 3-4 pairs of rather faint veins.

Distribution: Szechuan, Shensi, at altitude 2500 m.

2. **Sinarundinaria murielae** (Gamble) Nakai

Arundinaria murielae (Gamble) Nakai

Culms yellow with waxy bloom when young; stem-sheaths glabrous, ciliate; leaves petioled, 7-12 cm long, 1-1.5 cm broad, long acuminate into a setaceous point.

Distribution: Western Hupei, at altitude of 2300-3300 m.

Genus (5) **Semiarundinaria** Makino

Upright shrubs; stems terete; upper internodes flattened; stem-sheaths with appendages, deciduous; branches several at each node; leaf-sheaths with rigid smooth bristles; lemma tessallate; stamens 3; style short, with 3 stigimas. Three species in Japan and Southeastern Asia.

1. **Semiarundinaria farinosa** McClure

Culms erect, 7-15 m tall, internode hollow, 3.5-8 cm in diameter, terete, the upper inter nodes flattened; dark green marked with purplish-brown erect branches; stem-sheaths to 22 cm long, purplish, pubescent at first, early deciduous.

This species is distinguished by its pale color imparted to the young shoots, by a fine mealy covering alluded to in the specific epithet.

Distribution: In provinces Southeastern of the Yang-tsze River, at lower altitude; locally called Kong Naam Chuck shoots used as foods; Culms used for making split-bamboo products.

2. **Semiarundinaria gracilipis** McClure

Culm 2 meters tall, 1 cm thick; internodes purple, occurring in Kwangtung, Hainan.

3. **Semiarundinaria henryi** McClure

Culms 7 m tall, 3.6 cm in diameter; internodes red; occurring in Kwangtung, Tsin-Yuean Hsien.

4. **Semiarundinaria lima** McClure

Culms 3 m tall; internodes prominent, glabrous.; Occurring in Hainan, Hun-Mao Shan

5. **Semiarundinaria nuspicula** McClure

Culms 2 m tall, 1 cm in diameter at the base; internodes terete, glabrous; spikelet in allusion to the nodding spikelets, occurring in Hainan, Ling-Shue Hsien.

6. **Semiarundinaria scopula** McClure

Culms erect, 2–5 m tall, 1–1.5 cm thick, monopodial, a little broom alludes to the prominent, brush–like row of cilia along each deel of the exserted palea. Occurring in Hainan.

7. **Semiarundinaria shapoensis** McClure

Culm 2 m tall, 1 cm in diameter; internodes glabrous occurring in Hainan called Shan Chuk Tsai.

8. **Semiarundinaria venusta** McClure

Small shrub with culm of 1.4 m tall, internodes terete, 8.5 mm in diameter.

This species deviates from the genus Semiarundinaria in the common occurrance of 6 stamens in the florets and those without producing 6 stamens may be prematured. Occurring in Kwangtung Hwa Hsien.

Genus (6) **Indocalamus** Handel–Mazz.

This genus is very much like Sasa, but differs in the number of stamens and stigimas: Sasa has 6 stamens and sometimes with 3 stigmas and 3 stamens, where as Indocalamus has 3 stamens and 2 stigmas; All other generic characters are similar to that of Sasa, seven species occurring in India, China, Philippines, and Taiwan.

1. **Indocalamus confusus** McClure

Culm 1–2 m, internodes 7.3 cm long, 2.5 cm in diameter, terete, glabrous nodes prominent; branches 1–3, appressed; branchlets solitary.

Distribution: Hupei Fan Hsien at altitude 2000–3200 m.

2. **Indocalamus fargesii** Nakai

Arundinaria fargesii E. C. Camus

Leaves 3–5, 15–20 cm long, 25–30 mm wide, lanceolate, linear, acuminate, short petoiled, attenuated at the base, margin serrate, sub–hirsute; inflorescences paniculates, terminal, tessellate; flowers 6–10, linear, oblong; rachis angulate.

Distribution: Szechuan.

3. **Indocalamus herklotsii** McClure

Culms reed–like 2 m tall, 5–6 cm in diameter, rhizome monopodial; Leaf – sheaths overlapping; inflorescence terminal; fruits deciduous when matured.

Distribution: Hongkong New Territory.

4. **Indocalamus nanunicus** McClure

Culms dwarfed, erect, up to 4 m tall, 1 cm thick.; branches solitary; internodes cylindric, glabrous; specimens growing in favorable conditions often produce the primary branches in 3. Occurring in Kwangsi.

5. **Indocalamus longiauritus** Handel–Mazz.

Arundinaria (Indocalamus) longiauritus Hand.–Mazz.

Culms 1–1.5 m tall, with very small hollowed center; Leaves pale green, lanceolate, 15–22 cm long, 4–6 cm wide, oblong with acuminate apex, broadly cuneate at base; leaf-sheaths fringed with brown hairs; leaves mostly on the upper part of the culms, while those below generally reduced to small ligules of about 1 x 5 cm attached to culm bracts.

Distribution: Hunan Yun Shan and Kwangsi, Kwei-Yang at altitude of 1200 m.

6. **Indocalamus mairei** (Hack.) McClure

Culms 24 cm long; inflorescences in long panicles of 12 cm long, erect. Occurring in Yunnan, at altitude of 3600 m.

7. **Indocalamus niitakayamensis** (Hayata) Nakai

Arundinaria niitakayamensis Hayata

Sasa niitakayamensis Camus

Sasa niitakayamensis var. *microcarpa* Camus

Bush, 1-5 meters tall, forming a jungle with rootstocks forming a mat.

Distribution: Taiwan and Philippines, at altitudes 300-3600 meters.

8. **Indocalamus pallidiflorus** McClure

Culms 1 meter tall, erect; internodes 3 mm thick, glabrous, terete; nodes prominent; the first three branches 1, 2, or 3 appressed; branchlets solitary; leaves glabrous, 15 cm long, 19 mm wide; flowers pale.

Distribution: Kwangtung Naam-Kwan Shan.

9. **Indocalamus rigidulus** (Camus) Nakai

Arundinaria rigidulus Camus

Small shrub, branches in fascicles; branchlets erect appressed; leaves lanceolate; apex acuminated, short petioled, attenuated, 8-10 cm long, 15-20 mm wide.

Distribution: Szechuan.

10. **Indocalamus scariosus** McClure

Leaves 12 cm long, 15 mm wide; flower panicles 9 cm long, composed of 15 flowers; pedicels 15 mm long; anthers 3; styles 2.

11. **Indocalamus sinicus** (Hance) Nakai

Arundinaria sinica Hance

Plant with neat simple culms springing from a creeping root stock, terminated by a single panicle, or bearing large leaves only. Wright mentioned in a note about branching at the nodes.

Distribution: This species is confined to Hongkong.

Genus (7) **Indosasa** McClure

This genus is closely affiliated with the genus Sasa Makino et Shibata. It is distinguished by having 3 stamens and 1-2 leaves on the branchlet. Sasa has three leaves on each branchlet and 6 stamens.

1. **Indosasa hispida** McClure

Culms 2-3 m tall, internodes glabrous, nodes densely hispidous, small nodes persistent hispidous; branches medium large, rigid; leaves glabrous, lanceolate, oblong-lanceolate; apex acuminate, 6-9 cm long, 22-28 mm wide; base attenuated-rotundate.

Distribution: Kwangtung Lung-Men Hsien.

2. **Indosasa shibataeoides** McClure

Culms 2 m tall; branches with 1-2 leaves; internodes glabrous; leaves 5-10 cm long,

10-18 mm wide.

Distribution: Kwangtung Lau Fu Shan.

Genus (8) **Bambusa** Schreb. (See orig. text page 131)

1. **Bambusa angustata** Munro

   Culms almost herbaceous; branches angulated, green, striated; leaves 3-7 cm long, 6-8 mm broad, apex setaceous-acumunated.

   Distribution: Taiwan.

2. **Bambusa basihirsuta** McClure

   Culms 12 m tall, 7.6 cm in diameter, with dense dark hairs at the middle of the base of the culm sheaths; ligule 15 mm broad; internodes somewhat appressed; branches rigid; leaves glabrous above, pilose beneath; inflorescence deciduous.

   Distribution: Kwangtung Ho Yean Hsien and Lung Keng, local name Pin Chuk.

3. **Bambusa beecheyana** Munro

4. **Bambusa blumeana** Schult. (See orig. text page 131)

5. **Bambusa boniopsis** McClure

   Culms 2 meters tall, 1 cm in diameter; internodes teretes, somewhat curved, glabrous; leaves ovate-lanceolate, erect, acuminate, glabrous above, densely pilose beneath.

   This species is somewhat closely related to *Bambusa fecunda* McClure. It differes in having smaller status, strong triangular culm sheaths, auricules more completely hidden by the sheath-blade which is larger and larger in proportion to the sheath proper than in the case in *Bambusa fecunda*. The specific name alludes to the resemblance of the culm sheath to that of the type species *Bonia Balansa* of the genus *Bonia* Balansa.

   Distribution: Kwangtung Ling-Shui Hsien Chim Shan, Fan Maan Ts'ueng.

6. **Bambusa breviflora** Munro

   Culm large, subsolid; internodes 10-16 cm long; branches at nodes in fascicles, terete; leaves lanceolate, 6-10 cm long; flowers small, 5-7 florets.

   Distribution: Taiwan, and discovered by Oldham.

7. **Bambusa cornigera** McClure

   Culms up to 13 m tall, 6-9 cm in diameter, with rather dwarfed slender, curvative, horn-like or spine-like structure, nodes prominent, glabrous; leaf-sheath apex truncate, deciduous; auricules small, oblong-hispidous, margin ciliated or denticulated; florets deciduous.

   Distribution: Kwangsi Ts'ang-Wu Hsien, Cheung-Chow Island and West river regions above Wu-Chow.

8. **Bambusa dissemulator** McClure

   Culms 9 m high, 6 cm in diameter; sympodial, thorny.

   Distribution Kwangtung Honan Island, and Pan-Yu Hsien.

9. **Bambusa dolichoclata** Hayata

   Leleba dolichclata Odashima

   Distribution: This species was found in Taiwan.

10. **Bambusa dolichomerithalla** Hayata

    Lebela dolicho merithalla Nakai

      Distribution: This species was found in Taiwan.

11. **Bambusa eutuldoides** McClure

   Culms 12 m high, 6.3 cm in diameter the internodes covered by white powder; ligule 7 mm long, ciliate.

      Distribution: Kwangtung T'sing-Yuen Hsien.

12. **Bambusa fecunda** McClure

   Culms 6.6 m tall, 7 cm in diameter; internodes glabrous, terete, tips curved; branchlets angular, fistulose; inflorescence deciduous. The species name is alluded to its unusual rapid rate of new culm reproduction.

      Distribution: Kwangtung Hainan, Naam Foung.

13. **Bambusa fimbriligulata** McClure

   Culms 6 m, 3 cm in diameter; sheaths deciduous; nodes prominent, auricules small, glabrous; Leaves oblong-lanceolate; glabrous above, pubescent beneath, 3-16 cm long, 26-28 mm broad.

      Distribution: Kwangsi Ch'uan Hsien, local name Tan Chuk.

14. **Bambusa funghomii** McClure

   Culms 15 m tall, 6.5 cm in diameter; ligula cover 1/4 of the internodes, 1.5 cm wide; nodes elevated; plant very thorny. The local name is Hen's nest thorny bamboo. This appearently alludes to the dense clusters of long thorny branches which invest base of the clumps and render access to the interior difficult.

      Distribution: Kwangtung Honan Island and Pan-Yu Hsien.

15. **Bambusa gilba** McClure

   Culms 7-10 m tall, 5-6 cm in diameter. The specific epithet alludes to the characteristic high point on the shoulder in sheaths from the middle nodes of the culms.

      Distribution: Kiangsi, South of Kan-Chow.

16. **Bambusa lapidia** McClure

   Culms erect, 17 m tall, 6.5 cm in diameter. Local name means "Stone bamboo" occurring in Honan Island Kwangtung.

17. **Bambusa malingensis** McClure

   Culms erect, 10 m tall, 6 cm in diameter.

   Occurring in Kwangtung, Hainan Yai Hsien.

18. **Bambusa multiplex** (Lour.) Raeusch.

   Culms 3 m tall, 7.5 cm in diameter.

   Occuring in Kwangsi.

19. **Bambusa mutabilis** McClure

   Culms 4-5 m tall, 3 cm in diameter; internodes elongated, terete, glabrous.

      Distribution: Hainan Ling-Shui Hsien.

20. **Bambusa nana** Roxb. (See orig. text page 131)

21. **Bambusa oldhamii** Munro

Culms erect, striate, purplish at base; Branches 2-4 on each node, never solitary; Leaves 6-10 cm long; young shoots edible.

Distribution: Taiwan, Tan-Shui.

22. **Bambusa pachinensis** Hayata

Leleba pachinensis Nakai

This species is found in Taiwan.

23. **Bambusa pervariabilis** McClure

The shape and pubescence of the sheaths of culms and branches and the pubescence of the internodes, are variable. The species may represent a hybrid between *Bambusa tuldoides* and *Bambusa eutuldoides*.

Distribution: Kwangtung Pan-Yu Hsien.

24. **Bambusa piscaporum** McClure

Culms 10 m tall, 3 cm in diameter; internodes elongated, terete, glabrous; sheath apex convex; leaves glabrous above, pilose beneath; inflorescence deciduous. The culm with gradual tapering is fitted for use as fishing rods.

Distribution: Hainan Wen-Chang Hsien.

25. **Bambusa rutila** McClure

Culms erect, 12 m tall, 6 cm in diameter, spikelet in purplish-red tint.

This thorny bamboo is cultivated in the New Territory of Hongkong and wild in Kwangtung Shui Chow District.

26. **Bambusa shimadai** Hayata

Leleba shimadai Nakai

A small bush, 2-4 m tall; branches in dense clusters on nodes.

Occurring in Taiwan.

27. **Bambusa spinosa** Roxb.   (See orig. taxt page 132)

28. **Bambusa stenostachya** Hack.

A large bamboo with culms of 20 m high, 6-8 cm. in diameter.

Occurring in Taiwan.

29. **Bambusa striata** Loddiges et Lindl.

A gradual tufted very glabrous, slender species, 2-7 m tall, as thick as a thumb; internodes 10-25 cm long, shining striped yellow and green; leaves 15-20 cm long, 3-4 cm broad, linear-oblong or oblong-lanceolate from an obtuse unequal base, glabrous, margin finely ciliated, rather glabrous beneath; sheaths slender, smooth, glabrous; ligule short, truncate, ciliate; panicles with 3 sessiled spikelets, 3-5-flowered; glumes and lower palea similar, acuminated with many obscured nerves, smooth; stamens 6; anthers almost as long as the glumes; upper palea slender, 2-nerved, ciliated; scales 3, oblong, pilose; ovary hairy; stigmas 2.

Distribution: Kwangtung.

30. **Bambusa tessellata** Munro

Very small bamboo. Leaves membraneous, oblong-lanceolate, tessellate, apex acuminate.

Occurring in Kwangtung.

31. **Bambusa textilis** McClure

Culms 9-10 m tall, 5-6 cm in diameter; internodes elongated cylindric; branches in fascicles on nodes.

Occurring in Kwangsi T'sang Wu Hsien.

32. **Bambusa tuldoides** Munro   (See orig. taxt page 132)

33. **Bambusa verticillata** Blume

A large bamboo occurring in Taiwan.

(The following species of bamboos are reported to be found in China, but no type specimens have been seen and further studies about them are needed.)

1. **Bambusa contori** Munro   In Kwangtung.

2. **Bambusa flexuosa** Munro   in Kwangtung.

3. **Bambusa vulgaris** Schrad.   No definite locality.

Genus (9) **Phyllostachys** Sieb. et Zucc. (See orig. text page 125)

1-10.   (See orig. text pages 125-130)

11. **Phyllostachys cerata** McClure

Culms erect, 5 m tall, 2 cm in diameter, internodes elongated, glabrous; nodes prominent; leaves very long, with truncate apex, and ciliated margin, hispidous; ligule small.

Distribution: Hunan Sin-Yang, at altitude of 800 m.

12. **Phyllostachys filifera** McClure

Culms 8 m tall; branches 30 cm long internodes terminal curvatured, slender; leaves 8-10 cm long, 6-8 mm wide.

Distribution: Fukien Shao - Wu.

13. **Phyllostachys formosana** Hayata

14. **Phyllostachys henryi** Rendle

Culms 2 m tall; branches quadrangulary, glabrous; leaf-sheathes glabrous; leaves lanceolate; apex acute, pointed, 4-6 cm long, 1-15 cm wide; characteristically near *Phyllostachys stauntenii* Munro, but differs in shorter ligule and shorter finibriae at the mouth of the sheath and in solitary dense panicules at the end of short leafy branches.

Distribution: Hupei Nanto.

15. **Phyllostachys hispida** McClure

Small bamboo, 2 m tall, 2 cm in diameter, leaves broad-ovoid, bright-green above, glabrous beneath, 8-12 cm long, 4-6 cm wide, with ciliated prickly margin; 1-2 leaves on each branchlet.

Distribution: Growing on open hill side of Anhwei Ma Chi. at altitude 400 meters.

16. **Phyllostachys lithophila** Hayata

A small bamboo with very slender branchlets, bearing 1-2 leaves on each.

Occurring in Taiwan.

17. **Phyllostachys mundae** Dunn

Culms 3–10 m tall, 2 cm in diameter; leaves linear with acute apex; petioles 3–6 mm long, attenuated; culm sheaths foliated, 14–18 cm long; panicles terminating, peduncles 30–40 cm long; stigmas 3; styles 3; ligules 3 cm long.

Distribution: Forming extensive groves on the dry hills along the Han River and Fun Huang Shan and Honan.

Genus (10) Dendrocalamus Nees

Culms 2–10 meters tall; culm sheaths striate; Rootstock or rhizome sympodial; Stamen 6 rarely more; Palea 2-keeled; fruit a nut or berry; pericarp crustaceous and separable from the seeds.

This genus consists of more than 20 species. Occurring in Burma, India and Himalayan regions. 5 species occur in China.

1. **Dendrocalamus affinis** Rendle

A small shrub of 4 meters tall with a striate culm sheath; rhizome sympodial; fruit nut–like.

Occurring in Kwangsi.

2. **Dendrocalamus brandisii** Kurz

A small shrub of 8 meters high.

Occurring in Yunnan.

3. **Dendrocalamus flagellifera** Munro

A small bamboo, 5 m tall, with sympodial rhizomes.

Occurring in Kwangsi.

4. **Dendrocalamus giganteus** Munro

Culms 5–10 m tall with very large leaves; leaves 12 – 25 cm long, 4 – 6 cm wide, lanceolate, base rotundate, petiolate, upper surface glabrous, pubescent below, margin serrate; ligule elongated; internodes hirsute; stamens 6; stigma bifidous; fruit nut–like with a rugose hirsutous crown; seeds enveloped in a periginium.

Distribution: Yunnan.

5. **Dendrocalamus latiflorus** Munro

A small bamboo occurring in Taiwan.

Genus (11) Shibataea Mak.

Shrubs to 1.5 m tall; stems zigzag, much flattened, nearly solid; branches very short, 3–5 at each node; leaves terminal on short branches, short petioled; sheaths without bristles; inflorescences on leafless branches; spikelets 1 – 2 flowered; lodicules 3; stamens 3; style long, with 3 stigmas. Two species in East Asia.

1. **Shibataea kumasasa** (Steud.) Nak.

Culms 1–2 m tall, upright, very zigzag, much flattened, narrow fistulose, green; internodes 2–8 cm long; branches 2–5 at each node; leaves distinctly stalked, ovate-oblong to ovate-lanceolate, 6–12 cm long, 1.5–2.5 cm broad, long-pointed, broadly cuneate at the base, lustrus dark green above, slightly glaucescent, and at first puberulous beneath, with 6-7 pairs of veins.

Distribution: Japan and Northeastern provinces of China.

Genus (12) Sasa Makino et Shibata (See orig. text page 135)

1. **Sasa japonica** Makino (See orig. text page 135)

2. **Sasa longiligulata** McClure

Culms 1.5 m tall, 1 cm in diametr; rhizomes monopodial; branches solitary, 15-300 cm long; branchlets 3-15-foliated; leaf-sheaths hirsute, liguea very long, 6.5-25 cm long. 15-33 mm broad. The specilic name is alluded to the color of the young culm-sheath; locally called Chek Chuk.

Distribution: Kwangtung Loh-Fau* Shan, at altitude of 900 m in shaded ravines, usually in isolated clumps.

3. **Sasa tessellata** Makino (See orig. text page 135)

4. **Sasa veithii** Rehder (See orig. text page 136)

Genus (13) Lingnania McClure

Plants caespitose, rarely climbing; Culms erect or climbing; Rhizomes sympodial; branches slender, rigid, cylindric, terete, glabrous, shining bright-green; internodes elongated and restricted, somewhat curved; nodes prominent, elevated; culm-sheaths deciduous with truncated apex; leaves 5-7 on each branch, 10-25 cm long, 2-5 cm wide, sharply pointed, margin entire; lodicules 3, hispidous; flowers scarlet-green-pale-yellow, fragrant; glumes 2-4; palea convolute minutely 2-dentate; keels indistinct; anthers 6, style united; ovary glabrous, with 3 long plumose stigmas.

Distribution: Mostly in Indo-China; Some species in Hainan Island, and other in Kwangtung.

1. **Lingnania chungii** McClure

Bambusa chungii McClure

Bambusa cerosissima McClure

A tall erect bamboo of 12 meters high. Occurring in Hainan and Kwangtung.

2. **Lingnania fimbriligulata** McClure

Culms 12 m tall, 7.2 cm in diameter; ligule 9 mm broad; leaf-sheaths deciduous, glabrous, occurring Hainan Hung Mo Shan.

3. **Lingnania funghomii** McClure

Culms 3 m tall; sheaths deciduous, glabrous, with its base densely papillose; leaves lanceolate with margin ciliated. Occurring in Kwangtung Hain-An Hsien.

4. **Lingnania parviflora** McClure

Culms 10 m tall, 5 cm in diameter, purplish-red in color; internodes terete, glabrous; nodes prominent; branches each with 7 leaves leaf-sheath elevated, striated, 4-8 cm long, 8-12 mm wide; flowers very small; spikelets conspicuously purplish-red tinted when fresh.

Distribution: Hainan Island.

5. **Lingnania scandens** McClure

Culms climbing very thin; spikelets few, lemmas obtuse, apically purple-tinted lod-dicules hispidous and frequently occurrance of 2 stigmas.

Distribution: Hainan, Yai District.

6. **Lingnania sericea** McClure

Culms erect, 3 m tall, 2 cm in diameter; branches slender; leaves oblong-lanceolate, sharp-pointed, 5-12 cm long, 2-3 cm wide; margin entire, bright green, glabrous; leaf-sheath very long, glabrous.

Distribution: Growing in woods or on slopes near streams in Hainan Island.

Family 14. Palmae
(See orig. text 137)

Genus (1) Phoenix (See orig. text page 140)

1. **Phoenix hanceana** Naud.

> Var. 1. **Phoenix hanceana** Naudin var. **formosana** Beccari
> This variety occurs in Taiwan.

2. **Phoenix humilis** Roxb.

Small shrub 80 cm tall; Leaves simple pinnatedly compound, with white dots; Fruit drupe-like, greenish-yellow.

Distribution: In the margin of thickets on dry slopes among pines in Yunnan, at altitude 1280-1460 m Kin-tung Chai and Lan-T'sang Hsien.

3. **Phoenix roebeleni** O'Brien (See orig. text page 141)

Genus (2) Trachycarpus (See orig. text page 144)

Genus (3) Rhapis

1. **Rhapis excelsa** A. Henry (See orig. text page 147)

2. **Rhapis filiformis** Burret

Segments of petiole 21 cm long, acute pointed; leaves 37 cm long, 10 cm broad, very robust; ligule rotundate, glabrous; male inflorescences 23 cm long, filiformis; male flowers small, 3 mm long; calyx 1 mm high, 3-lobed; corolla tubular, cylindric, 2 mm in diameter; stamens 6, biseriated; anthers ovate, laterally dehiscent, sessile; stamen 3 united at base, linear-lanceolate to linear, 3 cm broad; main ribs 4 attenuated at the apex; fruit unknown.

Distribution: Kwangsi.

3. **Rhapis gracilis** Burret

Stems 1 cm. in diameter; sheaths slenderly and gradually fibrous; leaf-segements 3 or 4, apex acutely toothed; spadix about 20 cm long, simple or lower parts again branched; fruits globose, 8-9 mm in diameter.

Distribution: Kwangtung.

4. **Rhapis mutifida** Burret

Stems with leaves 2 meters tall, 1 cm in diameter; sheaths with exterior fibers brown, regularly disposed, inner fibers stouter; leaf - segements 12; main ribs 2, narrowly linear-lanceolate, about 1.5 cm broad, attenuate at the apex, point at base; spadix about 28 cm long, partially exposed from the tubular, spathe much branched; rachillae furfuraceous; fruit subglogbose to oval, 9 mm long.

Distribution: Kwangsi, at altitude 1000–1500 m.

5. **Rhapis robusta** Burret

Stem with leaves 2 m or more tall, 1 cm in diameter; sheaths brown, with regularly disposed slender fibers; leaves segments 4, cut near to base; the main ribs 3 or 4, lanceolate to broad-lanceolate, 5 cm long, 2.5 cm broad; spadix 25 cm long, 3-forked; rachillae slender and brownish furfuraceous; matured fruit not described.

Distribution: Kwangsi.

Genus (4) Licuala

1. **Licuala fordiana** Beech. (See orig. text page 148)
2. **Licuala spinosa** Wurmb.

Corypha pilaria Lour. et Fl.

Licuala pilaria (Lour.) Bl.

Licuala spinosa var. *cochinensis* Becc.

Erect palm 1.5–4 m tall. 2–3 cm in diameter; leaves green above; rachis with spines; infloerescence upright in axil of a leaf; flowers yellow; fruit red.

Distribution: Hainan, Yai Chow, at altitude 460–1800 m.

Genus (5) Livistona R. Br.

1. **Livistona chinensis** Mart. (See orig. text page 149)
2. **Livistona saribus** (Lour.) Merr. et Chevalier

Corypha saribus Lour. et Fl.

Saribus cochinensis Bl.

Livistona cochinensis (Bl.) Mart.

Tree 20 m tall, 20 cm in diameter, bark ringed; fruit greenish-yellow.

Distribution: Hainan Mocheung Ling; growing in forest at altitude 900–1000 m.

3. **Livistona speciosa** Kurz

Tree 30 meters high with green fruit, occurring in Yunnan You Lau Shan, at altitude of 1100 meters.

Genus (6) Calamus L.

1. **Calamus formosanus** Becc.

Calamus margaritae Hance

Calamus quenquesetinerus Burret

A climber up to 30 meters long; with rigid spines and shining yellow leaves; fruit white, occurring in Taiwan.

2. **Calamus hoplites** Dun.

Calamus walkeri Hance

A small erect tree of a climber of a few meters long; leaves oblong, 2–3 m long; leaves segments linear; petiole glabrous, no spine; flower pale yellow, very fragrant.

Distribution: Fukien, Hongkong in woods. This species is near to *Calamus thy-sanolepis* Hance, but distinguished by the armatures of the leaves and by its smaller flowers.

3. **Calamus tetradactyloides** Burret   (See orig. text pages 151-152)

4. **Calamus thysanolepis** Hance   (See orig. text page 152)

5. The following new species of Calamus are desposited in European Herbaria ---Botanical Museum, Berlin-Dahlem: (See orig. text page 152)

   (1) **Calamus egrigius** Burret ----- in Hainan.

   (2) **Calamus henryanus** Becc. ---- in Yunnan.

   (3) **Calamus macrorrhynehus** Burret---- in Kwangtung.

   (4) **Calamus melanochrous** Burret ---- in Kwangsi.

   (5) **Calamus multispicatus** Burret ---- in Hainan.

   (6) **Calamus oxyxarpus** Becc. ---- in Yunnan.

   (7) **Calamus pulchellus** Burret ---- in Hainan.

   (8) **Calamus platyacanthoides** Merr.----- Climber in Hainan and Yunan.

Genus (7) Caryota L. (See orig. text pages 152-153)

Genus (8) Arenga (See orig. text pages 153-155)

1. **Arenga engleri** (Warb.) Becc.

   Didymosperma engleri Warb.

A small bush 4-6 m tall; fruit orange to reddish color, cultivated in Hongkong and in Fukien.

2. **Arenga pinnata** Merr. (See orig. text page 155)

Genus (9) Areca L. (See orig. text pages 155-156)

1. **Areca catechu** L. (See orig. text page 156)

Family 15. Liliaceae Adans.
(See orig. text pages156-157)

Genus (1) Cordyline

1. **Cordyline terminales**   (See orig. text page 157)

Division B. Dicotyledonae
(See orig. text pages 157-158)

Family 16. Salicaceae Lindl.
(See orig. text page 158)

Genus (1) Populus L. (See orig. text page 159)

1-10. **Populus adenopoda** Max. (See orig. text pages 159-167)

9. **Populus macronthela** Levl. et Vant.

Stem 15-20 meters high, glabrous; leaves ovate, small petioled, acuminated, dentate, ciliated, rotundate at base; male aments 15-20 cm long, pediculary; lobes 5-8, acute; stamens 3-8; female aments 20-24 cm long, stigmas 4, capsules glabrous, dentate, asymetrical; when adult glabrous.

This species is closely related to *Populus adenopoda* Maxim. It differes only in the repantly denticulated serration of the leaves, and the fruits, being glabrous and eglandular.

Distribution: Yunnan, Kweichow. at altitude 1000-2000 m.

11. **Populus nigra** L.

Tree 30 m or more tall, with wide-spreading stout branches and usually short trunk; bark deeply furrowed, often with large spurs, branchlets terete, glabrous, orange changing to ashy-gray the second year; buds viscid, reddish, elongated and curving outward the apex; leaves rhombic-ovate, long acuminate, broad-cuneate, finely crenate-serrate, non-ciliate, 5-10 cm long, 4-8 cm wide, glabrous, light green beneath; those on short branches, smaller and broader and often truncate or rounded at base; petiole slender; staminate catkins 4-6 cm long; scales laciniate; stamens 20-30; fruiting catkins 10-15 cm long; capsules 2-valved; pedicel slender, 3-5 mm long.

Distribution: Western Kansu Plain.

12-14 (See orig. text pages 169-172)

15. **Populus purdomii** Rehder

A large leaved handsome popular; leaves ovate to narrow-ovate, 10-13 cm long, or on short shoots oblong-ovate and to 25 cm long, rounded to sub-cordate at base, pilose on the distinctly raised veins and veinlets beneath or sometimes glabrous, more coarsely glandular-serrate.

This is a closely related species of *Populus cathayana* Rehder.

Distribution: North-Western China, at altitude of 1200-2200 meters.

16-19. (See orig. text pages 172-176)

20. **Populus tremula** L. European aspen.

Tree to 30 meters tall, usually much smaller, with round open head; suckering; branches terete, glabrous; buds ovoid, acute, slightly viscid; leaves thin, suboribcular, or ovate, rounded or acuted at apex, truncate or subcordate at base, sinuately crenate-dentate, 3-8 cm long, tomentose when unfolding, quickly glabrous, glaucescent beneath; petioles compressed, glabrous, often as long as blade; leaves of suckers ovate, to 15 cm long, pubescent beneath; catkins 8-10 cm long; scales deeply lobed and fringed; stamens 5-12, stigmas 2, 2-parted; fruiting catkins to 12 cm long.

Distribution: Europe, North Africa, West Asia to Siberia and its variety *P. t.* var. *davidiana* Schneider.

Distributed in Western and North China. It is closely related to *P. rotundifolia* Griff. of the Himalayan Region.

Genus (2) **Salix** L. (See orig. text page 167)

1-17. **Salix amygidalina** L. (See orig. text pages 177-192)

18. **Salix cantonensis** Hance

Leaves lanceolate, 4-7.5 cm long, 1-1.7 cm wide, serrate, with acuminate apex, glabrous, lower surface somewhat glaucous; catkins about 1.5-2 cm long; ovary sessile. It is closely related to *S. babylonica*.

Distribution: Kwangtung, at altitude 400-800 m.

19. **Salix calyculata** Hooker

Salix microphyta Franch.

A very small shrub of 10-25 cm tall, with ascending branchlets, the branchlets and leaves covered with silky hairs; bracts oblong glabrous ciliate and somewhat emarginate at the apex, male flowers with two very long and narrow glands, the dorsal one being scarcely smaller than the ventarl, half as long as the bracts, filaments free, glabrous 1/3 longer than the bracts; ovaries narrowly oblong, stigmas sessile, the gland broad, ovate-rectangular, truncate or emarginate at the apex, nearly enveloping the ovaries.

Distribution: Yunnan Dali and Tibet, at altitude 3300-3800 meters.

Var. 1. Salix calyculata Hook. var. **glabrifolia** Hand.-Mazz.

A dwarf creeping shrub 8-16 cm tall, on moist alpine moore land and is closely related to *Salix flabellaris* Anderss. Distributed in Yunnan, at altitude 4000-4500 meters.

20. **Salix caprea** L. (See orig. text page 192)

21. **Salix cavaleriei** Levl. (See orig. text page 192)

22. **Salix cercifolia** Goerz

A shrub 1.8 m tall, with a habit of growth resembling that of *Salix tenella* Schnieder, but differs in the staminate flowers having only one nectary and in the leaves being glabrous from the beginning.

Distribution: Kansu Tao River Basin, at altitude 2700-3000 m.

23. **Salix chang-chowensis** Metcalf

Tree 2-3 m tall; leaves scattered strigose or short pilose on upper surface; older leaves somewhat reticulated, lower surface with white bloom and abundant strigose hairs, elliptic 2-3 cm long, 8-12 mm wide, margin serrate; petioles and young branchlets densely pilose; male catkins 3-5 cm long, mostly on short branches; rachis pilose; bracts almost naked above, white pilose beneath, stamens 4-7, glabrous.

This species is closely related to *Salix cantonensis* Hance.

Distribution: Fukien Chang-Chow, Cloudy Hill.

24. **Salix chekiangensis** Cheng

This species belongs section to Tetraspermae or Pentadrae and is related to *Salix wilsonii* from which it differs in the leafless staminate inflorescences, lanceolate or ovate-lanceolate pilose flowering bracts, the shaped of glands, and the long acuminated leaves. It is also near to *Salix mesnyi* Hance but differs in the obovate flowering bracts which are glabrous outside and obtuse or rounded at the apex, the more numerous (6-10) stamens, and the usually subcordate leaves.

25. **Salix characta** Schneider (See orig. text page 193)

26. **Salix cheilophila** Schneider (See orig. text page 193)

27. **Salix chingiana** Hao

Small tree or shrub up to 6 m tall; occurring in Kansu near Sining, at altitude 2650–3100 meters.

28. **Salix chikungensis** Schneider (See orig. text page 193)

29. **Salix chuniana** Fang

Tree 3–5 m tall; branches terete. It is closely related to *Salix rehderiana* Schneider in general appearence but it differs in the habit of flowering after the leaves and in the pedunculate long and narrow pistillate catkins, which are leafless at the base. The flower of *S. rehderiana* are precocious and the sessile catkin is just 2.5 cm long and 8 mm in width and provided with 2 or 3 normal lancelate leaves at the base of the inflorescences.

Distribution: Szechuan, Mt. Omei, at altitude 2000 m.

30. **Salix chieni** Cheng

Tree 8 m tall; characterized by upright branching habit with usually elliptic leaves distinctly glaucous and sometimes pilose beneath, short staminate inflorescence, flowers with 2 stamens slightly connate at base; pistillate flowers with ovate–oblong–ovate bracts, and glabrous ovary with distinct style. It is closely related to *S. babylonica*, but differs in the upright branching growth habit and usually shruby form.

Distribution: Chekiang Tien Mo Shan and Anhwei Chu Hua Shan at altitude 100–350 meters.

31. **Salix denticulata** Anders. (See orig. text page 193)

32–46 (See orig. text pages 194–198)

47. **Salix formosa** Willdenow

> *Salix punifolia* Smith
>
> *Salix arbuscula* (Willd.) Wier
>
> *Salix cineraea* Willd.

A small tree with stomata on the upper surface of the leaves; leaves seritate, glabrous

Distribution: Mt. Altai and Siberia.

48. **Salix franchiana** (Burkill) Hand. –Mazz. (See orig. text page 198)

49. **Salix fulvopubescens** Hayata

Small shrub with very slender branches; leaves oblong–lanceolate, obtuse at the apex; short petioled; margin entire.

Distribution: Taiwan and Alisan.

50. **Salix glandulosa** Seem. (See orig. text page 199)

> Var. 1.
> Var. 2. (See orig. text page 199)

51. **Salix gracilistyla** Miquel (See orig. text page 199)

52. **Salix hsinhsuaniana** Fang

Shrub 1–2m tall; branches terete, pubescent, bracts of both male and female flower glabrous on both surfaces, ciliate; the ventral glands shorter than the bracts.

Distribution: Sikang Tien-Chun Hsien and Omei Mts.

53. **Salix hsiana** Goerz

Shrub 1.8m tall with branches roughly wrinkled. It is closely related to *Salix tenella* Schneider but differs in having thinner branchlets, smaller and thicker leaves, and short petioles.

Distribution: Szechuan Wen-Chuan Hsien at altitude 2780-3100 meters.

54. **Salix bylonoma** Schneider (See orig. text page 199)

55. **Salix hypoleuca** Seem. (See orig. test page 200)

56. **Salix inamoena** Hand.-Mazz. (See orig. text page 200)

57. **Salix juparica** Goerz (See orig. text page 201)

58. **Salix kusanoi** Schneider

Salix oldhamiana Henry

Tree 3-6 meters tall; branches purplish glabrous; leaves ovate or ovate-elliptic, rotundate at the base, with acute apex; male aments pedunculate, 5-10 cm long; female aments 3 cm long, 1 cm broad. This species is distinguished by its brownish pubescent in its young parts and coarse serrate multinerved leaves, the short fruiting aments, and by its nervation of the old leaves. It is closely related to *Salix tonkinensis* Seem. and *Salix tetrasperma* Roxb.

Distribution: Taiwan.

59. **Salix kouychensis** Schneider (See orig. text page 201)

60-64 (See orig. text pages 201-202)

65. **Salix mairei** Levl.

Small shrub 4 m tall, stems 1 cm thick; stigma slightly bi-lobed; occurring in Yunnan at altitude 3000 meters.

66. **Salix magnifica** Hemsl.

Bush 1-6m tall, with large broad leaves, appearing more like a poplar than a willow, with very long catkins, glabrous in all parts; branches straight, dark purple, sparingly lenticellate; leaves coriaceous when mature, abruptly and obtusely acuminate, rounded at the base; primary lateral veins 12-15 pairs, slightly curved; male catkins shortly stalked, 10-12 cm long; flowers diandrous; female catkins 20 cm long, erect; capsules 2-valved.

Distribution: Western Szechuan, at altitude 2600-3000 m.

67. **Salix mesnyi** Hance (See orig. text page 203)

68. **Salix microphyta** Fr. (See orig. text page 203)

69. **Salix microstachya** Turcz.

Small shrub up to 3 m tall; branches purplish red; leaves narrow, slender, green above, pubescent beneath. Occurring in Kansu Ho Lan Shan, at altitude 2750 m.

70. **Salix miyabeana** Seem. (See orig. text page 203)

71-88 (See orig. text pages 204-210)

89. **Salix pseudo-ernestii** Goerz

Small tree 2-4 m tall and is affiliated with *Salix balfouriana*, occurring in Szechuan

Wen–Chuan Hsien at altitude 3000 meters.

90–98 (See orig. text pages 210–214)

99. **Salix schneideriana** Hao

Small tree of a few meters tall; leaves oblong, 2.5–4.5 cm long, 4–9 mm wide, margin revolute, glandular, denticulate; bracts elliptic, white pilose or scarcely villous, ventral gland on male plant cylindrical, half as long as bracts.

Distribution: Chekiang, Yen Tan Shan.

100. **Salix siberica** Pallas (See orig. text page 214)

101. **Salix sikkimensis** Anderss. (See orig. text page 214)

102. **Salix souliei** Seem. (See orig. text page 214)

103. **Salix spathulafolia** Seem. (See orig. text page 215)

104. **Salix sphaeronympha** Goerz

Shrub 2–3 m tall; bark yellow–green; branchlets dirty green; stipules ovate, 1–15 mm long; petiole 2–3 mm long, densely tomentose, occurring in Szechuan Pan Lan Shan, at altitude 3000–3700 m.

105. **Salix sqaurrosa** Schneider (See orig. text page 215)

106. **Salix subpycnostachya** Burkill

Small tree; bark cortically fissured; leaves oblanceolate pilose. It is distinguished from *Salix pycnostachys* Anderss. by its long style, more acute bracts and less hairy leaves. The leaves are produced much later than the flowers.

Distribution: Szechuan Ta–Chien–Lu, at altitude 3000–5200 m.

107. **Salix tangii** Hao

Shrub 2 meters tall; bark grayish black, smooth; leaves obovate, tomentose below; brachlets purplish brown.

Distribution: Shansi at altitude 1800 meters.

108. **Salix taoensis** Goerz (See orig. text page 215)

109–112 (See orig. text pages 215–216)

113. **Salix vaccinioides** Hand.–Mazz.

A small shrub with obovate leaves, triangular stipules, dark brown branches, long slender aments.

Distribution: Yunnan, Tibet and Burma, at altitude 3275 m.

114. **Salix variegata** Franch. (See orig. text page 217)

115. **Salix wangii** Goerz

Shrub 3 meters tall; leaves lanceolate, 3–9 cm long, 1–3 cm wide, obtuse at the base, margin revolute, tomentose beneath, occurring in Szechuan Wen Chuan Hsien, at altitude 3560 meters.

116. **Salix warburgii** Seem.

Bushy tree, 2–15 meters tall, 2–50 cm in diameter, occurring in Taiwan.

117. **Salix wallichiana** Anderss. (See orig. text page 217)

118. **Salix wenchuanica** Goerz

Tree 3-5 m tall; branchlets brown; leaves oblong-ovate, 5-8 cm long, 2-4 cm wide, finely serrate, densely tomentose beneath, apex obtuse; female catkins hairy, 8 cm long, 1 cm thick. Distributing Szechuan, at altitude 2300 m.

119. **Salix wilhelmsiana** M.B. (See orig. text page 218)

           Var. 1. Salix wilhelmsiana var. microstachya Turcz. (See orig. text page 218)

120. **Salix wolohoensis** Schneider (See orig. text page 218)

121. **Salix wuiana** Hao

Tree 10 m tall; branches dark gray; leaves oblanceolate, 4 cm long, 1.5 cm broad, entire, glabrous; female catkins short petioled, 3 cm long, 6 mm thick.

Distribution: Kansu Li-Chen, at altitude 2150-2950 meters.

Family 17. Myricaceae L.
(See orig. text pages 218-219)

Genus (1) Myrica Linn.

1. **Myrica esculenta** Buch.-Ham.

2. **Myrica nagi** Thunb.

A small shrub; branches rigid, dark brown; leaves alternate, spatulate, acuminate or mucronate at the apex, 6-10 cm long, 2-3 cm wide, short petioled; catkins reddish brown, occurring in Taiwan.

3. **Myrica rubra** S. et Z.

4. **Myrica adenophora** Hance

           Var. 1. Myrica adnophora Hance var. **kusanoi** Hayata

                Shrub with thick rigid and grey-brown branchlets; leaves small, obovate-lanceolate, recurved at margin, occurring in Hengchun, Taiwan.

Family 18. Juglandaceae Lindley
(See orig. text pages 221-222)

Genus (1) Platycarya S. et Z.

Genus (2) Engelhardtia Leschen.

Pterilema Reinw. (See orig. text page 223)

1. **Engelhardtia aceriflora** Bl. (See orig. text page 223)

2. **Engelhardtia chrysolepis** Hance

3. **Engelhardtia spicata** Bl.

           Var. 1. Engelhardtia spicata Bl. var. **aceriflora**

           Var. 2. Engelhardtia spicata Bl. var. **colebrookiana** K. et V. (See orig. text page 226)

           Var. 3. Engelhardtia spicata Bl. var. **gernera** K. et V.

                A small tree 10-12 meters tall; occurring in Yunnan.

4. **Engelhardtia fenzelii** Merr.

    This species is closely related to *Engelhardtia wallichiana* Lindl. and to *Engelhardtia chrysolepis* , but differs particularly in shorter leaves, fewer elliptic to oblong–opposite leaflets, and in the smaller fruiting bracts.

Distribution: Kwangtung near Kaufung.

5. Engelhardtia **wallichiana** Lindl. (See orig. text pages 226–228)
6. Engelhardtia **mollis** Manning

Tree 10 meters tall; 15 cm diameter; branches robust rugose, striate, glabrous, lenticelled, whitish gray; branchlets tomentose; leaves 25 cm long, petioled, terete; leaflets 7–8 pairs, subsessile or short petioled, tawny–brown tomentose, carioceous, oblong–lanceolate, 9 cm long and 3.5 cm broad, acuminate, obliquely rounded at base, slightly revolute and crenate–serrate along the margin, midrib elevated above, secondary veins and reticulations, densely pilose along the midrib and veins fruiting bracts densely hirsute at base, 3 cm long, 6.5 mm broad.

Distribution: South–western Yunnan Yenn–Yeh Hsien, at altitude 1080 meters.

Genus (3) **Pterocarya** Kunth (See orig. text page 228)

1–8 (See orig. text page 228)

Genus (4) **Juglans** L. (See orig. text page 233)

1. **Juglans cathayensis** Dode (See orig. text page 233)
2. **Juglans formosana** Hayata

Large tree 12–20 m tall; bark brownish–grey; leaves odd–pinnate, large, bluntely acuminate, 40–80 cm long, 6–8 cm wide; leaflets 7–13, oblong–ovate, brownish, densely pubescent beneath, especially along the midrib and veins; rachis very long and densely pubescent. Distribution: Taiwan.

3. **Juglans hopeiensis** Hu

Tree 25 meters tall; branches glabrous, leaves 45–80 cm long; rachis glabrous; leaflets 7–15, elliptic–oblong–ovate, 10–23 cm long, 6–9 cm wide; acute–acuminated, obscure dentate–serrate; male flowers 24 cm long, pubescent; fruit 1–3, globose, tetrapartial, 5 cm long, 4 cm in diameter, apiculate.

Distribution: Hopei, Hsia Chow.

4. **Juglans manchurica** Maxim. (See orig. text pages 233–234)
5. **Juglans regia** L. (See orig. text pages 234–236)
6. **Juglans sinensis** Dode (See orig. text pages 236–237)

Genus (5) **Carya** (See orig. text page 237)

1–2

3. **Carya sinensis** Dode

Carya integrifolialata Kuan.

Tree 13 meters tall; 30 cm in diameter; leaves short, leaflets 5–11 in number, 8–16 cm long, 4–6 cm wide, oblong–lanceolate, brownish pubescent along the midribs beneath, acuminate at the apex; nut round.

Distribution: Yunnan, at altitude 500 meters.

4. **Carya tsiangii** Chun

Tree 13 meters tall, 6 cm in diameter; bark dark gray; barnchlets lenticulate; leaves mostly 9 leaflets, deep lustrous green above, light green below; fruit green, small.

Distribution: Kweichow.

Family 19. Betulaceae Agardh.

(See orig. text page 239)

Genus (1) Ostryopsis Dcne. (See orig. text page 242)

Genus (2) Ostrya Scop.

Key to the Species of Ostrya

A. Leaves with 18–20 pairs of lateral veins ---------------------- *O. multinervis*.

AA. Leaves with no more than 15 pairs of lateral veins.

B. Involucre contracted into a slender stipe at base, to 2.5 cm

long -- *O. rehderiana*.

BB. Involucre not contracted into a slender stipe at base, up to 15

cm long.

C. Involucre obovate-oblong, 1.5 cm long, 8 mm braod --------- *O. japonica*.

CC. Involucre elliptic-oblong, 1–1.5 cm long, 6 mm broad

---- -------------- --(2) *O. liana*.

1. **Ostrya japonica** Sargent (See orig. text page 243)

2. **Ostrya liana** Hu

A deciduous tree up to 16 m high; trunk 60 cm in diameter; bark grayish black longitudinally fissured; branchlets terete, straite, glabrous, covered with minute white rounded lenticels; buds ovoid, acute, with imbricate broadly ovate obtuse glabrescent scales; leaves membraneous, elliptic-ovate to elliptic, acute to acuminate at apex, subcordate to rounded at base, coarsely, irregularly and doubly mucronate - serrate along the margins, glabrous above, glabrescent except puberulent along the elevated midrib and lateral veins beneath, about 47.5 cm long, 2–4 cm broad; lateral veina 10–11 pairs, straight and slightly arching and leading into the teeth at the margins, divergent at 45 degrees; veinlets slender but distinct, petioles slender, 1 cm long, tomentollate; staminate aments 2–5 in a cluster, pedunculous, 5 cm long, 7 mm broad; bracts reniform, cuspidate, red, 3 mm long, 4 mm broad; stamens numbrous, yellow; anthers long, pilose at apex; fruiting aments 2 cm long, peduncle 2–2.5 cm long, with 8–10 fruits; involucures laterally compressed, elliptic-ovate, with an oblique pointed apex, 1–1.5 cm long, 6 mm broad; nutlets laterally compressed, oviod, 7 mm long, shiny yellowish-green, glabrous at apex.

Distribution: Eastern Tomb of Chahar province, in Jehol and Southern Manchuria; wood good for making farm implements, constructions, and fine furnitures; seeds usually do not germinate until the second year.

3. **Ostrya multinervis** Rehder

A deciduous tree 16 m high; matured branches purplish-brown sparcely and appreseedly pilose, lenticelled. buds or oblong-ovoid, 6-6 mm long, scales striate, glabrous; leaves membraneous, oblong-lanceloate, 8 - 12 cm long, 3-4.5 cm broad, caudate-acuminate at apex, rounded to broadly cuneate at base, sharply and unequally and subsimply serrate with aristate teeth, upper surface with scattered appressed long hairs and pubescent along the midrib, lower surface glabrous, except sparcely pilose along the midrib and lateral veins, lateral veins 18-20 paris, 3-4 mm distant, divergent at 45 degrees; veinlets quite conspicuous; petioles 5-7 mm long, sparcely appressedly pilose, 1.5-2 cm long; immatured staminate aments 4.5-6 cm long, dense; peduncle sparcely appressedly pilose, 1.5-2 cm long; involucre elliptic, about 1.5 cm long, acute, mucronate, broadly cuneate and setulose at base, ribbed, sparcely appressedly pilose; nutlets narrowly ovoid, compressed, 6-7 mm long, 3-3.5 mm broad, very smoothly striate, ciliate at apex, pale brown.

Distribution: Hupeh, Huana, in mixed forest at altitude 650 m.

4. **Ostrya rehderiana** Chun

A deciduous tree up to 18 m high. Trunk straight, 45 cm in diameter; branches horizontally spreading; bark intensely brown-gray, rough; branchlets slender, terete, brown, lenticelled, at first serioceous-pubescent, soon glabrous and intensely purplish; buds cylindrical-ovoid, shiny-green, acute, with pubescent scales; leaves membranaceous, elliptic-oblong, 4-10 cm long, 3-4 cm broad, caudate-acuminate at apex, cuneate to rounded at base, simply and irregularly sharply serrate to obsecurely doubly serrate with aristate teeth, upper surface green and glabrous except on the lower part of the midrib, lower surface pale green and sparcely pubescent; lateral veins 13 pairs; straight and slightly arching and leading into teeth.; staminate flowers 1-3 in a cluster, pedulous, sessile, 10-13 cm long; bracts broadly ovate, caudate-acuminate, 4 mm long, and broad, red and ciliate along the margins, pilose inside, glabrous outside; stamens 10; anthers pilose at apex; fruiting aments loose, pedulous, 2-3 cm long, sericeous-pubescent; involucres brown, elliptic-oblong, 2-2.5 cm long, 8 mm broad, rounded and apiculate at apex, contracted into a stipe at base, minutely pubescent along the midrib; nutlets narrowly ovoid compressed, 8-10 mm long, sericeous-pilose at apex, brownish-green.

Distribution: Western Chekiang Tien Mo Shan, at altitude 400 to 500 meters.

Genus (3) **Carpinus** Linn.

Key to the species of Carpinus

A. Fruiting aments with bracts densely imbricate like Ostrya; bracts with or without a ligule distinctly inflexed and totally covering the nutlets; mature nutlet distinctly ellipsoid with very faint ribs. -------------- Sect. *Distegocarpus*

B. Leaves elliptic-oblong to oblong-lanceolate, to 27 cm long, with 24-34 pairs of veins; fruiting aments long-cylindrical, to 45 cm long; bracts without a distinct ligule at base of inner margin. ------------------- *Carpinus fangiana*

BB. Leaves ovate, ovate-elliptic to subovate, less than 13 cm long, with 15-20 pairs of veins; fruiting aments broadly ovoid to cylindrical, less than 13 cm long; bracts with an inflexed ligule at base of inner margin.

    C. Fruiting aments 12 cm long, long cylindrical; bracts rhombic-ovate, acute at apex, indistinctly serrulate on the upper part of the outer margin.

        D. Bracts ovate, 13 mm long, broad 7 mm ------------------------------------ ---------------------------------- (36) *C. rankanensis*

        DD. Bracts lanceolate, 12-15 mm long, 4-5 mm broad ------------------------ -------------------------------- (36-1) *C. rankanensis* var. *matsudae*

    C. Fruting aments oblong or shortly cylindrical; bracts ovate-oblong, coarsely dentate-serrate at apex.

        D. Leaves soft-long-pilose beneath, to 8 cm long, with 14-21 pairs of veins; fruiting aments shortly cylindriceal ---------------------------------- ------------------------------ (27) *C. mollis*

        DD. Leaves slightly pubescent along the veins or glabrous, to 12 cm long; fruiting aments oblong, to 15 cm long.

            E. Branchlets and petioles slightly pubescent, sonn glabrous; leaves to 15 cm long and 7 cm broad ----------- *C. cordata*

            EE. Branchlets and petioles densely pubescent; leaves smaller ---------- --- *C. cordata* var. *chinensis*

AA. Fruiting aments lax, with bracts not densely imbricate; bracts 3-lobed, or without basal lobes; nutlets not completely covered by the basal lobe of inner margin, prominently ribbed. ------------------------------- Sect. *Carpinus*

B. Nutlets with face scarecly pilose, but usually coverd with minute resinous glands.

    C. Bracts distinctly lobed at base of inner margin, outer margin dentate to lobulate, often lobed at base.

        D. Bracts distinctly lobed at base of outer margin.

            E. Leaves ovate-oblong to lanceolate, caudate-acuminate.

                F. Petioles less than 5 mm long; leaves lanceolate, less than 5 cm long; bracts usually I cm distant from each other ----------------- ------------------------------ (20) *C. lanceolata*

                FF. Petioles 8-10 mm long; leaves larger and broader; bracts more close

                    G. Leaves ovate-oblong to ovate-lanceolate, broadest below the middle; petioles of the larger leaves 10 mm long, glabrous to sparcely pilose -------(52) *C. vinimia*

                    GG. Leaves elliptic-oblong to elliptic-lanceolate, broadest at or above the middle; petioles of larger leaves no more than 8 mm long, tomentose to nearly glabrous.

    H. Midlobe of bracts obtuse or rounded at apex ─────────── ───────────── (23) *C. loudoniana*

    HH. Midlobe of bracts acute or subacute at apex. ─────────── ───────────────────────*C. poilanei*

EE. Leaves shorter and broader, ovate to ovate-oblong.

    F. Leaves distinctly and often abruptly caudate-acuminate; bracts usually 3-lobed at base, with a distinct subacute lobe at the base of inner margin.

        G. Leaves distinctly cordate at base.

            H. Fruiting aments no more than 10 cm long; bracts to 2 cm long; outer margin coarsely dentate-serrate, inner margin entire. ───────────── *C. fargesii*

            HH. Fruiting aments to 16 cm long; bracts to 2.5 cm long, inner margin serrate ─── *C. fargesii* var. *macrostachya*

        GG. Leaves rounded to subcordate at base; bracts often less than 2 cm long, outer margin of the narrow midlobe sharply serrate, inner margin entire ────*C. fargesii* var. *davidii*

    FF. Leaves short-acuminate, acute or subacute at base.

        G. Leaves broadly ovate, to 4 cm broad; bracts distinctly 3-lobed at base. ───────────── (45) *C. tientaiensis*

        GG. Leaves much narrower.

            H. Leaves to 5.5 cm long; bracts with outer margin coarsely incised-dentate-lobulate──*C. fargesiana*

            HH. Leaves to 4 cm long; bracts with outer margin coarsely and sparesly lobate-dentate ─────────────────────── ─────────────────────── *C. chowii*

DD. Bracts not lobed at base of otuer margin.

    E. Leaves broadly ovate to broadly-obovate. ───────────────────── ──────────────────────────── (35) *C. putoensis*

EE. Leaves ovate to ovate-lanceolate.

    F. Leaves to 11 cm long.

        G. Leaves oblong, to 5 cm broad; bracts to 4 cm long, with nutlets 6 mm long──────(17) *C. kweichoensis*

        GG. Leaves oblong to ovate-lanceolate, 3-4 cm broad; bracts to 2 cm long, with much smaller nutlets ──────────────────── ───────────────────── (28) *C. monbeigiana*

    FF. Leaves much shorter.

        G. Leaves sharply mucronate-dentate-serrate, over 8 cm long; bracts lanceolate, often slightly falcate ───────────────────

––––––––––––––––––– (47) *C. tschonoskii*

GG. Leaves not or slightly mucronate-dentate-serrate, 4–7 cm long.

    H. Leaves pubescent beneath ––––––––––––––––––––––––––––

––––––––––––––– (44) *C. sunpanensis*

    HH. Leaves not pubescent beneath, but long pilose along the midrib and lateral viens. ––––––––––––––––––––––––––

––––––––––––––– (16) *C. kawakamii*

        J. Bracts lanceolate; leaves 4–5 cm long.

        JJ. Bracts semi-ovate; leaves 5–7 cm long. –––––––––

–––––––––––(13) *C. huana*

    II. Leaves shortly acuminate at apex; bracts semi–ovate; inner margin with or without an obtuse basal lobe ––––

––––––––––––––––––– *C. turczaninowii*

CC. Bracts with inner margin not distinctly lobed at base, frequently with slightly inflexed margin.

    D. Leaves at maturity scarcely 5.5 cm long.

        E. Leaves broadly ovate, ovate–oblong to ovate–lanceolate; bracts with inner margin entire –––––––––(15) *C. hwai*

        EE. Leaves elliptic–oblong to obovate–elliptic; bracts with inner margin serrate at apex. ––––––––––– (29) *C. oblongifolia*

    DD. Leaves at maturity 6–11 cm long.

        E. Bracts over 2 cm long.

            F. Leaves ovate–lanceloate to elliptic–lanceolate;bracts ovate–oblong to ovate–lanceolate. ––––––(50) *C. tungtzeensis*

           FF. Leaves ovate–elliptic.

                G. Leaves 8–11 cm long; bracts with inner margin remotely dentate–serrate to the base –––––––––––––––––––––––––––

––––––––––––––––––––––––– *C. chuniana*

               GG. Leaves 5–9 cm long, bracts with entire inner margin.

                   H. Leaves 6.5–9 cm long, ovate–oblong, ovate–elliptic or lanceolate, mucronate–serrate; bracts mucronate–dentate–serrate –––––––––– (40) *C. shensiensis*

                   HH. Leaves 6.5–8 cm long, callose–dentate–serrate. Bracts callose–dentate–serrate ––––––––––––––––––––––––

–––––––––––––––––(48) *C. tsiangiana*

        EE. Bracts 1–15 cm long.

           · F. Leaves lanceolate, minutely doubly–serrate; nutlets puberulent at apex, resinose–glandulose –––––––––––––––––––––––––––––––––

–––––––––––––––––––––––– (25) *C. minutiserrata*

           FF. Leaves ovate, simply mucronate–serrate; nutlets glabrous, not resinose–glandulose ––––––(42) *C. simplicidentata*

BB. Nutlets with total face sub to distinctly pilose or puberulent (sometimes with resin-glands and long hairs at apex)

C. Leaves to 11 cm long.

D. Leaves oblong to broadly lanceolate; bracts to 3 cm long, with a large spreading basal lobe on the inner margin; nutlet large, compressed, not resinose-glandulose ---
--------------------------(2) *C. austro-yunnanensis*

DD. Leaves ovate-elliptic, cordate at base.

E. Bracts to 3 cm long; nutlets large, 7 mm long, 6 mm broad, resinose-glandulose ----- (46) *C. tsaiana*

EE. Bracts 2 mm long; nutlets much smaller ----------------------
------------------------ (41) *C. sichourensis*

CC. Leaves, bracts and nutlets much smaller.

D. Leaves sharply mucronate-serrate, or setose-serrate.

E. Leaves sharply mucronate-serrate; bracts 2 cm long.

F. Leaves ovate-lanceolate.

G. Bracts lanceolate, coarse-dentate with few teeth on the outer margin, with 1-2 teeth on the inner margin ------
------------------(39) *C. sekii*

GG. Bracts semi-ovate, with many teeth on the outer margin and inner margin entire ------------------------------
---------------- (19) *C. kweiyangensis*

FF. Leaves ovate -------(31) *C. pinpienensis*

EE. Leaves setose-serrate; lateral veins 15-16 pairs; bracts much smaller ----------------(32) *C. polyneura*

DD. Leaves not sharply mucronate-serrate or setose-serrate, if so, then simply serrate.

E. Leaves doubly serrate.

F. Leaves ovate, elliptic or oblong.

G. Bracts acute or obtuse at apex.

H. Bracts usually obtuse at apex. -------------------
------------ (34) *C. pubescens*

HH. Bracts acute at apex

I. Leaves thickly chartaceous, acute or obtusish at apex; petioles 5 mm long. ---------------------
---------- (8) *C. firmifolia*

II. Leaves chartaceous, acuminate at apex, petioles to 12 mm long --------------------------------
---------- (49) *C. tsoongiana*

GG. Bracts coarsely dentate-lobulate at apex --------------

------------------- (14) *C. hupeana*

FF. Leaves elliptic-lanceolate or lanceolate.

　G. Leaves elliptic-lanceolate, with 16–17 pairs of lateral veins; petioles pubescent, 5 mm long. ---------------------------- ------------------- (9) *C. handelii*

　GG. Leaves lanceolate.

　　H. Leaves to 2 cm long; petiolea to 1.5 cm long ------------ ---------------- (18) *C. kweitingensis*

　　HH. Leaves less than 6.5 cm long.

　　　I. Bracts coarsely dentate-lobulate at apex ------------ ---------------(10) *C. hebestroma*

　　　II. Bracts not coarsely dentate-lobulate at apex

　　　J. Leaves with more than 10 pairs of veins.

　　　　K. Nutlets not densely resinose-glandulose.

　　　　　L. Nutlets puberulent; Bracts obtuse at apex --------- *C. austro-sinensis*

　　　　　LL. Nutlets densely long pilose; bracts acutish at apex ---------------------------- ---(30) *C. pilosinucula*

　　　　KK. Nutlets densely resinose-glandulose; Leaves simply dentate-serrate on the upper part----- ------ (24) *C. marlipoensis*

　　　JJ. Leaves with 8–9 pairs of veins. ------------------ ---------- (21) *C. lancilimba*

EE. Leaves simply serrate.

　F. Leaves setose-serrate.

　　G. Leaves ovate, 6 cm long, densely pilose on both surfaces ---- --------------------- (26) *C. mollicoma*

　　GG. Leaves lanceolate, densely pilose or pubescent beneath -------- --------------------- (37) *C. rupestris*

　FF. Leaves not setose-serrate.

　　G. Leaves to 7 cm long, with 16 pairs of veins ----------------- --------------------- (11) *C. henryana*

　　GG. Leaves to 5.5 cm long with 10 pairs of veins ---------------- ------------------------------- *C. wangii*

1. Carpinus austro-sinensis Hu (See orig. test page 244)

2. Carpinus austro - yunnanensis Hu

A deciduous tree 10 m high; branchlets slender, terete, densely tawny- tomentose, finally glabrescent, dark purple, covered with many minute elongated white lenticels; Buds large, elliptic- ovoid, acutish, covered with many imbricate, carioceous, ovate-elliptic sparsely pilose and ciliate bracts; Leaves chartaceous, ovate-oblong to broadly lanceolate, acutish or shortly acuminate at apex, rounded to subcordate at base, doubly serrate along the margins, with 2-3 secondary teeth between the veins, intensely green and tomentose along the midrib and sparsely pilose on the rest of the surface above, pale green and densely sericeous-pilose along the midrib and lateral veins and bearded in the axils of the veins and sparsely black-glandulose beneath, 6.5-10 cm long, 3-4 cm broad; midrib and lateral veins slightly elevated above, distinctly so beneath, lateral veins 15-16 paris, alternate or opposite, straight, and slightly arching and leading to teeth at the margins, 5-8 mm distant; petioles rather stout, 12 mm long, densely tawny-tomentose; fruiting aments to 12 cm long, peduncle and rachis densely tawny-tomentose; bracts ovate-lanceolate, acute, outer margins remotely denticulate, inner margin straight, with a large spreading obtuse basal lobe of 5 mm long, sparsely pilose above, densely sericeous-pilose along the midribs and veins beneath, to 3 cm long, 1 cm broad; nutlets compressed, or trigonal, prominently ribbed, densely white- sericeous-pilose and sparsely resinose-glandulose, crowned with perigonium at the apex, 7 mm high and broad.

Distribution: Southeastern Yunnan, at altitude 1100 meter.

3-7. (See orig. text pages. 245-250)

8. **Carpinus firmifolia** Hu

Carpinus turczaninowii Hance var.*firmifolia* Winkler

A tree 10 meters high; young branchlets slender, terete, striate, tomentose-pilose, finally become sparsely pilose, grayish-black, covered with many white rounded lenticels; buds ovoid-lanceolate, acute, with many imbricate subcoriaceous scales sericeous-pilose outside; leaves firmly coriaceous, ovate to ovate-oblong, acute to obtusish, subcordate or rounded at base, doubly callose-dentate-serrate along the margins, with 1-2 secondary teeth between the veins, deeply shiny green and pilose along the midrib and lateral veins and slightly bearded in the axils of the veins beneath; lateral veins impressed above, elevated beneath, 11-12 pairs, straight and slightly arching and leading into teeth; veinlets scarcely distinct; petioles slender, 5 - 7 mm long, tomentose pilose; bracts semi-ovate, acute, outer margin dentate-serrate, inner margin entire, straight slightly involute at base, 1.5 cm long 6 mm broad, sparsely pilose on both surfaces. Nutlets ovoid, slightly compressed, crowned with perigonium and long pilose at apex, pubescent on the rest of the surface, 4 mm long, 3 mm broad.

Distribution: On open hillside of Kweichow

9. **Carpinus handelic** Rehd. (See orig. text page 250)

10. **Carpinus hebestroma** Yamamoto

A deciduous tree with very slender purplish-brown, branchlets covered with very sparse minute lenticels; leaves subchartaceous, lanceolate, acuminate at apex, obtuse to rounded at base, simply and very rarely doubly serrate along the margin and entire at base, 5-5.5 cm long, 1.6-18 cm broad, midrib scarsely elevated above, distinctly so beneath, lateral veins 11-12 pairs, divergent at 30-35 degrees, straight and slightly arching and leading into teeth at the margin; petioles very slender 7-10 mm long, sparsely hirsute; fruiting aments with peduncles 1.5-2 cm long, about 3-3.5 cm long; bracts 3 mm distant, broadly semi-ovate, 9-10 mm long, 5 mm broad, outer margin incised-dentate-serrate, inner margin straight and entire, inflexed at base, hirsute along the ribs outside, glabrous inside; nutlets compressed, oviod, 2.5 mm high, 2 mm broad, minutely pubescent, 9-10-ribbed, resinose-glandulose.

Distribution: Taiwan.

11. **Carpinus henryana** Winkl. (See orig. text page 250)

12. **Carpinus hogoensis** Hayata

This tree is about 8-10 meters high and 20-60 cm in diameters, occurring at Mo-Sha, Taiwan Taipei, at altitude 50-100 meters.

13. **Carpinus huana** Cheng

A deciduous tree 8 m high; bark smooth black; young branchlet slender, terete, grayish-brown, pilose, covered with small yellow lenticels, finally glabrous, brownish gray to gray; buds elongated, acute, 3-5 mm long; scales ovate brown, imbricate coriaceous, ciliate; leaves chartaceous, firm, oblong - lanceolate to ovate - lanceolate, rarely elliptic-lanceolate, obliquely subcordate to subcordate rarely obtuse at base, caudate-acuminate at apex, 5-7 cm long, 2-2.7 cm broad, upper surface intensely green and glabrous or pilose and sericeous-pilosulose along the midribs and lateral veins, irregularly and doubly at apex, simply crenate-serrate to serrate, with 1-3 secondary teeth between the veins; lateral veins 15-18 pairs 2-3 mm distant, slightly elevated above, distinctly so beneath; petioles tomentose, 10-14 mm long; stipules caducous, linear-lanceolate, subacute, pilose on both surfaces, 10 mm long, 1 mm broad; fruiting aments 7.5-11 cm long, peduncles 8-10 mm long, rachis pilose; bracts semi-ovate to ovate-lanceolate, 17-21 mm long, 9-10 mm broad, acute, outer margin remotely serrate, inner margin entire to subundulate with a short inflexed basal lobe; nutlets ovoid, compressed, 9-11-ribbed, crowned with perigonium at apex, sparsely pilose and puberulent and resinose-glandulose on the upper half, and glabrous on the lower part, 5 mm long, 4 mm broad.

Distribution: Endemic to Northwestern Chekiang.

14. **Carpinus hupeana** Hu

A tree 6 m high; bark gray, smooth; branchlets slender terete, dark purple, glabrous; buds small, elliptic-ovoid, subacute, 4 mm long, with many imbricate subcoriaceous scales ciliate along the margin; leaves chartaceous, ovate. to ovate-oblong or ovate-lanceolate, acute to acuminate at apex, subcordate at base, intensely green and sparsely pilose above, pale green and sericeous-pilose along the midrib and lateral veins and bearded in the axils of the veins beneath, doubly callose-dentate-serrate along the margins except at the apex, 5-6 cm long, 3-3.5 cm broad; midrib and lateral veins slightly elevated above, distinctly so beneath; lateral veins 14-16 paris, straight and slightly arching and leading into the teeth near the margins; divergent 60 degrees; veinlets reticulate on both surfaces; petioles pilose, 8-10 mm long; fruiting aments about 6 cm long, 2.5 cm broad; peduncle 7-8 mm long, densely sericeous-pilose; rachis densely sericeous-pilose; bracts semi-ovate to broadly oblong, prominently incised-dentate at apex, outer margin incised-dentate-sublobulate, inner margin entire, straight, scarsely or slightly involute at base, sericeous-pilose along the midrib and lateral veins above, 10-15 mm long, and 8-10 mm broad; nutlets ovoid, compressed, crowned with perigonium and long pilose at apex, minutely perulent on the rest of the surface, about 5 mm long, and 3 mm broad.

This species is allied to *C. fargesiana* Winkler, differing in narrower leaves subcordate at base and in bracts being prominantly incised-dentate-serrate at apex.

Distribution: Western Hupeh at altitude 1250 meters.

15. **Carpinus hwai** Hu et Cheng

C. turczaninowii var. *ovalifolia* Winkler

A tree to 17 meters high; branchlets terete, slender, striate, glabrous, dark-purple; buds small, elliptic-ovate, subacute, 4 mm long, with many subcoriaceous ciliate scales; leaves chartaceous, ovate-oblong, ovate-lanceolate, or lanceolate, acute at apex, rounded to obliquely subcordate at base, intensely green and sparsely long pilose along the midrib above, pale green and long sericeous-pilose along the midrib and lateral veins and bearded at the axils of the viens beneath, doubly callose-dentate-serrate, 4-6 cm long, 1.5-2.5 cm broad; lateral veins elevated beneath, 14-16 pairs, 2.5-4 cm distant; divergent 45 degrees; petioles glabrous, 10-15 mm long; fruiting aments dense, 7 cm long 2.5 cm broad; rachis pilose; bracts semi-ovate to oblong, obutse or acute at apex, outer margin denticulate-serrulate, inner margin entire, straightly involute at base, sericeous-pilose along the ribs and veins, 15 mm long, 7 mm broad; nutlets ovoid, crowned with perigonium and long pilose at apex, glabrescent and sparsely resinose-glandulose on the rest of the surface, about 2.5 mm long and 3 mm broad.

Distribution: Szechuan, Hupeh, Yunnan, Kweichow, Honan and Kansu, at altitude of 2300-2600 meters.

16. **Carpinus kawakamii** Hayata

Bush or a small tree 10-13 meters tall, occurring at Arisan, Taiwan, at altitude 2130 meters.

17. **Carpinus kweichowensis** Hu (See orig. text pages 250-251)

18. **Carpinus kweitingensis** Hu (See orig. text pages 251)

19. **Carpinus kweiyangensis** Hu

A deciduous tree to 10 m high; bark gray, branchlets slender, terete, striate, sparsely pilose, grayish-purple; leaves thin, chartaceous, ovate-elliptic, elliptic to lanceolate, acuminate at apex, rounded to subcordate at base, irregularly doubly-dentate-serrate glabrous above, densely long pilose along the midrib and lateral veins and sparsely so on the rest of the surface beneath, bearded at the axils of the veins, 3.5-7 cm long,

1.7 cm broad; lateral veins 11–12 pairs, 3–5 mm distant; petioles slender, 8–10 mm long, sparsely long pilose; bracts semi-ovate, slightly falcate, acute, outer margins incised-dentate-serrate to sublobulate, inner margin entire, slihgtly involute at base; nutlets compressed, ovoid, minutely puberulent, crowned with perigonium and long pilose at apex, resinose-glandulose, 4 mm long and broad.

Distribution: Chen lin Shan of Kweichow

20. **Carpinus lanceolata** Hand.-Mazz.

A small shrub or tree of 4–15 meters tall growing in thicket; flowers green or yellow; fruit green with wings. It is related to C. viminea Wall. but differs in shorter petioles (less than 5 mm), more distant bracts each furnished with one prominent lobe on each side at the base.

Distribution: Hainan, at altitude 350 meters.

21. **Carpinus lancilimba** Hu

22. **Carpinus lexiflora** Bl.

Var. 1.–3. Hu (See orig. text page 253)

Var. 4. **Carpinus lexiflora** Bl. var. **tientaiensis**

A tree, few meters high; leaves broadly ovate, to 4 cm broad; short-acuminate, acute or subacute at base, bracts distinctly 3-lobed at base; fruiting aments lax, with bracts not densely imbricate; bracts 3-lobed or without basal lobes; nutlets not completely covered by the basal lobe of inner margin, prominently ribbed.

Distribution: Tien tai shan, and Chekiang.

23. **Carpinus loudoniana** Winkl. (See orig. text pages 253–254)

24. **Carpinus marlipoensis** Hu

A deciduous tree 8 m high; branchlets very slender, terete, striate, sparsely pilose, finally glabrous, grayish-purple, covered with many obscure lenticels. Buds small, ovoid, obtuse, with several imbricate broadly-ovate obtusish scales ciliate along the margins; leaves chartaceous, ovate to ovate-lanceolate, acute to long acuminate at apex, subcordate at base, irregularly and doubly and on the upper part simply serrate along the margins, intensely green and glabrescent above, pale green and long pilose along the midrib and lateral veins and bearded at the axils of veins beneath, 3.5–7.5 cm long, 1.5–2.5 cm broad; midrib slightly elevated above, distinctly so beneath; lateral veins 6–12 pairs, alternate or subopposite, straight or slightly arching and leading into teeth at the margins, 3–6 cm distant; veinlets distinct on both surfaces; petioles slender 5–10 mm long, pilose; fruiting aments 6 cm long, peduncle and rachis slender, pilose; bracts semi-ovate, acute; outer margins coarsely dentate-serrate-sublobulate, inner margin straight, entire, with a very small acute lateral lobe at base, glabrous above, long pilose and gladulose along the ribs and veins beneath, 2 cm long, 1 cm broad; nutlet compressed, ovoid, strongly ribbed, long pilose and crowned with perigonium at apex, sparsely pilose and densely resinose-glandulose on the rest of the surface, 5 mm long, 4 mm broad.

Distribution: Marlipo of Southeastern Yunnan, at altitude 1600–1750 m.

25. **Carpinus minutiserrata** Hayata

A medium-sized deciduous tree 20 m tall and 30 cm in diameter, branches and branchlets fusco-purplish, glabrous, covered with many minute rounded lenticels; leaves chartaceous, ovate-oblong, acuminate and obtuse at apex, obtuse and slihgtly cordate at base, 6 cm long, 2.5 cm broad, minutely and doubly-serrate along the margins; lateral veins 15–17 pairs, divergent at 40 degrees, straight and slightly recurved and extending into teeth at the margins, upper surface glabrous except sparsely long-pilose along the midrib and lateral veins, reticulate on both surfaces; petioles 7 mm long, terete, subglabrous to sparsely pubescent; fruiting aments 3–4 cm long, loose; peduncles 1.5 cm long, rachis very slender, pubescent; bracts semi-angulate-ovate, strongly oblique 13 mm long, 6–7 mm broad, reticulate on both surfaces, glabrous, the veins inside sparsely hirsute, and those outside densely hirsute, outer margin subdoubly serrate, inner margin with 1–2 teeth; nutlets ovoid-globose, 3 mm long, 10-ribbed, crowned with perigonium and pubescent at apex, resinose-glandulose and glabrous on the rest of the surface.

Distribution: Endemic to Taiwan, at altitude of 1000–3000 m.

26. **Carpinus mollicoma** Hu

Carpinus polyneura Franch. var. *wilsoniana* Winkler

A deciduous tree 7 m high; branchlets very slender, terete, densely long pilose, finally glabrescent, purplish, covered with minute elongated lenticels; buds very small, ovoid, acutish, with many imbricate acute ovate scales; leaves chartaceous, lanceolate 5–8 cm long, 1.5–3 cm broad; long caudate-acuminate at apex, rounded to rarely subcordate at base, simply to rarely subdoubly recureved-setoserrate along the margins, appressedly long-pilose above, softly pubescent and long sericeous – pilose along the midrib and lateral veins beneath, midrib slightly elevated above, distinctly so beneath; lateral veins 16–17 pairs, alternate or subopposite, straight and slightly arching and leading into teeth at the margins, divergent at 45 degrees; petioles densely sericeous-pilose; bracts semi-ovate, acute, outer margin coarsely dentate-serrate-sublobulate, inner margin straight, entire, long pilose and reticulate on both surfaces, 15 mm long, 7 mm broad; nutlets very slightly compressed, ovoid-oblong, prominently ribbed, densely long pilose, 4 mm long, 2.5 mm broad.

Distribution: Western Szechuan and Yunnan.

27. **Carpinus mollis** Rehder (See orig. text page 254)
28. **Carpinus monbeigiana** Hand.-Mazz. (See orig. text page 254)
29. **Carpinus oblongifolia** (Hu) Hu et Cheng

Carpinus turczaninowii Hance var. *oblongifolia*. Hu

A tree 12 m high, 15 cm in diameter; bark light brownish-gray, exfoliating into small irregular flakes; young branchlets slender, terete, densely tawny-pilose, finally glabrous, dark purple, covered with very small elongated whitish lenticels; buds ovate-lanceolate, acute, with many imbricate subcoriaceous scales ciliate along the margins;

leaves chartaceous, ovate-lanceolate,elliptic-oblong to obovate-oblong, 3.5-7 cm long, 2.5-3.5 cm broad, acute to subobtuse at apex, rounded to subcordate at base, doubly callose-serrate along the margin, long pilose along the midrib and sparsely pilose on the rest of the surface above, long pilose along the midrib and lateral veins and bearded in the axils of veins and glandulose on the rest of surface beneath; lateral veins 11-13 pairs, straight and slightly arching leading into the teeth near the margins; divergent at 45 degrees; veinlets reticulate on both surfaces; petioles very slender, 12 mm long, densely tawny-pilose; fruiting aments loose, 7 cm long; peduncle 15 mm long, pilose; bracts semi-ovate, acute to subobtuse, 10-16 mm long, outer margin irregularly obtusely serrate, inner margin entire or remotely and obscurely serrate, scarcely involute at base; nutlets ovoid, compressed, crowned with perigonium and long pilose at apex, minutely puberulent, and sparsely resinose-glandulose, 4 mm long and broad.

Distribution: In the vicinity of Nanking, Kiangsu, at altitude 450 m.

30. **Carpinus pilosiducula** Hu

Tree 8 m tall; bark gray; young branchlets slender, terete, grayish-purple, pilose becoming glabrescent, covered with minute obscure lenticels. Leaves chartaceous, lanceolate, 4.5-6 cm long, 18-2.5 cm broad; rounded to subcordate at base, acute to acuminate at apex, irregularly and doubly mucronulate-serrate along the margins, with 1-2 secondary teeth between the veins, glabrous except long pilose along the midrib and lateral veins on both surfaces, lateral veins 11-12 pairs, 4 mm distant, straight and slightly arching and leading into the teeth near the margins; petioles slender, 4-6 mm long, long pilose; fruiting aments 8 cm long, rachis slender, long pilose; bracts semi-ovate, acute, 1.5 cm long, 6 mm broad, outer margin dentate-sublobulate, inner margin entire, involute at base; nutlets ovoid, slightly compressed, crowned with perigonium and densely long pilose and sparsely resinose-glandulose, 3 mm long and broad.

Distribution: Kweichow Anlung Hsien on rocky hills.

31. **Carpinus pinpienensis** Hu

A deciduous tree 8 m high; trunk 30 cm in diameter; young branchlets slender, terete, striate, blackish-purple, deeply long pilose, finally glabrous, covered with numerous small elongated lenticels; leaves chartaceous, ovate, acuminate at apex, cordate at base, doubly and sharply mucronate-dentate-serrate, long pilose especially along the midrib and lateral veins beneath, reticulate on both surfaces, 5-6.5 cm long, 2.5-3 cm broad; lateral veins 14-16 pairs, impressed above, elevated beneath, straight and slightly curved and leading into teeth at the margins; petioles 3-6 mm long, densely long pilose; fruiting aments subdense, 8-9 cm long; peduncles and rachis long pilose; bracts semi-ovate, aucte, outer margin remotely serrulate to lobulate or subentire, inner margin straight and entire, densely long pilose along the ribs and veins on both surfaces, 15-18 mm long, 7-8 mm broad; nutlets slightly compressed, ovoid, pilosulose and long pilose and crowned with perigonium at apex, 4 mm long, 3 mm broad.

Distribution: Yunnan, Ping-Pien Shien, at altitude 1500 m.

32. **Carpinus polyneura** Franchet (See orig. text page 255)

        Var. 1. **Carpinus polyneura** var. **wilsoniana** Winkl. (See orig. text pages 255–256)

33. **Carpinus potanini** Bobr.

A tree 20 m in height; branches sparsely lenticeled; leaves 3–10 cm long, 2.5–9 cm broad, subcoriaceous, orbicular-ovate, subcordate at base, rounded or acuminate at apex, margin serrulate, sparsely pilose; petioles 0.4–1.3 cm long dense pilose.

    Distribution: Hunan, Hupeh, Szechuan, Yunnan, Kweichow and Tibet, at altitude.

34. **Carpinus pubescens** Burkill (See orig. text page 256)

35. **Carpinus putoensis** Cheng

A tree; branchlets brown, pilose, covered with small yellow elliptic lenticels, becoming glabrous and gray; leaves chartaceous, broadly-ovate to elliptic-ovate, rounded to cuneate at base, acute to acuminate at apex, upper surface pilose, lower surface puberulent, and pilose along the midrib and lateral veins, very finely reciculate; lateral veins 11–13 pairs, about 5 mm distant, irregularly mucronate-dentate-serrate, 5–9 cm long, 3–5 cm broad; petioles densely pilose 5–10 mm long; fruiting aments 8 cm long and 4–5 cm in diamenter, pilose peduncles 2 cm long, rachis pilose; bracts falcate to subfalcate, oblong to ovate-oblong, 3–3.2 cm long and 1 cm broad, obtuse to subobtuse at apex, outer margin remotely serrate, inner margin entire to subundulate, basal lobe shortly dentate, inflexed; nutlets ovoid, crowned with perigonium and long pilose at apex, sparsely pilose and resinose-glandulose, about 6 mm long.

    Distribution: Endemic to Puto Island, and Chekiang.

36. **Carpinus rankanensis** Hayata

A medium-sized deciduous tree; branchlets brown covered with numerous minute yellowish, elevated to linear lenticels, finally smooth, yellow, glabrous; leaves membranaceous-chartaceous, ovate-oblong, oblong to elliptic, 8–10 cm long, 3–4 cm broad, cuspidate-acuminate to caudate-acuminate at apex, deeply cordate at base, irregularly setose-serrate along the margins with ascending to recurved teeth, midrib and lateral veins impressed above, elevated beneath, and glabrous, hirsute along the midrib above, appressedly soft-pilose along the midrib and lateral veins beneath lateral veins 20–25 paris, 3–4 mm distant, straight and slightly recurved and extending to the teeth at the margins; petioles 5–10 mm long, glabrous; fruiting aments terminal, pendulous, narrowly cylindrical, 10–12 cm long, 2 cm broad; peduncles 2–3 cm long, slender, hirsute; bracts densely imbricate, more or less obliquely ovate, acute at apex, 13 mm long, 7 mm broad, outer margin fewdentate on the upper part, inner margin entire and with an inflexed basal lobe embracing the nutlet, densely bearded at base, 3-ribbed, reticulate and hirsute on both surfaces; nutlets ovoid, 10-ribbed, glabrous, bearded at apex.

    Distribution: Endemic to Taiwan, and growing at altitude of 1300 meters.

      Var. 1. **Carpinus rankanensis** var. **matsudae** Yamamoto

        This variety differes from the typical form in having narrower bracts and suboblong nutlets; occurring in Taiwan.

37. **Carpinus rupestris** A. Camus (See orig. text pages 256-257)

38. **Carpinus seemeniana** Diels (See orig. text page 257)

39. **Carpinus sekii** Yamamoto

A deciduous tree with very slender purplish-brown branchlets covered with minute elongated lenticels; leaves membranaceous-chartaceous lanceolate to oblong-lanceolate acuminate at apex, obtuish at base, doubly serrate along the margins, 5-8 cm long, 1.8-2 cm broad, hirsute along the midrib above, pilose along the midrib and lateral veins and bearded in the axils of the veins beneath, midrib slightly elevated above, manifestly so beneath, lateral veins 14-15 pairs, divergent at 30 degrees, straight and slightly arching and leading into the teeth at the margins; petioles slender, subterete, 8-15 mm long; fruiting aments with peduncles 2-3 cm long, about 4-6 cm long, fruiting bracts about 1 cm distant, semi-ovate, 18 mm long, 5-6 mm broad, outer margin dentate-serrate, inner margin srtaight except few-dentate at apex, inflexed at base, hirsute along the midribs on both surfaces, densely so at base beneath; pedicels 4 mm long, hirsute; nutlets slightly compressed, ovoid, crowned with perigonium and long pilose at apex, 9-10-ribbed, minutely pubescent on the upper part, resinose-glandulose.

Distribution: Endemic to Taiwan, at altitude of 1000 m.

40. **Carpinus shensiensis** Hu

A small tree; branchlets terete, slender glabrous, reddish-purple; buds elliptic-lanceolate, acute, to 1 cm long, with many subcoriaceous ciliate scales; leaves chartaceous, ovate, oblong or lanceolate, 5.5-8 cm long, 2.5-4.5 cm broad, acute to acuminate at apex, round or subcordate at base, sparsely pilose above, pubescent along the midrib and lateral veins and sparsely pilose on the rest of the surface and bearded at the axils of the veins beneath, doubly-callose-dentate-serrate with 1-2 secondary teeth between the teeth along the margins, lateral veins elevated beneath, 14-16 pairs, 2.5-5 mm distant, divergent 35-45 degrees; petioles slender, pubescent to glabrous, 12-15 mm long; fruiting aments subdense, 7-9 cm long, 4 cm broad, rachis slender, densely pilose; bracts semi-ovate, acute, outer margin dentate-serrate, scarsely lobulate, inner margin entire, straight, slightly involute at base, not lobulate, pilosulose and glandulose along the rib and veins, 2.5-2.8 cm long, 1-12 cm broad; nutlets ovoid, compressed, crowned with perigonium and pilose at apex and glabrous on the rest of the surface and sparsely pilose, 5 mm long, 3 mm broad.

This species is closely related to *Carpinus fargesii* Winkler, differring in larger leaves and bracts scarsely lobulate on the outer margin and not lobulate at the base of the inner margin. From *C. turczaninowii* Hance it differs in having much larger leaves and bracts.

Distribution: Shensi province.

41. **Carpinus sichourensis** Hu

A deciduous tree 8 m high; branchlets slender, terete, densely pilose, covered with rather obscured lenticels; buds small, ovoid, acute, with many imbricate coriaceous ovate, acute glabescent scales; leaves chartaceous, ovate to ovate-elliptic, acute to short-acuminate at apex, slightly unequal and cordate at base, callose-serrulate along the margins, intensely green and densely pilose along the midrib and sparsely so on the rest of the surface above, pale green and densely pilose along the midrib and lateral veins and bearded at the axils of the veins and sparsely pilose on the rest of the surface beneath, 6-10 cm long, 4-5 cm broad; midrib slightly elevated above, prominently so beneath; lateral veins 12-17 pairs, alternate or subopposite, straight and slightly acrhing and leading into teeth at the margins, divergent 45 degrees, 3-6 mm distant; petiole 10-12 mm long, densely pilose; fruiting aments to 12 cm long, peduncles and rachis densely pilose; bracts semi-ovate-lanceolate, outer margins remotely serrate-lobulate, inner margin straight, entire, with a small inflexed obtuish basal lobe embracing the nutlets, 2 cm long, 1 cm broad; nutlets slightly compressed, subglobose, 8-ribbed, densely pilose and crowned with perigonium at apex, sparsely pilose and sparsely resinose-glandulose on the rest of the surface, 4 mm long, 3 mm broad.

Distribution: Yunnan, Sichour Hsien; common in the mixed forests at altitude 1300-1500 meters.

42. Carpinus simplicidentata Hu

A tree 8 m high, with smooth gray bark, branchlets terete, glabrous, dark-purple; buds very small, ovoid, acutish, with many impricate subcoriaceous scales ciliate along the margins; leaves chartaceous, ovate to ovate-lanceolate, acute to short acuminate at apex, rounded to suncordate at base, simply to rarely slightly doubly mucronate-dentate-serrate along the margins, sericeous-pilose especially along the midrib and lateral veins beneath, 3-4 cm long, 1.8-2.2 cm broad; petioles very slender, 7-10 mm long, densely sericeous-pilose; lateral veins 11-13 pairs, straight and slightly arching and leading into teeth at the margins, divergent 45-60 degrees; fruiting aments to 5 cm long, subdense, peduncle about 1 cm long, densely sericeous-pilose; bracts semi-ovate, acute to 15 mm long, 7 mm broad, outer margin dentate-sublobulate, inner margin entire, slightly involute at base; nutlets ovoid, compressed, crowned with perigonium and long pilose at apex, resinose-glandulose, and glabrescent, 4 mm long, 2.5 mm broad.

Distribution: Western Hupeh, growing at altitude of 2100 meters.

43. Carpinus stipulata Winkler

Carpinus turczaninowii var. *stipulata* Winkler

This is a small tree with very pubescent branchlets and very prominent stipules, occurring in Shensi province.

44. Carpinus sunpanensis Hsia

A deciduous tree 10 m high; bark gray, smooth; branchlets slender, pale brown, pilose when young, finally glabrescent to sparsely pilose; leaves chartaceous, ovate, acuminate at apex, obliquely rounded or subcordate at base, doubly and sharply-mucronate-dentate-serrate along the margins, intensely green and glabrous to strigose above, pubesecnt and along the midrib and lateral veins pilose beneath, 4–5 cm long, 2–3 cm broad; lateral veins 12–15 paris, divergent 40–45 degrees; petioles slender, pubescent, 7–18 cm long; stipules linear, acute, glabrous to strigose, quite persistent; fruiting aments 4–6 cm long, peduncle slender, sparsely pilose, 2.5 cm long; bracts semi–ovate to lanceolate, the outer margin mucronate – dentate – serrate to sublobulate, inner margin entire or with 1–2 teeth at the apex and a small inflexed lobe at base, pubescent at the midribs and veins on both surfaces, 15–18 mm long, 5–8 mm broad; nutlets ovoid, slightly compressed, crowned with perigonium and long pilose at apex, glabrescent and resinose– glandulose on the rest of the surface, 4 mm long and 3 mm broad.

Distribution: Sun–pan Hsien, Szechuan province, at altitude 2050 m.

45. Carpinus tientaiensis (Hu) Cheng

Carpinus laxiflora Bl. var. *tientaiensis* Hu

A tree 16–20 m high; bark smooth, pale–ashy–gray; young branchlets terete, slender, brownish–yellow, pilose becoming glabrous the second year, faintly lenticelled; leaves membranaceous, firm, ovate to elliptic–ovate or oblong ovate, acute, obliquely subcordate to cordate, irregularly, shortly and obtusely doubly serrate, glabrous except pilose along the midrib and lateral veins and barbulate at the axils beneath, more or less minutely reticulate on both surface, 5.5–10 cm long, 3–3.5 cm broad; lateral veins 12–15 pairs, 4–7 mm distant, more or less elevated above, distinctly so beneath, curving and leading to the teeth; petioles pilose 8–15 mm long, pilose; stipules caducous, linear–oblong to ovate–oblong, pilose outside, glabrous inside, obtuse to subacute at apex, 10–12 mm long, 3–4 mm broad; pistillate aments 2–3 cm long, pilose, peduncle 1–1.4 cm long, scales of peduncles linear, 10–12 mm long, 2 mm broad, pilose outside, glabrous except pilose at base inside, bract 4 mm long, distinctly 3–lobed, midlobe linear oblong, nearly glabrous inside, densely pilose inside; ovary glabrous, ciliate at apex, 1 mm long, style pilose, 1.5 mm long; stigma 2. 1 mm long; fruiting aments cylindrical; rachis very slender, pilose to perulent; bracts 3–lobed, 5–7–ribbed, reticulate, middle lobe oblong to lanceolate, suboblique to straight, subobtuse, rarely acute at apex, outer margin obtusely serrate with 1–5 teeth, inner margin entire to subundulate, rarely remotely serrate to obscurely mucronate, lateral lobes usually unequal, acute to subacute, outer lobes larger, upper margin with 1–3 teeth, lower margin entire, inner–lobe smaller, entire; nutlets broadly ovoid, slightly compressed, pilose and coronated with perigonium at apex, glabrous on other parts 7–11–ribbed, 5 mm long, 6 mm broad.

Distribution: Chekiang, Tien Tai Shan at altitude 850 m.

46. Carpinus tsaiana Hu

A deciduous tree to 25 m high; trunk 70 cm in diameter; branchlets terete, slender, glabrescent, purplish–red; buds ovoid obutse, with several imbricate broadly–ovate obtuse ciliate scales, 2.5 mm long; leaves chartaceous ovate to ovate–elliptic, acuminate at apex, obliquely cordate at base, irregularly doubly callose–serrate, with 2–3 secondary teeth between the veins, glabrous above, sparsely pilose along the midrib and lateral veins and bearded at the axils of veins beneath, glandulose-punctate and reticulate on both surfaces; lateral veins 14–15 pairs, 5–7 m distant, straight and slightly arching and leading into teeth at margins, divergent at 45 degrees; petioles 4–12 mm long glabrous; fruiting aments dense, 10–13 mm long, 4 cm broad, rachis sparsely pilose to glabrous; bracts quite densely imbricate broadly semi – ovate, broad, acute, outer margins shortly and coarsely dentate-sublobulate, inner margins remotely serrulate and slightly involute at base, reticulate and long pilose along the ribs and veins on both surfaces; nutlets slightly compressed, trigonal-ovoid, 7 mm long, 6 mm broad, conspicuously 13-ribbed and with scattered orange-resinose glands and long pilose at apex.

Distribution: Southern Yunnan, at altitude 1500 m.

47. **Carpinus tschonoskii** Maxim. (See orig. text page 258)

48. **Carpinus tsiangiana** Hu (See orig. text pages 258–259)

49. **Carpinus tsoongiana** Hu

A deciduous tree, 10 m high; bark dark gray; bud very small, ovoid, acute, 2 mm long, with many imbricate ovate cilitate scales; leaves chartaceous, ovate–elliptic, elliptic, ovate–oblong to lanceolate, acuminate at apex, subcordate or rounded at base, doubly callose–dentate–serrate along the margins, glabrescent above densely long pilose along the midrib and lateral veins and sparsely so on the rest of the surface beneath; lateral veins 8–9 pairs, 4–6 mm distant; petioles slender, densely long pilose; fruiting aments 7 cm long, 2.5 cm broad, rachis sparsely long pilose; bracts semi–ovate, acute, outer margin dentate-serrate, inner margin straight and entire, with the basal lobe embracing the fruit, glabrous above, pilose beneath, 13 mm long, 5 mm broad; nutlet slightly compressed, ovoid, minutely pubescent, crowned with perigonium and long pilose at apex, 4 mm long, 3 mm broad.

Distribution: Yunnan, Kweichow, on rocky slopes along the rivers.

50. **Carpinus tung-tzeensis** Hu (See orig. text page 259)

51. **Carpinus turczaninowii** Hance (See orig. text page 259)

Var. 1 and var. 2. (See orig. text page 260)

52. **Carpinus vinimia** Wall. (See orig. text page 261)

Genus (4) Corylus Linn. (See orig. text page 261)

Key to the Species of Corylus

A. Segments of the involucre transformed into dense branching spines.

    B. Branching spines with a short trunk; involucre wall scarcely visible --(4) *Corylus tibetica*

    BB. branching spines with a trunk as long as the soine-branches; involucre wall visible --(3) *Corylus ferox*

AA. Involucre segments not transformed into dense branching spines.

B. Involucre campanulate, not constricted above the nut.

    C. Leaves pubescent along the midrib and lateral veins beneath involucre glandulose-setose near base ---------- (5) *C. heterophylla*

    CC. Leaves softly tomentose or densely pubescent beneath; involucre gray-tomentose and glandulose ------------ (6) *C. yunnanensis*

BB. Involucre constricted above the nut.

    C. Involucre limb deeply divided into linear, often forked and pinnately lobulate lobes --------------------------- (7) *C. jacquemontii*

    CC. Involucre limb not deeply divided.

        D. Involucre foliaceous, limb divided at apex into 7-8 broad pungent lobes ------------------------------------ (9) *C. kweichowensis*

        DD. Involucre tubular, limb divided into linear lobes.

            E. Leaves ovate to ovate-oblong--(1) *C. chinensis*

            EE. Leaves oblanceolate to oblong--(2) *C. fargesii*

1. **Corylus chinensis** Fr. (See orig. text pages 261-262)

    Var. 1. Corylus chinensis Franch. var. **macrocarpa** Hu

        This variety differes from the typical form in having reddish-brown involucres with the tube 3.5 cm long, only slightly constricted above the nut and forked linear lobes 2.5 cm long, and with globose nuts 2.2 cm in diameter.

    Distribution: Northwestern Yunnan, at altitude of 3400 m.

2. **Corylus fargesii** Schn. (See orig. text pages 262-263)

3. **Corylus ferox** Wall. (See orig. text pages 263-264)

    Var. 1. Corylus ferox Wallich var. **tibetica** Bat. (See orig. text page 264)

        A shrub or a small tree 4-12 meters high; bark reddish - brown; branchletd slender reddish-brown; lenticels spotted; leaves large, 5-8 cm long, 3-4 cm wide, doubly-serrate, long-acuminate at apex, a little lapsided at base; fruit covered with dense spines, yellowish-brown or greenish-brown.

    Distribution: Yunnan and Southeastern Tibet, at altitude of 2500-3400 meters.

4. **Corylus tibetica** (See orig. text pages 264-265)

5. **Corylus heterophylla** (See orig. text pages 264-265)

    Var. 1. Corylus heterophylla var. **sutchuanensis** (See orig. text pages 265-266)

    Var. 2. Corylus heterophylla var. **crista-galli** Burkill (See orig. text page 266)

        A small tree with very slender brownish branchlets; branchlets densely yellowish pubescent; leaves obovate 3-5 cm long and 3-4 cm broad, with long attenuate-acuminate apex and doubly-dentate-serrate margin, reddish-brown pubescent on the lower surface; fruits solitary, on rigid peduncles; petioles and peduncles covered with dense brownish haris.

Distribution: Hupeh.

6. **Corylus yunnanensis** (Franch.) A. Camus   (See orig. text page 266)

7. **Corylus jacquemontii** (DC.) Decaisne

   Corylus colurna var. *jacquemontii* De Candolle

   A small deciduous tree 7 m high, 10 cm in diameter; branchlet slender, terete, densely pilose when young, soon glabrous, purplish-brown, covered with scattered lenticels; buds ovoid to ellipsoid, obtuish, with imbricate scales ciliate along the margins; leaves membranaceous, ovate to ovate-lanceolate, long-acuminate at apex, obliquely subcordate at base, sharply and doubly-serrate, 6-9 cm long, 3.5-6.5 cm broad; midrib and lateral veins impressed and glabrous above, elevated and pubescent beneath; lateral veins 12 pairs, divergent at 45 degrees, lower ones with tertiary veins; veinlets slender, elevated, closely spaced; petioles slender, pilose and glandulose, 1.3 cm long; fruit 4-5 in a cluster; involucre striate, constricted above the nut, covered with long and pungent spines, the stipitate-glandulose tube short, limb deeply divided into linear lobes, 2 cm long, 1 mm broad, lobes often forked and pinnately lobulate, pubescent; nuts subglobose, 1.5 cm in diameter.

   This hazel nut is found in the Himalayan Region and in Northwestern Yunnan it grows at altitudes of 2300-3400 m.

8. **Corylus kawakamii** Hayata

   A small tree, few meters high; branchlets slender, brownish gray; leaves oblong-ovate, acuminate at apex and rounded at base, coarsely serrate, occurring in Taiwan, at altitude of 300-600 meters.

9. **Corylus kweichowensis** Hu

   A small deciduous tree, 3.5 m high; trunk 8 cm in diameter; bark dark gray, finely fissured; young branchlet slender, terete, finally glabrous, covered with scattered elongated lenticels; leaves chartaceous, ovate to ovate-oblong, acuminate at apex, obliquely cordate at base, unequally and doubly mucronate-serrate along the margins, 9-11 cm long, 5-7 cm broad, glabrous above, very sparsely pilose along the elevated midrib and lateral veins beneath; veinlets elevated beneath; petioles 1-1.5 cm long, sparsely pilose; fruit in pairs on a peduncle 1.5 cm long; involucre foliaceous, much constricted above the nut, divided at apex into 7-8 pungent lobes; nut subglobose, 1 cm in diameter.

   The leaves of the species are quite like those of *Corylus chinensis,* but the fruits are smaller. It's involucres are not tubular and not divided into linear lobes as in the latter species. Furthermore it lacks the stipitate-glands.

   This species is closely related to *Corylus fargesii* Schneides, differring in having smaller nuts, and somewhat foliaceous involucre with a very short tube and 7-8 broad and more or less furcate and serrate lobes pungent at apex.

   Distribution: Kweichow province.

10. **Corylus minuteserrata** Hayata

Small tree or shrub with very slender branchlets; leaves dense, short petioled, obovoid–lanceolate, acute to acuminate at apex and rounded at base, finelly serrate at margins; occurring in Taiwan.

11. **Corylus potanini** Bobr.

A tree, 20 m high; branch coarsely furrowed, sparsely lenticelled; leaves 3–10 cm long, 2.5–9 cm borad, orbicular–ovate, subcoriaceous, rounded–acuminate at apex and subcordate at base, serrulate, veins 5–8 on each side, sparsely pilose; petioles 0.4–1.3 cm long, densely pilose, stipitate–glandulose; stipule lanceolate, dense pilose; fruits 2–4 in a cluster; involucre densely pilose, stipitate–glandulose.

Distribution: Sikang, Ta–Tsien–Lu, Tibet, Hupeh, Kweichow, and Yunnan.

12. **Corylus rankanensis** Hayata

A small tree with very slender branchlets; bark grayish brown; leaves oblong–ovate, finelly serrate, acute–acuminate at apex and cordate at base, petioles long and pilose, aments very long and large, pendulous; occurring in Taiwan.

13. **Corylus rostrata** Ait. var. **fargesii** Franch.

A small tree of 15 m high; leaves oblique, doubly–serrate, pubescent along the veins beneath, obtuse at base, acuminate at apex; fruits globose, occurring in Szechuan, at altitude of 1400 m.

14. **Corylus sieboldiana** Bl. var. **manchurica** (Maxim.) Schneider (See orig. text pages 266–267)

15. **Corylus wangii** Hu

A small tree 7 m high; branchlets slender, densely villose when young, soon glabrous; leaves membranaceous, ovate to ovate–lanceolate, to 7.5 cm long, 4.5 cm broad, long acuminate at apex, obliquely subcordate at base, sharply and doubly serrate, midrib and veins impressed and glabrous above, elevated and pubescent beneath, lateral veins 12 pairs, veinlets closely spaced; petiole slender, pilose and glandulose, 1.3 cm long; fruits 4 in a cluster; involucre striate, covered with long bristles, tube short, limb deeply divided into linear lobes 2 cm long, 1 mm broad, lobes often forked and pinnately lobulate, pubescent; nutlets globose, to 1.5 cm long.

This species in characterized by the rather small and sharply serrate ostrya–like leaves and involucres deeply divided into narrow linear lobes. It differs in this respect from all other species of the section *Avelana*.

Distribution: Northwestern Yunnan, at altitude 3400 m.

Genus (5) Betula Linn.(See orig. text pages 267–268)

Key to the Species of Betula

A. Fruiting aments 2–4 in a raceme or solitary, pendulous, long and narrowly cylindrical; lateral lobes of bract strongly reduced or distinct; samara with broad wings, exceeding the nutlets nearly 3 times, leaves many-veined--- Sect. I. *Acuminatae*

B. Fruiting aments racemose —————————— (5) *B. alnoides*

BB. Fruiting aments solitary.

    C. Leaves broadly deltoid-ovate or ovate-elliptic, usually more than 6 cm long; fruiting aments 3.5-11 cm long. —————————*B. luminifera*

    CC. Leaves oblong to ovate-oblong, 5-6 cm long; fruiting aments 3-7 cm long. ——————————————————————————————————————(3) *B. baeumkeri*

AA. Fruiting aments solitary, rarely 2, pendulous, spreading or erect, the lateral lobes of bracts distinct; samara with wings scarcely broader than the nutlets, usually very narrow, leaves few-veined.

    B. Fruiting aments erect, usually subglobose, ovate to narrowly elliptic (in *B. schmidtii* cylindric); lateral lobes of bracts nearly always erect to erect-spreading, more or less shorter than the midlobe; leaves with 6-14 pairs of lateral veins ——— Sect. 2. *Costatae*

        C. Samara with quite distinct wings, 1/2 rarely 2/3 times narrower than the nutlet; fruiting aments ovate-cylindrical to subcylindrical, 2-3 times longer than broad; peduncle quite distinct and slender ——— Subsect. ———— *Ermanianae*

            D. Flowering and fruiting branchlets more or less abundantly glandulose and villose; leaves quite thick, midrib prominent beneath, sericeous to bearded-villose; petioles sericeous-villose; fruiting aments elliptic to shortly cylindrical —————————— (21) *B. utilis*

            DD. Flowering and fruiting branchlets, glabrous (in some varceties distinctly glandulose); leaves thinner, midrib and lateral veins slightly prominent beneath, sparsely sericeous to subglabrous; petioles glabrous to sparsely sericeous; fruiting aments quite cylindrical ——— (2) *B. albo-sinensis*

      CC. Samara with narrowest wings, 4-5 times narrower than the nutlets; peduncle very short and thick; leaves triangular, breadest at base.

        D. Large leaves 6-14 cm long, ovate-rounded; petioles usually more than 1 cm long; tall trees.

          E. Fruiting aments cylindrical, 2-3 cm long and 8 mm broad; peduncle quite slender; leaves very shortly and unequally denticulate ——— Subsect. ——Asperae. (20)
                                                      B. schmidtii

          EE. Fruiting aments thickly ovate-elliptic, to subglobose, subsessile or with short and thick peduncles; leaves with distinct more or less acuminate teeth —————————————— Subsect. —— *Grossae*

            F. Leaves narrowly ovate, long caudate at apex; samara with distinct wings, 1/2 to 2/3 narrower than the nutlet ——————————————————————————————————— *B. costata*

            FF. Leaves ovate to ovate-elliptic, usually more or less acuminate at

apex; Samara with narrow wings ----------------------------
------------------------------ *B. insignis*

DD. Leaves at maximum 6 cm long; petioles 4–8 cm long,

    E. Large tree -------------------------*B. fargesii*

    EE. Small tree or shrubs. --------------- Subsect. Chinenses.

        F. Leaves ovate–oblong, or ovate–elliptic or obovate; lateral veins 10–22; petioles scarcely more than 6 mm long.

            G. Leaves usually with 14–22 pairs of lateral veins, white-and red-sericeous beneath; lateral lobes of bracts quite obtuse suberect -------------(19) *B. potanini*

          GG. Leaves usually with 10–14 pairs of lateral veins; lateral lobes of bracts acute and divargent.

              H. Leaves, ovate to obovate sparsely sericeous or glabrous above, more or less loosely white-sericeous beneath ---- ------------------------ *B. delavayi*

              HH. Leaves broadly ovate or broadly obovate, densely sericeous or glabrous above, densely sericeous along the midrib and lateral veins beneath.

                I. Branchlets and fruiting bracts sericeous-villose; small tree or shrub--------- *B. forrestii*

                II. Branchlets and fruiting bracts densely sericeous-villose, a shrub. -----*B. forrestii* var. *calcicola*

      FF. Leaves ovate to ovate-rounded, lateral veins of large leaves 6–10 petioles 6–12 mm long. -----------*B. chinensis*

BB. Fruiting aments pendulous or suberect, cylindrical to subelliptic; lateral lobes of bracts suberect to spreading, sometimes slightly recurving, shorter than the midlobe; leaves with 4–8 pairs of lateral veins ----Sect. 3. *Excelsae*

    C. Leaves ovate to ovate-oblong; fruiting aments suberect, elliptic to subcylindrical; samera with wings 1/2 narrower than the nutlet rarely subequal. ------- -- Subsect. Dahuricae, *B.davurica*

    CC. Leaves triangular to ovate to rhombic–triangular; fruiting aments pendulous to subpendulous; samara with wings as broad as the nutlet or twice as broader-- -- Subsect. *Albae*

      D. Leaves ovate to triangular-ovate.

        E. Leaves glabrous on both surfaces, ovate to triangular-ovate, truncate to broadly cuneate at base-----(18) *B. platyphylla* var. *manchurica*

        EE. Leaves puberulent or glabrous usually bearded at the axils of veins beneath, triangular-ovate to broadly ovate, truncate or subcordate at base ----------------------------- *B. platyphylla* var. *japonica*

      DD. Leaves rhombic-ovate.

E. Leaves ovate to rhombic-ovate, unequally dentate-serrate along the margins ------------------------------ *B. platyphylla* var. *szechuanica*

EE. Leaves rhombic-ovate, doubly-serrate sometimes lobulate along the margins ------------------------------ *B. platyphylla* var. *rockii*

1. **Betula acuminata** Wallich var. **pyrifolia** Franch.

A small tree with grayish bark and slender and lenticelled branchlets; leaves 10-12 cm long, pubescent on lower surface, 7-8 cm broad, roundate-ovate at base, acuminate at apex and subequally serrate at margins; female aments 7-8 cm long; peduncles 10-15 mm long, solitary, pendulous.

Distribution: Szechuan, at altitude of 1400 meters.

2. **Betula albo-sinensis** Burk. (See orig. text page 286)

Var. 1. **Betula albo-sinensis** var. **septentrionalis** Schneider (See orig. text page 269)

3. **Betula baeumkeri** Winkler

A deciduous tree, young branchlets densely tomentose with spreading hairs; leaves obliquely oblong to ovate-oblong, acute to shortly acuminate at apex, obliquely rounded at base, unequally sharply serrate along the margins, upper surface dark green, glabrous except tomentulose along the midrib and reticulate, lower surface light green, resinose-punctate and long pilose along the midrib and lateral veins, 5-6 cm long, 2.5-3.5 cm broad; lateral veins 10-11 pairs, elevated beneath, petioles densely tomentose, 6-8 mm long; fruiting aments solitary, pendulous, 3-4 cm long, 6-8 mm in diameter; bracts small, midlobe spatulate, obtuse, about twice as long as the lateral lobes, ciliate; nutlets olbong to oblong-ovate, pubescent, with wings 2-3-times as broad.

Distribution: Yunnan, Sikang, Szechuan and Hupeh.

4. **Betula bhojpattra** Wall. var. **sinensis** Franch.

A tree; leaves 5-6 cm long, coriaceous, glabrous beneath, roundate at base, callose-acuminate at apex, doubly-dentate-serrate at margin; fruiting aments cylindrical, solitary, glabrous; bracts lobed, obtuse obovate glandulose.

Distribution: Szechuan.

5. **Betula alnoides** Hamilton ex D. Don. (See orig. text page 269)

6-14. (See orig. text pages 270-276)

15. **Betula kwangsiensis** F. P. Metcalf

A tree 20 m high, trunk 60 cm in diameter; branches deep green above, brownish-green below, lenticelled; leaves 4-6 cm long, 3-5 cm broad, oblong-ovate, margin, doubly-dentate-serrate, lateral veins 11-13 pairs, acuminate at apex, truncate to slightly cordate at the base, glabrous on both surfaces; female aments cylindrical, erect, browish, 2-4 cm long, 1 cm thick, on short and stout peduncles.

Distribution: Kwangsi, Tzu-Yuen Hsien, at altitude 1200 m.

16. - 17. **Betula** (See orig. text pages 277-280)

18. **Betula platyphylla** Sukatchev var. **manchurica** (Regel) Hara

Betula alba subsp. *manchurica* Regel

A deciduous tree 20-27 m high, trunk to 2.5 m in diam.; bark white, branchlets slender, terete, striate, grayish-purple, covered with numerous minute white rounded lenticels, resinose-glandulose; leaves ovate to deltoid-ovate, truncate to broadly cuneate at base, acuminate at apex, simply or doubly mucronate-crenate-serrate along the margins, deep green above and pale green beneath, glabrous on both surfaces, glandulose and sometimes bearded in the axils of the veins beneath, 4-7 cm long, 3.5-6 cm broad; midrib and lateral veins elevated on both surfaces; lateral veins 6-7 pairs, straight and slightly arching and leading to the teeth at the margin, divergent 35 degrees; veinlets reticulate on both surfaces; petioles 1.5-2 cm long, staminate aments in pairs, about 8 cm long, 5 mm thick, subsessile; bracts rounded, peltate, frienged with glandulose hairs; stamens numerous; pistillate aments cylindrical, 3 cm long, 7-10 mm broad; bracts 3-lobed, midlobe shorter than the divaricate lateral lobes; wings broader than the nutlet.

Distribution: Widely distributed in Ussuri, Korea and Manchuria of China.

19. **Betula potanini** Batalin (See orig. text page 281)
20. **Betula schmidtii** Regel

Betula bhojpattra var. *typica* Shirai

Betula bhojpattra var. *jacquemontii* Shirai

Betula dahurica Shirai

Betula punctata Levl.

A deciduous tree to 35 m high, trunk to 2.7 m in circumference; bark nearly black, falling off in thick, rather small plates of irregular shape; young branchlets slender, terete, pubescent and glandulose, finally glabrous, brown; leaves ovate, 4-8 cm long, 2.5-3 cm broad, acuminate, rounded or broadly cuneate at base, finally and irregularly serrate, resinose-glandulose beneath, lateral veins 9-11 pairs, slightly pilose above when young; petioles 5-10 cm long, pilose; fruiting aments cylindric, erect, 2-3 cm long, 8 mm broad; bracts 3-lobed, lobes linear-oblong, acute, ciliate, midlobe twice as long as the lateral ones; nutlets with very narrow wings.

Distribution: This remarkable birch is found in Ussuri, Korea, Japan and Manchuria in China.

21. **Betula utilis** D. Don. (See orig. text pages 281-282)

Var. 1. **Betula utilis var. prattii** (See orig. text page 282)

Genus (6) Alnus Mill. (See orig. text pages 282-283)

Key to species of the genus Alnus.

A. Staminate and pistillete aments singular, axillary, buds stipitate, with 2 scales, obtuse; strobiles with very long peduncles, nutlets with broad hyaline wings-------- --- Subgen. I. *Cremastogyne*

    B. Peduncle of strobile to 8 cm long, slender, glabrous; leaves glabrescent, adult sparsely pilose to glabrous, slightly bearded in the axils of veins. -- *A. cremastogyne*

  BB. Peduncle of strobile 2–4.5 cm long, sparsely hisute or pilose, reddish–villose when young, adult more or less distinctly red–pubescent -- (8) *A. lanata*

AA. Staminate and pistillate aments several to solitary; strobiles with rather short peduncles; nutlets with narrow wings -------------------- Subgen. 2. *Alnus*

    B. Staminate aments 2–9, racemose–aggregate at the apex of flowering branchlets; nutlets with narrow coriaceous marginate wings ---Sect. *Gymnothyrsus*

      C. Staminate aments precocious.

        D. Leaves not lobulate along the margin.

          E. Leaves elliptic, ovate to lanceolate, broadly ovate to broadly oblong, acuminate to cuspidate at apex, cuneate, rounded or subcordate at base ------------------------------ (10) *A. trebeculata*

         EE. Leaves elliptic, ovate to lanceolate, acute at apex, acute to rarely subrounded at base ----------- (7) *A. japonica*

        DD. Leaves lobulate along the margin --(5) *A. hirsuta* var. *sibirica*

      CC. Staminate aments flowering in summer or autumn.

        D. Strobiles solitary --------- ----------- *A. ferdinandi-coburgii*

        DD. Strobiles several to many, racemose–paniculate ----------------------- -------------------------------- (4) *A. formosana*

  BB. Staminate aments numerous, paniculate–racemose at apex of flowering branchlet; flowering in autumn; strobiles numerous, paniculate; nutlets with distinct hyaline wings --- Sect. *Clethropsis*

                                      (*A. nepalensis*)

1–3. (See orig. text pages 283–285)

4. **Alnus formosana** Makino

        Alnus maritima var. *formosana* Burkill

        Alnus japonica var. *formosana* Callier

        Alnus henryi Schenider

A large deciduous tree; trunk 1.8 m in diameter; bark dark gray brown, smooth; branchlet terete, striate, glabrous, purplish black covered with many minute white lenticels; leaves ovate to elliptic, acute to acuminate at apex, slightly unequal and rounded at base, glandulose-serrate, along the margins, glabrous on both surfaces, 4.5–10 cm long, 1.7–4.5 cm broad; midrib and lateral veins impressed above, elevated beneath; lateral veins about 8 pairs, slightly arching and anastomosing near the margins; veinlets very fine, obscure; petioles 1–2 cm long; staminate aments flowering in autumn or spring, 3–4 in a cluster, pendulous, with slender peduncles about 1 cm long, cylindric, to 7 cm long; bracts ovate, acutish, glabrous; strobiles many, racemose-paniculate, rarely few, with short peduncles, ellipsoid, 2 cm long; bracts short – lobed: samara broadly obovate, with narrow membranaceous wings.

> Distribution: This species is very common throughout the island of Taiwan, usually occurring in river beds, along banks of stream; sometimes forming pure stands.

5. **Alnus hirsuta** Turcy. var. **sibirica** Schneider (See orig. text page 285)

6. **Alnus jackii** Hu (See orig. text page 285)

A tree 10 m high; trunk and branches glabrous and lenticelled; leaves elliptic–ovate to elliptic–obovate, 4–7.5 cm long, 2–2.5 cm broad, acute–cuspitate at apex, subrounded at base, glandulose–serrate, glabrous; petioles 2 cm long; flowering aments 5–6 in a cluster, in autumn, cylindrical, 2 cm long, 1.2 cm in diameter; bracts truncate at apex, with minute lobulate; samara orbicular compressed, 3.5 mm long and broad, coriaceous, apex acutish.

This species is affiliated to Alnus formosana Makino but differring by having solitary strobiles.

> Distribution: Chekiang Tien Tai Shan and Fukien.

7. **Alnus japonica** Sieb. et Zucc.

> *Alnus maratama* var. *japonica* (Sieb. et Zucc.) Regel
>
> *Alnus japonica* var. *latifolia* Callier
>
> *Alnus japonica* var. *reginosa* Nakai

A deciduous tree, 20 m high; trunk 60 cm in diameter; bark light purplish – brown, rough and irregularly fissured, branchlet terete, light reddish–brown, glabrous, covered with grayish–white lenticels; buds stipitate, obovate–elliptic, 3–ribbed, with 3 glabrous scales; leaves elliptic to obovate–elliptic, acuminate or abruptly acuminate at apex, cuneate at base, serrulate along the margin, intensely green above, light green beneath, glabrous or slightly pubescent when young, 6–12 cm long, 3–5.5 cm broad; midrib and lateral veins slightly elevated and glandulose above, prominently elevated and glandulose beneath; lateral veins 8–10 pairs, slightly arching, often forking, anastomosing near the margins; petiole channeled above, glabrous or slightly pubescent, 2.5–3.5 cm long. Staminate aments precocious, pendulose, 2–5 in a cluster; bracts ovate–rhombic, purplish–red; strobiles 1–3, on rather stout peduncles, ovoid or broadly ellipsoid, about 2 cm long, 13 mm broad, dark brown; pedicels 7–8 mm long; scales 5–lobed; samara broadly elliptic to obovate, with very narrow wings.

> Distribution: Ussuri, Korea and Japan, also in Manchuria, Shantung, Kiangsu and Kwangtung of China. It grows very rapidly, and is good for reforestation in wet area. The timber is soft and good for fuel and cheap furnitures.

8. **Alnus lanata** Duthie (See orig. text page 285)

9. **Alnus napalensis** D. Don (See orig. text page 286)

10. **Alnus trebeculosa** Hand.–Mazz. (See orig. text page 287)

Family 20. Fagaceae A. Br.

(See orig. text pages 287–288)

Genus (1) Fagus L.

1. **Fagus chienii** Cheng   (See orig. text page 289)

   Tree 25 m high; trunk 1 m in diameter; branchlets pendulous; Leaves oblong–elliptic to ovate–lanceolate, obtuse–acute to obtuse, or acuminate at apex, oblique at base, sinuate–dentate, 5–9.5 cm long, 3–5.2 cm broad, glabrous above, somewhat pubescent beneath.

   This species is closely related to *Fagus longipetiolata* Seem. and *F. lucida* R. et W. It may be a hybrid between these species. It's leaves with pubescence on the lower surface, and it's involucre with subulate recurved scales show clearly its relationship with *F. longipetiolata*, while its oblong–elliptic, ovate–lanceolate, or ovate leaves with broadly cuneate to subcordate base, and sinuate margin with the veins projected from the base of the sinuses and forming small teeth and involucre with short scales indicate its relationship with *F. lucida*.

   Distribution: Szechuan, at altitude 1300 meters.

2. **Fagus engleriana** Seem. et Diels   (See orig. text page 289)

3. **Fagus hayatae** Palib. ex Hay.

   A small tree with light gray and smooth bark; branchlets slender, glabrous; leaves oblong lanceolate to oblong ovate, glabrous above, pubescent along the veins beneath; lateral veins 9–11 pairs, acunminate at apex, acute to cuneate at base, sinuate or doubly dentate–serrate, fruit solitary, stalk as long as the fruit, glabose, 1 cm long and broad.

   Distribution: Taiwan Nan Hu Ta Shan, at altitude 1600 m.

4–5. (See orig. text pages 290–293)

6. **Fagus tientaiensis** Liou   (See orig. text page 293)

   Tree with very glabrous bark; branchlets sparsely lenticelled; leaves ovate–oblong with attenuated base, acuminate at apex. 7–8.5 cm long, 3–4.2 cm wide, denticulated, lateral veins, 9–11 pairs glabrous; flowers pendulous, 1–2.5 cm long; involucres 4–parted, 1–2 cm long, 1–15 cm broad.

   Distribution: Chekiang, Tien Tai Shan, and Fukien province.

Genus (2) Castanea Mill. (See orig. text pages 293–296)

Genus (3) Castanopsis Spach (See orig. text pages 296–297)

Key to the species of Castanopsis

I.

A. Fruit spiny.

  B. Branchlets of second year glabrous.

    C. Leaves oblong–lanceolate, ovate–lanceolate, or lanceolate, glabrous, 5–8 cm.

D. Leaves ovate-lanceolate, long acuminate, glabrous, 5-8 cm long, 2.5-4 cm broad ------------------------------ *C. eyrei*

DD. Leaves oblong-lanceolate or lanceolate, acuminate, densely fulvus pubescent, rarely glabrescent beneath, 8-10 cm long, 2-3 cm broad ------------ ----------------------------------(31) *C. hystrix*

CC. Leaves oblong, 10-22 cm long, 4-7 cm broad; lateral veins prominent on both sides ------------------------------ (56) *C. tibetana*

BB. Branchlets of second year densely dark yellowish-brown tomentose; leaves densely brownish-yellow tomentose beneath, oblong or oblanceolate-oblong rarely oblong-lanceolate, acute, subcordate at base ------------ *C. fordii*

AA. Fruits with transverse ridge of samll tubercles.

B. Leaves 4-8 cm long, long acuminate, entire or crenate-serrate toward the apex.-- ------------------------------------- (17) *C. cuspidata*

BB. Leaves 8-15 cm long, usually caudate-acuminate, coarsely serrate above the middle ------------------------------- *C. scelrophylla*

II.

A. Fruit composed of interupted transverse ridges or tubercles.

B. Leaves large, more than 8 cm long, usually 8-12 or more.

C. Fruit covered with transverse ridges of appressed tubercles.

D. Leaves 8-12 cm long, usually 2.5-5.6 cm wide, oblong-ovate to lanceolate-elliptical; margin serrate above the middle; lateral veins 9-11 pairs; fruit almost enclosing the nuts. --------- *C. scerophylla*

DD. Leaves 15-20 cm long, 5-8 wide, lanceolate to oblanceolate; margin remotely crenate-serrate; lateral veins 13-18 pairs; fruit entire enclosing the nuts ----------------------(22) *C. fissa*

CC. Fruits with irregular, erect, branched tubercles; leaves ovate to oblong-lanceolate; margin subentire; lateral veins 9-12 pairs. --------------------- ------------------------------- (37) *C. lamontii*

BB. Leaves smaller, less than 8 cm long, usually 4-8 or less.

C. Leaves usually serrate, usually less than 2 cm rarely over 2.5 cm wide, glabrous; fruit small, covered with short tubercles ------------------------- ----------------------------(9) *C. carlesii*

CC. Leaves entire or serrate, 2.5-3.5 cm wide, rarely less, glabrous above, covered with grayish, scally tomentum beneath; fruit with irregular transverse ridges, with irregular appressed excrescences ------------------------- -------------------------- (17) *C. cuspidata*

AA. Fruit spiny.

B. Leaves glabrous throughout, the lower surface approximately same color and without tomentum.

    C. Leaves 5–10 cm long; fruit with erect branched spines distinctly separated from each other —————————————————— *C. eyrei*

    CC. Leaves 12–19 cm long; fruit with numerous groups of stout, radiating flatted spines, arranged in imperfect radiating curving zones ——————————————————————————————————— (3) *C. armata*

BB. Leaves often glabrous above but lower surface covered with grayish, brownish, yellowish, or reddish tomentum.

    C. Leaves ovate–lanceolate to lanceolate with cordate base (lower surface of leaves and branchlets covered with dense yellowish–orange, gray or rufous tomentum;); fruit large ———————————— *C. fordii*

    CC. Not as above.

        D. Leaves broad–lanceolate, 5–10 cm wide, and 20–25 cm long. ———————————————————————————————— (56) *C. tibetana*

        DD. Leaves 2.5–5 cm wide and less than 20 cm long.

            E. Leaves with lower surface and young branchlets covered with reddish tomentum; fruit covered with long pilose spines ——————————————————————————————— (31) *C. hystrix*

            EE. Leaves with lower surface covered with brownish tomentum; young branchlets glabrous, fruit covered with many branched spines. ———————————————————— (20) *C. fabri*

1. **Castanopsis acuminatissima** Rehder

    A large tree up to 48 m tall, trunk 1 meter in diameter; bark dark gray; branchlets slender; leaves oblong–lanceolate, long acuminate at apex, semi–rounded at base, entire thick, coriaceous, glabrous, or slightly pubescent along the midribs beneath; fruits 2–3 in a cluster, obovoid, minutely ovoid mucronate.

    Distribution: Taiwan, Arisan, at altitude 1866–2833 m.

2. **Castanopsis argyrophylla** King

    A tree 5–12 meters high; trunk 10–25 cm in diameter; bark gray and rough; branchlets stout and lenticelled; leaves yellowish green, large, 10–15 cm long, 6–8 cm broad, ovate–elliptic in shape, acute to acuminate at apex and cuneate at base, densely yellowish–brown pubescent beneath, especially dense along the midribs and veins, margin entire, coriaceous and short petioled.

    Distribution: Yunnan at altitude of 1540 meters.

3. **Castanopsis armata** (Roxb.) Spach (See orig. text page 313)

4. **Castanopsis brachyacantha** Hayata

    This species is distinguished by having acorns in densely spined cups and by the upper portion of the leaves irregularly dentate–serrate; occurring central parts in Taiwan, at altitude of 1000–2000 meters.

5. **Castanopsis brevispina** Hayata

This species is distinguished by having oblong-lanceolate leaves with subentire margin the tip-portion spinely serrate; occurring in Heng chun peninsula, Taiwan, at altitude of 400-1000.

6. **Castanopsis** brevistella Hayata et Kanehira

This species is closely related to Castanopsis brachyacantha Hayata but difers in having cupules with densely stellate spines; occurring in Taiwan at altitude above 1000-2000 m.

7. **Castanopsis** blumeneana (Korth.) Rehder (See orig. text page 297)

8. **Castanopsis** calathiformis (Skan.) Rehd. et Wils. (See orig. text pages 297-298)

9. **Castanopsis** carlesii (Hemsl.) Hayata

Tree 7-9 m tall; leaves oblong-lanceolate, serrate, 5-8 cm long, rarely over 2.5 cm wide, usually 2 cm or less, glabrous, with caudate-acuminate but rounded apex; involucre tuberculate cinerous-pubescent; nut entirely enclosed, 7 mm long, 6 mm wide, ovoid-globose, cracking open irregularly; fruit very small.

Distribtuion: Kwangtung Tai Mo Shan, Hainan, Kwangsi and Fukien, at altitude 1130 m.

10. **Castanopsis** caudata Franch. (See orig. text page 298)

11. **Castanopsis** ceratacantha Rehd. et Wilson.(See orig. text page 299)

12. **Castanopsis** chevalier Hick. et Camus

A tree 20 m tall; leaves large, oblong-elliptic 20-25 cm long, 6-8 cm broad, acuminate at apex, cuneate at base, margin entire, glabrous on both sides, slightly pubescent along the midrib; lateral veins 11-13 pairs; petioles 2 cm long.

Distribution: Southwestern Yunnan, at altitude 1500 m.

13. **Castanopsis** chinensis Hance (See orig. text page 299)

14. **Castanopsis** chingii Camus

15. **Castanopsis** concinna (Pamp.) A. DC. (See orig. text page 300)

16. **Castanopsis** concolor Rehd. et Wils.

17. **Castanopsis** cuspidata (Thunb.) Schottky

18. **Castanopsis** delavayi Franch.

19. **Castanopsis** diversifolia (See orig. text pages 302-304)

20. **Castanopsis** fabri Hance

21. **Castanopsis** fargesii Franch. (See orig. text pages 304-305)

22. **Castanopsis** fissa Rehd. et Wils.

23. **Castanopsis** fohaiensis Hu

Tree 10 m high; branchlets rather stout, terete, striate, lenticelled, brownish-black, tawny-tomentose, glabrous in age; leaves coriaceous, elliptic-oblong, lanceolate to obovate-lanceolate, short acuminate at apex, unequal and broadly cuneate at base, entire except very remotely mucronultae-serrate near the apex, shining yellowish green and glabrous except tomentulose along the lower part of midrib above, tawny-tomentose especially along the elevated midrib and secondary veins beneath, 8-16 cm long, 3-6 cm broad, lateral veins 11-14 pairs, slightly arching and divergent at 45 degrees, connected by the close elevated parallel veinlets; petioles rather stout, tomentose, 14 mm long; fruiting spikes rather short, with few fruits; rachis tomentose; cupules subglobose, symmetrical, 3.5 cm long, including the spines, densely covered with slender straight pubescent, spines to 1 cm long, connate at base into a common trunk 4 mm long, cupules thick, woody, indehiscent; walls tawny - tomentose; young fruit conforming with the cupule, with a very large basal scar.

Distribution: Southwestern Yunnan, Fohai Hsien, at altitude of 1800 m.

24-27. (See orig. text pages 305-309)

28. **Castanopsis henryi** Skan

Tree 20-30 m high; branches glabrous, purplish, with whitish lenticels; leaves ovate lanceolate to oblong, 3.5-5 cm long, 1.5-2.5 cm broad, glabrous, rotundate-cuneate at base, acuminate at apex, remotely dentate-serrate at margin; petioles 7-8 mm long; styles 9; fruits solitary, pendulous, 3/4 cm long and broad.

Distribution: Hupeh province.

29. **Castanopsis heterophylla** Hu

Tree 8-15 m high; 7-15 cm in diameter; bark light greenish-gray, branchlets whitish lenticelled, stout, brownish pubescent; leaves oblong-elliptic, 6-10 cm long, 3-5 cm broad, glabrous above, densely pubescent below, acuminate at apex, unequal cuneate at base, margin entire; petioles 2-3 cm long, pubescent; flowers solitary on short pedicels; nut entirely covered by spiny cupule.

Distribution: Yunnan Fohai Hsien, at altitude 1100-1540 m.

30. **Castanopsis hickelii** A. Camus

Small tree 6 m tall; bark grayish-brown, longitudinally fissured; leaves small narrowly-lanceolate usually serrate above the middle, with acuminate apex, glabrous above, minutely papillous or glandular dotted beneath.

Distribution: Kwangtung Tung Koo Shan, at altitude 540 m.

31. **Castanopsis hystrix** DC. (See orig. text page 309)

32. **Castanopsis incana** (See orig. text pages 310-311)

33. **Castanopsis indica** DC.

34. **Castanopsis junghuhnii** Hayata

A tree with very slender branchlets; leaves oblong-lanceolate, long acuminate at apex, rotundate-cuneate at base, minutely serrate-above the middle portion of the margin; acorns globose.

Distribution: Taiwan, Arisan.

35. **Castanopsis jucunda** Hance

36. **Castanopsis lancilimba** Hu

Tree up to 14 m high, 12 cm in diameter; bark rough, brownish gray, stout; branchlets densely yellowish pubescent; leaves oblong - lanceolate, rotundate - cuneate at base, margin, entire, and recurved, glabrous above, brownish-yellow pubescent beneath; lateral veins 12-14 pairs.

Distribution: Yunnan, Fohai Hsien, at altitude 1530 m.

37. **Castanopsis lamontii** Hance (See orig. text page 312)

38. **Castanopsis longicaudata** (Hay.) Kanehira et Hatusima

Shrubs, shoots with slender branchlets crowded on the tips; bark dark gray, glabrous; leaves obovate-elliptic, acuminate at apex, cuneate at base, recurved, entire, occurring in Taiwan.

39. **Castanopsis longispicata** Hu

Large tree to 23 m high, trunk to 60 cm in diameter; branchlets rather slender, terete, striate, glabrous, marked with many small whitish lenticels; leaves coriaceous, oblong-lanceolate, lanceolate or ovate-lanceolate, 6.5-14 cm long, 2-4 cm broad, long caudate-acuminate at apex, the acumen 3 cm long, broadly cuneate to rounded at base, remotely dentate-serrate to subentire near the apex and revolute along the margin, glabrous, shining green above, pale green and opaque midrib impressed above, elevated beneath, secondary veins 8-10 pairs, slender, slightly arching or striate, dissolving near the margins; petiole slender, glabrous, 1.5 cm long; staminate aments in terminal panicles to 11 cm long; rachis slender, gray, sericeous-tomentulose, staminate flowers minutes in rather distant glomeruluse, perigonium glabrescent outside, the lobes, ciliate stamens exserted; pistillate inflorescences 14 cm long, rachis slender, striate, glabrous, lenticelled; pistillate flowers numerous, distant, sessile; cupule spiny, gray, tomentulose; ovary solitary, glabrous, in axils of obtuse bracteoles; styles 2, very short; fruiting spikes 30 cm long, paniculate; rachis slender; cupules sessile, thin, conical-subglobose, 1.5 cm high, 1.2 cm in diameter covered with short stout simple broadly conical mucronulate gray-tomentose spines, 1 mm long, more or less arranged in sones, dehiscent; fruit conical-globose, 1.3 cm high, 10 mm in diam. glabrous, light chestnut brown.

Distribution: Yunnan, Che-Li-Hsien, at altitude 1200 m.

40. **Castanopsis kawakamii** Hayata

Tree 10-20 m tall; leaves oblong-lanceolate, subentire, recurved, with one dentate-serration on each side of the leafapex, short acuminate at apex, unequal cuneate at apex; lateral veins 8-12 pairs; fruits rather small on Taiwan specimen, but with stouter spines on the involucres.

Distribution: Hainan, and Taiwan, at altitude of 900-1000 m.

41. **Castanopsis matsudae** Hayata

Shrub with small leaves crowded on the top-part of the branchlets; leaves elliptic-lanceolate; petioles long and slender, apex sharply acuminate, margin coarsely serrate on the part above the middle, occurring in Taiwan.

42. **Castanopsis megaphylla** Hu

Tree 9 m high, trunk 20 cm in diam.; branches stout, terete, striate, pendulous, densely covered with small whitish lenticels, purplish black, young branchlets stout, angular, grooved, puberulous; leaves thin coriaceous, oblong to elliptic–oblong, short acuminate at apex, acute and subrounded at base, entire, and slightly revolute along the margin, glabrous, shining green with impressed midrib and prominent secondary veins above opaque and pale green with stout midrib and prominent secondary veins and elevated close subparallel veinlets beneath, 23–35 cm long, 10–13 cm broad; lateral veins 18–20 pairs; fruiting spikes to 25 cm long, covered with scattered subsessile fruits; rachis stout, striate, covered with numerous lenticels; immature cupules subsessile, asymmetrical, obovate–hemispherical, flat on the side against the rachis, convex on the opposite side, to 1 cm high and 2 cm in diameter including the spines; wall thick, woody, adnate to the fruit, large basal scar, covered with dense puberulous spines to 1 cm long; young fruit 2 in each cupule.

Distribution: Southern Yunnan, at altitude 1100 m.

43. Castanopsis namdinhensis Hickel et Camus

Tree 17 m high, 30 cm in diameter; bark gray and smooth; leaves lanceolate, 6–9 cm long, entire, acuminate at apex, glaucescent beneath; fruits green, 3 cm in diameter, with branched pubescence and not closely spaced spines.

Distribution: Kwangsi Nanning Hsien, at altitude 800 meters.

44. Castanopsis neo-cavalerier A. Camus (See orig. text page 312)
45. Castanopsis orthocantha Franch. (See orig. text pages 312–313)
46. Castanopsis rockii A. Camus (See orig. text page 314)
47. Castanopsis sinsuiensis Kaneh.

Small tree with dark gray bark; branchlets very rigid, whitish dotted; leaves elliptic–lanceolate, long acuminate at apex, cuneate at base, entire, glabrous; fruits 5–8 in a cluster, covered with short black spines.

Distribution: Taiwan.

48. Castanopsis stellato-spina Hayata

This species is distinguished by its stellate spines on the cupule; leaves oblong–lanceolate with 2–3 large teeth on each side of the leaf–apex. The rest of the leaf–margin entire.

Distribution: Taiwan.

49. Castanopsis stipitata (Hayata) Kanehira et Hatusima

Quercus stipitata Hayata

Large tree with grayish bark; branchlets slender; leaves oblong–lanceolate, coarsely serrate above the middle, acuminated at apex, dark green above, purplish green beneath; flowering aments short and erect; acorns globose, sessile, 1.5 cm long, 1 cm broad; nuts covered with very short scales, mucronate at the apex.

Distribution: Taiwan.

50. Castanopsis subacuminata Hayata

This species is distinguished by its oblong–elliptic to oblong–lanceolated leaves, subacuminate at apex, coarsely serrate, or dentate–serrate; fruits many crowded in a cluster, covered with dense black spines.

Distribution: Taiwan.

51. Castanopsis **sclerophylla** Schottky (See orig. text page 314)

52. Castanopsis **tenuinervis** A. Camus (See orig. text page 315)

53. Castanopsis **tenuispinula** Hickel et A. Camus

Large tree 20 m high; bark light gray; branchlets slender, yellowish pubescent when young; leaves elliptic-lanceolate, glabrous above, yellowish-brown pubescent beneath, 10-15 cm long, 3-5 cm broad, acute-acuminate at apex, unequally cuneate at base, entire, somewhat recurved; flowering spikes 10-18 cm long, pendulous.

Distribution: Yunnan, Fohai Hsien, at altitude 1530 m.

54. Castanopsis **trinervis** A. Camus

This species is distinguished by its nut-bracts 3-nerved and leaf-apex attenuated acuminate and with few dentate teeth above the middle of the leaves.

Distribution: Kweichow.

55. Castanopsis **taiwaniana** Hayata

A small tree 4-8 m high; 30-40 cm in diameter; bark dark gray, very rough; branchlets stout, sparsely lenticelled; leaves oblong-lanceolate, thick, coriaceous, acute or acuminate at apex, cuneate at base, entire, green above, brownish-yellow beneath, 15-20 cm long, 3-5 cm broad; petioles 1-15 cm long, glabrous; fruit spikes rigid, erect, terete, 15-20 cm long, covered with forked bract-like long spines; fruits 4-12 on each spike.

Distribtution: Taiwan.

56. Castanopsis **tibetana** Hance (See orig. text page 315)

57. Castanopsis **tribuloides** DC. (See orig. text pages 316-317)

Vars. 1-2. (See orig. text page 317)

58. Castanopsis **uraiana** (Hayata) Kanehira et Hatus.

Small tree, 5-10 m high; bark gray; branchlets slender, brownish gray, glabrous; leaves oblong-lanceolate, 6-10 cm long, 2-3 cm wide, attenuate long acuminate at apex, oblique obovate at base, distinctly coarse serrate above the middle; petioles slender, 1 cm long; fruit globular, 1/4 covered by the cupule, 1 cm long and 8 mm broad, mucronate at apex, sessile on spikes; spikes rigid, erect, 6 cm long.

Distribution: Taiwan, Taipei Urai.

59. Castanopsis **wangii** Hu

Tree 13 m high; trunk 90 m in circumference; young branchlets stout, terete, aciculate-pilosulose, lenticelled; leaves coriaceous, obovate-oblong to oblong-lanceolate, of two sizes, the smaller ones 8-11 cm long, 3.5-4 cm broad, the large ones 14-17 cm long, 5-8 cm broad,; acuminate at apex, slightly asymmetrical and acute to subrounded at base, entire, and slightly revolute along the margins, shining green and glabrous except tomentulose along the lower part of the slightly elevated midrib and with impressed secondary veins on the upper surface, densely tawny velutinous tomentose on the lower surface and fasciculose-pilosulose along its stout midrib and elevated secondary veins, 13-17 pairs, straight and abruptly arching toward the margin, connected by numerous slender close parallel veinlets; petioles stout, flattened above, 1-2 cm long; pitillate flowers paniculate; rachis rather stout, striate, densely tawny tomentose; pistillate flowers scattered sessile; involucre with many tomentose scales; fruits depressed-globulose, light chestnut brown.

Distribution: Southwestern Yunnan, Fohai Hsien, at altitude 1300 m.

This species is closely related to *Castanopsis ridleyi* Gamble and *C.fohaiwensis* Hu in the Sect. *Alleocarpus*, but it differs from both species in having larger leaves, cupules and fruits. From *C. megacarpa* Gamble it differs in having smaller cupules and fruits and densely set longer straight spines.

60. **Castanopsis wattii** (King) A. Camus (See orig. text pages 317-318)

Genus (4) Lithocarpus Bl. (See orig. text page 318)

Key to the species of Lithocarpus

A. Branchlets glabrous and petioles glabrous or glaucous; leaves for the most part glabrous or rarely glaucescent.

  B. Nut entirely enclosed by globose cupule or only open slightly at the top. ---------- -- *L. amygdalifolia*

  BB. Nut not enclosed by the shallow saucer or shaped cupule.

    C. Nut small ovoid-conical, about 1.5 cm in diameter and 1-1.3 cm high; leaves thick, very coriaceous, glabrous, lower surface with prominent raised reticulation; ----------------------------- (31) *L. hancei*

    CC. Nut large ovoid, over 2 cm long and about 2 cm wide.

      D. Leaves entire, 3.5-5.5 cm wide, oblong-elliptic; petioles 2 cm or less; fruit 2 cm wide ---------------------- (5) *L. brevicaudata*

      DD. Leaves undulate to undulate-serrate, 2.5-4 cm wide, elliptic; petioles 2.5-5 cm.; fruit 1.5 cm wide. ------- (32) *L. harlandii*

AA. Branchlets and petioles usually pubescent; leaves for most part pubescent beneath, but may be glabrous.

  B. Cup of fruit flat-topped or turbinate, nuts hemispheric, or decidedly depressed-globose.

    C. Leaves usually entire, 2.5-8 cm wide; branchlets pubescent.

      D. Leaves 2.5-4 cm wide (rarely to 6.5 cm) elliptic to lanceolate, acuminate; branchlets grayish or cinerous yellow pubescent, ------------------------ ------------------------------------- (21) *L. elliptica*

      DD. Leaves 5.5-8 cm wide, oval to oblong with rounded or broadly - acute, rarely acuminate apices; branchlets stout, densely yellowish pubescent;

nut 2.75 cm long, 1.75 cm broad -----(78) *L. uvarifolia*

CC. Leaves undulate or serrate above the middle, rarely over 5.5 cm wide; branchlets glabrous or grayish pubescent.

D. Lateral veins 17-25 on each side; leaves serrate, lanceolate-elliptical, pubescent on lower surface ----------(28) *L. fordiana*

DD. Lateral veins, rarely, if ever, over 13 on each side; leaves entire or undulate-crenate, pubescence confined mostly to veins on lower surface--(11) *L. cornea*

BB. Cup of fruit shallow, saucer-shaped or cup-shaped; nuts ovoid, conical, or depressed-globose, partly or almost enclosed.

C. Leaves oblong-ovate to oblanceolate and densely villous-tomentose beneath as on petioles and branchlets --------------(65) *L. skaniana*

CC. Leaves lanceolate to elliptic-oblong and usually glabrous throughout, but petioles and branchlets villous-tomentose ----(30) *L. glabra*

1-2. (See orig. text page 319)

3. **Lithocarpus bacqiangensis** Hickel et Camus

Tree 14-27 meters high, 30-90 cm in diameters; leaves oblong lanceolate 10-20 cm long, 5-10 cm broad, acute-acuminate at apex, cuneate at base, margin slightly recurved whitish green and somewhat grayish-yellow pubescent beneath; fruit subglobose, 2 cm long and broad; cups covering 1/3 of the acorns; acorns mucronate, sessile, minutely scally; spikes stout short, nuts many, crowded.

Distribution: Yunnan, at altitude 1300-1900 meters.

4. **Lithocarpus brachystachya** Chun

Lithocarpus microphylla Chun

Shrub or tree, 4-20 meters or more high, sometimes scandent or climing; leaves small, flowering and fruiting spikes, short small, fruits pedicelled, in a shallow fragile cup marked by the minutely denticulate spines; fruit brown.

Distribution: Hainan Island.

5. **Lithocarpus brevicaudata** (See orig. text page 320)

6. **Lithocarpus brunnea** (See orig. text page 320)

7. **Lithocarpus carolinse** (See orig. text page 321)

8. **Lithocarpus castanopsisifolia** Hayata

Tree 24-35 m tall, trunk 30 cm in diameter; bark dark gray; branchlets rigid, terete, sparsely lenticalled; leaves oblong-lanceolate, 10-20 cm long, 4-6 cm wide, acute to acuminate at apex, acute at base, entire, margin, slightly recurved grayish green above and slightly tomentose along the midribs below; lateral veins 5-11 pairs on each side; fruit large, sessile, globular, 4-5 cm long and 3-4 cm broad, maturing in pairs, or solitary on the pedicels; scales of the cups broadly flattened; nuts with a saucer-like depresshon on top.

Distribution: Taiwan, at altitude 1000-1500 meters.

9. **Lithocarpus   caudatilimba** (Merr.) Canus

    Pasania caudatilimba Merr.

    Tree 3–20 m high, trunk 12–20 cm in diameter; bark gray; leaves obovate, acute at apex and base, 6–10 cm long, 4–6 cm wide, thick coriaceous, entire; petioles 2–3 cm long; fruits with stout and thick pedicels; cupules covering the nuts completely.

    The species is characterised by having shining caudate – acuminate leaves, with decurrent–acuminate base, and cupules as long as the acorn; with few, free, rather distant scales arranged in 12 rows.

    Distribution: Hainan Island, at altitude 450–500 meters.

10. **Lithocarpus   cleistocarpa** Rehd. et Wils. (See orig. text page 322)

11. **Lithocarpus   carnea** Rehder (See orig. text pages 322–323)

12. **Lithocarpus   cystocarpa** Chun

    Tree 5–12 meters tall; bark dark gray; branchlets tomentose; leaves gray, thin, glabrous, green above, pale green beneath; fruits large edible, globose, covered with brownish reflexed scales.

    Distribution: Kwangsi Nan–ning, Kwangtung, at altitude 900 m.

13. **Lithocarpus   chifui** Chun et Tsiang

    Tree 12 m tall, trunk 3/4 m in diameter; leaves dull green above, grayish green beneath; pistillate inflorescence as seen in the fruiting state, with flowers clusterd in more or less pentagonal groups, all those on the under side of the rachis remaining abortive, of those more advantageously placed in relation to light, only one in each cluster reaching maturity; the individual flowers being contigous but no confluent; ripe acorns alternately juxtaposed in two ranks all facing one direction.

    This new species may be compared with Lithocarpus megastachya Hick. et. Camus from which it is amply distinct by isolated, not ternately coalescent acorns.

    Distribution: Kwangtung, Yu–Yuen Hsien, and Mo Tung Shan.

14. **Lithocarpus   chrysocoma** Chun et Tsiang

    Tree 6–8 m tall. This species is easily distinguished from its nearest allies, *L. amygdalifolia* (Skan) Schottky and *L. dealbata* Rehd. by the golden to reddish yellow pulverulent indumentum on the under surface of the leaf.

    Distribution: Kwangtung Yu–Yuen Hsien, and Hunan.

15. **Lithocarpus   cheliensis** Hu

    Tree 7 m high, trunk 25 cm in diameter; branchlets stout, terete, striate, glabrous, dark purple; leaves coriaceous, oblanceolate to lanceolate, long-acuminate at apex, cuneate at base, very slightly revolute and entire along the margins, glabrous on both surfaces, shining green with elevated flat midrib and impressed secondary veins above; lateral veins 10–14 pairs, divergent at about 60 degrees, arching toward the margins; petioles flat, glabrous, 3–5 cm long; pistillate inflorescences 20 cm long, 3–flowers together, distant, each enclosed by numerous tomentose scales and bracteoles; styles 3, erect; fruiting spike 20 cm long, densely covered with fruits, to 6 cm on diameter;

rachis stout, 1 cm in diameter; cupule platelliform, slightly triangular or rounded on the mouth, covering the basal part of the gland, to 8 mm high, 2.2 cm in diam., covered with spirally arranged very broadly ovate acute gray-tomentose scales; glands depressed triangular-globose, scarcely apiculate at the spex, with a large concave basal scar to 1.5 cm in diam. at base, tawny tomentose, light chestnut brown, very slightly spetate inside, longitudinally fissured.

Distribution: Southwestern Yunnam Che-Li Hsien, at altitude of 1050 meters.

16. **Lithocarpus dealbata** (Lindl.) Rehder (See orig. text page 324)

17. **Lithocarpus dictyoneuora** Chun

Tree of 18 m tall,

This species falls into the group of *Lithocarpus fenestrata* (Roxb.) Rehder, from which it differs in thinner leaves with more numerous and unusually prominent, strongly etched lateral veins and veinlets., smaller cups with minute scales, and hemispheric, not ovoid acorns. *Lithocarpus paviei* (Hickel et. A.Camus) Chun is not unlike in certain respects but in that species the silky pilose acron is borne on a pedicellate cup.

Distribution: Kwangsi Yao Shan.

18. **Lithocarpus dodoniaefolia** Hayata

A tree with whitish gray bark; branchlets with white lenticels; leaves lanceolate, 6-10 cm long and 1.5-2 cm wide, acute at apex, margin entire, recurving, glabrous, shining green above, slightly pubescent beneath, acuminate at base, with short petioles acrons broad-pyramidal with acute and mucronated apex and rounded truncate base, 2-2.5 cm long, 1.5-2 cm broad; cupule shallow, saucer-shaped, with fine-flaky scales; fruits often in two setting opposite on the peduncle, sessile.

Distribution: Taiwan.

19. **Lithocarpus dunnii** Metcalf (See orig. text page 324)

20. **Lithocarpus eleaegnifolia** (Seem.) Chun (See orig. text page 325)

21. **Lithocarpus ellitptica** Metcalf

Tree; leaves ellitiptic to lanceolate, 8-12 cm long, 2.5-4 cm wide, on young shoots and suckers larger, to 20 cm long and to 6.5 cm wide and oblanceolate, coriaceous, olive green above and paler, grayish or chestnut beneath, acute to acuminate, entire, glabrous above, densely tomentose pubescent beneath; veins somewhat obscure, depressed above but prominently elevated and reticulate beneath, 15-20 on each side petioles 1-2 cm long, pubescent; branchlets and inflorsecence pubescent, grayish or cinerous yellow; cup and nut similar to *L. cornea* (Lour.) Rehder

This species is closely related to *L. cornea* (Lour.) Rehd. from which it is distinguished by the more numerous veins on the thicker leaves more pubescent beneath; to *L. wariifolia* (Hance) Rehd. it is distinguished by much larger, consistently broader, oval to oblong leaves usually with rounded or broadly acute, rarely acuminate apices.

Distribution: Kwangtung at altitude 730 m to 1000 m.

22. **Lithocarpus elmerrillia** Chun

Tree 12–25 m tall; bark brown; leaves oblong–ovate, 18 cm long, 6 cm wide, acute to acuminate at both ends, margina entire, lustrous green above, glaucous beneath, coriaceous; cups thin and fragile.

Distribution: Kwangtung Hainan, at altitude 450–1000 m.

23. **Lithocarpus elisabethae** (Tutcher) Rehder (See orig. text page 325)

24. **Lithocarpus eyrei** (Champ.) Rehder (See orig. text page 326)

25. **Lithocarpus fenestrata** (Roxb.) Rehder (See orig. text page 327)

26. **Lithocarpus fenseliana** A. Camus

Pasania longana Chun

Tree 8–10 meters tall; bark blackish; branchlets thick, stout; leaves elliptic–lanceolate, 6–10 cm long, 3–4 cm wide, long acuminate at apex, acute at base; thick coriaceous, shining green above, silvery green and slightly pubescent below, entire, somewhat recurved along the margin; flowers white; fruits globose, 1.5–2 cm long and broad, completely enclosed by cupule, sessile.

Distribution: Hainan, at altitude of 700 meters.

27. **Lithocarpus fohaiensis** Hu

Tree 5 meters high, trunk 6–8 cm in diameter; branches very robust and terete; branchlets minutely lenticelled; leaves lanceolate to oblanceolate, long falcate–acuminate at apex, cuneate at base, margin undulate, coriaceous; veins prominent beneath and impressed above.

Distribution: Yunnan Fohai Hsien.

28. **Lithocarpus fordiana** (Hemsl.) Chun (See orig. text page 327)

29. **Lithocarpus formosana** Rehder

Quercus (Pasania) formosana Skan

Branch terete, rugose, glabrous; leaves ovate–elliptic, rarely narrow ovate, 1.5–2 cm long, 8 mm broad, coriaceous, glabrous, rounded at apex, margin revolute.

This species is closely related to *Quercus glabra* Thunb., but its leaves are never acuminate as in that species. The primary lateral nerves are less prominent, the male flowers more denesly crowded in shorter spikes, and the cupule and acorn also differ considerably.

Distribution: Taiwan.

30. **Lithocarpus glabra** (Thunb.) Rehder (See orig. text page 328)

Var. 1. **L. glabra var. thalassica** (See orig. text page 328)

31. **Lithocarpus hancei** (Benth.) Rehd. (See orig. text page 329)

32. **Lithocarpus harlandii** (Hance) Rehd. (See orig. text page 329)

33. **Lithocarpus haipinii** Chun

Tree 10–12 m; branches terete and rugose; leaves oblong lanceolate to elliptic–ovate, 8–12 cm long, 3.5–7 cm wide, abruptly acuminate at apex, rotundate at base, shining green above, pale green and tomentose beneath, coriaceous; margin recurved, glabrous; petioles 2–3 cm long; fruiting spike 6–13 cm long, rigid; flowers white; cupules cupulifermis, very shallow, 6 cm high, 2.2 cm broad, globular.

Distribution: Kwangtung, and Kwangsi.

34. **Lithocarpus henryi** (Seem.) Rehd. et Wils. (See orig. text page 330)

35. **Lithocarpus howii** Chun

Tree 3-5 m high; bark dark brown ; branchlets reddish brown, stout, whitish lentic-elled; leaves oblong-lanceolate, 12-16 cm long, 3-5 cm wide, acute at apex, ovate to cuneate at base, coarsely dentate, serrate and revoluted at margin, shining green above, brownish pubescent below, coriaceous; petioles slender, 2-3 cm long, brownish pubescent; fruits pale green, crowded at the apex of branchlets.

Distribution: Kwangtung king ping Shan, and Hainan, at altitude 3200 m.

36. **Lithocarpus hui** A. Camus

Tree 22.7 m tall, trunk 73 cm in diameter; bark dark brown; leaves large, 16-27 cm long 6-10 cm broad, oblong-lanceolate, to obovate-oblong, acute to acuminate at apex, acute to rounded-acute at base, undulate, entire coriaceous, shinning green above, pale green below; petioles 1.5-2 cm long; acorns globose, 1.5 cm long and 1 cm broad completely covered by cupule, sessile; cups spiny.

Distribution: Yunnan Chiu kiang Valley, at altitude 2500 m

37. **Lithocarpus hypoglauea** Hu

Tree 7-10 m high; bark brown; leaves oblong lanceolate, 10-16 cm long, 3-5 cm broad acuminate at apex, acute at base, entire, shinning green above, pale green and slightly pubescent beneath; coriaceous; male inflorescences reddish brown, very rugose, 10-12 cm long, pendulous; female inflorescences 20-25 cm long stout and pendulous; acorns sessile.

Distribution; Yunnan at altitude 1100-1800 m.

38. **Lithocarpus induta** (Bl.) Rehder (See orig. text page 330)

39. **Lithocarpus irvinii** (Hance) Rehder (See orig. text page 338)

40. **Lithocarpus iteaphylla** (Hance) Rehder (See orig. text page 332)

41. **Lithocarpus iteaphylloides** Chun

Tree 12-18 m high; leaves lanceolate to elliptic-lanceolate, 5-10 cm long, 2-3 cm wide long obtuse at apex, obtuse acuminate at base, undulate on the margin.

This species differs from *L. hancei* (Benth.) Rehd. in having slender blackish not grayish branchlets, much thinner and smaller leaves, smaller cups with less distinct scales arranged in few sones. It seems to be more closely allied to *L. iteaphylla* (Hance) Rehd, from which it is at once distinguished by the ternately coalescent (not solitary) acorn *L. ternaticupula* Hayata, of shich we have authentic specimens from Taiwan, differs in having a thicker deeper cup with prominent swollen scales and larger acorns, These 4 species belong to a closely related group, but it seem that they are specifically distinct.

Distribution: Kwangtung Sin-I Hsien

42. **Lithocarpus kawakamii** Hayata

Tree with short and stout branchlets; leaves large, 16-26 cm long, 8-10 cm broad oblong-lanceloate, acute at apex, rounded somewhat obligue at base, margin entire glabrous, coriaceous; branchlets fissured, deeply grooved; petioles 4-6 cm long, pubescent along the midrib below; fruits globular, sessile, crowded on the stout and rigid rachis acorns covered by the cupules to about 1/3 - 1/4 of the length of the nuts; cupules saucer-shaped, scaly; nut globular, 2 cm long, 1.5 cm broad, with minute projecting tips.

Distribution: Taiwan.

3. **Lithocarpus kodaihoensis** Hayata

Tree with slender and terete branches; bark dark gray, glabrous; leaves oblong-lanceolate, acuminate at apex, aucte at base, coarsely dentate-serrate above the middle of the leaves; fruits globular, solitary, sessile; cupules covered the acorns to 2/3 length of its heights.

Distribution: Taiwan.

4. **Lithocarpus konishii** Hayata

Quercus konishii Hayata

Synaedrys konishii (Hayata) Koidz.

Small tree 2-10 m high; bark light gray; branchlets whitish gray, minutely lenticelled, slender; leaves elliptic-lanceolate, long-acuminate at apex, broadly acute at base, coarsely dentate-serrate at margin only above the middle of the leaves, shinning green above, pale green beneath, glabrous; petioles slender, 1 cm long; acorns flattened globular, 2 cm broad, 1.5 cm high; cupules saucer-shaped, scaly, solitary, sessile.

Distribution: Taiwan.

5. **Lithocarpus leucostachya** A. Camus

Tree 14-20 m high, 32 cm in diameter; bark grayish white; branchlets stout, brownish gray, densely covered with round spots; leaves elliptic to elliptic-oblong, 8-12 cm long, 3-6 cm wide, acute at apex, acute or acuneate at base, margin revolute, glossy shinning green above, pale green slightly pubescent beneath; fruit aments very stout, rigid, with numerous acorns crowded on the rachis; fruit globular, mucronate at apex, scaly; acorns completely enclosed by cupules.

Distribution: Northwestern Yunnan, at altitude 2000-3200 m.

6. **Lithocarpus litseifolia** (Hance) Chun (See orig. text page 333)

7.- 49. (See orig. text pages 333-334)

9. **Lithocarpus nakai** Hayata

Shrub or small tree with slender, dense greenish gray branchlets; Leaves elliptic-lanceolate, long acuminate at apex, acute at base, margin entire, glabrous, light green on both surfaces; petioles 1-2 cm long.

Distribution: Taiwan.

10. **Lithocarpus nantoensis** Hayata

Small tree, 10 m high, 30 cm in diameter.; bark light gray; branchlets slender, reddish-brown; leaves lanceolate, long and sharply acuminated at apex, acute at base, entire, and undulate, dark green above and light green below, glabrous on both surfaces.

Distribution: Taiwan, Nanto.

52. **Lithocarpus naraikii** Hayata

   Pasania naraikii Hayata

   Tree 8-10 meters high; leaves lanceolate to oblanceolate, entire or undulate, with peculiar bloom beneath; flowers white, whitish-brown to yellow; acorns ovoid about 1 cm in diameter, half enclosed by cupule.

   Distribution: Kwangtung, Lao Fu Shan, Haiana, at altitude 700 m.

53. **Lithocarpus paihengii** Chun et Tsiang

   Tree 12 meters tall, trunk 22 cm in diam.; bark gray brown, irregularly fissured peeling off in plates; branchlets angular and lenticelled; leaves oblong lanceolated; 15-20 cm long, 5-8 cm wide, acuminate at apex, cuneate at base, deep green above, whitish green beneath; lateral veins 50 degrees in divergency; petioles 2.5-5 cm long; cupule depressed; fruits globose, 18 mm long, 15 mm broad.

   This species is most closely related to *Lithocarpus cleistocarpa* (Seem.) Rehd. e Wils. from which it differs in having thick coriaceous leaves with fulvous furfuraceou indumentum beneath, which persists more or less into the second year. In *L cleistocarpa* the acorn is completely adnated to the cupule except the exposed apex while in *L. paihengii* the nut is attached to the envolucre at base only. The specie yields hard and durable wood which is highly valued in making carrying poles.

   Distribution: Hunan, I-Chang Hsien, at altitude 930 m.

54. **Lithocarpus paniculata** Hand. – Mazz. (See orig. text page 335)

55. **Lithocarpus podocarpa** Chun

   Tree up to 20 m high; trunk 40 cm in diameter; bark gray; branchlets lenticelled leaves persistent, silver green, coriaceous, oblong to elliptic-oblong, 8-10 cm long 3-4 cm wide, abruptly obtuse acuminate at apex, cuneate at base, margin entire an revolute; male aments 10-15 cm long; flowers white; perigonium cupule-like, 1 mm deep fruits 7-9 aggregated on the pedicels; cups grayish white; acorns wholly exerted; gland hemispheric depressed, globose, 14-15 mm broad and deep.

   Distribution: Kwangtung, and Hainan, at altitude 800 m.

56. **Lithocarpus picta** Hand.–Mazz.

   Large tree with whitish gray, lenticelled, angular branches and branchlets; leave ovate-oblong, 7.5-14 cm long, coriaceous, caudate at base, acute at apex, margi recurved; lateral veins pilose, 5-9 pairs, divergent 40-45 degrees; petioles 2-7 m long; acrons globose; style 4-5 mm long.

   Distribution: Kweichow, at altitude 6500 m.

57. **Lithocarpus polystachya** (Wall.) Rehd. (See orig. text page 335)

58. **Lithocarpus randaiensis** Hayata

   A small tree with brownish bark and very slender reddish brown branchlets; leave elliptic, 5-8 cm long, 2-3 cm wide, acute or acuminate at apex, cuneate at base, margi entire, thick, coriaceous, dark green on both surfaces; petioles slender, 1 cm long.

Distribution: Taiwan, Ran dai Shan.

59. **Lithocarpus rehderiana** Hand.-Mazz.

A tree with silvery gray bark; leaves small, glabrous, rotundate-obovate, occurring in Yunnan and Szechuan.

60. **Lithocarpus rhombocarpa** Hayata

Large tree with brownish bark; branchlets reddish brown and terete; leaves elliptic-ovate, acute at apex, acute and slightly oblique at base, entire or little undulated, light green above, brownish green and pubescent along the veins beneath, thick coriaceous; petioles slender, 2-3 cm long; female aments crowded with acorns along the pedicels forming a long spike; acorns half enclosed by cups, very small, globular, 3-5 mm high and broad (immature).

Distribution: Taiwan.

61. **Lithocarpus rosthornii** Schottky

Pasania rosthornii Schottky

Small tree with dense pilose branchlets; leaves lanceolate, abruptly acuminate at apex, undulate lustrous glabrous, 15-18 cm long, 4-4.5 cm wide; petioles pilose, 1-1.5 cm long.

Distribution: Szechuan, Nan-Chuan Hsien.

62. **Lithocarpus shinsuiensis** Hayata et Kaneh.

Tree with dark brown bark and very slender branchlets; Leaves elliptic-lanceolate to oblong-lanceolate, sharply acuminated at apex, acute to rounded at base, entire, dark green above, light green beneath; petioles slender, 1-1.5 cm long; fruits globose; acorns half enclosed by cupule; fruits short pedicelled, solitary.

Distribution: Taiwan.

63. **Lithocarpus silvicolarum** (Hance) Chun

Quercus silvicolarum Hance

Tree to 20 m high; trunk 1 m in diameter; branchlets angled, sulcate, fuscous, puberulous, lenticellate; leaves long petiolate, subcoriaceous, glabrous, entire, elliptic to elliptic-oblong, caudate-acuminate, base obliquely-obtuse, decurrent down the petiole, upper surface light green, sublustrous, lower surface whitish green, becoming brownish when dry; midrib flattened above, elevated on the lower surface, lateral veins 8-11 pairs, slender, diverting 45 degrees, ascending, curving, transverse veinlets indistinct above; petioles flattened above, base dilated, 2-2.8 cm long.

Distribution: Hainan.

64. **Lithocarpus suishanensis** Kanehira et Yamamoto

Tree with dark brown bark, branchlets brown, lenticelled, glabrous, terete; leaves elliptic-ovate, 10-16 cm long, 4-6 cm broad, acute at apex, broadly cuneate at base, entire, dark green and shinning glossy above, pale green and slightly pubescent beneath; petioles slender, 2-3 cm long; flowering aments short, stout, erect; fruits 5-9 on each

pedicel, globular, 1–1.5 cm high and broad, mucronate; cupule shallow covering th
acorn up to 1/4 of its length, light grayish, scaly, sessile.

Distribution: Taiwan.

65. **Lithocarpus skaniana** (Dunn) Rehd. (See orig. text page 336)

66. **Lithocarpus spicata** R. et W.

Vars. 1–5. (See orig. text pages 336–339)

67. **Lithocarpus stipitata** Koidz.

Small tree with dark gray bark and slender lenticelled branchlets; leaves elliptic-
oblong, 8–12 cm long, 3–5 cm wide, long acuminate at apex, ovate and lapsided at base
coarsely toothed along the margin, lustrous light green above, pale green beneath, thick
coriaceous; petiole slender, 1 cm long; female ament short, erect, 5–10 cm long; acorn
globular, small, 5–8 mm high and broad, half enclosed by the scaly cupule; Cups bowl-
shaped; acorns 7–11 on each pedicel, sessile.

Distribution: Taiwan.

68. **Lithocarpus synbalanos** (Hance) Chun

Tree with angular branchlets; leaves coriaceous, entire, elliptic, about 9 cm long
short cuspidate–acuminate at apex, glabrous above, glaucescent beneath; fruiting spikes
10 cm long, mature fruits usually 2–3 , bases connate, depressed globose; cup scales
about seriate, ovate–triangular, mucronate, thick, fuscous–tomentose, the uppermos
scales incurved, acorn densely tawny–tomentose, top convex, apiculate.

Distribution: Hong Kong Happy Valley, and Kwangtung Wan Shiu Shan.

69. **Lithocarpus taitoensis** Hayata

Tree 10–18 m tall, 32 cm in diameter; bark borwn; branchlets thick reddish brown,
lenticelled; leaves elliptic to elliptic–oblong, 8–12 cm long, 3–5 cm wide, acute at apex,
cuneate at base, entire, thick, coriaceous, dark green above, pale green beneath,
grayish pubescent below; petioles slender, 1–1.5 cm long, glabrous; fruiting spikes
thick, stout, 6–16 cm long with 6–17 acorns on each pedicel; acorn flattened, globose,
1–1.5 cm high and broad; cupules very shallow, adhering to the base of the acorn and
smaller than the acorn's base; acorns minutely mucronated.

Distribution: Taiwan.

70. **Lithocarpus ternaticupula** Hayata

Tree 17–25 m high, 32–38 cm in diameter; bark dark gray, branchlets densely lenticelled, reddish brown, slender; leaves oblong lanceolate, 10–14 cm long, 3–6 cm wide,
acute at apex, cuneate at base, entire, glabrous, coriaceous, slightly brownish pubescent along the midrib beneath; petioles slender, 1–2.5 cm long, glabrous; fruiting spikes
short, stout, 10–14 cm long; acorns globular, 1 cm long and broad, densely crowded on
the pedicels, sessile. half enclosed by the cupules, mucronate; cupules arranged in
zones with grayish scales.

Distribution: Taiwan and Hanian, at altitude 2600–2800 m.

71. **Lithocarpus thalssia** Hance (See orig. text page 339)

72. **Lithocarpus trachycarpa** Hickel et Camus

Small tree 6 meters high; bark dark gray; branchlets slender, grayish brown; leaves large, 20–30 cm long, 6–10 cm wide, lanceolate to oblong–lanceolate, acute at apex, cuneate at base, entire, light green above, pale green beneath, reddish pubescent along the midrib below; lateral veins 15–19 pairs divergent 45–50 degrees, curving upward near the margin; petioles stout, 1–2 cm long, glabrous; fruits round, acorns completely enclosed by the cupules, sessile, brown, scaly, numerous on the pedicels.

Distribution: Southwestern Yunnan at altitude 1000–1400 m.

73. **Lithocarpus tremula** Chun

Tree 6–8 m high; bark gray; leaves ovate to elliptic – lanceolate, acute at apex, cuneate at base, 6–9 cm long, 2–3.5 cm wide; petiole flat; pistillate flowers whitish, hairy; fruiting cups reddish brown.

Distribution: Hong Kong.

74. **Lithocarpus truncata** (King) Rehder et Wilson

Quercus truncata King

Tree 5–17 m high, 32 cm in diameter; bark dark brown, branchlets glabrous; leaves persistent, oblong–lanceolate to lanceolate, long acuminate at apex, acute at base, 18–30 cm long, 3–4.5 cm wide, entire, dark green above, pale green and pubescent reddish brown beneath; petioles 2 cm long, flattened; lateral veins 9–10 pairs; male flowers solitary. erect, stout pedicelled; female ones very short pedicelled, erect, thick, stout, densely crowded with acorns; fruits completely enclosed by cupules.

Distribution: Yunnan, at altitude 1500 m.

75. **Lithocarpus tsangii** A. Camus

Tree 5–10 meters high; leaves oblong–lanceolate or elliptic, 10–17 cm long, cuspidate-acuminate, glabrous or sparsely pubescent beneath, distinguished by the turbinate cups, which simulate those of *L. cornea* (Lour.) Rehder, somewhat roughened but not with the projecting tubercles.

Distribution: Kwangtung Sha Lo Shan and Kwangsi province.

76. **Lithocarpus unicinata** Camus

Trees; leaves oblong lanceolate, 7–8 cm long, short acuminate, glabrous or sparsely pilose beneath, shallowly cinate–dentate, resembling *L. tsangii* Camus but cups with numerous prominent, curved, stout, woody tubercles.

Distribution: Kwangsi, Shap Ma Shan.

77. **Lithocarpus uraiana** Hayata

Shiia uraiensis Kaneh. et Hatus.

Large tree; bark dark gray; branchlets slender, brownish gray; leaves elliptic lanceolate, 5–10 cm long, 3–5 cm wide, long acuminate at apex, cuneate and lapsided at base, coarsely serrate along the margin above the middle, glabrous, slightly pilose beneath, dark green above, light green below; petioles short, 5 mm long; fruiting aments 3–5 cm long; acorns globular, small, 2–5 mm long and broad, mucronate, about half enclosed by cupules, covered by scales, arranged in zones; pedicels short, stout, erect.

Distribution: Taiwan, Taipei Urai, in forest along Kango.

78. **Lithocarpus uvariifolia** (Hance) Rehder (See orig. text page 340)

79. **Lithocarpus variolosa** (Franch.) Chun (See orig. text page 340)

80. **Lithocarpus vestida** (Hickel et Camus) Metcalf

Tree 8-17 m high, 15-30 cm in diameter; bark gray, brown to black, narrowly elliptic, glabrous; leaves bluish green below; 13-15 cm long, up to 5 cm wide, long gradually acuminate at apex; flowers yellowish, acorn 1.5 cm in diameter and in height; cupules covered with closely arranged spines.

Distribution: Kwangsi and Kwangtung Yam Na Shan.

81. **Lithocarpus viridis** Rehder et Wilson (See orig. text page 341)

82. **Lithocarpus wilsonii** Seem.

Tree, bark smooth, gray; branchlets grayish brown, slender; leaves with petioles of 1.5 cm long, oblong-lanceolate, 17.5 cm long, 8 cm wide, sharply acuminate at apex, cuneate at base, entire along the margin; lateral veins 11 pairs; fruiting aments 8 cm long; female aments usually on the tips of branchlets; cupules saucer - shaped, very shallow.

Distribution: Western Hupeh.

83. **Lithocarpus yunjensis** Hu

Tree 7.5 m high; branchlets slender, terete, striate, sparsely pilose, purplish-black; leaves coriaceous obvate-lanceolate, caudate-acuminate at apex, acuminate at base, entire and slightly revolute along the margins, glabrous and shinning green with slightly elevated midrib and secondary veins above, very sparsely pilose to glabrescent with elevated midrib and secondary veins beneath, 9-11 cm long, 2.5-4 cm broad; secondary veins 10-11 pairs, divergent at 45 degrees, abruptly curving forward and forming loops near the margins; petioles flat, 1-1.5 cm long, glabrous; fruiting spikes 10 cm long, 1.5 cm in diameter with numerous fruits; rachis sparsely pilose; cupules connate in 3's on a very short peduncle, 5 mm high, 6-7 mm in diameter, enclosing 2/3 of the nut, with many imbricate broadly ovate tomentulose scales acuminate at apex, and with a concave svar at base; pericarp thin, deeply septate inside, longitudinally fissured.

Distribution: Yunnan Yung-Jen Hsien, altitude 1700 m.

This species seems to alley to *Pasania paniculata* Hand.-Mazz. in the small gland and cupule, but distinguished by larger leaves and larger pruinose olive fruits.

Genus (5) **Pasania** Oersted

Trees, branchlets more or less angular, grooved, covered with elevated small purple lenticels; leaves chartaceous, lanceolate or elliptic-lanceolate, long acuminate at apex, acute, acuminate to cuneate at base, entire, slightly revolute and undulate along the margins; staminate aments solitary, axillary; staminate flowers sessile, perigonium-lobes 6, obovate, rounded at the apex, tomentulose outside; stamens 12; filaments slender to 3 mm long; fruiting aments to 14 cm long, rachis terete, glabrous; cupules isolated, subsessile, truncate at the apex, 1.3 in diam., with spines, lower spine recurved to 6 mm long, uppermost incureved, all minutely gray sericeous tomentulose, young fruits completely enclosed by the cupules, turbinate, with 4 glabrous styles at the apex, truncate at base and with a large slightly nearly flat basal scar, light chestnut-brown, densely covered with yellowish gray sericeous tomentum, pericarp thin, septate much developed.

1. Pasania echinothola Hu

Tree to 10 m high, 60 cm in diameter; branchlets more or less angular, grooved, glabrescent, covered with purple small lenticels, dark purple; leaves chartaceous, elliptic-lanceolate, lanceolate to narrow lanceolate, long acuminate at apex, acute to cuneate at base, entire, slightly revolute and undulate along the margins, glabrous and slight green with slightly elevated flat channelled midrib and secondary veins and very close and very slender parallel veinlets above; secondary veins 12–13 pairs, curving abruptly toward the margins; staminate aments solitary, axillary, up to 11 cm long, sessile.

Distribution: S. E. Yunnan, at altitude 1200 m.

Pasania echinothola Hu is in the section Eupasania. It is distinguished by the large leaves glabreacent beneath and with short petioles and by the isolated cupules probably nearly completely enclosing the fruit which is turbinate in shape and has a large nearly flat basal scar, In this respect it seems to be closely allied to P. wrayi Gamble

Genus (6) Quercus Linn. (See orig. text pages 341–342)

I. Key to the species of Quercus

A. Cups with the scales connate into concentric rings --------------------------------
-- Subgenus I Cyclobalanopsis
 B. Leaves entire or entire-undulate, glabrous throughout; branches and petioles glabrous.
  C. Leaves small, (7–12 cm long, 2.5–5 cm wide), oblong-ovate to oblong lanceolate
  -- (2) Q. acuta
  CC. Leaves large (15–20 cm long, 6–8 cm wide), broadly elliptic to ovate lanceolate
  -- (58) Q. jensentiana
 BB. Leaves subentire with few undulate crenate to shallow crenate teeth or 4–6 sharp serrations below the apex.
  C. Leaves with undulate-crenate to shallow – crenate teeth below the abruptly caudate-acuminate apex; glabrous above, pubescent beneath; branchlets to-

mentose; petioles usually 1.5 cm or more long; leaves with 5-6 pairs of secondary veins, cups of fruit with 4-5 rings --- ------------------------------------- (13) *Q. chungii*

    CC. Leaves with 4-6 sharp serrations below the short acute apex, glabruos, petioles 0.6-1 cm long, leaves with 9-10 pairs of secondary veins; cups of fruit with 5-7 rings ----------------------(81) *Q. nubium*

BBB. Leaves serrate (rarely crenate-serrate) at least the upper 1/3; glabrous or pubescent; branchlets glabrous or pubescent.

    C. Acorns 2 cm or more long.

        D. Acorns 2-2.5 cm long; branches, petioles pubescent; leaves tomentose when young to glabrous -------------- (85) *Q. pachyloma*

      DD. Acorns 3.75-4.5 cm; branches, petioles glabrous at least when mature; leaves glaucous below -------------- (31) *Q. edithae*

    CC. Acorns less than 2 cm long, usually 1-15 cm

        D. Leaves narrow, 2-3.5 cm wide, elliptic or elliptic-lanceolate, serrate, dull above, glabrous ---------------- (78) *Q. myrsinaefolia*

      DD. Leaves broad, 2-5.6 cm wide, elliptic oblong, or elliptic-lanceolate to oblanceolate, coarssly serrate above the middle, shiny above. ---------- ------------------------------------- (47) *Q. glauca*

AA. Cup shallow, with the scales (tubercles) not connate into concentric rings, but appressed or spreading ---------------------------------- Subgenus II *Euquercus*.

    B. Leaves sinute-dentate or sinute-shallow lobed

        C. Branchlets glabrous; margin of leaves with 10-15 pairs of usually obtuse teeth ------------------------------------- (4) *Q. aliena*

      CC. Branchlets pubescent.

        D. Leaves 5-7 cm wide, shallow sinuate with 6-10 pairs of short rounded lobes; cups with apressed scales; acorns 2-2.25 cm long --------------- ------------------------------------- (33) *Q. fabri*

      DD. Leaves up to 20 cm wide, sinuate-dentate, with 4-9 broad lobes; cup with spreading scales; acorns 1.5-2 cm long ------------------------------- ------------------------------------- (25) *Q. dentata*

    BB. Leaves serrate or crenate-serrate.

        C. Branchlets, petioles pubescent; leaves small, 2.5-6 cm long 1.5-2.75 cm wide ------------------------------------- (92) *Q. phillyraeoides*

      CC. Branchlets, petioles glabrous; leaves larger, 7-14 cm long 3-10 cm wide.

        D. Leaves serrate with bristle tips.

           E. Leaves tomentose beneath; scales (tubercles) recurved; acorns 1.5-2 cm long ----------------------- (127) *Q. variabilis*

          EE. Leaves subglabrous beneath tubercles or scales spreading; acorns 2 cm long ----------------------- (3) *Q. acutissima*

DD. Leaves only serrate, without bristle tips; scales appressed ------------
-------------------------------- (43) *Q. glandulifera* Blume

II. Key to the Species of Quercus of Chekiang

A. Leaves deciduous.

    B. Leaves serrate or crenate-serrate with bristle like teeth or with acute gland-tipped teeth.

        C. Leaves serrate or crenate serrate with macronate or bristle like teeth.

            D. Leaves glabrous at maturity, or with a sparse pubescence along the veins, or with axillary tufts of hairs beneath.

                E. Leaves ovate-oblong, oblong, rarely oblong-lanceolate; scales of cup thick, subulate spreading and recurved; acorns usually globose or globose-ovoid at maturity --------(3) *Quercus acutissima*

                EE. Leaves lanceolate or elliptic-lanceolate, rarely oblong - lanceolate; scales of cup thin, scale - like; acorns usually elliptic - oblong or obovoid at maturity --------------------*Q. chenii*

            DD. Leaves glabrous or stellately pubescent above, with a sparse stellate, scaly pubescence or with a dense stellate pubescence beneath.

                E. Leaves 4-7 cm long, serrate with a short bristle-like teeth, glabrous or stellately pubescent above, stellately scaly-pubescent and densely tomentose near the base on midrib beneath; scales of cup slender ---
-------------------------------- *Q. baronii*

                EE. Leaves 8-15 cm long, serrate with bristle-like teeth, glabrous above, densely stellately pubescent beneath; scales of cup stouter ----------
-------------------------------- (127) *Q. variabilis*

        CC. Leaves serrate or crenate-serrate with acute gland-tipped teeth, obovate, oblong-obovate or acute-lanceolate; scales of cup appressed----------------
-------------------------------- (105) *Q. serrata*

    BB. Leaves sinuate-dentate, with rounded lobes or with acute teeth

        C. Branchlets more or less pubescent.

            D. Leaves 6-12 or sometimes up to 18 cm long; scales of cup ovate, appressed; acorns cylindric-oblong -------------- (33) *Q. fabri*

            DD. Leaves 10-20 or sometimes over 30 cm long; scales of cup lanceolate, free, spreading; acorn globose-ovoid ------(25) *Q. dentata*

        CC. Branchlets glabrous; leaves with obtuse teeth (with acute teeth in var. acutiserrata) ---------------------------- (4) *Q. aliena*

AA. Leaves evergreen.

    B. Leaves glabrous at maturity.

        C. Leaves oblong, elliptic-lanceolate, oblong-ovate or lanceolate, entire, or with a few serrated teeth below the acuminate apex, not glaucous beneath --(81) *Q. nubium*

CC. Leaves oblong-lanceolate to lanceolate, sharply serrate, glaucescent beneath --- (78) *Q. myrsinaefolia*

BB. Leaves more or less hairy beneath.

C. Leaves pubescent with simple hairs beneath or only on midrib above and at its base beneath; fruit mature in two years.

D. Leaves glabrous above, somewhat hairy beneath; scales of cup connate into concentric rings.

E. Leaves serrate above middle (less deeply serrate in var. gracilis), 6-13 cm long, 2-5.5 cm broad; fruiting spike 0.5-1 cm long. --(47) *Q. glauca*

EE. Leaves entire or semewhat undulate, 12-20 cm long, 5.5-12.5 cm broad; fruiting spike 5-7 cm long. --(58) *Q. jenseniana*

DD. Leaves pubescent on the midrib above and at its base beneath, broad-elliptic, to ovate-oblong, serrate, 2.5-6 cm long; scales of cup appressed, not connate into rings. -------------- (92) *Q. phillyraeoides*

CC. Leaves densely stellate pubescent beneath, oblanceolate or obovate-oblong, rarely oblong; fruit mature in one year.-- (42) *Q. gilva*

III. Key to the species of Quercus in the Kunming Region

A. Leaves small, coriaceous and persistent.

B. Cup scales connate into concentric rings.

C. Branchlets, lower surface of the leaves, inflorescence, and cup more or less densely covered by a light yellow indumentum; leaves oblong-lanceolate, serrulate usually above the middle ---------- (22) *Q. delavayi*

CC. Branchlets and inflorescence glabrous.

D. Leaves glabrous on both surfaces, elliptic-lanceolate, entire, or obscurely crenulate-denticulate, glaucescent beneath; rings of cup 3-5, obscurely puberulent; fruit matures in the second year-- *Q. augustinii*

DD. Leaves glabrous above, minutely whitish wooly tementose beneath at least when young, elliptic or elliptic-ovate, sharply dentate; rings of cup 6-8, densely silky pilose------------------(100) *Q. schottkyana*

BB. Cup scales distinctly imbricate, not connate into concentric rings.

C. Leaves entire, crenulate or irregularly spinulose-denticulate, sessile or sub-sessile.

D. Leaves with dense yellowish tomentum beneath; inflorescence less than 5 cm long; fruit matures in the first year; acorns 1/2 enclosed by the cup. --

---------------------------------- (104) *Q. senescens*

DD. Leaves with thin yellowish pubescence beneath, inflorescence more than 5 cm long; fruit natures in the second year; acorn 1/4 enclosed by the cup-

--- *Q. semicarpifolia* var.

longispica

CC. Leaves sharply serrate above the middle, distinotly petiolete; acerns 2/5 enclosed by cup -------------------------(40) *Q. franchetii*

AA. Leaves large, chartaceous and deciduous.

B. Cup scales short, compressed.

C. Branchlets tomentose, cup scales fringed at the apex; leaves obovate, obtuse-dentate ------------------------------ (49) *Q. griffithii*

CC. Branchlets glabrous.

D. Leaves dinuate-dentate; acorn oblong-ovoid, 1/2 enclosed by cup -------

--(4) *Q. aliena*

DD. Leaves coarsely and acutely serrate; acorn cylindric, 1/3 enclosed by cup

------------------------------------- *Q. aliena* var. *acutiserrata*

BB. Cup scales long, linear or lanceolate.

C. Leaves oblong-lanceolate, sharply serrate with bristle-pointed teeth; fruit matures in the second year.

D. Leaves glabrous and light green beneath; acorn oblong-ovoid ------------

------------------------------------ (3) *Q. acutissima*

DD. Leaves white tomentose beneath; acorn globose-ovoid --------------------

---------------------------------(127) *Q. variabilis*.

CC. Leaves obovate, lobulate-dentate along the margin; fruit matures in the first year.

D. Leaves obtusely lobulate-dentate; cup straight to form a tube; acorn entirely enclosed by cup ------------ (129) *Q. yuii*

DD. Leaves sharply lobulate-dentate along the margin; cup scales spreading and recurving; acorn 2/3 enclosed by cup --- *Q. dentata* var. *oxyloba*

1. **Quercus acrodonta** Seemen (See orig. text page 342)

2. **Quercus acuta** Thunberg

Tree 15-30 m tall, 30-40 cm in diameter; leaves oblong-ovate to oblong-lanceolate, 7-12 cm long, 2.5-5 cm wide, rounded at base, entire, usually undulate, apex abrupt, green and glabrous on both sides; petioles 2.25-3 cm long; cup pubescent, of connate concentric rings; acorn about 2 cm long, narrowly ovoid.

Distribution: Fukien, and Kweichow, at altitude 300-1100 m.

3. **Quercus acutissima** Carruth (See orig. text page 342)

4. **Quercus aliena** Blume (See orig. text pages 344-346)

Vars. 1,2, 3, 4.

5. **Quercus amygdalifolia** Skan

Small trees with brownish bark; branchlets short, stout, reddish brown, glabrous; leaves oblong-ovate, 4-6 cm long, 2-3 cm wide, acuminate at apex, ovate at base, basal postion entire, minutely serrate above the middle, pale green above, brownish green and slightly pubescent below; petioles red, short, 1 cm long; flowering aments in longer slender spikes, 5-10 cm long; aments crowded along the peduncles; flowers red-dish brown.

Distribution: Kwangtung, Loh Fau Shan.

6. **Quercus aquefolioides** Rehd. et Wils. (See orig. text page 346)

7-11. (See orig. text pages 346-350)

12. **Quercus carlesii** Hemsl.

Small tree; branchlets glabrous at tips; leaves distinctly petioled, coriaceous, glabrous, oblong lanceolate, caudate-acuminate; petioles 2-3 cm long; veins inconspic-uous; female flowering spikes axillary slightly longer than the leaves; involucre white pubescent; nut spherical, pea-size 3-4 mm in diameter.

This species is closely affiliated to *Quercus cuspidata* Thunb, but differs in the less coriaceous leaves and the nuts spherical.

Distribution: Fukien, and Foo-chow.

13. **Quercus chungii** Metcalf (See orig. text page 350)

14. **Quercus chrysocalyx** Hickel et Camus

Tree 40 m high; completely glabrous; branchlets gray, the current year's growth 3-4 mm in diameter; winter buds oblong, 4 mm long; leaves ovate-elliptic, 6-12 cm long, 2.5-5 cm wide, coarsely serrate, the base obtuse or acute, the apex acuminate, the acumen 0.5-2 cm long, the lateral veins 9-10 pairs, evident on both surfaces; cup patelliform, 20-25 mm in diameter, gray with 7 concentric rings, pubescent; nuts hemis-pheric, 1 cm from base to apex, 2 cm in diameter, pubescent, mucronate.

Distribution: Hainan, at altitude 300 m.

15. **Quercus cenduplicans** Chun

Tree 22 m high; branchlets subangular, terete, glabrous; leaves dark green above pale green beneath, acorn dark brown; cup with brownish velvety indumentum.

This species is unlike any others known to us in the peculiar structure of cupule. The cupule is composed of two parts different from each other in texture. It has a hemis-pheric and woody cup preper and an abruptly expanded broad circular limb which, in the living state must presumably by flesh, eventually becomes thickly coriaceous and strongly undulate with conduplicate upwardly curving folds alternating with decidedly indented and more or less revelute intervals.

Distribution: Kwangtung Yao-Ping Hsien.

16-17. (See orig. text pages 351-352)

19. **Quercus cornea** Lour.

Quercus hemisphaerica Drake

Tree 3 meters tall, trunk 6 cm in diameter; leaves elliptic-lanceolate, 10-16 cm long,

3-4 cm wide, acuminate at apex, acute at base, serrate, pale green above and yellowish brown beneath; fruit edible, sold in the markets of Canton.

Distribution: Kwangtung and Kwangsi.

20. **Quercus cuspidata** Thunb.

  Castanopsis cuspidata Thunb.

Small tree; elliptic-lanceolate and long cuspidate, leaves entire, sometimes with undulate or irregulary small serrations, petioles 1 cm long; male flowers in slender clusters of terminal aments.

Distribution: Kwangtung.

21. **Quercus cambodiensis** Hickel et Camus

Tree of 12 meters high, 18 cm in diameter; bark grayish-brown; leaves elliptic-lanceolate, 10-16 cm long, 2.5-4 cm wide, glabrous, serrate, dark green above, brownish green below, acuminate at apex and acute at base; fruit smoky colored.

Distribution: Kwangsi and Hainan.

22. **Quercus delavayi** Franch. (See orig. text pages 352-353)

23. **Quercus delicatula** Chun et Tsiang

Tree 13 meters tall; leaves thin, glabrous, relatively small, entire, caudate-acuminate cupule small, the upper half of the annual rings glabrescent and the lower half densely tomentose; fruit light yellow.

Distribution: Kwangtung, Cheng Hsien, scattered in mixed forest in dense shade.

24. **Quercus densiflora** Abl.

(May be a *Lithocarpus* or a *Castanopsis densiflora* not surely determined as yet, for the present leaving in the *Quercus*)

Its fruits in the long upright spikes and terminating the branches certainly suggest to be *Lithocarpus* or *Castanopsis*.

25. **Quercus dentata** Thunb. (See orig. text page 353)

  Var. 1. Quercus dentata var. **oxyleba** Franch. (See orig. text page 354)

  Var. 2. Quercus dentata var. **stewardii** Rehder

    This variety differs form the typical form by leaves of nearly triangular shape and obliquely cuneate at base, breadly truncate acute apex and wedge-shaped below, and irregularly coarsely dentate at margin.

  Var. 3. Quercus dentata var. **yunnanensis** Camus

    This variety differs from the typical form by oblique - ovate leaves, fanshaped, 10-14 cm long, 8-12 cm wide above the middle, acute at apex, cuneate at base, pale green above, yellowish green below, hairy, and rounded lobulated-dentate at margin; midribs and veins very prominent beneath and depressed on the upper surface; style and stigma 5-lobed; nuts cylindrical and 1/2 enclosed by the cupule.

26. **Quercus dilatata** Lindl. (See orig. text page 353)

Var. 1. Quercus dilatata var. yunnanensis Franch.

A tree closely similar to *Quercus semicarpifolia* var. *glabra* Franch.
occurring in Yunnan and having the characters of *Quercus dilatata* Lindl.

Distribution: Yunnan.

27. **Quercus dilatata** Seem. (See orig. text page 355)

Lepidobolanus, dielsiana Seemen

Tree 6.5 meters or more high; bark and branches gray-brown to light gray; leaves 5.5 cm long, 1.5 cm wide; long acuminate at apex, olive green above, light green below, entire margin, acute at base; petioles 1/2 cm long; fruits solitary or 2-3 in short spikes, grayish pubescent; acorns enclosed entirely by the cupules.

Distribution: Southwestern China.

28. **Quercus dispar** Chun et Tsiang

Tree 8-16 meters high; branchlets pale gray; leaves deep green above, pale green beneath, young inflorescence white; leaves 8-10 cm long, 3 cm wide; elliptic-oblong to obovate-lanceolate, acute or obtuse at the apex, obtuse or cuneate at the base, crenate-dentate; fruit depressed globose; cupules with concentric annular zones.

This species is related to *Quercus vestita* Rehd. et Wils. from which it differs in indumentum, smaller differently shaped leaves with much more regular venations, and sessile deeper cup with more numerous annular rings. *Quercus dasaudii* Hick. et Camus has similar fruits. Besides being glabrous, it differs in having an acorn with a deeply intruded basal scar.

Distribution: Kwangsi, Shang-Si Hsien, and Feng-Hwang Hsiang.

29. **Quercus djiringensis** Chun et Tsiang

Tree; branchlets slender, reddish, glabrous, lenticelled; leaves elliptic, acuminate, 5-9 cm long, 2-3 cm wide, glaucescent beneath, shallowly dentate teeth above the upper half, acuminate at apex and acute at base, potioles 2-3 cm long, slender; fruits hemispherical or ovoid, 1.2-1.5 cm high, 1 cm wide cups shallow.

Distribution: Kwangsi Yao Shan.

30. **Quercus disciformis** Chun et Tsiang

Tree 10-19 m tall, trunk 32-40 cm in diameter.

This species is distinguished from all other species known to us by thin flat broad involucre, velvety tomentose inside (except the basal scar), supporting, but not at all embracing, a slightly narrower more or less depressed acorn. The acorns as described are evidently immature. Those collected later in the season are fully 1.5 cm long and uniformly hemispheric. In most specimens the fruits are solitary but in others they are borne, back to back, in pairs from the same level on opposite sides of a short spike.

Distribution: Kwangtung Hsin-I Hsien and Kwangsi Shang-Hsi Hsien Shi Wan-Ta Shan.

31. **Quercus edithae** Skan. (See orig. text page 355)

32. **Quercus engleriana** Seem. (See orig. text pages 355-356)

33. **Quercus fabri** Hance (See orig. text page 356)

34. **Quercus fargeii** Franchet.

Cyclobalanopsis fargesii Franchet

Tree with grayish bark and glabrous branchlets; leaves oblong-obovate to oblong-lanceolate, 13-15 cm long, broadly-rounded at apex, and broadly-cuneate at base, regularly coarse dentate-serrate, chartaceous; lateral veins 13-16 pairs; petioles 3 cm long; flowers 5-9 on one spike, pubescent; fruits 7-8 mm long; cupules recurving with concentric cyclic margin; nut globular, 3/4 enclosed by cupules; styles and stigmas 3-lobed.

Distribution: Szechuan, at altitude 1400 m.

35. **Quercus fenseliana** Chun

Tree 6 m tall; branchlets gray, slender, glabrous; leaves elliptic-lanceolate, acute at apex and base, entire or somewhat undulate-serrate above the middle, shining pale green above, brownish green beneath; fruits globular, 1.5 cm long, 1 cm broad; nuts completely enclosed by cupules; cupules with cyclic concentric rings; fruits with a cup-like depression on the top, brown, sessile.

Distribution: Kwangtung.

36. **Quercus fissa** Champ. ex Benth.

Small tree with gray bark and dark grayish branchlets, lenticelled; leaves oblong-ovate, 10-20 cm long, 4-10 cm wide, rounded at apex and acute at base, undulate and somewhat recurving, minutely notched at margin, shining pale green above, brownish green beneath; petioles 2-3 cm long; fruiting spikes short, erect, 10-15 cm long; nuts sessile, solitary or in opposite pairs.

Distribution: Kwangtung and Hong Kong.

37. **Quercus flavescens** Hickel et Camus

Tree 14 m high; bark grayish brown.

This species is closely related to *Quercus poilanei* Hickel et Camus and *Quercus championi* Benth. It is distinguished from these species by the pale yellow, not golden yellow indumentum. From *Q. championi* Bentham it is distinguished by its oval, not oboval leaves.

Distribution: Hainan, at altitude 600-1000 m.

38. **Quercus fordiana** Hemsl.

Tree 10-30 m high; leaves elliptic-oblong, long acuminate at apex, acute at base, irregularly undulate-serrate at margin; fruits crowded at tips of the branchlets, flattened globular, almost completely enclosed by cupules; stigmas 3-lobed; pericarp with ingrowth cavity, nearly dividing it into separate cells and causing the cotyledons to become lobed as in the walnut.

Distribution: Yunnan, at altitude 1000-1300 m.

39. **Quercus fleuryi** Hickel et Camus

Large tree 12-43 m high, trunk 1-1.2 m in diameters; bark gray brown; branchlets whitish gray; leaves oblong-lanceolate, acute at apex, oblique acute at base, lustrous light green above, pale glaucous green beneath, entire and recurving at margin, 16-20 cm long, 3-6 cm wide; petioles 3 cm long; fruits large cylindrical, 5-8 cm long, 2-3 cm broad, 2/3 of the acorns enclosed by the cupule, solitary, sessile; cupules reddish brown, thickly hairy.

Distribution: Hinana at altitude 800 meters.

40. **Quercus franchetii** Skan (See orig. text page 356)

41. **Quercus gillina** Rehd. et Wils. (See orig. text page 358)

42. **Quercus gilva** Blume

43. **Quercus glandulifera** Blume

Tree 10-20 m tall, 3-4 m in girth, with stout wide spreading branches; bark dark gray rough and fissured, but never corky; leaves very greatly in shape, in length of petiole densely hairy, when young, glabrous at maturity; fruits matures the second season.

This is a species of considerable economic importance to the people. Its wood is valued for boat building, and for general construction. Much has been used as fuel and for making charcoal. The cups are used for dyeing silk-yarn black. In north-central Szechuan and Kweichow a species of silk-worm (*Antheraea pernyi*) is fed by the leaves. It is locally called Ching-kang. In Hupeh it is called the Hwa-li or occasionally Hung (red) Hwa-li.

Distribution: Shangtung, Honan, Hupeh, Kiangsi, Fukien and Szechuan, at altitude 300-2000 m.

Var. 1. **Quercus glanduligera** var. **glanduligera**

Small tree; leaves oblong-obovate to oblong-lanceolate.

This variety is almost similar to *Quercus glauca, Quercus glaucina*, and *Quercus ciridia*, but it is distinguished by having sparsely stellate-pilose leaves with veins prominent and hirsute. The petioles are 5-25 mm long.

Distribution: Hupeh and Szechuan, at altitude 300-3000 meters.

Var. 2. **Quercus glanduligera** var. **brevipetiolata** Nakai

A tree, 5 meters tall, with whitish gray bark; branchlets slender grey; leaves oblong-lanceolate, 8-10 cm long, 3-4 cm wide, acute at apex, cuneate at base, densely hairy beneath, veins and veinlets covered by silky hairs, coarsely serrate dark shining green above pale green below; lateral veins 11-15 pairs; petioles 5 mm long; fruits mature in opposite pairs, globular, 1-1.5 cm long, 8 mm high; nuts grayish brown in color, enclosed about 2/3 by brownish scaly cupules.

Distribution: Shangtung, Honan, Kiangsi, Hupeh, Chekiang, Kiangsu, Szechuan, Yunnan and Kwangsi, at altitude 200-1800 m.

44. Quercus glabra Thunb.

Small tree; bark grayish brown; branchlets gray, slender, with yellowish pubescence; leaves elliptic-oblong, 4-6 cm long, 3-4 cm wide, acute or acuminate at apex, cuneate at base, entire, shining brownish green above, light green beneath, glabrous; petioles 1-2 cm long; male flowers clustered in terminal spikes; fruiting aments short, 3-6 cm long; nuts small, globular, sessile, 2/3 enclosed by cupule; cupule cup-shaped, bristly scally; nuts with mucronated at apex.

Distribution: Kiangsi, I-Hsing.

45. Quercus glaucoides Koidz.

Cyclobalanopsis glaucoides Schottky

Quercus sckottkyapa Rehd. et Wilson

Small tree 6 m tall, trunk 12.5 cm in diameter; bark reddish brown; branchlets slender, brownish pubescent; leaves elliptic lanceolate, long acuminate at apex, acute at base, finely serrate, pale shining green above, yellowish pubescent below; fruit very small, glabrous, globular 2 mm high and broad (immature); nuts completely enclosed by cupules, sessile, crowded along the short and erect peduncles.

Distribution: Taiwan, at altitude 1740-2000 m.

46. Quercus glacilenta Chun

Tree 15 m tall, trunk 40 cm in diameter; Leaves lanceolate to elliptic-lanceolate or oblong-lanceolate, 6-9 cm long, 1.5-3 cm wide, acute or acuminate at apex, oblique cuneate at base, crenate-dentate on the apical portion of the margin, lustrous deep green above, dull pale green beneath; long petioles; pistillate flowers and fruits brown tomentose.

This species differs from *Quercus pachyloma* Seem. in the thin elliptic leaves with the margin sharply crenate-dentate from the middle, in the more numerous lateral veins distinct on the upper surface, and in the large acorns. In *Quercus pachyloma* the leaves are thicker, not distinctly veined on the upper surface with fewer veins ending in callose not apiculate teeth.

Distribution: Border of Kwangtung and Kiangsi.

47. Quercus glauca Thunb. (See orig. text pages 358-359)

Var. 1. Quercus glauca Thunb. var. **hypargura** V. Seem. (See orig. text page 359)

Var. 2. Quercus glauca Thunb. f. **gracilis** Rehd. et Wilson

Tree with grayish bark, and leaves definitely pubescent beneath. It is distinguished from the typical form of the species by having much smaller, evergreen, elliptic leaves, slender petioles. It should not be confused with *Quercus myrsinaefolia* Bl., the leaves of which are glabrous beneath, lighter green and usually more elongated.

Distribution: Anhwei, Kiangsi, Chekiang, Hunan, Kwangtung. at altitude 1800-2700 m.

Var. 3.   Quercus glauca Thunb. var. **micrococca** Maxim. ex Camus

This variety is distinguished from the typical form of the species by the very small cups which are 7 mm in diameter, 4 mm high. The nuts are obovoid, 10-12 mm high, 7-8 mm in diameter; leaves glaucous.

Distribution: Chekiang.

Var. 4.   Quercus glauca Thunb. var. **lineata** Bl.

Quercus chinensis Abel.

Quercus serrata Thunberg

Quercus sessilifolia Blume

This variety differs from the typical form of the species by glaucous linear leaves, hairy glands on the serrated margin and the fruits cylindrical and ovoid.

Distribution: Hopei, Shantung, Kiangsu, Chekiang, Hong kong, and Szechuan, at altitude 2800 m.

Var. 5.   Quercus glauca Thunb. var. **nudata** Bl.

Tree with dark gray bark and branchlets; leaves oblong-lanceolate, acuminate at apex, obovate at base, coarsely serrate, glassy dark green above, pale green below; petiole slender, 2-3 cm long; fruiting aments terminal on the branchlets; fruits oblong cylindrical, 1-1.5 cm long, 1 cm. broad; nuts half enclosed by cupules.

Distribution: Northwestern China.

48. Quercus gomesiana Camus

Quercus vestita Rehder et Wilson

Tree 10-20 m tall; bark brown; branchlets stout, densely yellow pubescent; leaves oblong-ovate, 10-15 cm long, 3-5 cm wide, acute at apex, obovate at base, undulate at margin; petioles 1-2 cm long, densely pilose; female aments on very short erect peduncles; fruits globular, 1-1.5 cm broad, enclosed by yellowish pubescence encircling the nuts, forming a cup-like depression on the top, densely yellowish hairy in 3 rings, 4 or 5 fruits crowded on the tips of branchlets.

Distribution: Yunnan and Szechuan, at altitude 1200 m.

49. Quercus griffithii Hook. et Thom. (See orig. text page 561)

Var. 1.   Quercus griffithii var. **glandulifera** Fr. (See orig. text page 361)

Quercus griffithii var. *glandulifera* Blume

Tree; leaves elliptic, oblong-acuminate at apex, acute at base, serrate margin; petioles 1.15 cm long, glabrous; fruits cylindrical, 1-1.5 cm long, 7 mm broad, mucronate, almost completely enclosed by cupules.

Distribution: Yunnan, at altitude 2800 m.

Var. 2.   Quercus griffithii var. **urticaefolia** Franch.

Tree with brownish bark; branchlets short, stout, brown; leaves elliptic-ovate to oblanceolate, 6-10 cm long, 2-3 cm wide, acute to rounded at apex, cuneate at base, coarsely serrate at margin, dark green and glabrous above, yellowish green and pubescent beneath; petioles 5 mm long; fruits small, oblong-cylindrical, 1.5-2 cm long, 1 cm broad, 2/3 of the nuts enclosed by the cupules.

Distribution: Yunnan

50. **Quercus guayavaefolia** Levl.

Tree; leaves of this species agree exactly with those of *Quercus semicarpifolia* Smith, but the cupules have thick closely appressed scales, which are different from the thin scales forming a fringed margin in *Quercus semicarpifolia*. There is, however, a possibility that the cups of the specimen are not attached to the branches.

Distribution: Yunnan at altitude 2600-3000 m.

51. **Quercus hainanensis** Merr. (See orig. text page 361)

52. **Quercus handliana** A. Camus

Small tree 4-7 meters tall; branchlets slender, grayish; leaves small, elliptic to elliptic-oblong, 4-6 cm long, 2-3 cm wide acute at apex, rounded at base, entire rarely coarsely serrate above the middle; fruits oblong-cylindrical; acorns 2 cm long, 1 cm broad, 1/3 enclosed by cupule; the cupules scaly; stigma 3-lobed.

Distribution: Southwestern China.

53. **Quercus henryi** Seemen

Tree 10 meters tall; bark gray; branchlets short, thick, lenticelled; leaves oblanceolate, 12-22 cm long, 3-4 cm wide, acute at apex, narrow cuneate at base, entire thick coriaceous, brownish green on both surfaces; petioles 2-4 cm long; male flowers in long slender axillary, pendulous, yellow spikes of 10-20 cm long; fruits globular, solitary, sessile, 1.5-2 cm high and broad, densely hairy; acorns enclosed 1/4 by the cupules.

Distribution: Hupeh and Szechuan.

54. **Quercus helferiana** A. DC.

Tree 7-10 meters tall; leaves oval-elliptic 13-22 cm long, 5-5.9 cm wide, with undulate-crenate or distantly crenate-serrate margin, densely tomentose beneath; acorn 1.7-2.5 cm in diameter, appearing very flat, 1.2-1.5 cm high, the shallow tomentose cups. with 8-12 rings. It is related to *Quercus mespilifolioides* Camus of Yunnan which has similar bases but the acorns are much higher in proportion to the cups.

Distribution: Hainan, and Southwest Yunnan, at altitude 1000-1800 m.

55. **Quercus hui** Chun (See orig. text page 362)

56. **Quercus hunanensis** Hand.-Mazz. (See orig. text page 362)

57. **Quercus fluryi** Hickel et Camus

Quercus tsoi Chun

Tree 10-16 meters tall; bark grayish brown; branchlets purple to dark brown, stout; leaves elliptic-oblong, 16-20 cm long, 4-6 cm wide, dark shining green above, pale brown and yellowish pubescent beneath, acute both at apex and base, margin entire and slightly revolute; midrib yellowish hairy; petioles 3-4 cm long, purple, glabrous; aments axillary, short, terminal, and densely covered by yellow hairs, 10-18 cm long; flowers yellow and white, fragrant; fruits brownish yellow, solitary, globular, hairy, short peduncled.

Distribution: Kwangsi, Kwangtung and Kweichow.

58. **Quercus jenseniana** Hand.-Mazz. (See orig. text page 363)

59. **Quercus junghunii** Miq.

Small tree with grayish bark; branchlets slender, gray; leaves elliptic-lanceolate, 5-8 cm long, 2-3 cm wide, acuminate at apex, obtuse at base, entire margin; petioles 6 mm long, shining green above, brownish green beneath; midrib and veins with brownish pubescence; fruits solitary, globular, 1-15 cm long, 1 cm broad; acorns enclosed 2/3 by the cupule.

Distribution: Taiwan Arisan, at altitude 2500 m.

60. **Quercus kawakamii** Hayata

Tree, bark whitish gray; branchlets gray; lenticelled, short, stout; leaves large, oblong-ovate, 15-20 cm long, 4-6 cm wide, acute at apex and base, entire margin, slightly revolute, coriaceous, brownish green above, light green with midrib and veins very prominent beneath, slightly whitish pilose along the veins and mirdib; petioles 3-4 cm long, brown, glabrous.

Distribution: Taiwan Arisan, at altitude 1200-1600 M.

61. **Quercus kerrii** Craib

Cyclobalanopsis kerrii (Craib) Hu

Tree 12 m tall, trunk 30 cm in diameter; bark gray and rough; branchlets short, thick and stout, brownish hairy; leaves elliptic-lanceolate, 12-18 cm long, 5-7 cm wide, acute at apex and base, dark shining green above, brownish hairy beneath, undulate-dentate at margin; veins and midrib very prominent, lateral veins 11-13 pairs, thick, coriaceous; fruit flattened globular, 2 cm broad, 1 cm high; cupules saucer-shape, covering half of the nut, sessile, solitary; cupules bearing grayish scales arranged in 3 rings.

Distribution: Yunnan, at altitude 1500 m.

62. **Quercus kangsiensis** A. Camus

Tree, 15 meters tall; leaves lanceolate to elliptic, glabrous, deep green above, pale green and densely tomentose beneath, entire but undulate or coarsely serrate in the apical portion, acute at apex, acuminate at base; fruits, entirely enclosed, globose half exposed, nut large ellipsoid 3.5 cm long, 2 cm wide; cupule gray, 4 or 5 broad and widely spaced rings.

Distribution: Kwangsi Yao Shan, Ma Ta Shan, and Hainan, at altitude 300-1000 meters.

63. **Quercus lammellosa** Smith (See orig. text page 363)

64. **Quercus lanata** Smith (See orig. text page 363)

65. **Quercus liaotungensis** Koidz. (See orig. text page 364)

66. **Quercus lineata** Bl. var. **macrophylla** Seemen

Tree with grayish bark; branchlets slightly hairy; leaves large, 19 cm long, 6.5 cm. wide, elliptic-lanceolate, dark green above, pale green below; petioles 5 cm long; lateral veins 20–22 pairs.

Distribution: Szechuan, Nan-Chuan Hsien.

67. **Quercus liseoides** Dunn

Shrub, 2 meters high, bark dark reddish; branchlets slender, reddish gray, short, clustered at tips of branches; leaves small elliptic-ovoid, 3.5 cm long, 1.5–2 cm wide, rounded at apex, acute at base, entire, slightly revolute at margin, dark green above, reddish green beneath, thick coriaceous; petioles short, 1–2 cm long; flowers yellow, fragrant; fruit brownish black.

Distribution: Kwangtung and Hongkong, at altitude 300 m.

68. **Quercus longispica** Camus

Quercus semicarpifolia var. *longispica* Hand.-Mazz.

Tree 20 m tall; bark reddish gray; branchlets purplish red, densely lenticelled, slender, glabrous; leaves oblong-lanceolate, 5–12 cm long, 4–6 cm wide, broadly acute at apex, entire and undulate, glassy light green above, brownish pubescent below, thick coriaceous; petioles 1–2 mm long, pubescent; fruit greenish yellow, globose, 2 cm long, 1 cm broad, half enclosed by spiny-scaly cupule.

Distribution: Northwestern Yunnan and Sikang, at altitude 2300–3000 m.

69. **Quercus longinux** Hayata

Tree with grayish bark; branchlets very slender, greenish gray, glabrous; leaves elliptic-lanceolate, 6–12 cm long, 2–3 cm wide, acuminate at apex and base, regularly sharp-serrate, dark green above, light green below; petioles slender, 1–2 cm long, reddish, glabrous; fruits globose, mucronate at apex, 1–1.5 cm long and broad; 3 covered, by cupules; 2 or 3 fruits born on each short peduncle.

Distribution: Taiwan, at altitude 600–1100 meters.

70. **Quercus macrocalyx** Hickel et Camus

Tree 8–10 m tall, bark grayish black; branchlets slender, dark purple, lenticelled, glabrous; leaves elliptic-lanceolate, 10–16 cm long, 3–5 cm wide, acute at both ends, serrate above the middle, deep green above, pale green beneath; petioles slender, 1–2 cm long; staminate flowers yellow, pistillate flowers greenish brown; fruit small, globose. 5 mm broad and high (immature), gray.

Distribution: Kwangtung and Hainan, at altitude 1100 meters.

71. **Quercus malacotrica** Camus

Tree; leaves oblong lanceolate, acute at apex, cuneate at base, coarsely serrate; petioles short, 1 cm long, glabrous; fruit globose-cylindric, 1/3 to 1/2 of the nuts enclosed by the cupule.

Distribution: Yunnan.

72. **Quercus   meridionalis** Liou

Tree with reddish brown bark; branchlets purplish, lenticelled; leaves oblong-lanceolate, 15–25 cm long, 5–8 cm wide, acute at apex, cuneate at base, coarsely-dentate serrate at margin, glossy shining green above, pale green beneath, glabrous on both sides; petioles 2 cm long; fruit small, globular, 1 cm broad and high, solitary; acorns nearly completely encolsed by cupules.

Distribution: Chekiang.

73. **Quercus   mespilifolia** Wall.

Tree 12–18 m tall; bark gray and rough; branchlets grayish brown, rough, thick, stout; leaves oblong lanceolate, 12–18 cm long, 4–5 cm wide, acute at apex, obovate at base, undulate or coarsely dentate–serrate at margin, light green above, brownish green below, brownish pilose along the midrib and veins beneath, thick coriaceous; petioles stout, 2 cm long; male aments yellowish, slender, 8–12 cm long, clustered at the tips of the branchlets.

Distribution: Yunnan.

74. **Quercus   microphylla** Chun

Tree 8 m tall, trunk 35 cm in diameter; bark gray; branchlets short, stout, light gray; leaves elliptic–lanceolate, 5–8 cm long, 1.5–3 cm wide, acuminate at apex and base, entire, lustrous green above, silvery gray beneath; petioles 1 cm long; fruits globose, 1.5–2 cm long and broad; cupules saucer–shaped, lustrous greenish slightly scaly.

Distribution: Hainan, at altitude 3100 m.

75. **Quercus   mongolica** Fish. et Turcz. (See orig. text pages 364–365)

76. **Quercus   monimotricha** Hand.–Mazz. (See orig. text page 365)

77. **Quercus   morii** Hayata

Tree 40 m tall, 60 cm in diameter; bark gray, peeling off in scaly plates; branchlets light gray, stout; leaves elliptic–obovate 8–12 cm long, 3–4 cm wide, apex long acuminate, base cuneate, sparsely serrate above the middle, lustrous green above, light green below, glabrous; petioles slender, long, 3–4 cm long; fruits globular, 1–1.5 cm broad and high; cupules scales arranged in 3–4 rings; cup bowl–shaped, 1/2 embracing the nut, silvery brownish.

Distribution: Taiwan Arisan, at altitude 2160–2600 m.

78. **Quercus   myrsinaefolia** Bl. (See orig. text pages 365–366)

79. **Quercus   nariakii** Hayata

Pasania nariakii Hayata

Tree with grayish bark; branchlets slender, glabrous; leaves elliptic–lanceolate, acuminate at apex, cuneate at base, entire, thin, dark green above, light green beneath, 5–8 cm long, 2–3 cm wide; petioles 1–1.5 cm long; fruits globular, clustered on short, erect peduncles; cupules embracing the nut completely.

Distribution: Hainan.

80. **Quercus nemoralis** Chun

Tree 15 m tall; bark gray; leaves oblong laceolate, 10–16 cm long, 3.5–5 cm wide, crenate–dentate at margin, coriaceous; petiole 2–4 cm long; fruits solitary.

This species is close to *Quercus zanthoclada* Hick. et Camus from Indo-China, from which it is easily distinguished by the dense yellowish to grayish indumentum on the branchlets, petioles and lower surface of the leaves and by the hemispheric cup with many concentric erose zones.

Distribution: Hainan, and Ting–An Hsien, at altitude 800 m.

81. **Quercus nubium** Hand.–Mazz. (See orig. text pages 366–367)

82. **Quercus oxyodon** Miquel (See orig. text page 367)

> **Var. 1. Quercus oxyodon** var. **fargesii** Rehd. et Wils. (See orig. text pages 367–368)

> **Var. 2. Quercus oxyodon** var. **tomentosa** Hu (See orig. text pages 367–368)

> > *Cyclobalanopsis oxyodon* Oerst. var. *tomentosa* Hu

> > Shrub 6 m tall; leaves densely tawny velutions–tomentose on the lower surface. It should be distinguished as a variety from the glabrous–and glaucous–leaves. The typical form of the species has and differs the type.

> > Distribution: Northwestern Yunnan, at altitude 2900 m.

83. **Quercus oxyphylla** Hand.–Mazz. (See orig. text page 368)

84. **Quercus obscura** V. Seemen

Tree with dark brown bark; branchlets brownish pubescent; leaves oblong–lanceolate or obovate, 13 cm long, 5.5 cm wide; deep grayish green above, yellowish brown beneath, margin entire; lateral veins 13 pairs; petioles 2.2 cm long; fruits not gray but similar to that of *Q. acuta* Thunb.

Distribution: Hupeh.

85. **Quercus pachyloma** Seem. (See orig. text page 368)

> **Var. 1. Quercus pachyloma** Seem. var. **tomentosicupula** (Hay.) Metcalf

> > Tree 10–12 meters tall.

> > This variety is distinguished from the species by the entirely leaves, glabrous, the much larger and usually somewhat reflexed margins to the cups, very variable with leaves almost entire or somewhat serrate toward the apex, and usually elongated slender petioles.

> > Distribution: Taiwan.

86. **Quercus pachylomicarpoides** Metcalf

Tree 5 meters high; leaves entire and noticeably cinnamon–brown beneath serrate at apex, wavy margin, not reflexed; acorns globose–ovoid or ellipsoid–cylindrical.

It is closely related to *Quercus pachyloma* Seem. but can be easily distinguished by much larger leaves and fruits.

Distribution: Kwangsi, and Shap Man Taai Shan.

87. **Quercus pannosa** Hand.-Mazz. (See orig. text page 369)

88. **Quercus parvifolia** Hand.-Mazz. (See orig. text page 369)

89. **Quercus pauhanii** Chun et Tsiang

Tree 5-15 m tall. leaves oblong ovate to elliptic-lanceolate, 5-8 cm long, 1.5-2 cm wide, cuneate at apex, rotundate at base,, coriaceous; acorns small, edible, wood durable for making handles of various kinds of tools, and especially good for making charcoal.

Distribution: Kwangtung Yu-Yean-Hsien and South Hunan, An evergreen oak with usually small acorn found in South Hunan I-Chang-Hsien, from level-land to 1000-meter inter-mixed with deciduous species and conifers.

90. **Quercus patelliformis** Chun

Tree 12 m tall; bark blackish gray; leaves elliptic-oblong, 5-12 cm long, 2.5-6 cm wide, acuminate at apex, rotundate at base, crenate-dentate-serrate, glabrous, coriaceous; petioles 2-4 cm long; fruits brownish tomentose; styles highly connate columnar; acorns hemispheric, depressed, born on a shallow cup, with a narrow rim.

Distribution: Hainan Yui Hsien.

91. **Quercus phanera** Chun

Tree 10 m tall; bark grayish black; leaves oblanceolate-elliptic, 3.5-7 cm long, 1.5-3 cm wide, abruptly acute at apex, cuneate at base, rigid coriaceous, reticulated, deep lustrous green; petioles very short; acorn cylindrical, 1.5-2 cm broad, 2.5 cm high, hairy.

This species is closely affiliated to *Quercus edithae* Skan and *Quercus combodiensis* Hickel et Camus, but differing from both in the glabrous vegetative parts, the strong reticulated leaves, the more numercus annular rings on the cups, and the much larger cylindrical acorns.

Distribution: Hainan Heng-Po-Po.

92. **Quercus phylliraeoides** (A. Gray) Franch. (See orig. text pages 369-370)

93. **Quercus platycalyx** Hickel et Camus

Tree 15 m tall, trunk 32 cm in diameter; bark dark brown; branchlets slender, lenticelled; leaves elliptic-lanceolate, acuminate at apex, acute at base, crenate-dentate-serrate above the middle, dark green above, pale green beneath, 5-16 cm long, 3-5 cm wide, glabrous; lateral veins 7-11 pairs; petioles 1-2 cm long; flowering buds greenish yellow; fruit large, oblong cylindric, 4-5 cm long, 2-3 cm broad; cups saucer-shape, embracing $\frac{1}{4}$ of the acorns. cup-scales forming 3-5 rings, brownish hairy; fruits solitary.

Distribution: Kwangsi Sup Man Ta Shan.

94. **Quercus poilanei** Hickel et Camus

Tree 10 m tall; bark whitish gray; branchlets short, stout; leaves oval (not oboval) acute at both ends, margin entire, shining green above, with orange yellow (not pale yellow) indumentum beneath, 5–8 cm long, 3–4 cm wide; petioles stout, 1.5–2 cm long, pubescent; fruit brown.

This species is closely related to *Quercus championi* Benth. and *Quercus flevescens* Hickel et Camus

Distribution: Kwangtung Sam Kok Shan.

95. **Quercus prainiana** Levl.

This species is near to *Quercus engleriana* Seem. but this species belongs to the section *Lepidobalanos*, while *Quercus prainiana* belongs to the section *Cyclobalanopsis*. It is appreatly near to *Quercus vestida* Rehd. et Wils., but it is less pubescent and has broader more coarsely toothed leaves.

Distribution: Kweichow.

96. **Quercus pseudomyrsinaefolia** Hayata

Tree 12 m tall; bark gray; branchlets short, thick, grayish red, lenticelled; leaves lanceolate, 10–16 cm long, 2–5 cm wide, acuminate at apex, broadly cuneate at base, sharply-coarsely-serrate above the middle, coriaceous, shining lustrous green above, pale green beneath; petioles 2–5 cm long, reddish brown; fruits glabrous, 2 cm long, 1 cm broad; cupule-scales gray, forming 3 concentric rings and covering the nuts half way; fruits solitary.

Distribution: Taiwan, at altitude 2500 m.

97. **Quercus pseudocarpifolia** A. Camus

Tree 6–10 m tall; bark brownish gray; branchlets short, stout, rough, brown, lenticelled; leaves obovate, 3–4 cm long, 2–3 cm wide, rotundate-ovate at both ends, entire or sharply toothed all the way along the margin above the middle, thick coriaceous, lustrous shining green above, brownish green beneath; petioles 5 mm long; fruits small, long and broad, cupule covering the nut to 2/3 the length, crownded on short and stout peduncles.

Distribution: Yunnan Li-Kiang, at altitude 2800–3000 m.

98. **Quercus quangtriensis** Hickel et Camus

Tree 10 m high, 24 cm in diameter; bark reddish gray; branchlets short, bushy, reddish gray, glabrous; leaves elliptic-lanceolate or elongated ellitptic, 4–6 cm long, 2–3 cm wide, acute or pointed at both ends, coarsely serrate above the middle, thick coriaceous, shining green above, brownish green beneath; lateral veins 10 pairs; petioles 1 cm long; fruits large, ovoid, 3 cm long, 2 cm broad, 1/3 of the nut embraced by the cupule; solitary; cupule covered by 8–9 concentric ringed scales.

Distribution: Hainan Manning.

99. **Quercus rex** Hemsley (See orig. text page 370)
100. **Quercus schottkyana** Rehd. et Wils. (See orig. text page 371)
101. **Quercus scleophylla** Lindl.

Small tree with whitish gray bark; branchlets whitish gray, short, stout, glabrous; leaves oblong elliptic, 4–6 cm long, 2–3 cm wide, acute at apex, ovate at apex, 3–5 sparsely serrate above the middle, thick, coriaceous, shining green above, pale green beneath, glabrous; petiols 1.5 cm long.

Distribution: Kiangsu I-Hsing.

102. Quercus silvatica L. var. **chinensis** Franch.

Fagus silvatica var. *chinensis* Franch.

Tree with ovate-lanceolate, acute pointed leaves; lateral veins 10-12 pairs; petioles 10-12 mm long; peduncles 6-7 cm long; involucre bract acuminate-lanceolate reflexed at margin.

Distribution: Szechuan.

Var. 1. Quercus silvatica L. var. **longipes** Oliv.

Tree; leaves ovate-lanceolate, 10-11 paris of lateral veins; very similar to variety *chinensis* Franchet, occurring in Szechuan.

103. Quercus semicarpifolia Smith (See orig. text page 371)

Var. 1. - 2. (See orig. text pages 372-373)

104. Quercus senescens Hand.-Mazz. (See orig. text page 373)

105. Quercus serrata Thunb. (See orig. text page 374)

Var. 1. Quercus serrata Thunb. var. **brevipetiolata** Nakai (See orig. text page 374)

106. Quercus sessilifolia Blume

Tree 10-20 m tall, trunk 30 cm in diameter; leaves oblong to elliptic-oblanceolate, 7-11 cm long, 2.5-3.5 cm wide, almost entire, or margin with 4-6 sharp teeth below the short acute apex; petioles 1 cm long, glabrous; male aments clustered at the tips of the young shoots, pendulous, 6-8 cm long; young fruits in short spikes, 0.5-1.5 cm long, surrounded by pubescent cups; cupule covered by 5-7 connate concentric rings; whitish tomentose; acorns green.

Distribution: Kwangtung, Kwangsi, Hunan, Kweichow, Kiangsi, Fukien, and Taiwan at altitude 800 m.

107. Quercus sinii Chun

Small tree 6 meters tall; bark gray; leaves ovate, dentate from near the base, terminated by an unusually broad acumen; fruits with tumid cup-scales, borns on a stout short peduncle.

Its nearst all seems to be *Quercus setulosa* Hickel et Camus, from which it differs in longer petiolate leaves and enlarged cupule scale.

Distribution: Kwangtung Yun-Fon, at altitude 130 m.

108. Quercus spathulata Seem. (See orig. text page 376)

109. Quercus spicata var. **yunnanensis** Schottky

Small tree 5 meters tall; bark gray, smooth; branchlets, long, slender, gray; leaves elliptic-lanceolate, 6-8 cm long, 2-4 cm wide, acuminate at apex, acute at base, 5-6 sparsely serrate above the middle, shining green above, pale green beneath, thick coriaceous, glabrous; petioles 5 mm long; male flowers clustered on short spikes, 5 cm long, axillary, brownish.

Distribution: Yunnan, and Fun-Nan Hsien, at altitude 2000-3000 m.

110. **Quercus spinosa** David et Franch. (See orig. text page 377)

Var. 1. **Quercus spinosa** var. **monimotricha** Hand.-Mazz.

Small tree, leaves 1.5-8 cm long, similar to those of the species in shape, except having more tomentose indumentums.

Distribution: Yunnan, at altitude 1750-3400 m.

111. **Quercus stenophylloides** Hayata

Small tree with slender grayish branchlets; leaves oblong-lanceolate, acuminate at apex, rotundate and cuneate at base, sharply serrate, dark green above, light green below; petioles 1-2 cm long, glabrous.

Distribution: Taiwan, at altitude 2500 m.

112. **Quercus stewardii** Rehder (See orig. text pages 377-378)

113. **Quercus stewardiana** Camus

Tree 8 m tall. 20 cm in diameter; bark gray and rough; branchlets dark gray, lenti-celled, thick, stout; leaves oblanceolate, 8-10 cm long, 2-3 cm wide, long acuminate at apex, cuneate at base, 3-4-toothed above the middle, shining green above, brownish and slightly pubescent beneath; petioles 2-3 cm long; fruit globular 1-1.5 cm long, 1 cm broad; cupule saucer-shaped, covering half of the nut; cupule-scales arranged in 5-6 concentric rings; fruits small, 4 or 5 in a clustered, sessile, gray.

Distribution: Kweichow Niu Tao Shan, at altitude 2200 m.

114. **Quercus sutchenensis** Franch.

Small tree with glabrous branchlets; leaves oblong 6-9 cm long, rotundate-obtuse at apex, coriaceous; fruits small, sessile, 4-5 aggregate together.

Distribution: Szechuan.

115. **Quercus taichuensis** Hayata

Small tree with slender and bushy branchlets; bark dark gray; leaves elliptic-oblong, 4-6 cm long, 2 cm wide, acuminate at apex, cuneate at base, entire margin, with 3-4 teeth, coarsely-serrated below the apex, glabrous; petioles slender, 1-2 cm long.

Distribution: Taiwan Tai-Chun.

116. **Quercus taitoensis** Hayata

Lithocarpus taitoensis Hayata

Small tree with slender branchlets; leaves elliptic-lanceolate, 8-12 cm long, 3-4 cm wide, acuminate at apex, cuneate at base, entire margin, thick, coriaceous, dark green above, pale green beneath; petioles 1-2 cm long.

Distribution: Taiwan Tai-Tung.

117. **Quercus taliensis** A. Camus (See orig. text page 378)

118. **Quercus tarokoensis** Hayata

Tree with dark gray bark and very slender branchlets; leaves elliptic ovate, 3-6 cm long, 2-3 cm wide, acute at apex, obutse at base, 3-4 serrate above the middle; petiole 3 mm long.

Distribution: Taiwan, Tairoko.

119. **Quercus thalassica** Hance

Small tree with dark grayish glabrous branchlets; leaves elliptic-lanceolate, long acuminate at apex, acute at base, entire 6-12 cm long, 3-4 cm wide, coriaceous, glabrous; petioles 1-2 cm long; male flower aments terminal to the branchlets, short, erect; female spikes clustered with dense globular fruits on short, erect peduncles; nuts oblong-cylindrical, 2 cm long, 1 cm broad; cups shallow and spiny scaly.

Distribution: Hong Kong, Kuan-Yin-Chiao.

120. **Quercus thorlii** Hickel et Camus

Cyclobalanopsis thorlii Hu

Tree 15 m tall, trunk 30 cm in diameter; bark dark gray, rough; branchlets slender, gray lenticelled; leaves oblong lanceolate, 10-15 cm long, 3-4 cm wide, long acuminate at apex, cuneate at base, sharply serrate at margin, lustrous shining green above, pale green beneath, brownish pilose along midrib below, coriaceous; petioles 2-3 cm long, slender, brownish pubescent; fruits flattened globose, 4 cm broad, 2 cm high, almost completely enclosed by cupules with 3-4 concentric scaly rings; fruits solitary, sessile.

Distribution: Yunnan and Kwangsi.

121. **Quercus tinfanensis** A. Camus

Tree, branchlets glabrous, lenticelled; leaves oblong-lanceolate to lanceolate, 5.5-7 cm long, 1.5-2.5 cm wide, attenuate at apex, rotundate at base, dentate; lateral veins 8-9 pairs; petioles 1.5-3 mm long.

It is closely affiliated to *Quercus phylliraeoides* Gray, but differs in glabrous and lenticelled branchlets and leaves.

Distribution: Tin-Fan Hsien.

122. **Quercus tomentosicupula** Hayata

Tree; leaves lanceolate, acute at apex, margin entire or with 3-5 teeth below the apex; lateral veins 8-10 pairs; petioles 1-2 cm long, glabrous; fruits cylindric; nuts embraced by shallow cups covering 1/4 its length; cupules with long tomentose scales; fruits solitary on short and erect peduncles.

Distribution: Taiwan.

123. **Quercus tranninghensis** Hickel et Camus

Tree 4 m tall, trunk 15 cm in diameter; branchlets stout, short, gray; leaves elliptic-oblong, 5-8 cm long, 3-4 cm wide, acuminate at apex, obovate at base, serrate; petioles 2-3 cm long.

This species is closely related to *Quercus glauca* Thunberg, but distinguished by buds with 5 (not 4) longitudinal rows of scales, larger and wider (3-7 mm.) nuts, and lanceolate acuminate subglabrous leaves.

Distribution: Kwangtung, Hainan, and Kwangsi.

124. **Quercus tsaii** Hu

Cyclobalanopsis tsaii Hu

Tree, bark dark gray, rough; branchlets short, stout, brownish gray, lenticelled; leaves lanceolate, 20-32 cm long, 5-6 cm wide, long acuminate at apex, cuneate at base, sharply serrate, lustrous deep green, glabrous above, brownish pilose beneath; lateral veins 20-25 pairs, thick coriaceous; petioles 3-4 cm long, brownish pubescent; fruits clustered on short erect peduncles, solitary, sessile; cupule covering the nut almost completely, bearing scaly concentric rings.

Distribution: Kweichow, at altitude 1300 m.

125. Quercus tsoi Chun

Tree 10 m tall; bark dark gray; branchlets gray, rusty, slender; leaves elliptic-oblanceolate, 20-25 cm long, 5-7 cm wide, acute at apex, cuneate at base, undulate and recurved along margin, lustrous shining green above, brownish pilose beneath, coriaceous; lateral veins 10-12 pairs; petioles 3 cm long; male aments axillary, clustered on tip of branchlets, brownish yellow, slender, 8-16 cm long.

Distribution: Kwangtung Fan-Chang Hsien.

126. Quercus uvariifolia Hance

Tree, bark brownish gray; branchlets short, thick, pubescent; leaves oblong-obate, 6-10 cm long, 4-5 cm wide, mucronate at apex, cuneate at base, entire, shining green above, brownish pubescent beneath, coriaceous; petioles 2 cm long, pubescent; fruits globular, 3-4 cm high and broad; cupules cup-shaped bearing coarsely toothed scales.

Distribution: Kwangtung.

127. Quercus variabilis Blume (See orig. text page 379)

128. Quercus vestita Rehd. et Wils. (See orig. text pages 380-381)

129. Quercus yuii Liou

Deciduous tree up to 10 m tall; bark dark gray, with irregular deeply fissured plates; branchlets stout, dark gray tomentose in the first year, later gray and glabrous; buds globose, with dense grayish hairs; leaves obovate, acute or rounded at apex, cuneate or slightly rounded at base, obtuse-dentate, dark green with sparse stellate hairs especially along the veins above, glaucescent and densely tomentose beneath, 12-18 cm long, 8-12 cm broad; petioles short, about 5 mm long, grayish tomentose; staminate catkin 5 cm long, clustered on the apex of the current years shoots, densely tomentose; fruits 1-3, in the axils of upper leaves, ripening the first year, sessile; acorn oblong-ovoid, wholly enclosed by the cup or exposed only at the apex; cup deep with straight, linear-lanceolate yellowish gray, pubescent scales, projecting beyond the acorn.

Distribution: Yunnan and Szechuan, at altitude 2300 m.

130. Quercus yunnanensis Franch.

Tree with brownish gray bark; branchlets short, stout, rough, brownish - yellow pubescent when young; leaves broadly fan-shaped, obovate, 18-25 cm long, 8-10 cm wide above, and 3-4 cm at the lower end, coarsely dentate-serrate, coriaceous, lustrous shining green above, acute at apex, cuneate at base, brownish pubescent beneath; fruits cylindrical obovoid, 2-3 cm long, 2 cm broad, 1/2 enclosed by long scaly cupules.

Distribution: Yunnan.

Family 21. Ulmaceae Mirb.

(See orig. text page 381)

Genus (1) Ulmus.

1. **Ulmus bergmaniana** Schneider (See orig. text pege 383)

   Var. 1. (See orig. text pages 383–384)

2. **Ulmus castanaefolia** Hemsley (See orig. text page 384)

3. **Ulmus changii** Cheng

   Tree 10 m tall, trunk 30 cm in diameter; bark rugose; branchlets glabrous; sparsely pubescent; leaves ovate, elliptic-oblong or obovate, subcordate and asymetric at base, acuminate at apex, glabrous above, sparsely pubescnet beneath, serrate, glandular, 6.5–10 cm long, 3.5–4.5 cm wide; lateral veins 14–24 pairs, scariceous; petioles 3.5 mm long; petioles 2–7 mm long; inflorescences in small clusters forming racemes; pedicels pilose, 2.5–3.5 cm long; samara obovate, orbiculate-obovate, rarely orbiculate, 2–2.5 cm long, 1.6–2.1 cm wide, pilose, margin ciliate, stipitate, emarginate at apex; perigonium inferior.

   This species is related to *U. macrocarpa* Hance from which it differs chiefly by its acuminate leaves, with obtuse serrate margin, more numerous veins, glabrous on the lower surface except with tufts of hairs in the axils of the secondary lateral veins, and by its elongated cymose on short racemose inflorescences. In general appearance of the leaves it resembles *U. lanceaefolia* Roxb. which has persistent coriaceous leaves and glabrous obovate samara with the seed touching apical the notch.

   Distribution: Hang-Chow, Lung-Ching.

4. **Ulmus davidiana** Planch. (See orig. text pages 384–385)

5. **Ulmus glaucescens** Fr.

   Var. 1. (See orig. text page 385)

6. **Ulmus japonica** Sargent (See orig. text pages 385–386)

   Var. 1. (See orig. text page 386)

7. **Ulmus lanciniata** Mayr (See orig. text pages 386–387)

8. **Ulmus lancenaefolia** Roxb. (See orig. text page 388)

9. **Ulmus macrophylla** Hance (See orig. text pages 388–389)

10. **Ulmus manshuria** Nakai

    Tree 6–7 m tall, trunk 60–80 cm in diameter; bark dark gray, irregularly fissured; branchlets greenish with reddish pubescence; leaves oblanceolate, 3–8 cm long, 2–5 cm wide, acute at apex, cuneate and asymmetric at base, doubly serrate, green above, light green below; lateral veins 11–17 with stiffy hairs; samara hairless; seed ovoid, 10–16 mm high and broad.

    Distribution: Hopei, and East Mongolia, Hailungkiang.

11. **Ulmus parvifolia** Jacq. (See orig. text pages 389–390)

12. **Ulmus pumila** Linn. (See orig. text page 390)

Var. 1. (See orig. text pages 390-391)

13. **Ulmus szechuanica** Franch.

Tree 10-12 m tall; branchlets hairy at base; young leaves yellowish green, leaves ovate-obovate, doubly serrate; samara green, fascicles with 17-flowers, bracts brown, oblong-elliptic, firmbriate towards apex, 1-2 mm long; pedicels pubescent, 1.2 mm long; calyx tube cylindrical campanulate, glandular, 1.5-2 mm long, glabrous, lobes 4, broadly oblong truncate at apex, long ciliate; staments 4; young fruits obovate.

This species is closely related to *Ulmus wilsoniana* , but differs chiefly in the glabrous obovate or ovate leaves, which are oblique and broadly cuneate at the base, with 12-16 pairs lateral veins.

Distribution: Szechuan.

14. **Ulmus tonkinensis** Gagnep.

Small tree 8-10 m tall, 15-20 cm in diameter; folowers reddish with large oboval to suborbicular fruits,about 2 cm long and 15 mm wide.

Distribution: Kwangtung, Hainan and Kwangsi Chen-Pien Hsien at altitude 400-600 meters.

15. **Ulmus uyematsuii** Hayata (See orig. text pages 391-392)

16. **Ulmus wilsoniana** Schneid. (See orig. text page 392)

Vars. 1.-2. (See orig. text pages 392-393)

enus (2) **Celtis** Linn. (See orig. text page 393)

According to Planchon's desposition the genus *Celtis* has been divided into the following groups.

Section I. *Euceltis* Planchon in Ann. Sci. Nat. ser. 3 10; 263 (1848); in De Candolle, Prodr. 17: 169 (1873); Schneider. in Pl. Wils. 3: 283, (1916)

Section 2. *Sponiocellis* Planchon in Ann. Sci. Nat. ser. 3,.10: 263 (1848); in De Candolle, Prodr. 17: 180 (1873); Schneider in Pl. Wils. 3: 283, (1916)

The chief difference between section, *Sponiocellis* and *Euceltis* is that the latter has elongated-cymose female inflorescences.

Key to the species of Celtis in Chekiang

A. Fruits. large, 10-15 mm long; pediceles stout, 2-3 times longer than the petioles.

B. Leaves more or less pubescent beneath:

C. Branchlets, petioles, and pedicels, densely brownish or yellowish pubescent --------------------------------------(18) *C. juliance*

CC. Branchlets, petioles, and pedicels glabrous or glabrescent. -- (18-1) *C. juliance* var. *clavescens.*

BB. Leaves glabrous except the axillary tufts of hairs beneath; branchlets, petioles and pedicels glabrous ---------------------- (28) *C. vandervoetiana*

AA. Fruits smaller, 6–8 mm long; pedicels slender, as long as, or longer than the petioles

 B. Pedicels 2–3 times longer than petioles.

  C. Leaves with impressed veinlets beneath; fruits yellow; seeds pitted; pedicel slender; branchlets brownish pubescent or glabrescent. -------------------- ------------------------------------- (4) *C. biondii*

  CC. Leaves with elevated veinlets beneath; seeds smooth; pedicels very slender branchlets yellowish pubescent ----------(10) *C. chekiangensis*

 BB. Pedicels as long as, or slightly longer than petioles; fruits dull red; seeds pitte and ribbed; leaves with elevated veinlets beneath ----------------------------- ------------------------------------- (26) *C. sinensis*

1. **Celtis amphibola** Schneider (See orig. text page 394)

2. **Celtis aurantiaca** Nakai

Tree with pubescent branchlets and leaves; petioles 10–14 mm long, pubescent leaves, ovate 10–20 cm long, 9–16 cm wide; margin sharply toothed above the middle long acuminate and mucronate at apex; fruits solitary, axillary, 20–24 mm long, 1–1. mm thick, globular and orange when riped.

This species is closely allied to *Celtis koraiensis*, from which it is distinguished having pubescent shoots, leaves and orange mature fruits.

  Distribution: Chiefly in Korea but the range extending to the lowlands Manchuria, Shangtung, Hopei and Honan.

3. **Celtis benthamiaca** Metcalf

Small tree 3 m tall; bark brownish gray; branchlets slender, brownish gray, dense lenticelled; leaves elliptic–obovate, 3–5 cm long, 2–3 cm wide, entire margin, mucro nate at apex, obovate at base, dark green above, reddish brown beneath, glabrous petioles 5–7 cm long, brownish; fruits solitary, 3–5 mm. long and broad, black; pedice 1–2 cm long, brownish pubescent.

  Distribution: Kwangtung and Hongkong.

4. **Celtis biondii** Pampanini (See orig. text pages 394–395)

  Var. 1. Celtis biondii var. **cavaleriei** Schneider (See orig. text page 395)

  Var. 2. Celtis biondii var. **heterophylla** Sehneider

    Celtis bungeana var. *heterophylla* Levl.

    Celtis leveillei var. *heterophylla* Nakai

    This variety is well characterised by the peculiar shape of its leav which are mostly breadest at the upper end below the caudate apex. T specimen from Fukien agrees well with those from Korea. Nakai in h flora Koreana appearently confused it with *Celtis sinensis* Pers., whi is easily distinguished by the shape of its leaves, their different pube cence and serration and also by its glabrous ovaries and the more i regularly and more deeply pitted stones. It is most nearly related to the typical *Celtis biondii* Pamp., which has same nervation and pubescence of the leaves and the same fruits and stones.

Distribution: Fukien and Korea.

5. **Celtis bodinieri** Leveille (See orig. text pages 395–396)

6. **Celtis bungeana** Blume (See orig. text page 396)

7. **Celtis caudata** Hance

Small tree with purplish tomentose bark; leaves small, rotundate, ovate–elliptic in shape, caudate at apex, doubly serrate many–nerved; petioles short; stipules glandular; fruits solitary, ellipsoid, 4 mm long and broad.

Distribution: Taiwan, Tam–Sui.

8. **Celtis cerasifera** Schneider (See orig. text pages 396–397)

Var. 1. **Celtis cerasifera** var. **glaberrima** Schneider

Tree 8 tall, 20 cm in diameter, bark gray, smooth; branchlets slender, greenish gray leaves elliptic–ovate, acute or cuadate at apex, roundate at base, entire or coarsely toothed near tip, dark green above, light green below; petioles 1 cm long, grooved, pubescent; fruit elliptic–ovoid, 5 mm long and broad, green to dark when riped.

Distribution: Yunnan, at altitude 980 meters.

9. **Celtis cersidifelia** Schneider (See orig. text pages 397–398)

0. **Celtis chekiangensis** Cheng

Tree 20 m tall; bark gray, smooth; leaves elliptic–oblong, 3–11 cm long, 2.7–4.7 cm wide, long acuminate at apex, obtuse–truncate at base, minutely crenate–serrate at margin, dark green above, yellowish green beneath; petioles 4–9 mm long, densely villous; fruits solitary, ovoid, apiculate, 6 mm long 5 mm broad; pedicels 12–19 mm long

This species belongs to the section *Euceltis* and is related to *Celtis biondii* Pamp. from which it differs by its densely yellowish pubescent branchlets, thinner leaves with elevated small veins beneath, much slender pedicels and smooth stones.

Distribution: Chekiang, West Tien Mu Shan, at altitude 1000 m.

1. **Celtis cheliensis** Hu

Tree 11 m tall; bark chalky white; branchlets slender chalky white; leaves elliptic–lanceolate, long acuminate at apex, asymetric, obovate at base, irregularly serrated dark green above, light green beneath; veins depressed above, elevated and slightly pubescent beneath; petiole 6–8 mm long, brownish; fruit solitary, globose, black at maturity, 3–5 mm long and broad; pedicels 1–1.5 cm long.

Distribution: Yunnan, at altitude 720 m.

2. **Celtis chuanchewnensis** Metcalf

Tree with yellowish–pubescent branchlets; leaves elliptic to ovate–elliptic, 3–5 cm long, 2 cm wide, strigose pubescent above, more so beneath, crenate above the middle, abruptly acuminate; fruit distinctly pubescent, subglobose, 4 mm long, pubescent.

It is closely related to *Celtis leveillei* var. *holophylla* Nakai and *Celtis chekiangensis*

Cheng. It is easily distinguished from *C. chekiangensis* by the oblique cross veins which are not elevated in *C. chekiangensis* the cross veins are distinctly elevated a[?] horizaontal. From *C. leveillei* var. *holophylla* Nakai it is distinguished by the pube[?] cent fruits and smaller leaves.

Distribution: Fukien, Chuan-Chow.

13. **Celtis cinnamomefolia** Hu

Tree 10 m tall, 50 cm in diameter; bark gray, smooth; branchlets slender, whitis[?] brown; leaves elliptic-lanceolate, 6–12 cm long, 3–5 cm wide, acute at apex, obovate base, 3-nerved, entire margin, thick, dark green above, brownish below, glabrou[?] fruit 3 mm long and broad, green to red at maturity, pedicels 3–4 cm long, browni[?] pubescent.

Distribution: Yunnan, at altitude 1000 m.

14. **Celtis emuyaca** Metcalf

Tree, branchlets terete, glabrous; lenticels round to elliptic, pale; leaves fa[?] shaped, or obovate, 3–4 cm long, 2–3 cm wide, truncate with crenate to dentate apice[?] base broadly acute to obtuse or even rounded to subcordate in the smaller leaves, roug[?] scabrous-papilose above, sometimes with appressed whitish hairs, subglabrous slightly pubescent beneath; fruit axillary, in twos, 4.5 mm long, 4 mm wide, orang[?] pedicels 10 mm long, scabrous.

Distribution: Fukien, Kulangsu Island, and Amoy.

15. **Celtis formosana** Hayata

Tree 20 m tall, 50 cm in diameter; bark dark reddish brown, very rough; branchle[?] slender reddish green, smooth, lenticelled; leaves elliptic-ovate, 8–12 cm long, 4–6 [?] wide, mucronate at apex, oblique at base, somewhat pubescent along the nerves a[?] midribs, margins entire or finely serrated, glabrous, dark green above, light gre[?] beneath; petioles 1–1.6 cm long, pubescent; fruits subglobular, 8 mm long, 5 mm broa[?] orange to black at maturity; pedicels 1–2 cm long, brownish pubescent.

Distribution: Taiwan, at altitude 600–1000 m.

16. **Celtis hunanensis** Hand.-Mazz. (See orig. text page 398)

17. **Celtis integrrima** Merr.

Tree 4–5 m tall, 24 cm in diameter; bark grayish brown, densely lenticelled; leav[?] oblong-elliptic, 4–6 cm long, 2–3 cm wide, acute at apex, cuneate at base, prominen[?] 3-nerved, entire margin, lustrous green above, pale green beneath, brownish pubesc[?] along the midrib below; petioles 5 mm long; flowers green monoecious; fruits small s[?] globose, 3 mm long, 2 mm broad, dark; stone ridged.

Distribution: Kwangtung and Hainan.

18. **Celtis julianae** Schneider (See orig. text pages 398–399)

    Var. 1. Celtis julianae var. **calcescens** Schneider (See orig. text page 399)

19. **Celtis koraiensis** Nakai (See orig. text page 400)

20. **Celtis labilis** Schneider (See orig. text page 400)

21. **Celtis leveillei** Nakai (See orig. text page 401)

        Var. 1. Celtis leveillei var. **holophylla** Nakai (See orig. text page 401)

22. **Celtis nevosa** Hemsley

Tree up to 8 m tall; leaves elliptic-ovate, 2–5.5 cm long, 2.5 cm wide, ridged, prominently veined, somewhat rough on both surfaces, the midribs and nerves being not so glabrous as in the other specimens; the fruits glaucous; stones ovate–ellipsoid, solitary, laterally compressed, 5 mm long, 3.5 mm broad.

    Distribution: Taiwan.

23. **Celtis philippiensis** Blanco (See orig. text page 402)

24. **Celtis rockii** Rehder

Tree 6 m tall; branchlets subangular, densely villose, lenticelled; leaves elliptic-rhombic – ovate, 4–8 cm long, 2.3–4.5 cm wide, minutely acuminate at apex, slightly oblique-cuneate at base, trilinear-veined, dentate-serrate above the middle; petioles 3–5 mm long; peduncles 2–5; pedicels 3–5 mm long; fruits small, subglobose, 4 mm in cirounferic diameter, glabrous at maturity.

This species is closely related to *C. salvana* Schneid. and also to *C. cinnamomea* Lindl., but from both it is easily distinguished by the rather dense pubescence of the leaves; the densely pubescent branchlet and inflorescence and the pubescent fruits. From the *C. cinnamomea* it differs in the serrate broader leaves, the few flowered short-peduncled inflorescence and small fruit.

    Distribution: Yunnan, and Kwangsi.

25. **Celtis salvatiana** Schneid. (See orig. text page 402)

26. **Celtis sinensis** Persoon (See orig. text pages 402–403)

        Var. 1. Celtis sinensis f. major, Hand.-Mazz. (See orig. text pages 403–404)

27. **Celtis wightii** Planch.

Shrub 3 m tall with reddish brown bark and 3 cm in diameter; branchlets grayish red, glabrous; leaves oblong-lanceolate, 3–5 cm long, 2–3 cm wide, acute at apex, cuneate at base, green above, light green beneath, prominently trinerved, entire, thick, chartaceous; petioles 2–5 mm long; flowers yellowish orange; fruits whitish green.

    Distribution: In dense wood of Hainan.

        Var. 1. Celtis wightii var. **censimilis** (Blume) Cagnap.

Tree 5–15 m tall; bark whitish gray; leaves obovate, 3–6 cm long, 4–5 cm broad, truncate at top, obovate at base, entire, lustrous green above, pale green below, glabrous; petioles 3–5 mm long; flowers green; fruit globose, 5 mm long and broad; pedicels 5 mm long.

This variety occures in India, Cylon, Indo-China, Siam and Java, but also found in Hainan Island on the slopes near the seashores.

    Distribution: Hainan Island.

28. **Celtis vandervoetiana** Schneider (See orig. text page 404)

29. **Celtis yunnanensis** Schneider (See orig. text page 404–405)

Genus (3) Pteroceltis Max. (See orig. text page 405)

1. **Pteroceltis tatarinoveii** Max. (See orig. text page 405)

   Var. 1. Pteroceltis tatarinoveii var. pubescens (See orig. text page 406)

Genus (4) Hemiptelea Planch. (See orig. text page 406)

1. **Hemiptelea davidii** Planch. (See orig. text pages 406-408)

Genus (5) Zelkova Spach (See orig. text pages 408-410)

1. **Zelkova formosana** Hayata

  Small tree; bark brown; branchlets slender, reddish brown; leaves elliptic lanceolate, 3-15 cm long, 1.5-4.5 cm wide, long acuminate at apex, acute at base dentate-serrate, dark green above, brownish green beneath; lateral veins 10-12 paris very prominently elevated beneath, slightly brownish villose, firm, sub-coriaceous petiole 5-10 mm long, silky pubescent; fruit irregularly rhombic-ovoid, solitary, sessile, 1-2 mm long and broad, dark brown in color.

  Distribution: Taiwan, Nanto, at altitude 1000-2000 m.

2. **Zelkova schneideriana** Hand. - Mazz. (See orig. text page 410)

3. **Zelkova serrata** Makino (See orig. text page 411)

4. **Zelkova sinica** Schneider (See orig. text page 412)

   Var. 1. Zelkova sinica var. australis Hand.-Mazz. (See orig. text page 412)

Genus (6) Trema Lour. (See orig. text page 414)

1. **Trema amboinensis** (Decne.) Blume

  Tree 15 m tall, 40 cm in diameter; branchlets terete, slender, reddish brown; lenticelate; leaves alternate, 2-ranked 3-nerved at base, lanceolate, 4-6 cm long, 2-2. cm wide, long, acuminate at apex, ovate at base, finely serrate, short petiolate, glabrous; fruits solitary, subglobose, 1 mm broad and high, yellowish brown.

  Distribution: Taiwan, and Kwangtung, at altitude 50-600 meters.

2. **Trema augustifolia** Blume (See orig. text page 414)

3. **Trema cannalina** Lour.

  Trema virgata Blume

  Celtis virgata Roxb.

  Sponia virgata Planchon

  Sponia timorensis Kurz

  Small shrub to tree of 16 meters tall; leaves pubescent, reticulated 7-11 cm long, 2- cm wide; flowers yellowish green, fragrant; fruits large, brownish-orange on long stout stalk.

   Distribution: Kwangtung, Hongkong, Kwangsi, Yunnan and Kiangsi, at altitud 200-300 m.

4. **Trema dielsiana** Hand. - Mazz. (See orig. text pages 414-415)

5. **Trema hainanensis** Merr. et Chun

  Tree 8 m tall; branchlets slender, yellowish pubescent; leaves oblong-lanceolate 14-16 cm long, 3-4 cm wide, acuminate at apex, subcordate at base, serrate 3-nerve dark green above, grayish green beneath; flowers yellowish pubescent and pale green.

Distribution: Hainan, Po-Ting, at altitude 100 m.

6. **Trema lavigata** Hand. – Mazz. (See orig. text page 415)

7. **Trema orientalis** Blume (See orig. text pages 415-416)

8. **Trema politoria** Blume (See orig. text page 416)

Small tree or shrub with slender brownish pubescent branchlets; leaves lanceolate, 6-10 cm long, 1-15 cm wide, long acuminate, truncate at base, serrate, dark green above, light green pubescent beneath; petioles 8 mm long; flowers yellowish green.

Distribution: Yunnan.

9. **Trema sampsonii** (Hance) Merr.

Sponia sampsonii Hance

Small shrub with purplish pubescent branchlets; leaves small, narrow lanceolate, 4 cm long, 1-1.5 cm wide, long acuminate, truncate and 3-nerved at base, serrate, deep green above, pale green, many-nerved, and glabrous below; petioles 2 mm long; flowers yellowish green; fruits orange color.

Distribution: Hainan Yai-Chow and Kwangsi.

10. **Trema velutina** Planch.

Small tree; branchlets slender, reddish brown, densely whitish hairy; leaves large, obovate-lanceolate, 10-16 cm long, 5-10 cm wide, long acuminate 3-nerved at base, finely serrate, dark green above, pale green below; petiole 1 cm long, densely whitish hairy; flowers yellowish green; fruits solitary, subglobose, 1-2 mm broad and high; pedicels 3 mm long, brownish pubescent.

Distribution: Hongkong.

11. **Trema virgata** Blume (See orig. text page 416)

Genus (7) Aphananthe Planch. (See orig. text page 416)

1. **Aphananthe aspera** Planch. (See orig. text pages 416-418)

Genus (8) Gironniera (Thwaites) Gaudich. (See orig. text page 420)

1. **Gironniera cuspidata** (Blume) Kurz

Tree 10-18 m tall, trunk 45-70 cm in diameter; branchlets slender, graysih brown, glabrous; leaves elliptic-oblong, 8-12 cm long, 3-4 cm wide, acute, obtuse at base, entire, lustrous deep green above, pale green below, coriaceous, glabrous; lateral veins 4-6 pairs; petioles 1 cm long; flowers yellow in short cymes; calyx 5, filaments white; fruits solitary, globose, 1-1.5 cm long, 1 cm broad and high, mucronate at apex, green and red when ripe; pedicels 1 cm long. glabrous.

Distribution: Hainan.

2. **Gironniera nitida** Bentham (See orig. text page 420)

3. **Gironniera subsequalis** Planch. (See orig. text pages 420-422)

4. **Gironniera yunnanensis** Hu

Tree 15 m tall, 60 cm in diam.; branchlets slender, terete, striate, scabrid; leaves chartaceous, ovate, oblong to elliptic, caudate-acuminate, rounded to broadly cuneate at

base, subentire to remotely glandulose-denticulate along the margins, shining green an
glabrous except scabrid along the impressed midrib, and with slender secondary vein
and veinlets above, pilosulose beneath, 10-19 cm long, 4-7 cm broad, lateral veins 12
20 pairs, arching and forming loops near the margins, veinlets closed, parallel; petiole
slender, channelled, 12 mm long, scabrid; flowers monoecious, staminate ones in axil
lary many-flowered corymps or panicles, 7.5 cm long, petals 5, orbicular, 1.5 mm i
diam., scarbid outside, yellowish green; stamens 5, subequalling the sepals; pistil
late flower solitary, axillary, or rarely forming terminal flowered cymes; pistil with
tuft of hairs; pedicels very slender, 1-3 mm long, scarbid; young fruits with 5 sub
orbicular sepals, densely scarbid, stigmas long, widely divergent, recurved, densel
dark brown, papillose; mature fruits ovoid, searbid, beaked, yellow, 2 cm long, 1.2 c
in diam.; pedicels slender 1.5-2 cm long.

Distribution: Southwestern Yunnan, at altitude 1180-1300 m.

Family 22. Rhoipteleaceae Hand.-Mazz.

(See orig. text pages 422-423)

Genus (1) Rhoiptelea Diels et Hand.-Mazz.

1. **Rhoiptelea chiliantha** Diels et. Handel-Mazz. (See orig. text pages 423-424)

Family 23. Moraceae DC.

Genus (1) Morus Linn. (See orig. text pages 425-427)

1. **Morus alba** Linn. (See orig. text pages 427- 428)
2. **Morus australis** Poiret (See orig. text page 429)
3. **Morus cathayana** Hemsley
4. **Morus laevigata** Wall. (See orig. text page 430)
5. **Morus mongolica** Schneider

    Var. 1.-2. (See orig. text page 431)

6. **Morus nigra** Linn. (See orig. text page 432)
7. **Morus notabilis** Schneid.
8. **Morus rubra** Linn.

    Shrubs, 2 meters high; bark grayish brown, rough; branchlets very slender, gree
glabrous; leaves ovate, 8-12 cm long, 6-8 cm broad, mucronate-acuminate, caudate a
base, coarsely serrate 3-nerved at base, dark green above, light green and slightl
pubescent below; fruits dark, edible.

    Distribution: Kwangtung Hwei-Yang Hsien.

9. **Morus serrata** Roxb.

    Small shrub, 2 m tall; bark light brown, smooth; branchlets slender greenish brown
leaves obovate, 6-8 cm long, 4-5 cm broad, acute, obtuse at base, serrate, dark gree

above, light green below; petiole very long, 4–5 cm in length glabrous; fruits reddish, 1–2 cm long, 1 cm broad; pedicels 2–2.5 cm long, glabrous.

Distribution: Tibet.

10. **Morus yunnanensis** Koidz.

Large tree 12–17 meters high; branchlets very long, terete, slender, smooth, reddish brown; leaves large, obovate, 20–25 cm long, 16–20 cm broad, acute, caudate and 3-nerved at base, coarsely serrate slightly pubescent along the midribs on both surfaces, dark green above, light green beneath; petioles stout, 3–4 cm long, greenish brown, glabrous.

Distribution: Northwestern Yunnan, at altitude 4000–4300 m.

Genus (2) **Allaeanthus** Thwait. (See orig. text pages 433–434)

1. **Allaeanthus kursii** Hook.

Genus (3) **Malaisia** Blanco (See orig. text pages 434–435)

1. **Malaisia scandens** (Lour.) Planch.

Genus (4) **Broussonetia** Vent. (See orig. text pages 435–436)

1. **Broussonetia kazinoki** Sieb. (See orig. text pages 436–437)

2. **Broussonetia papyrifera** L'Heritier (See orig. text pages 437–438)

Genus (5) **Taxotrophis** Blume (See orig. text page 438)

1. **Taxotrophis caudata** Hutch.

Phyllochlamys taxoedes (Heyne) Koord.

Shrub 2 meters high, branchlets stout, rigid, with stout spines, whitish gray, smooth; leaves elliptic-ovate, 5–8 cm long, 2.5 cm wide, acute serrate above the middle, acuminate, cuneate at base, deep green above, light green, slightly brownish pubescent beneath; petioles 1–2 mm long, brownish pubescent; flowers yellowish white; fruits globular, 4–6 in clusters, fresh berries borne on a 4-parted involucre, 2–4 mm long and broad, brownish pubescent; pedicels 2 cm long, brownish pubescent.

Distribution: Hainan, growing in thicket, at altitude 450 m.

2. **Taxotrophis ilicifolia** Vidal (See orig. text page 439)

Genus (6) **Streblus** Lour. (See orig. text pages 439–440)

1. **Streblus asper** Lour. (See orig. text page 440)

Cudrania crenata Wright. (See orig. text page 440)

Genus (7) **Cudrania** Trecule (See orig. text page 440)

1. **Cudrania furticosa** Wight et Kurz (See orig. text page 441)

2. **Cudrania cochinchinensis** (Lour.) Kudo et Masam.

3. **Cudrania pubescens** (See orig. text pages 442–446)

4. **Cudrania rectispina**

5. **Cudrania tricuspidata** (Carr.) Bureau

Genus (8) **Artocarpus** Forst (See orig. text page 444)

1. **Artocarpus chaplasha** Roxb.

Artocarpus milinoxylus Gagnep.

Large tree, bark gray and rough; branchlets stout, thick, grooved, yellowish villose leaves large, elliptic-ovate, 25-35 cm long, 25-30 cm broad, acute, cuneate at base undulate margins, thick leathery, dark green above, light green and brownish pubescen beneath; petioles thick, stout, 2-3 cm long, 1 cm thick, yellowish hairy; fruits globular 5-8 cm long, 4-6 cm broad, fleshy, solitary,; pedicels slender, 5-8 cm long, .5-8 m thick, yellowish hairy.

Distribution: Yunnan.

2. **Artocarpus hypargyrea** Hance (See orig. text pages 444-445)

3. **Artocarpus nitidus** ssp. **griffithii** (King) Jarrette

Tree 13 meters high, trunk 15 cm in diameter; bark reddish brown, very rough branchlets rough, reddish brown, lenticelate; leaves spatulate-lanceolate, 10 - 22 c long, 5-10 cm wide, entire, mucronate-acute, cuneate at base, lustrous deep gree above, pale green with whitish pubescent along the veins and midrib beneath; petiole stout, 1-1.5 cm long, glabrous; fruits globular, terminating the branchlets, solitary fleshy and yellow.

Distribution: Yunnan.

4. **Artocarpus heterophyllus** Lamb.

5. **Artocarpus integrifolia** Linn. (See orig. text page 446)

6. **Artocarpus lakoocha** Roxb.

Artocarpus yunnanensis Hù

Tree 12 meters high; young branchlets stout, tawny sericeous, glabrescent when old striate, lenticelled; leaves large, chartaceous, oblong to obvate, rounded and slightl oblique at base, round or short acuminate at apex, remotely and obscurely denticulat along the revolute margin, to 26 cm long, 16 cm broad, sparsely scabrid and pilosulos along the slightly elevated midrib and secondary veins, tawny tomentose along the thic midrib and elevated secondary veins and veinlets, appressedly tomentulose on the res of the surface beneath, secondary veins about 15 pairs, alternate, curving far up an forming loops near the margin and sending short branches to end in the teeth, trabecula and reticulation prominent and close; petioles stout, 2.5 cm long; staminate inflores cence unknown; pistillate inflorescences 3-4-lobed; lobes to 8 mm long, to 1.5 cm diameter; tawny tomentose; flowers coalescent, inconspicuous, style filiform, 2 m long; syncarps unequally lobed, more or less globose, 3.5 cm in diam.; peduncles to 1 mm long; flowers forming short obtuse umbels, tawny tomentose; seed to 1 cm long, 7 m broad.

This species is closely related to *Artocarpus melinoxyla* Gagnepain, differing smaller syncarps on much shorter peduncles.

Distribution: Yunnan, at altitude 1400 m.

7. **Artocarpus lingnanensis** Merr.

Artocarpus nitidus ssp. *lingnanensis* (Merr.) Jarrette

Tree 15 meters high; bark gray, glabrous; branchlets sparsely pubescent, terete leaves elliptic to oblong–elliptic and obovate–elliptic 7–15 cm long, 3–7 cm wide, obtuse–acuminate at apex, acute at base, margin glabrous; petioles 8–12 mm long, glabrous; male flower solitary, axillary, pedunculated; fruits ovoid, solitary, smooth, 1.3 cm in diam., edible; pedicels 1 cm long.

Distribution: Kwangtung, Honan, and Campus of Lingnan University.

8. **Artocarpus setacifolius** Pierre

Artocarpus bicolor Merr. et Chun

Tree 17 meters tall, trunk 80 cm in diameter, bark gray, fissured; branchlets glabrous, terete; leaves coriaceous, oblong–elliptic, subcaudate–acuminate, acute decurrent–acuminate at base, 4.5–7.5 cm long, 2–2.5 cm wide, entire margin, lustrous green above, pale brown beneath, glabrous, slightly puberulose, glaucous; petioles 6–7 mm long, slender; syncarp terminal, solitary, globose, 2.5 cm in diam., grayish pubescent, 2–3.5 mm long, obtuse, lower part 1 mm in diam.; seed few; peduncle puberulouse, usually to 2 cm long.

This species in closely affiliates with *Artocarpus hypargyrea* Hance which differs in the indumentum of the young branchlets, petioles, and lower surface of the leaves being much dense and more conspicuous, the branchlets and petioles much stouter; the leaf–blade much larger and more coriaceous, not so acute at the base, with nervation much more prominent beneath.

Distribution: Kwangtung Hainan, Kwangsi and Yunnan, at altitude 900 m, locally known as Kai-Nang-Shui.

9. **Artocarpus tonkinensis** Chev. et Gagnep.

Tree 12 meters tall, 30 cm in diameter, bark blackish gray, rough; branchlets reddish brown, rough; leaves elliptic–oblong–ovate, 18–22 cm long, 6–8 cm wide, thick leathery, entire, recurved, acute to acuminate at apex, narrow ovate to cuneate at base, lustrous pale green above, brownish green below; midrib, secondary veins, and veinlets forming prominent elevated network and brownish tomentose on the lower surface; petioles thick, stout, round; 1–1.6 cm long, densely brownish pubescent; fruits, globular, fleshy sulphur yellow; pedicels 2–3 cm long, brownish pubescent.

Distribution: Hainan, Kwangsi and Kweichow in mixed woods; at altitude 280–450 m.

Genus (9) Ficus Linn. (See orig. text page 447)

Explanation to the classification of the genus *Ficus* (Espec. formosan species) from the viewpoint of economic botany is specially made.

The flowers which are mostly unisexual, are sitting on the inner walls of the receptacle. They may be sessile or pedicellate. Five kinds of flowers are found in the genus as follows;

1. The male flower.

2. The pseudo–hermaphrodite flower.

3. The neuter flower.

4. The fertile (or true) female flower.

5. The gall flower.

Among the Formosan species, the neuter flower is very rarely found.

The pseudo-hermaphrodite flower is found only obscruely. The male, gall and female flowers are common.

Pseudo-hermaphrodite flowers occur in an imperfect form. Such flowers have perianth, like that of the ordinary male flowe. Along with the stamen, there present a pistil with perfect style and ovary. Hower the ovary does not contain a seed. It may be found containing a pupa.

Neuter flowers are long pedicellate and have 3-leaved perianth. None of them possesses any anther or pistil. Some authors have used the characteristics of these 5 kinds of flowers in *Ficus* classification. More recent worker have questioned its value as the basal idea in dividing the genus into groups, because, it appears that the peculiarities of flowers are very variable. They can not be relied upon. Natural, grouping has been deviced on more constant characters, such as the sexual arrangement of flowers on the receptacle:

Model 1. -- Male, gall, and fertile (or true) female flowers always on the same wall in a cavity of the receptacle ----------- Subgenus *Urostigma* Miquel

Model 2. -- Distinctly two sets of receptacles are found

set. 1. The set of receptacles constitutes of receptacles Type A. and Type B. ------------------------------- Subgenus *Metamophe* Sata

set. 2. The set of receptacles constitutes of receptacles Type C. and Type B. ------------------------------- Subgenus *Palaeomorphe* (King) Sata

Type A. --- male and gall flowers in one set of receptacle.

Type B. --- fertile male flowers in one set of receptacle.

(the female flowers are rarely associated by the neuter flowers)

Type C. --- Pseudohermaphrodite and gall flowers on one set of receptacle.

The new subgenus *Metamorphe* includes five sections as defined by King, i.e. *Synoecia*, *Sycidium*, *Covellia*, *Eusyce*, and *Neomorphe*.

The model 1. Subgenus *Uroltigima* is subdivided into the following 2 sections:

Section 1. Stilpnophyllum (Endl.) Sata

Section 2. Gasparriniella Sata

The model 2. *Metamophe* is subdivided into 2 subgenera or sects:

Section 1. *Metamorphe*

Section 2. *Palaeomorphe*

Key to the Sections of the Genus Ficus

Group 1. -- Flowers unisexual; male flowers without rudimentary pistils; male, gall, and fertile flowers on the same receptactles---Subgenus 1. Urostigima

A. Receptacles axillary ----------------------- Sect. *Stilpnophyllum*

B. Receptacles axillary and in fascicles from stem and branches --------------
--- Sect. *Gaspariiniella*

Group 2. -- Flowers unisexual or pseudohermaphrodite;

Subgenus 2. -- Flowers unisexual; male flowers without rudimentary pistil; male
and gall flowers in one set of receptacle; fertile female flowers
in another set ---------------------Subgenus 2. *Metamorphe*

Type. 1. Flowers monandrous.

A. Receptacles chiefly axillary ----------------- Sect. *Sycidium*

B. Receptacles mostly in fascicles from stem and branches --------------------
--- Sect. *Convellia*

Type 2. Flowers di-tri-rarely polyandrous;

A. Receptacles chiefly axillary------------------Sect. *Eusyce*

B. Receptacles chiefly in fascicles from stem and branches ------------------
--- Sect. *Neomorphe*

Subgenus 3. Flowers pseudohermaphrodite; male flowers with 1 stamen and a
rudimentary pistil. ------------------ Subgenus 3. *Paleaomorphe*

Synoptical Key to the Species

Group 1.

Flowers unisexual; male flowers without rudimentary pistils; male, gall, and fertile females on the same receptacles.

Subgenus 1. Urostigima

Flowers unisexual; female flowers without rudimentary pistils; male, gall, and fertile female flowers always on the same receptacles (i.e. receptacles are of one kind, without the second set)

A. Receptacles axillary--------------------------- Sect. *Stilpnophyllum*.

Series 1. Receptacles pedunculate: without basal bracts, but with minute bracts only at the base of the peduncle.

a. Leaves elliptic, rather narrow, with lateral nerves 8-10 pairs, the base gradually narrowed; receptacles rather small -------------------------
--------------------------------- (45) *F. nervosa*

b. Leaves obovate, rather broad, with cuneately narrowed base, lateral primary nerves 5-8 pairs; receptacles rather large ---------------------
--------------------------------- (11) *F. cuneato-nervosa*

Series 2. Receptacles sessile with thickened basal bracts at its base.

a. Leaves rounded; apex long, cuspidate-caudate, petiole rather long -----
--------------------------------- (12) *F. cuspidato-caudata*

      b. Leaves obovate; apex short subcuspidate; petioles rather short ‒‒‒‒‒‒‒‒‒ ‒‒‒‒‒‒‒‒‒‒‒‒‒‒‒‒‒‒‒‒‒‒‒‒‒‒‒‒‒‒‒‒‒(58) *F. retusa*

B. Receptacles axillary and in fascicles from stem and branches ‒‒‒‒‒‒‒‒‒‒‒‒‒‒‒‒‒‒‒‒ ‒‒‒‒‒‒‒‒‒‒‒‒‒‒‒‒‒‒‒‒‒‒‒‒‒‒‒‒‒‒‒‒‒‒‒‒‒‒‒ Sect. *Gaspariiniella*

      a. Leaves elliptic; medium‒sized, gradually narrowed at base; receptacles large ‒‒‒‒‒‒‒‒‒‒‒‒‒‒‒‒‒‒‒‒‒‒‒‒‒‒‒‒‒(76) *F. wightiana*

      b. Leaves quite oblong, large‒sized, suddenly tapering at the base and apex; receptacles very small‒‒‒‒‒‒‒‒‒‒‒‒‒‒‒‒‒‒‒ *F. infectoria*

            Group 2.

Flowers unisexual or pseudohermaphrodite; receptacles of 2 kinds and each species has 2 sets (viz. one kind has 2 sets of receptacles, A. and B. another also has 2 sets of receptacles C. and B.)

            Subgenus 2. Metamorphe

Flower unisexual; male flowers without rudimentary pistils; receptacle being one kind with 2 sets; male and gall flowers in one set of receptacles (viz. set of receptacles A) fertile female flowers only (rarely confusing neuter flowers), in another set of receptacles B.

          Tribe I. Flowers monandrous.

A. Receptacles chiefly axillary ‒‒‒‒‒‒‒‒‒‒‒‒‒‒‒‒‒‒‒‒‒Sect. *Syncidium*

    Series 1. Trees or rarely shrubs, with large leaves;

      a. Receptacles nearly globular, smooth and fine, when ripe orange‒red ‒‒‒‒‒ ‒‒‒‒‒‒‒‒‒‒‒‒‒‒‒‒‒‒‒‒‒‒‒‒‒‒‒‒‒‒‒‒‒‒ (1) *F. antoensis*

      b. Receptacles often appressed and coarse, usually whitish green ‒‒‒‒‒‒‒‒‒‒ ‒‒‒‒‒‒‒‒‒‒‒‒‒‒‒‒‒‒‒‒‒‒‒‒‒‒‒‒‒‒‒‒ (65) *F. septica*

    Series 2. Usually shrubs with lanceolate leaves ‒‒‒‒‒‒‒‒‒‒‒‒‒‒‒‒‒‒‒‒‒‒‒‒‒‒ ‒‒‒‒‒‒‒‒‒‒‒‒‒‒‒‒‒‒‒‒‒‒‒‒‒‒‒‒‒‒‒‒(10) *F. cumingii*

B. Receptacles mostly in fascicles on trunks, stem and branches, or axillary ‒‒‒‒‒‒ ‒‒‒ Sect. *Convellia*

    Series 1. ‒‒‒ Usually trees.

      a. Receptacles rather small, axillary, and in fascicles of stem and branches, usually dark green, when ripe dark‒red, always shining; peduncles medium long; leaves obovate, oblanceolate, or subrounded, rather thick, very shining, dark green above, base subcordate ‒‒‒‒‒‒‒‒‒‒‒‒‒‒‒‒‒‒‒‒‒‒ ‒‒‒‒‒‒‒‒‒‒‒‒‒‒‒‒‒‒‒‒‒‒‒‒‒‒‒‒‒‒‒‒ (31) *F. harlandii*

      b. Receptacles large, usually in fascicles on stem and branches, never axillary; whitish or light green, dimly shining; peduncles long; leaves ovate to rhomboid, rather thin, faintly shining above; sub‒acute or rounded at base ‒‒‒‒‒‒‒‒‒‒‒‒‒‒‒‒‒‒‒‒ (37) *F. konishii*

Tribe II. Flowers di‒tri‒, or rarely poly‒androus ‒‒‒‒‒‒ Sect. *Eusyce*

  A. Receptacles chiefly axillary.

Series 1. Erect or spreading shrubs or rarely trees.

Sub-series 1. Leaves pubescent, erect shrub or rarely trees ------------
------------------------------- *F. beecheyana*

Sub-series 2. Leaves glabrous, erect spreading, or base creeping and
erect terminal shrubs or very rarely trees

    a. Leaves coriaceous, obovate, with entire margin, rounded apex;
erect, or basal-creeping and half erect (terminal-erect), shrubs or
very rarely tree -------------- (24) *F. garanbiensis*

    b. Leaves chartaceous or membranaceous; variable in shapes, margin
often entire or with 1, 2, or more large teeth, apex abruptly acuminate or cuspidate.

        i. Leaves oblong-lanceolate-obovate, with one or two teeth on
each edge, or entire, or lanceolate-linear with entire margin;
receptacles pyriform; basal bracts usually at the very tapering
base-at the base of the false-stalk (peduncle) on the top of the
peduncle proper --------(20) *F. formosana*

        ii. Leaves variable in malformation, with large 1 or 2 lobes, or
entire, lanceolate-linear with subrounded or auriculate base;
receptacle subglobose or subpyriform; basal bracts always
at the base of the receptacles, often united at the base of the
bracts --------------------- *F. tannoensis*

Series 2. Creeping and scandent shrubs.

Subseries 1. Receptacles small, stem slender and thin; leaves membranaceous or thinly coriaceous, shining, hairy above.

    a. Creeping and scandent shrubs, small; leaves very small, obovate
with more or less hyaline hairs above; lateral nerves 3-4 rarely 5
pairs; receptacles small, subpyriform or globular with more or less
hayline hairs on the surface, red or dark-red when ripe, always
soft -------------------------(73) *F. vaccinioides*

    b. Scandent shrubs, rather slender but elongated; leaves medium sized,
elliptic, smooth and shining above, rarely puberulous beneath, lateral
veins 8-12 pairs, subcuspidate at apex; receptacles medium sized;
nearly globular, half glabrous, soft ferruginous on both apex and
base, usually hard, dark brown or blackish-brown ------------------
----------------------------- (21) *F. foveolata*

Subseries 2. Receptacles large; stems usually thickened; leaves thickly
coriaceous, very shining above.

    a. Leaves rather large, elliptic or ovate-lanceolate, apex subacute,
narrow and elongated (less than 13 cm.); receptacles very large, more
or less elongated subclavate or subfusiformis ----------------------

---------------------------- (2) *F. awkeotsang*

    b. Leaves rather small, ovate with bluntish apex, broad and short, less than 10 cm; receptacles large, obovoid or fusiformis, rather short vertically ------------------(52) *F. pumila*

B. Receptacles chiefly in fascicles on stem and branches -------------------------

-- Sect. *Neomorphe*

Scandent shrubs; receptacles large, finely colored; stem very much thickened; leaves rather small, variable from ovate to obovate, rather rounded, rounded or sub-emarginate at apex, very shining above; receptacles nearly globular, more or less appressed, slightly or rarely obovoid; colors variable, from dark to red or scarlet, or orange-red. -------------- *F. terasoensis*

    Subgenus 3. Palaeomorphe.

Flowers pseudohermaphrodite; male flowers with 1 stamen and a rudimentary pistil (receptacles with 1 kind and 2 sets); Pseudohermaphrodite flower and gall flowers in one set of receptacle (viz. set or receptacles), fertile female receptacles only in another set (viz. set of receptacle).

Series 1. Erect or spreading shrubs.

    sub-series 1. Leaves smooth and shining.

        a. Tree-like shrubs on soils, or parasitic-epiphytal shrubs on the trees; leaves coriaceous, rather thin, elliptic or oblong, long-cuspidate-caudate apice; lateral veins 7–10 pairs; receptacles near globose, more or less appressed, with several vertically ridged, 2–4 pairs on the axils or leaf-less branches of large-small sizes -----

---------------------------- (8) *F. caudato-longifolia*

        b. Epiphytic shrubs, spreading, creeping or subscandent on the rocks; leaves coriaceous, thick, ovate, obovate, or elliptic, short bluntish apex, lateral nerves 5–8 pairs; receptacles globular, rarely slightly appressed, smooth, subscabrid, solitary or in pairs on axils, medium sized ------------------(64) *F. swinhoe*

    sub-series 2. Leaves very scabrous, but not hirsute, always opposite; erect rarely tree-like shrubs; leaves obovate, rhomboidal or elliptic, dentate margin, acute at apex; receptacles small, much gathered in pairs on one set of opposite axils ----------

---------------------------- *F. kusanoi*

Series 11. Usually trees.

    Sub-series 1. Leaves smooth and shining especially when young; receptacles shortly peduncled, smooth, orange to red colored; basal bracts none, but with several minutely bracts at the base of the peduncle; leaves coriaceous, thick, elliptic -----------

--------------------(75) *F. vasculosa*

Sub–series 2. Leaves scabrous.

a. Leaves rather narrow, obovate, oblong–lanceolate, gradually narrowed into the cuneate base; receptacles small with the basal bracts
at the very base, ovate, rather broad and suddenly narrowed into
the very gibbose base ---------(25) *F. gibbosa*

1. **Ficus antoensis** Hayata

   Ficus hiiranensis Hayata

   Large tree often reached 10 or more meters high and trunk with half a meter in diameter on the basal part; branches and branchlets rather thick; branchlets terete cortices
fulvo–rubescent, much rugolose, with many jointed and rubescent lenticels; leaf scars
semirotundate and yellowish pale brown, and slightly elevated with 2 prominent dilated
and rounded stipulescars; leaves alternate long petiolate, rather thin, chartaceous or
thinly coriaceous, glabrous and smooth on both surfaces, oblique or symmetrical variable from rotundate–cordate, cordate–ovate, to obovate–elliptic, or rhomboidal–rotundate
15–25 cm long, sub–entire or recurved along margin, narrowly acute or linear–acuminate
at apex, rotundate–cordate, cuneately truncate, or rarely slightly acute and usually 3–
nerved at base; lateral veins 3–5 pairs, impressed above and elevated beneath; petioles
long and slender, 7–10 cm long, 3 mm thick; receptacles axillary, solitary or in pairs,
short pedunculated, in 8 or 10 pairs on the apex of the branchlets or in 10 to 15 pairs,
subglobular or globose, with acute apex, 1.5–2.5 cm across, dark green to orange-
yellow changing from young to adult, smooth, glabrous; peduncles thick, 5–8 mm long;
male and gall flowers perhaps an one set of the receptacle, while the fertile female
flowers on an other set; fertile female flowers only in a cavity of the female receptacle;
male flowers never have a perianth, existing malformately, hidding poorly in the cavity
of the female flowers near the mouth, mixed together with numerous fertile female
flowers.

   This species is closely related to *F. konishii Hayata.* It is easily distinguished by the
receptacles always borne on the axils of the leaves, while in *F. konishii* they are situated on tubercles formed on the branches or the stem and never axillary.

   Distribution: Southern part of Taiwan.

2. **Ficus awkeotsang** Makino

   Ficus nagayamai Yamamoto

   A strong much branched, scandent or creeping shrub, with dimorphis leaves, climbing
stem, sometime very thick and flattened and doubly jointed vertically rooting readity,
fruiting branches and branchlets erect and spreading, densely foliated, cylidrical or
subglabrous, pale brown or fulvous, not rooting; leaves alternate, petiolate, thickly
coriaceous, dark green, glabrous, shining on the upper surface, slightly pubescent
along the middrib and veins, subhirsute or covered with pale–ferruginous minute hairs
specially on the promient midrib and nervations, and tomentose beneath, with numerous
minutes aerolars; usually lanceolate and slightly oblique, variable from broadly linear,

oblong-lanceolate, to narrowly ovate-lanceolate, and never rounded or obovate, gradually narrowed towards the shortly sub-acuminate or attenuate apex, which never round or much blunt, not suddenly acute and slightly truncate often emarginate at the end of the very apex; more or less oblique and usually cordate broadly acute or rotundate, never narrowly cuneate; the blade rather broad at the middle towards the base, 10-15 cm long, 4-7 cm wide, entire, slightly recurved and undulate-crisp along the margin; petiole pubescent; stipules deciduous, rarely persistent; receptacles large, 6-8 cm long, 3-5 cm in diameter, solitary or in pairs, always axillary; male and gall flowers both in one set of receptacles, while fertile females only in another set; male flowers pedicellate, perianth of 4, linear-lanceolate, segments acuminated at apex; stamen 1, anthers 2, linear-oblong, subsessile; gall flowers pedicellate, perianth of 4 or 5 segments, glabrous, linear, acute at apex; ovary smooth, very large.

Distribution: Taiwan.

3. **Ficus abellii** Miq.

Ficus schinzii Levl. et Vant.

Shrubs, leaves with acute apex, cuneate at base, entire margin, dark green above, pale brownish green and sparsely hirsute on the lower surface; receptacle hispid pubescent, subglobose, 1.5 cm long, 1 cm broad.

Distribution: Kwangsi, Hunan, and Kweichow, at altitude 200-800 m.

4. **Ficus altissima** Blume

Ficus hainanensis Hayata

Tree with massive straggling branches, 6-12 meters tall, 14-60 cm in diameters; bark gray, smooth; branchlets terete, gray, rough; leaves obovate-oblong, 12-26 cm long, 6-12 cm wide, acute apice, cuneate and 3-nerved at base, entire margin, thick, glossy green above, pale green beneath, glabrous; petioles 1-5 cm long, glabrous; fruit round, hard, orange-yellow to red.

Distribution: Kwangsi, Kwangtung, Hainan, and Yunnan, at altitude 400-1800 meters.

5. **Ficus auriculata** Lour.

Ficus roxburghii Wall.

Ficus macrophylla Roxb.

Ficus macrocarpa Levl.

Tree 10 m tall, with large dentate leaves and smaller receptacles; bark gray, smooth; leaves round, elliptic-ovate, 16-36 cm long and broad, 3-nerved at base, irregularly toothed along margin, acute at apex, round at base, hairy along the midrib and veins on both surfaces, lustrous green above, pale green below; petioles thick, 3-6 cm long, yellowish pubescent; flowers brownish green, 1-3 cm long; fruit globular, 2-3 cm long and broad, yellowish green; pedicels 1-1.5 cm long, yellowish green, scally.

Distribution: Kwangtung, Kwangsi, Hainan and Kweichow, at altitude 1500 m.

6. **Ficus benjamina** Linn.

Small leaved ficus, tree 20 m high, trunk 1 m in diameter.; branchlets and branches spreading; bark whitish gray, smooth; branchlets light gray, short, stout, smooth, glabrous; leaves elliptic obovate, 5–7 cm long, 3–5 cm wide, acute at apex, cuneate at base, enitre margin, light green on both surfaces, coriaceous, glabrous, petioles 1–1.5 cm long, grooved, glabrous; fruit small, globular, 5 mm in diameter borne in opposite pairs, on branchlets, sessile, yellow.

Distribution: Hainan at lowland to 660 m.

7. **Ficus caesia** Hand.–Mazz.

Small tree, 2–3 m tall, mostly cultivated for its edible fruits; bark dark gray, rough; branchlets thick, short, rough, dark gray; leaves palmately 5–lobed, 15 cm long and broad, thick, coriaceous; petioles flattened, yellowish pubescent, 2–3 cm long; fruit globose, 3–5 cm long and broad, with slender base on short pedicels, red, edible.

Distribution: Yunnan, at altitude 1890 meters.

8. **Ficus caudato-longifolia** Sata

Small tree or shrub, rarely occurring as parasites on other tree, sometimes spreading out numerous very short aerieal roots from the stems and branches or even from the branchlets; the young parts minutely pubescent or puberulous, ultimately all parts become glabrous except the petioles, leaves coriaceous, shining above and below, nearly smooth and glabrous, oblong or elliptic-lanceolate, ovate-elliptic, or oblanceolate, slightly inequilateral, twisted at the apex, 10–20 cm long, 4–6 cm broad, rather suddenly narrowed into the apex, acuminate or caudate or bluntly sub-emarginate, entire or slightly undulate, never dentae, somewhat revolute, suddenly narrowed tapering toward the inequilateral base, obtuse or rotundate, 3–5 nerved, lateral veins 7–10 paris, reticulations distinct on the lower and obscuredly appressed above; petioles slightly pubescent, rather slender and stout, 2–3.5 cm long; stipules fugaceous; receptacles in pairs or in 3 or 4 pairs, axillary, shortly pedunculate, seemingly subsessile when young, redish yellow to orange when subglobose, quite flattened, slightly puberulous, and verrucose, with few, brown or yellowish dotts and slender vertical ridges and warts, subglobose, yellowish green, 1–1.2 cm long, 0.8–1.1 cm broad; basal bracts none; male and gall flowers on one set of receptacles while fertile female flowers only on another set. Male flowers appear only near the mouth of the receptacles forming a pseudo-hermaphrodits flower together with a rudimentary pistil; perianths segments 4–6, nawrrowly-linear or lanceolate, anthers 2, ellipsoid or oblong-obovoid, more or less oblique; gall flowers numerous in the cavity of the receptacles, sessile or pedicellate, with 4 or more linear perianth segments.

This species is closely related to *F. somai* Hayata and to *F. gibbosa* Blume. It is distinguished in having leaves with oblique base, which is rounded on one side and acute on the other.

Distribution: Taiwan, Botel Tobago Island, and Hainan.

9. **Ficus cavalerei** Levl. et Vant.

Tree with whitish gray bark; branchlets whitish gray, smooth; leaves oblong lanceolate, 12-18 cm long, 4-6 cm wide, entire and recurve at margin, acute mucronat at apex, round, 3-nerved at base, dark green above, light green and slightly pubescen along the midrib and veins below; petioles flattened, 2 cm long, brownish; fruits small globular, 2 mm broad and high, short pedicelled.

Distribution: Botel Tobago, and Taiwan.

11. **Ficus cuneato-nervosa** Yamamoto

Large tree sometimes shrubs with pubescent branches; leaves elliptic-lanceolate o oblong-elliptic, 6-13 cm long, 6 cm wide, narrowly cuneate at base; receptacles shortl pedunculate, axillary, borne almost on the apex of the branchlets, globular apple shaped, 1.5-4 cm long and broad, umbilicus rather small, suddenly tapering at base oppositely attached in pairs to terminal branchlets.

Distribution: Botel Tobago, Taiwan.

12. **Ficus cuspidato-caudata** Hayata

Large evergreen tree, 30 m in height, with thick aerial roots from the spreading large thick main branches hanging down towards the ground, but aerial roots never fabrous aerial roots reach 10 cm in across; trunk less than 3 m high; few main branches sub- laterally or sub-erectly patent spreading near the ground or the base of the main stem all parts quite glabrous, slightly rugolose vertically and minutely brown notate; rathe white and variable in colors; leaves alternate, petiolate, thinly sub - coriaceous o thickly membranaceous, glabrous on both surfaces, waxy-powerish and dimly beneath, rounded, from broadly elliptic to ovate rotundate, always broader on the middle par towards the base and never obovate suddenly tapering towards the apex, sometime slightly oblique at the base, 10-14 cm long, 5-8 wide; petioles long and slender; re- ceptacles small, sessile, in pairs or solitary, about 1 cm broad and long.

This species is closely related to *Ficus retusa* L. but distinguished from it by the rounded leaves.

Distribution: Botel Tobago, Taiwan.

13. **Ficus delavayi** Gagnep.

Small tree, leaves sub-angular, alternate, lanceolate, linear-obtuse 3-nerved a base, attenuate apice, 6-9 cm long, 1.5-1.8 cm wide, glabrous, coriaceous, pilose beneath, lateral veins 8-10 pairs; petioles 5-7 mm long; fruits axillary, solitary, ovate- conical, 15 mm long, 10 mm in diameter; peduncle 20 mm long, pilose.

Distribution: Yunnan.

14. **Ficus chlorocarpa** (Blume) Bent.

Ficus vaerigata var. *chlorocarpa* Blume

Tree 7 m tall, 30 cm in diameter, containing milky juice forming substances as "Getah Lahoe" or Gutta Percha in Malaya; bark reddish brown; branchlets reddish; leaves entire rounded or cordate at base, broadly undulate-toothed at margin, 20-25 cm long, 10-14 cm wide; petioles 1.5-2.5 cm long; stipules 1-2 cm long; receptacle with constricted base when young; fruit yellow.

Distribution: Kwangtung, and Hongkong.

15. **Ficus clavata** Wall.

Ficus acanthocarpa Levl. et Vant.

Small tree, 2 m high; bark dark gray; branchlets slender, dark gray, glabrous; leaves elliptic-ovate to elliptic-lanceolate, variable in size, 6-16 cm long, 3-6 cm wide, acute-acuminate apice, cuneate at base, undulate to serrate at margin, coriaceous, thick, dark green above, light green, glabrous below; petioles 1 cm long; receptacle 1-1.5 cm long and broad, short pedicellate, axillary, solitary, black, edible.

Distribution: Yunnan, Szechuan, Kwangtung, and Kwangsi, at altitude 1000-1200 meters.

16. **Ficus comata** Hand.-Mazz.

Small tree; leaves deciduous, obovate-oblong, 5-12 cm long, 2.5-3 cm wide, caudate at base, chartaceous, attenuate at apex, brownish pubescent beneath; petioles 3-5 mm long; stipules fugaceous, acuminate-lanceolate, 8-10 mm long, brownish vilose; receptacle axillary, solitary; pedicels 2-4 mm long; bracts 3, triangular glabrous.

Distribution: Kweichow, at altitude 400 m.

17. **Ficus esquirelii** Levl.

This species is closely related to *F. pyriformis* Hook et. Arn. and to *F. stenophylla* Hemsl., from the former it differs in the narrow long caudate leaves, sub-sessile, subglobose receptacle, covered with short appressed hairs, and from the latter by the thinner caudate leaves, slightly hairy below and sub-sessile subglobose and hairy receptacles; fruit red.

Distribution: Kwangtung, Fukien, and Chekiang, at altitude 700-900 m.

18. **Ficus erecta** Thunb.

Small tree or shrubs; branchlets subglabrous hispidous pilose; leaves membraneous, broadly ovate, obovate-elliptic, sometimes sub-rhomboidal or elongate-lanceolate, apice acuminate or cuneat, gradually narrowed from the middle to the truncate, rounded, sub-emarginate or sub-cordate, slightly unequal and 3-nerved at base; lateral veins 4 pairs, minutely pubescent especially along the middrib and veins with few scabrid hairs below, entire margin or in upper half obscurely serrate, 8-10 cm long; receptacles in pairs, pedunculate, axillary, depressed, globose, glabrous; basal bract 3, ovate triangular shaped, puberulous; male flowers in the receptacles with the galls, shortly pedicellated or sub-sessile.

Distribution: Kwangtung, Kwangsi, Kiangsi, Fukien, Taiwan, and Korea.

Var. 1. **Ficus erecta** var. **beechyana** Hook. et Arn.

Ficus beechyana Hook. et Arn.

Shrub or small tree; branchlets spreading, tomentose especially at the annual node, ultimately subscabrid or glabrous when adult; leaves always alternate, petiolate, thick, membraneous, or chartaceous, some-

times slightly inequilateral, subovate, obovate-elliptic, often broadly rhom
boid, or obovate-oblanceolate, broadly linear or elongated-lanceolate
acute at apex, more or less cuspidate, and gradually narrowed fro
nearly middle towards the cordate sub-rotundate, emarginate, tuncate
or sub-acute, sometimes rather broad or cuneate, often more or le:
oblique at the base, 3-5-nerved base; lateral nerves 5-7 pairs, more
less tomentose or perulous and minutely tuberculate or with hirsutello
hairs along the midrib beneath, entire, undulate at margin, 15-20 c
long, 4-7 cm wide; petioles rather slender, medium long, very pubesce
or hirsutellous, 1.5-4 cm long; stipules caudaceous, rarely persisten
membraneous, puberulous, broadly ovate, convolute, acute apice, 1 c
long, 4 mm at base; receptacle solitary, pedunculate, or in pairs fro
the axil of the leaves, shortly hispid when young near the apex, with ol
scurely darker vertical stripes on the surface, pyriform or globula:
suddenly tapering into the dilated umbilious, 1.5-2 cm long and broac
male and gall flower on one set of receptacles, while fertile fema
flowers on another set; male flowers pedicellate in various lengths
perianth 2-4, segments broadly linear-lanceolate; stamens 1, 2, or :
thick, shortly pedicellate, long stipitate, anthers 2, more or less ol
lique, oblong or elliptic, recurved; gall flowers sub-sessile or short
pedicelled, with perianth of 3-5 segments, exceeding the ovary; stigin
dilated; fertile female flowers sub-sessile, shortly pedunculate, wi
4-6 perianths segments, broadly spathulate or lanceolate, sub-acutisl
short; ovary smooth shining, subsessile; stigima dilated, sometimes b
lobed.

Distribution: Kwangtung, Chekiang, Fukien, and Taiwan. ;
altitude 200-400 m.

19. **Ficus festulosa** Reinw.

Tree 2-5 m, bark reddish gray; branchlets reddish gray, glabrous; leaves elliptic
lanceolate, 14-18 cm long, 3-5 cm wide, acute apice, cuneate at base, entire and u:
dulate at margin, dark green above, pale green and brownish puberscent beneatl
petioles 2-3 cm long, red, glabrous; receptacles globular, 1.15 cm long, solitar
axillary, pubescent; pedicels 5 mm long, grayish pubescent.

Distribution: Kwangtung, Fukien, and Taiwan.

20. **Ficus formosana** Maxim.

Ficus taiwaniana Hayata

Small trees or shrubs one meter or more in height; branchlets rather slender, yellowi:
brown to reddish brown, slightly rugolose; leaf-scars below the nodal lines, prominen
rotundate, with 2 punctual stipule-scars above the nodal lines; young branchlets slight
pilose, ultimately quite glabrous; leaves chartaceous, membraneous, inequilateral ;

oblique, variable in forms from rhomboid-obovate to broadly linear, cuspidate-acuminate at apex, caudate at base, dentate or sinuate-serrate above the middle and entire downward, dull green above; veins 6-8 pairs below, light to dark brown beneath; petioles slender, 8 mm long; stipules fugaceous, membraneous, glabrous, slightly puberulous, triangular or linear-lanceolate; receptacles axillary, solitary, pedunculate, pyriform, variable from ovoid to obovoid, 1.2-1.8 cm long and broad.

Distribution: Kwangtung, Hainan, Kwangsi, Chekiang, Fukien, Hunan, An-hwei, Kiangsi and Taiwan, at altitude lowlands.

21. Ficus foveolata Wall.

Shrubs or climbers, 2-5 m long; leaves lanceolate, oblong-lanceolate, 6-20 cm long, 3-7 cm wide, long acuminate cuneate at base, entire, dark shining green above, bluish green beneath, thick leathery; petioles 1-2 cm long, slightly pubescent; fruits globular, solitary or in opposite pairs, axillary, 1-1.5 cm long and broad, mucronate at apex, bluish hairy, pedicels 1 cm long, glabrous; flowers orange to black colored.

Distribution: Kwangtung, Kwangsi, Yunnan, Hunan, Hupeh, Kiangsi and Chekiang, at altitude 200-2350 m.

Var. 1. Ficus foveolata var. arisanensis (Hayata) Kudo

Small shrub with slender branchlets; leaves lanceolate, shortly acuminate at apex, rounded at base, entire at margin; petioles 1 cm long, pubescent, receptacle globular, sessile, axillary.

Distribution: Arisan, Taiwan.

Var. 2. Ficus foveolata var. eburnea Gagnep.

Small tree with reddish bark and branchlets; leaves oblong-lanceolate, attenuate acuminate apice, entire and undulate, cuneate at base, thick, lustrous dark green above, pale green beneath 16-20 cm long, 4-6 cm wide, glabrous; petioles reddish, pubescent, 2-3 cm long; receptacle round, 1-1.5 cm long and broad, solitary, sessile, grayish pubescent.

Distribution: Yunnan, at altitude 1150 m.

Var. 3. Ficus foveolata var. henryi King et Oliv.

This variety differs chiefly in its sessile ovoid rather large fruits; leaves strongly coriaceous and pubescent beneath.

Distribution: Hupeh I-Chang, Chekiang, Anhwei, Kwangsi, Szechuan, and Fukien, at altitude 130-3000 m.

22. Ficus fruticosa Roxb.

Ficus scandens Roxb.

Scandent shrubs climbing on rocky cliffs; stem terete, reddish gray; leaves obovate, 8-10 cm long, 4-6 cm wide, acute apice, round at base, undulate entire, glossy pale green above, brownish green and pubescent below, thick, leathery; petioles 1.5-2 cm long, reddish pubescent; receptacles in pairs, axillary, globular, 5 mm long and broad, short pedicelled, reddish pubescent.

Distribution: Kwangtung, Hainan, Yunnan, and Hongkong, at altitude 660 m.

23. **Ficus fulva** Reinw.

Shrub 4 m tall; semi-woody, bark dark gray; leaves large, round, 3-nerved palmated lobe; dark green above, pale green and prominently veined beneath, 23-30 cm long and broad, somewhat acute at apex, cordate at base, finely serrate at lobes; midrib and veins covered with dense, long, and golden-reddish hairs, thick, coriaceous; petioles long, 8-10 cm long, round, 1 cm thick, densely golden-reddish hairy; fruit not seen.

Distribution: Kwangtung and Kwangsi.

24. **Ficus garanbiensis** Hayata

A small shrub about 50 cm tall, creeping on the ground, scandent or erect into the apex or rarely a tree; leaves always alternate, petiolate, thickly coriaceous smooth on both surfaces, obovate, slightly rounded or cuneate at base, apex rotundate never acutish, truncate and 3-nerved at base, entire or obscurely undulate, or revolute; lateral veins 4-6 pairs, reticulations distinctly impressed on the upper surface; receptacles in pairs, solitary by abortion, axillary, obovoid globular-pyriformis, acute obtuse, slightly truncate, 1.2 cm long; basal bracts 3, membraneous; male and gall flowers one set of receptacles while fertile female flowers on another set; pedicellate or sub-sessile; perianth segments 3-5 distinct.

Distribution: Endemic to Taiwan, confining to southern coastline.

25. **Ficus gilbosa** Blume

Ficus vasculosa Hayata

Small evergreen tree, 6 m tall, 20 cm in diameter; leaves oblong-lanceolate, 10-16 cm long, 4-6 cm wide, acute at apex, oblique cuneate at base, entire, thick, coriaceous; petioles 5 mm long; fruit globular, pale green, rough, axillary, solitary or several in clusters, 1 cm long and broad; pedicels 5 mm long.

Distribution: Kwangtung, Hainan, Kweichow, and Taiwan, at altitude 500 m.

26. **Ficus hainanensis** Merr. et Chun

Tree 4-11 m tall; branchlets terete, leaves alternate, oblong obovate, 15-25 cm long, 5-9 cm wide, acute-acuminate apice, obtuse and 3-nerved at base, crenate-dentate-serrate, coriaceous; petioles 4-6 cm long; stipules lanceolate, acuminate at apex; bracts 3, triangular ovate, 3 mm long; pedicels 2 cm long.

Distribution: Hainan, and Kwangtung.

27. **Ficus hayatai** Sata

Tree 10-13 m tall; bark reddish brown, glabrous; branchets slender, reddish brown; leaves elliptic-oblong, 6-10 cm long, 3-6 cm wide, acute at apex, cuneate 3-nerved at base, entire and undulate, thick coriaceous, dark green and glabrous above, pale green slightly pilose along the midrib beneath; petioles 5-8 mm long, grooved; receptacle globular, 5 mm long and broad, axillary, in pairs, or several in clusters; pedicels 5-8 mm long, brownish yellow.

Distribution: Common in Taiwan.

28. **Ficus henryi** Warb.

Tree with reddish gray bark; branchlets terete, reddish, glabrous; leaves oblong-lanceolate, 12–18 cm long, 3–5 cm wide, acuminate at apex, cuneate somewhat oblique at base, coarsely dentate-serrate above the middle, coriaceous, glossy, dark green above, light green and glabrous below; petioles 1–2 cm long, brownish pubescent; receptacle, globular, axillary, in pairs, 1 cm long, mucronate, shortly pedicelled, brownish.

Distribution: Hupeh I–Chang.

29. **Ficus heterophylla** Linn. f.

Shrub and climbers; fruit pale green, globular, 1 – 2 cm long and broad, long-pedunculate; leaves lanceolate, long acuminate at apex, truncate 3-nerved at base, or 2-lobed, irregularly dentate-serrate at margin, thick coriaceous; petioles 1 cm long, brownish.

Distribution: Hainan.

30. **Ficus hypoleucogramma** (Rehd.) Levl.

This species is closely related to *Ficus obtusifolia* Roxb, but the leaves are shorter, broader and petioles larger. Occurring in Kweichow.

31. **Ficus harlandii** Benth.

Ficus coronata Sasaki

Small tree 10 meters tall, 25 cm in diam.; branchlets slightly rugose, reddish brown; leaves alternate or opposite, often opposite in paris, long petiolate, obovate, elliptic ovate, 3–5-nerved some 7-nerved at base, margin entire and slightly sinuate on the upper third, often the teeth rather prominent, 15–28 cm long, 7–17 cm broad, obtuse at apex, broadly cuneate at base, membraneous, subcoriaceous, upper surface dull shining usually with numerous white spots and minute white dotts and seemingly pale and white; petioles thick, stout rugose, hispid, 1–4 cm long; receptacles solitary, in pairs or 3 or 4 pairs arising from the axils of the leaves.

Distribution: Taiwan, widely spreading over the island.

Var. 1. **F. harlandii** var. **harlandii** --- Leaves obovate oblong and narrowly or broadly oblanceolate, with more or less cuneate or subacute base, and short petioles; receptacles shortly pedunculate, basal bracts adhered to the very base which is never tapering.

Var. 2. **Ficus harlandii** var. **grandifolia** ---Leaves often conspicuously large, broadly ovate, rhomboid, or elliptic-rotundate with obtuse, truncate, cordate, or oblique base, often large and small leaves in alternate pairs with stout and long petiolate; basal bracts distinct with ferruginous hipid hairs. Occurring in Taiwan and Hongkong.

32. **Ficus harmandii** Gagnep.

Small tree 10 m tall, 20 cm in diam.; bark reddish gray, smooth; leaves elliptic-lanceolate, 16–20 cm long, 3–5 cm wide, long acuminate, entire, cuneate 3-nerved at base, glabrous; petioles 2-3 cm long, slender, glabrous; receptacles globular, solitary to many clustered along the branchlets, reddish brown, 1 cm broad and high; pedicels 1-1.5 cm long, glabrous.

Distribution: Kwangtung, Hainan, Kwangsi, and Fukien, at altitude 500-850 m.

33. **Ficus heteromorpha** Hemsl.

Tree deciduous and evergreen, widely distributed in Southern China; bark smooth, reddish brown; leaves exceedingly variable in size and in shapes, leaves oblong-ovate, broader or notched at middle, 16-20 cm long, 8-10 cm wide, coarsely toothed above the middle, broadly narrowing downward to a truncate base, sharply acute at apex, some leaves lobed or notched at the middle, slightly pubescent; petioles long and slender, 4-10 cm long, brownish, slightly pubescent.

Distribution: Kwangtung, Kwangsi, Hainan, Kweichow, Szechuan, Hunan, Yunnan, Hupeh, Shensi, Honan, Kiangsi, and Fukien, at altitude 700-2800 meters.

34. **Ficus hirta** Vahl.

Tree, bark gray brown; branchlets densely golden hairy; leaves oblong broadly lanceolated, 16-20 cm long, 5-6 cm wide, long acuminate, rounded at base, finely serrate or 3-lobed but with entire margins, coriaceous, dark green above, light green below, densely brownish pubescent and reticulated beneath; petioles slender, 3-5 cm long, reddish hairy; receptacle globular, sessile, solitary, or 2 in pairs, axillary, 1-2 cm broad and high, long reddish hairy or hirsute; fruits yellow.

Distribution: Kwangtung, Kwangsi, Kweichow, Hainan, and Yunnan, at altitude 1380 meters.

Var. 1. **Ficus hirta** var. **simplicissima** Lour.

F. hirsuta var. *brevipila* Corner

Tree 2 m tall; leaves more narrowly and long lobed and finely serrate along the margin of the lobes.

Distribution: Kwangtung.

Var. 2. **Ficus hirta** var. **hibiscifolia** Champ.

Small shrub; fruit green, ovoid, strigose; bark brown.

Distribution: Hainan.

Var. 3. **Ficus hirta** var. **roxburgii** (Miq.) King

Ficus esquiroliana Levl.

Ficus lous-esquiroliana Levl.

Tree 2 meters tall; leaves large, broad obovate; fruit green.

Distribution: Kwangtung.

35. **Ficus hispida** Linn. f.

Small tree, 5 m tall, 20 cm in diameter.; bark dark gray; branchlets stout, rugose, pubescent; leaves alternate, opposite, obovate, 20-35 cm long, 16-20 cm wide, acute, cuneate at base, shallowly serrate; thick, coriaceous, dark green above, pale and brownish reticulate beneath; petioles thick, stout, 28 cm long, brownish pubescent; fruit globular, 2-3 cm long and broad, solitary or in opposite pairs yellow; pedicels 1-2 cm long, bluish pubescent.

Distribution: Kwangtung, Kwangsi, and Yunnan, at altitude 600-1800 m.

36. **Ficus impressa** Champ. ex Benth.

Ficus bodinierei Levl.

Shrub or climber, 2 m high; fruit globular, yellow, small, 2 mm long and broad, short pedicelled, solitary or in opposite pairs, axillary; leaves elliptic-ovate, lanceolate, 4-8 cm long, 2-3 cm wide, acute at apex, cuneate at base, entire, lustrous glossy green above, light green and glabrous below; petioles 1 cm long, reddish pubescent.

Distribution: Kwangtung.

37. **Ficus konishii** Hayata

Ficus ochobiensis Hayata

Large tree, 15 m high, trunk half meter in diameter; branches and branchlets thick, pale white, with silght fulvo-pubescence, minutely vertical rugose, with many oblong or rotundate scars, glabrous except stipule slightly pubescent; leaves alternate, persistent both surfaces glabrous and smooth, shining, dimly on the upper surface, thin coriaceous or sub-coriaceous, usually ovate and never obovate or lanceolate, often ovate-lanceolate, more or less oblique; 10-20 cm long, 6-10 cm or more wide; margin sub-entire or undulate, rarely sub-dentate or sub-serrate, apex more or less curved, gradually or rather suddenly narrowed to the acute and cuspidate, caudate apex; the base rotundate or subacute 3-or rarely 5-nerved; lateral viens 6-10 pairs, reticulation rather prominent beneath and impressed above; petioles scurfy, long and slender, 4-8 cm long; stipules fugaceous, 1-2 to each leaf, situated near the terminal of the branchlet; receptacle usually in fascicles on tubercules of the leafless branchlets, or on the trunk, solitary or in pairs from 2 to 6 or more, never axillary, long pedunculate, glabrous, usually globose or slightly deppressed globose with slight vertical ridges obscurely and brownish papillose-punctate, usually green in color even after ripe 1.5-2 cm long.

Distribution: Taiwan, common throughout the Island.

38. **Ficus kingiana** Hemsly

A rather small tree; branchlets slight pendulous, slender, glabrous, ferruginous or very darkish brown, young branchlets, sub-hirsute on; leaves shortly petioled, more or less inequilateral, membraneous or chartaceous, rahter thin, scabrous on both surfaces, very variable in shapes and in colors, from narrow to broad-lanceolate to oblong-ellitptic, gradually narrowed to the cuspidate-caudate apex, more or less oblique at base and cuneate, 3-nerved, entire or slightly undulate along the margin; primary lateral veins 5-7 pairs, nearly at right angle to the midrib; petioles thick, slightly hispid, 3-6 mm long; stipules fugaceous 2 to each leaf near the end of the branchlets, thinly membraneous, triangular linear-lanceolate with acute apex, hirsute on the dorsal surface, 6-10 mm long, receptacle short pedunculated, always axillary, solitary or in pairs, rarely 3 or 4 pairs, globose or depressed globose or sub-pyriform-globose, smooth or scabrous, emarginate at the apex, tapering at the base, with a few minute bracts, on the slender peduncles. Pseudo-hermaphrodite flowers (containing male flowers) and gall flowers both on one set, while fertile female flowers only on another set; male flowers numerous, near the mouth of the receptacles, sessile or pedicellate, with 3-4 distinct perianths segments, lanceolated; stamen 1 rarely 2, with a short filament adnate to the abortive pistil and forming a pseudohermaphrodite flower; gall flower subsessile or shortly stipitate, with a perianth similar to the male flower; ovary stipitate, globular, obovoid, smooth; style short, lateral; fertile male flowers sessile, very short pedicellate, with 4-6 linear perianth segments; ovary smooth, subsessile, oblique, nearly globular; style thin, longer than that of the galls, lateral, or sub-eterminal.

Distribution: Endemic to Taiwan.

39. **Ficus laevis** Blume

Ficus jaminii Levl.

Shrub or semi-woody climber, 1-2 m long or high; fruit yellow; leaves obovate, 8-10 cm long, 6-8 cm broad, acuminate, rotundate, 3-nerved at base, finely serrate, dark green above, brownish pubescent below, coriaceous; petioles very slender, 5-7 cm long, brownish pubescent; receptacles or fruits round, 2 cm long and broad, dark; pedicels slender, 2-3 cm long, axillary, in pairs.

Distribution: Kwangsi.

40. **Ficus longepidata** Levl.

Ficus sordida Hand.-Mazz.

Ficus trechopoda Levl.

Shrub with brownish villose and reddish bark; leaves elliptic to oblanceolate, 4-10 cm long, 3-4 cm wide, coriaceous, glabrous, tomentose along the midrib beneath, acute at apex, undulate and entire at margin, cuneate at base; petioles 2 cm long, reddish hirsute; fruits globular, 1 cm long and broad, black, densely hirsute.

Distribution: Kwangsi, and Kweichow.

41. **Ficus lanceolatifolia** Levl. et Vant.

Shrub, 1-2 m high; bark red; branchlets slender; leaves elliptic-lanceolate, 8-12 cm long, 2-3 cm wide, acuminate at apex, acute at base, irregularly dentate-serrate at margin, thick, glabrous; petioles thin, 5 mm long; fruits globular 2 mm broad and high, green to black when ripe, solitary, or in pairs, edible.

Distribution: Kwangsi, Kweichow, and Szechuan.

42. **Ficus letaqui** Levl. et Vant.

Shrub with the receptacles on elongated appearently leafless branchlets and large leaves on slender petioles up to 15 cm long; leaves obovate 20-26 cm long, 16-18 cm broad, acute apice, cordate at base, irregularly coarsely dentate-serrate along the margin, dark green and rough on both surfaces.

Distribution: Kweichow.

43. **Ficus nomoralis** Wall.

Tree 5 m tall; bark and branches reddish; leaves elliptic-lanceolate 20-26 cm long, 6-8 cm wide, acuminate to acute at apex, narrowly rounded at base, enitre, very thick, dark green above, pale green with reddish reticulation beneath, glabrous on both surfaces; petioles 2-5 cm long, slender, reddish, glabrous; fruits globular, 2-10 mm long and broad, in opposite pairs, sessile, yellow.

Distribution: Yunnan, at altitude 2300 meters.

44. **Ficus martinii** Levl. et Vant.

Ficus kwangtungensis Merr.

Shrub upright or scandent, climbing to 25 m long; leaves lanceolate 7-11.5 cm long, caudate-acute at base, acuminate at apex, sub-reflexed and undulate at margin, coriaceous; fruits globular, small, axillary, solitary; pedicels 1 mm long.

Distribution: Kwangtung, Kwangsi, Kweichow, Hainan, Hunan, Szechuan, Chekiang, Anhwei, Hupei, and Kiangsu, at altitude 1000-1200 meters.

Var. 1. **Ficus martinii** var. **saxicola** Hand.-Mazz.

Ficus leucodermis Hand.-Mazz.

Shrub, bark whitish gray; leaves small, rigid, lanceolate, 3-6 cm long, 2-4 cm wide, acuminate apice, acute at base, entire, shining green above, pale green below, glabrous on both surfaces; petioles 1 cm long, brownish, glabrous; fruits solitary or in pairs, axillary, globular, 5 mm in diameter, grayish green; pedicels 1-2 mm long.

Distribution: Kweichow, and Hunan, at altitude 1000-1400 m.

45. **Ficus nervosa** Heyne

Ficus austro-chinensis Hutch.

Tree 30 meters tall, trunk 1 meter in diameter; bark grayish brown; leaves oblong-lanceolate, 16 cm long, 4 cm wide, acute apice, cuneate at base, entire; petioles 1 cm long, glabrous, red; fruits globular, 1 cm long and high, red.

Distribution: Kwangtung, Yunnan, Hongkong, Hainan, Fukien, and Taiwan.

46. **Ficus obscura** Blume

Ficus asymmetrica Levl.

Shrub, branchlets pubescent brownish; leaves asymmetric, oblong, from the midrib towards its right side being narrow and towards its left side being wide forming an asymmetrical rather crooked oblong-shape blade, narrowly acuminate at apex, oblique cuneate at base, irregularly coarsely-dentate serrate margin, dark green above, pale green densely whitish pubescent beneath, coriaceous; petioles 5-10 mm long, brownish pubescent, fruits subglobular, 1 cm long, 7 mm broad, brownish hirsute, mucronate; pedicels 1 cm long, brownish pubescent.

Distribution: Yunnan.

47. **Ficus pilosa** Reinw.

Tree 19 m tall, trunk 14 cm in diameter; branchlets rough, dark gray to reddish brown, glabrous; leaves obovate to oblanceolate, 16–20 cm long, 4–7 cm wide, blunt, acute apice, cuneate, rounded at base, entire margin, thick coriaceous, dark green above, light green and glabrous beneath; petioles 3–5 cm long, brownish, glabrous; fruits globular, small, 2 mm broad and high, solitary, axillary, short pedicelled.

Distribution: Hainan, and Kwangsi.

48. Ficus pseudo-botryoides (Rehd.) Levl. et Vant.

Shrub with rugose branchlets; leaves lanceolate, ovate, glabrous asymmetrical, 12–15 cm long, 5–6 cm wide, glabrous, acute-acuminate apice, entire and undulate margin, obtuse-cuneate at base; fruits ovoid, in pseudo-racemose clusters, solitary; peduncles 6–8 mm long.

Distribution: Kweichow.

49. Ficus pubinervis Blume

Shrub with whitish gray bark; branchlets thick, stout, short, reddish brown; leaves elliptic-ovate, 5–8 cm long, 3–5 cm wide, obtuse or acute at apex, cuneate at base, margin, entire and undulate thick, lustrous dark green above, pale green, pubescent along the midrib beneath, thick coriaceous; petioles 1–2 cm long, brownish pubescent; lateral veins 8–12 pairs with prominent reticulations, veinlets closed near margin; fruits flattened globose, 2 cm broad and 1 cm high, brown pubescent, solitary, short pedunculate.

Distribution: Botel Tobago, Taiwan.

50. Ficus pandurata Hance

Ficus cuneata Levl. et Vant.

Shrub 1–2 meters tall with milky juice; young branchlets hispidous-pilose, ultimately glabrous; leaves petiolate, membraneous, panduriform or pear-shaped, shortly cuspidate at apex, acute, 3-nerved at base, lateral veins 5–6 pairs, the lower one almost horizontal, the upper all oblique, prominent and like the midrib, sparsely adpressed-hispid below, the rest of the lower surface minutely tuberculate and scabrulous, the upper surface glabrous, 6–8 cm long, 3–5 cm wide; petioles 5–7 cm long; fruits axillary, solitary, or in pairs, pedunculate, ellipsoid or sub-obovate, with prominent umbilical bracts, smooth when ripe, 4–6 cm across; basal bracts 3, broadly ovate; peduncle 4–6 cm long; fertile female flowers sessile; perianth segments 3–4; style lateral elongate; stigma oblique; male flowers not seen.

Distribution: Kwangtung, Kwangsi, Chekiang, Fukien, and Taiwan, at altitude 300 meters.

51. Ficus parvifolia Miq.

Small tree with whitish gray bark; branchlets slender, white gray, smooth; leaves elliptic-ovate, 4–6 cm long, 2–3 cm wide, acute apice, cuneate at base, entire, light green above, pale green and glabrous beneath; petioles 1–2 cm long, glabrous; fruits globular, 5 mm long and high, sessile on bracts, solitary, greenish-brown.

Distribution: Kwangtung, Kwangsi, Fukien, and Taiwan, at altitude 370–400 meters.

52. Ficus pumila Linn.

Ficus stipulata Thunb.

Scandent shrub; stem and branches extensively creeping and rooting, much branched and spreading appressed to and clothing the trunk of trees, walls etc., glabrous, slender, hispid; fruiting branches suberect, free, stout, jointed, channelled, hispidly hairy; leaves close-set, distichous, shortly petioled, or sessile, appressed to the wall or support, obliquely ovate-cordate, sub-acute, unequal to the base, glabrous or scabridly pubescent; stipules glabrous, membraneous, bifid; leaves of fruiting branches 8–10 cm long, elliptic-oblong, petioled, spreading, coriaceous, obtuse at both ends or round at base and triple-nerved, smooth on both surfaces; receptacles peduncled, solitary, axillary, pear- or top-shaped, 5–8 cm long, narrowed at the base and tip, obscurely lobed, dark-blue or reddish purple when ripe, apparently pubescent; bracts ovate at the mouth, acute, spreading, inner surface villose; peduncle as long very hairy; ovary oblique rounded or dimidiater; style either capillary with an acute stigma or shorter with a peltate stigima.

Distribution: Kwangtung, Kwangsi, Kweichow, Hainan, Kiangsi, Hupeh, Anhwei, Hunan, Kiangsu, Fukien, and Taiwan, at altitude 100–600 meters.

53. Ficus pyriformis Hook. et Arn.

Small tree with milky juice; bark reddish brown, branchlets slender, reddish brown; leaves lanceolate, 4–8 cm long, 2 cm wide, acuminate apice, cuneate at base, entire, coriaceous, glabrous; petioles very short, 1–2 mm long; stipules triangular, small, brownish; fruits pyriform 1–2 mm long ang broad, borne on brownish bracts, solitary, axillary; pedicels 2–4 cm long, slender.

Distribution: Kwangsi, Kweichow, Yunnan, Kwangtung, Chekiang, and Hongkong at altitude 3000 meters.

Var. 1. **Ficus pyriformis** var. **ischnopoda** Miq.

Ficus macropoda Levl. et Vant.

Ficus pyriformis var. *ischnopoda* King

Leaves of this variety is similar to those of *E. sub-pyriformis* Miq. but glabrous; receptacles glabrous; the peduncles much elongated; branchlets rugose pubescent; leaves discolored, oblong, acuminate at apex, cuneate attenuated at base, margin sub-revolute; receptacle ovate, rugose; peduncle 3 cm long, pubescent.

Distribution: Kweichow, and Yunnan, at altitude 660 m.

54. Ficus rectinervia Merr.

Small shrubg glabrous except the distinctly hirsute branchlets; branchlets and branches dark reddish brown, rugose, marked with numerous, rather densely arranged, petiolar scars, the internodes very short; leaves lanceolate to linear-lanceolate, subcoriaceous, smooth, shining, olivaceous, brownish or somewhat greenish when dry, the lower surface paler than the upper and distinctly puncticulate, the apex slenderly acuminate, base obtuse and distinctly although minutely cordate, the margin recurved; lateral nerves spreading at nearly right angles from the midrib, about 20 pairs, straight, distinct, anastomosing directly with the somewhat arched, longitudinal nerves; petioles pubescent, 2–3 mm long; stipules lanceolate, acuminate, up to 4 mm long; fruits few, axillary, ovoid to somewhat obovoid, 15 mm long, somewhat narrowed below into a short pseudo-stalk above the bracts, glabrous, peduncles up to 12 mm long, sparingly pubescent, 3 bracts at the apex of the peduncle broadly triangular ovate, acute about 1 mm long; staminate flowers numerous but only in the upper part of the receptacle; pedicels 1–3 mm long in perianth segements 3, lanceolate, acuminate, brown; stamens 2, rarely 3; anthers as long as the perianth segements; ovary ovoid to obovoid, 1.2 in diameter; style very short.

Distribution: Kwangtung, and Hainan.

55. **Ficus ramentocea** Roxb.

Scandent shrub, 5 m tall, climbing on trees; bark whitish gray; leaves oblanceolate, 10–14 cm long, 4–7 cm wide, short acuminate at apex, round or obtuse at base, entire, undulate along the margin, thick leathery, dark green above, brownish pubescent beneath; petioles 1 cm long, brownish; receptacle globular, 1 cm broad and high, green to reddish brown, glabrous, solitary or in pairs; pedicels short and with reddish hairs.

56. **Ficus roxburgii** Wall.

Shrub, erect, 3 m tall, branchlets very rough and hirsute; leaves large obovate, 30 cm long, 25 cm wide, blunt at apex, cordate at base, irregularly shallowly-serrate at margin, 3-nerved, along the midrib brownish hairy on both surfaces and prominently reticulated beneath, thin coiraceous; receptacle 10 cm across, orange color.

Closely related to Ficus longiniformis of Taiwan.

Distribution: Yunnan, at altitude 1800 m.

57. **Ficus religiosa** Linn.

A large spreading tree; leaves triangular–ovate, broadest at base, long attenuate-acuminated at apex, obtuse and slightly cordate at base, entire, undulate, slightly revolute along margin, 10–18 cm long, 6–18 cm wide, 3-nerved at base, coriaceous, glabrous, dark green above, pale green prominently reticulated and brownish hairy along the midrib and veins beneath; petioles slender, exceedingly long, 8–15 cm long, 1 mm thick, glabrous; receptacles small, globular, mucronate on top, 1 cm broad and high, in pairs, borne on a 3–4 pieces reddish brown, bracts, glabrous; fruits clustered on branchlets arranged in pairs.

Distribution: Yunnan, at altitude 1950 m. Hongkong, cultivated in tewples.

58. **Ficus retusa** Linn.

Ficus indica Linn.

Tree 8 m tall, 80 cm in diameter, evergreen, with numerous aerial roots, some prop-like aerial roots assuming the size of trunks, quite glabrous; leaves shortly petiolate, shining, coriaceous, glabrous, thick, smooth, entire, broadly ovate or nearly orbicular to obovate-oblong, apex obtuse or obtusely-acuminate or slightly apiculate; base more or less narrowed ovately acute, or rhomboidal elliptic, with abrupt obtuse short cuspidate or with slight acute apex, much narrowed and 3-nerved at base, 4-9 cm long, 2.5-5.5 cm wide; petioles stout, 6-11 mm long; stipules fugaceous; receptacles closely sessile, solitary, originally in pairs in the axil of the leaves or of the scars of the fallen leaves, depressed globose, more or less pubescent, sitting on three spathulate bracts, purple dark reddish.

Distribution: Kweichow, Fukien, Taiwan, Kwangtung, Kwangsi, and Hainan.

9. **Ficus rigida** Jack

    Ficus glaberrima Bl.

    Ficus blinii Levl.

    Ficus suberosa Levl.

Tree 8-10 meters tall; fruit black; leaves oblanceolate, 16-26 cm long, 5-7 cm wide, acute acuminate at apex, broadly cuneate, 3-nerved at base, entire, dark green above, pale green, along the midrib and veins hairy beneath, thin coriaceous; petioles 1-3 cm long, glabrous; receptacles galbrous, globular, 1-2 mm broad and high, solitary, red, tapering towards both ends; pedicels 1 cm long, pubescent.

Distribution: Yunnan, Hainan, Kwangtung, and Kweichow, at altitude 600-1000 meters.

0. **Ficus rostrata** Lam.

Shrub 3 m tall; bark whitish gray, smooth, glabrous; leaves elliptic-oblong, 16 cm long, 5-7 cm wide, long attenuate-acuminate at apex, cuneate asymmetric at base, entire undulate at margin pale green beneath, depressed midrib, lustrous green above, prominently reticulated and curving upward, the secondary veins closing up the margin, pale green beneath, thick coriaceous; petioles 1-2 cm long, brownish rugose; receptacles globular, 1-1.5 cm long and broad, solitary or in pairs, axillary, brownish rugose; pedicels slender, 2 cm long, brownish rugose.

Distribution: Hainan

1. **Ficus sagitata** Vahl.

Climber, 2 meters long; bark whitish gray; branchlets whitish; leaves oblanceolate, 12-18 cm long, 6-8 cm wide, acuminate **apex**, **deeply cordate** at base, entire margin, thick, coriaceous, lustrous dark green above, pale green, brownish hairy along the midrib and veins beneath; petioles 2-3 cm long, brownish pubescent.

Distribution: Kwangtung.

2. **Ficus sikkimensis** Miquel

Tree 5 meters tall; branchlets very **slender, sweeping, gray;** leaves ellipti
oblanceolate, asymmetrical, acute-acuminate at apex, cuspidate at base, entire undula
along the margin, thin coriaceous; petioles 1 cm long, rugose pubescent; receptac
small oblong-cylindrical, solitary or in pairs, axillary, 1-2 mm long and broad; pedice
slender, 1 mm long.

Distribution: Kwangtung and Yunnan.

63. **Ficus swinhoei** King.

A hispid shrub; leaves petiolate, coriaceous, elliptic or sub-obovate-elliptic; t
apex subacute, margin slightly sinuate especially towards the apex; the base rounded
slightly contracted 3-nerved; lateral veins 5 pairs; both surfaces dull and covered wi
minute very short stiff hairs; leaves 8-12 cm long, 5-7 cm wide; petioles stout, scabri
stipules lanceolate, hispid; receptacles pedunculate solitary, axillary, globular, co
tracted at base; umbiliculous large and prominent, scabrid-hispid, with 3 spreadi
ovate bracts at base; female flowers with a 4-cleft scabrid perianth; fruits oblon
ovoid, oblique; style lateral.

Distribution: Endemic to Taiwan.

64. **Ficus septica** Maxim.

Tree, all parts glabrous; brnachlets thick, stout, annulate; bark rugose, whiti
yellow; leaves alternate or opposite, large whitish glabrous on both surfaces, abrupt
cuspidate **apex,** cordate at base, inequilateral, 3-5-nerved at base, entire margin, 1
25 cm long, 8-13 cm wide; petioles 1-4 cm long; stipules membraneous; receptacl
sub-sessile, solitary, more or less adpressed, 8-13 mm broad and high.

Distribution: Taiwan.

65. **Ficus siehentensis** Miq.

Ficus cyamus Levl.

Shrub 3-5 m tall; bark dark gray; branchlets slender, rugose; leaves ellipti
lanceolate 6-10 cm long, 2-3 cm wide, acuminate **apex,** cuneate at base, entire, thi
glabrous, 3-nerved; petioles 1-2 cm long, glabrous; receptacles small, globular, 1
mm broad and high, in pairs, sessile.

Distribution: Kweichow and Yunnan, at altitude 1200 m.

66. **Ficus simplicissima** Lour.

Ficus palmatiloba Merr.

Shrub 2 m tall, with brownish hairy branchlets; leaves narrowly 3-5-lobed, with lo
reddish hairs along the midrib below; the central narrow lobe up to 20 cm long and 2
wide; receptacle globular 1-2 cm long densely hairy, solitary, sessile.

Distribution: Kwangtung, and Hainan, at altitude 660 m.

67. **Ficus stenophylla** Hemsl.

Ficus retinerva Merr.

Erect shrub 1-2 m tall; leaves lanceolate, 16-20 cm long, 2 cm wide, acuminate ap
acute at base, undulate entire margin, dark green above, whitish green below, glabro

on both surfaces; petioles 1 cm long; fruit solitary, axillary, globular, 1–2 mm long and broad, green and red; pedicels 1 cm long, brown.

Distribution: Kwangtung, Kwangsi, Hunan, Fukien, Hainan, Chekiang, Anhwei, Hupeh, Szechuan and Taiwan.

Ficus subulata Bl.

Tree 3 m tall; bark whitish gray; leaves lanceolate, 12–18 cm long, 4–6 cm wide, asymmetric, oblique at base, acuminate **apex**, finely serrate thin coriaceous; petioles 1 cm long, brownish; receptacle globular, 1–2 mm broad and high, smooth, brownish yellow; pedicels 1 cm long, slender.

Distribution: Kwangtung and Hainan.

Ficus tsuii Merr. et Metcalf

Shrub 5 m tall, 70 cm in diameter; branchlets reddish gray, smooth; leaves obovate 20 cm long, 16 cm wide, acute **apex**, broadly cuneate at base, 3–nerved, undulate and entire margin, thin coriaceous, dark green above, light green and along the midrib and veins hairy beneath; petiole long, slender, 8–12 cm long, brownish pubescent; receptacle globular, mucronate apice, 2–3 cm broad and high, solitary, sessile.

Distribution: Kwangtung.

Ficus terminalis Merr.

Large tree, 26 m. tall, trunk 3–3.5 m in diameter; branches massive and spreading to form a broad rounded, flattened crown; bark dark gray, smooth; branchlets gray, rough; leaves fall late in the winter or retained until spring, oblong–lanceolate, 10–16 cm long, 4–6 cm wide, acute **apex**, broadly cuneate 3–nerved at base, entire somewhat recurved at margin, glabrous on both surfaces; petioles long, slender, 3–6 cm long, brownish; receptacle small, glabrous, 1–2 mm long and broad, short pedicelled or sessile, densely clustered along the branchlets, brone on brownish bracts.

Distribution: Kwangtung, Kwangsi, Hainan, Yunnan, Szechuan and Sikang, at altitude 1500 meters.

Ficus tikoua Bureau

Small vine creeping on the ground, forming a colony of 1–2 meters in diameter, brownish pubescent; leaves elliptic–oblanceolte, 4–6 cm long, 2 cm wide, acute narrowly truncate at base, irregularly serrate along the margin; petioles 2 cm long, brownish rugose; receptacle solitary, globular, 1–2 cm long and broad, brownish pubescent; pedicels 1 cm long, brownish.

Distribution: Kwangsi, Kweichow, Yunnan, Szechuan and Hunan, at altitude 1000–2300 meters. Ripe fruit sweet, edible.

Ficus vaccinioides Hemsley et King

A small creeping shrub, rooting from the stem and large branches, the young branches pendulous; leaves shortly petiolate, coriaceous, elliptic or obovate–elliptic, 3–4 cm long, 2–3 cm wide; wwith broad, rounded rarely sub–acute apex, entire edges and rounded or sub–emarginate, 3–nerved base; primary lateral veins 3–4 pairs, rather

broad and prominent beneath; lower surface with wide, sub-tesselate reticulatio
minutely punctate, perulous when young; upper surface sparsely adpressed-hisp
petioles adpressed pubescent, about 3 cm long; stipules 2 to each leaf, ovate acu
scarious, puberulous, twice as long as the petioles, deciduous; receptacles almost s
sile, solitary, axillary, ovoid, from 2-3 cm long and across; the umbilical scales lar
puberulous; basal bracts 3, ovate-acute, nearly glabrous; fertile female flowers
cupaying the whole receptacle, sub-sessile; the perianth segments 5; achene ov
reniformed, minutely papillose; style elongate when young; stigma slightly dilated; n
and gall flowers not known.

Distribution: Taiwan, at altitude 2000 meters.

73. Ficus varilosa Lindl.

A glabrous shrub, 2.5 meters high, stem 10 cm in diameter; leaves thinly coriace
oblanceolate or oblong-lanceolate; 6-14 cm long; petiole 1 cm long; apex sub-acute
obtusely acuminate, entire margin recurved, cuneate and 3-nerved at base; lateral
mary nerves 8-10 pairs, rather horizontal; reticulations wide, indistinct; stipule ov
acuminate, 1 cm long; receptacles pedunculate, axillary, in pairs, globular; the a
umbonate, especially when young; the umbilical bracts large; basal bracts 3, ov
triangular, spreading, united below; when ripe glabrous and more or less verruc
about 1 cm acrose; peduncles slender, 10-13 mm long; fertile female flowers pedicel
or sub-sessile, perianth segments 3 or 4, distinct; achenes trigonous, minutely wrinkl
style long, lateral; fruits black, edible.

Distribution: Kwangtung, Kwangsi, Hongkong, Hainan, Chekiang, and Hunan
altitude 100-1000 meters.

74. Ficus vasculosa Wall.

Ficus championi Benth.

Small tree usually shrub, 3-14 meters high; leaves varying in size and shape, al
alternate, very shortly petiolate, inequilateral, rather thick and cotriaceous, pal
brownish green, glabrous and smooth on both surfaces, elliptic to oblong-ovate, o
sub-rotundate or sub-rhomboid, sub-lanceolate, 5-10 cm long, 3-4.5 cm wide and o
15-22 cm long, 6.5-8.5 cm broad; apex acute, base, 3-nerved cuneate-acute entire
slightly revolute along the margin, often oblique, rarely gibbose but never rounde
base; petioles 3-10 mm long; receptacles axillary or on the scars of the fallen lea
solitary, in pairs or in 4's in small umbellate fascicles, pedunculate, almost globu
7-12 mm across, glabrous, tuberculate, constricted at the base; basal bracts none,
with few or 3 broadly ovate-acute, bracteoles, triangular, at their base the umbil
rather prominent and slightly emarginate; color changing from orange yellow to bril
red rather small, 7-12 mm across; peduncles short and slender, 7-12 mm long;
flowers few, near the mouth of the receptacle, with rudimentary pistil resembling
gall flowers; gall flowers sessile or very short pedicellate; perianth segments
distinct, linear or oblanceolate, blunt-acute and truncate apice, or bifid sub-toothe

apex; ovary smooth, more or less oblique, sub-globular, obovoid or ellipsoid with thickened pedicels; style lateral or sub-terminal, short, thick; stigma truncate, dilated; female flowers unkonwn, perhaps existing in other set of receptacles.

Distribution: Taiwan.

Ficus wightiana Wall.

Urostigma wightiana Miq.

Ficus infectoria var. *wightiana* King

Tree 6-12 meters high, 25 cm in diameter; all parts glabrous; bark rugose verically, pale brown or blackish; leaves alternate, petiolate, membraneous, sub-coriaceous, elliptic or oblong, 8-12 cm long, 4-6 cm wide, acute at apex, cuneate, 3-nerved at base, entire, slightly undulate, recurved at margin; lateral veins 6-8 pairs, prominent beneath; petioles 4-6 cm long; stipules fugaceous, membraneous, lanceolate with acute apex, convolute, 2 cm long; receptacle solitary, in pairs, or in 4's or more, axillary, or couliflorous globose, sometimes slightly adpressed, often more or less oblique, umbilicus rather prominent; apex acute, tapering at base; smooth, basal bracts 3, ovate-rotundate, with obtuse apex, 1-1.5 cm across; peduncles thick and short, 4-8 mm long.

This species is very common in Japan and the south cape of Taiwan and is closely related to *Ficus infectoria* Roxb. But easily distinguished by the rather small leaves and by the larger receptacles.

Distribution: Kwangtung, Hainan, Hongkong and Chekiang, at altitude of 100-1000 meters.

Family 24. Urticaceae Wedd.

(See orig. text pages 447-448)

us (1) **Debregeasia** Gaudich. (See orig. text page 448)

Debregeasia edulis (S. et Zucc.) Wedd. (See orig. text page 448)

Debregeasia longifolia Wedd. (See orig. text page 448)

Debregeasia obovata Wright (See orig. text page 449)

Debregeasia salicifolia (Roxb.) Rendle

Small shrub with reddish brown bark; branchlets slender, bluish green, hairy; leaves oblong lanceolate, 12-18 cm long 2-4 cm wide, acuminate apex, 3-nerved and cuneate at base, finely serrate, dark green above, whitish pale green below, bluish hairy on both surfaces, coriaceous; petioles 5-10 mm long, hairy; fruits fleshy drupe, pedunculate, yellow to orange juicy.

Distribution: Yunnan, at altitude 2200 meters.

Debregeasia squamata King

Debregeasia spiculifera Merr.

Shrub, 1-2 m high, with long spine-like spicules, 2-3 mm long; leaves obovate or rounded, 6-7 cm long, 5-6 cm wide, acute to acuminate at apex, dentate-serrate at margin, dark green, rough, hairy above, pale green, 3-nerved bluish green below, chartaceous; petioles 5-10 cm long, very slender, pubescent; flowers white, shad

to pale-rose color; fruits drupes, in pairs, forming a raceme on terminal pedunc

brownish, pubescent; pedicels slender, 1 cm long, glabrous.

Distribution: Yunnan, and Hainan, at altitude 900-1300 m.

Order XIII Ranunculales
(See orig. text page 449)

Family 25. Trochodendraceae Prantl.
(See orig. text pages 449-450)

Genus (1) Euptelea Sieb. et Zucc. (See orig. text page 450)

1. **Euptelea pleiosperma** Hooker et Thoms. (See orig. text pages 451-453)

Genus (2) Trochodendron Sieb. et Zucc.

Evergreen tree; terminal bud large, pointed, with imbricate scales: leaves altern

and clustered, long petioled, crenate; flowers perfect, without perianth, intermi

upright racemes; stamens numerous, spreading, with long filaments, carpels 5-10, i

whorl, inserted on a fleshy torus; stigma short, linear, spreading; ovules many; fru

consisting of 5-10 follicles, partly immersed in the torus and dehiscent at the free a

seeds linear, several in each follicle. One species in Eastern Asia.

1. **Trochodendron aralioides** Sieb. et Zucc.

Tree 20 meters tall, with spreading branches, glabrous; bark reddish brown; bra

chlets thick, stout; leaves rhomboidal-obovate to elliptic-lanceolate, 8-15 cm lo

obtusely acuminate, cuneate at base, crenate-serrate, dark lustrous green above, pa

beneath, coriaceous; petioles 3-7 cm long; flowers 1.5 cm across, bright green,

slender pedicels, 1.5-3 cm long, forming racemes 6-8 cm long; fruits brown, 1.52

across, terminal on branchlets; pedicels 4-6 cm long, brownish pubescent.

Distribution: Taiwan, at altitude 1,500m - 2,350m.

Family 26. Cercidiphyllaceae Van Tiegh.
(See orig. text page 453)

Genus (1) Cercidiphyllum Sieb. et Zucc. (See orig. text page 453)

Var. 1. **C. japonicum** Sieb. et Zucc var. **sinense** Rehder et Wilson (See or
text pages 453-454)

Family 27. Lardizabalaceae Lindl.
(See orig. text page 456)

Genus (1) Akebia Decne. (See orig. text page 456)

Deciduous or half evergreen twining shrubs, glabrous; bud with many imbric

glabrous scales; leaves palmately compound, long petioled, digitate; leaflets 3-5,

alked, emarginate at apex; flowers monoecious, in axillary racemes, the pistillate at

base, the staminate ones smaller, at the end of the racemes; sepals 3; stamens 6, w sub-sessile anthers; carpels 3-12, developing into ovoid-oblong fleshy pods opening along the ventral sature, with numerous black seeds in several rows. Two or three species in Eastern Asia.

4. Akebia micrantha Nakai

Climbing shrub with 5-foliated, digitate, petiolate leaves; leaflets oblong, obovate-oblong, broadly elliptic, 15-38 mm long, 7-20 mm wide, cuneate at base, obtuse and emarginate at apex; inflorescences in racemes; peduncle 30-40 to 70-80 mm long; pedicels 5-6 mm long; sepals 4 mm long, 3 mm wide, purplish; stamens 6, sub-sessile; anthers 2 mm long incurved.

Distribution: Chekiang.

2. Akebia quinata Decaisne

Woody vine climbing on trees, with 5-foliated leaflets, obovoid 3 cm long and broad; flowers deep red; fruit a large follicle 8 cm long, 3 cm broad, sweet, edible.

Distribution: Taiwan, Kiangsu, Anhwei, Hupeh and Szechuan.

Var. 1. Akebia quinata var. **longiracemosa** Mats.

A climber; leave 5-foliated; racemes with extremely long peduncles (15-15 cm). Occurring in Taiwan and Hunan.

3. Akebia trifoliata Koidz.

Akebia lobata Decaisne

A large glabrous climbing shrub; branches terete; bark brown, curved, lenticels scattered; buds covered with oblong-obtuse green and purple herbaceous, deciduous scales; leaves long petiolate, trifoliate, leaflets 10-15 cm long, 6-9 cm wide; flowers membraceous, crowded, pale purple; sepals ovate-acute, incurved; anther 6, sub-sessile; fruits 9 cm long, oblong cylindric, slightly curved, rounded at both ends; seeds few or many, black.

Distribution: Kwangsi, Hunan, Szechuan, Hupeh, Anhwei, Honan, Shansi, Chekiang, Kiangsi and Kweichow, at altitude 1300-2000 meters.

Var. 1. Akebia trifoliata var. **australis** (Diels) Rehd.

Large climber widely distributed over more or less lower elevation; appearing similar to Akebia quinata.

Distribution: Kwangtung, Yunnan, Kweichow, Hupeh, Szechunan Hunan and Kiangsi, at altitude 1000-1500 m.

enus (2) Decaisnea Hooker et Thoms. (See orig. text page 456)

1. Decaisnea fargesii Franchet (See orig. text pages 456-457)

enus (3) Holboellia Wall.

Evergreen twining shrubs, glabrous; leaves palmately compound, long petioled, digitate; leaflets 3-9, entire, stalked; flowers monoecious, in few flowered axillary racemes; sepals 6, petaloid, obtuish, fleshy; nectaries 6, small; staminate flowers with 6 free stamens and a rudimentary ovary; pistillate flowers with small staminodes and 3 carpels developing into indehiscent fleshy pods, with numerous black seeds in several rows. 5 species in China and Himalaya regions.

1. **Holboellia angustifolia** Wall.

Climbers 5-6 meters long; bark gray, smooth; leaves 3-foliated; leaflets lanceolate, 8-10 cm long, 2-3 cm wide, acute **apex**, cuneate or rounded and 3-nerved at base, inequilateral above the middle, entire, recurved at margin, thick coriaceous, dark green above, pale green and slightly pubescent beneath; petioles 5-6 cm long, petiolules 1-2 cm long, glabrous; inflorescencesin racemes of 3-flower each, axillary of the leaves, pedicellate; pedicels slender, 2-3 cm long, pubescent.

Distribution: Fukien.

2. **Holboellia coricea** Diels

Climbers 3-5 m long; leaflets in threes; female flower purple, male flowers white; fruits purple, somewhat tuberculate, rounded; 4.5-6 cm long, 2 cm broad; seeds apiculate, jet black, compressed, 4-5 mm high, 5-6 mm long, the inner pulp of the fruit white, watery, and sweet.

This species is closely related to *H. latifolia* Wall. but easily distinguished by its constant 3-foliated, more coriaceous less conspicuous veined leaves, by the larger peduncles and pedicels to the pistillate inflorescences, by filament as long as or lightly longer than the anthers and by the smaller seeds.

Distribution: Szechuan, Hupeh, Hunan and Anhwei; at altitude 600-1300 m.

3. **Holboellia fargesii** Reauburg

Stauntonia longipes Hemsl.

Climbers 3-6 m long; male flowers greenish white, female flowers purplish; leaves 3-9-foliated, leaflets 3.5-12 cm long; peduncles and pedicel 2-6 cm long and that of the female flowers 4-15 cm long, flower-parts of females flowers larger; fruits oblong, 7-9 cm long, rounded, tipped with a short point; seed somewhat verruculous, jet black, 4-5 mm high.

This species is closely related to *H. angustifolia* Wall. It is easily distinguished by its relatively thin leaves with prominent reticulations, much shorter peduncle and pedicles, different shaped sepals and by a somewhat different floral structure.

Distribution: Kwangtung, Yunnan, Szechuan, Hupeh and Fukien, at altitude 1300-2000 m.

4. **Holboellia grandiflora** Reauburg

Climbers 5-6 m long; bark gray, smooth; leaves 3-5-7-foliated; flowers white, fragrant; fruits 8-12 cm long, purple, edible.

This species is distinginshed by its large (3 cm long) flowers and by the strongly reticulated veins of the leaves, which are broadest above the middle and narrowed toward the ends.

Distribution: Hupeh and Szechuan, at altitude 1300-1600 m.

5. **Holboellia latifolia** Wall.

Climbers 3-4 m long; male flowers white, pistillate flowers purple; leaflet oblong-lanceolate, 14–16 cm long, 4–6 cm wide, broadest above the middle, narrowed, cuneate at base, mucronate–acute apice, entire, lustrous, dark green above, pale green, prominently reticulated and brownish pubescent along the midrib beneath; petioles 16 cm long and petiolules 2–3 cm long, glabrous; fruits pod–like fleshy follicle, 6–10 cm long , 2–3 cm broad; seed many, black, edible.

Distribution: Szechuan and Yunnan, at altitude 1600–2300 m.

Genus (4) Sinofranchetia Hemsley

Deciduous twinging shrub; terminal buds large, with 9 imbricate, mucronate glabrous outer scales; leaves palmately compound, long stalked; 3–foliated, lateral leaflets shortly stalked, oblique; flowers unisexual, probably dioecious, short pedicelled in long branchless racemes; sepals 6; carpels 3, developing into ellipsoid many–seeded berries, nectaries 6; stamens 6 free; seeds ovoid compressed. A meonotypic genus endemic to China.

1. **Sinofranchetia chinensis** Hemsl.

Holboellia cuneata Olv.

Parvatia chinensis Fr.

Holboellia chinensis Diels

A deciduous climber with inconspicuous whitish to chacolate white flowers and lavender purple colored fruit; leaflets large, 3–foliated, dark green above, glausecent beneath, with yellowish veins and darker veinlets, subchartaceous, the terminal leaflet rhomboidal–obovate to broad obovate, cuneate at base, on a stalk 2–3 cm long,the lateral ones oblique–ovate, 7–11 cm long, very oblique at base, nearly rounded; racemes with peduncle 10–30 cm long; flowers 5–6 mm across, white; seeds 5–6 mm broad, black.

Distribution: Hupeh and Szechuan, at altitude 2600–2800 m.

Genus (5) Stauntonia DeCandolle

Large woody climber; branches and branchlets winged; fruit pedicels usually paired; flowers perfect; sepales 6, arranged in two whorls, 3 larger ones outside and 3 smaller ones inside; flowers monoecious, axillary, in long racemes; filaments free, connate at base; leaves palmately compound leaflets 3–9, elliptic–ovate, obvate, oblong lanceolate, petiolate; peduncles usually long.

1. **Stauntonia alata** Merr.

A large climber with winged branchlets; leaves 3–foliated; leaflets elliptic–oblong–lanceolate, 6–8 cm long, 3–4 cm wide, acute apex, cordate sub–rounded at base, entire margin, dark green above, brownish green below, thick coriaceous; petioles 5 mm long; sepals 6, the 3 external ones ovate lanceolate, acuminate, the 3 internal ones smaller; petales 6–7 mm long in female flowers, 2.5 mm long in male flowers, linear lanceolate, acuminate; filaments 3–4 mm long, the base connected.

Distribution: Kwangtung and Kwangsi.

2. **Stauntonia brachyanthera** Hand.–Mazz.

Scandens climber; leaves 3–5–7–9–foliated; leaflets elliptic–lanceolate, 10–22 cm long,

3-5 cm wide, long attenuate, acuminate at apex, cuneate at base, broadest above the middle, entire, dark green glabrous above, pale green, with prominent reticulation and pubescent along the midrib and veins beneath; petioles 2-5 cm long, slender, yellowish pubescent; flowers in axillary long racemes.

Distribution: Szechuan.

3. **Stauntonia cavaleriana** Gagnep.

A large liana climbing on trees; stem 1-2 cm thick, glabrous; leaves 7-9-foliated; fruits subglobose, 6 cm long, 5 cm broad; seeds many, black, arranged in several rows; fruit solitary, on long peduncles.

Distribution: Kwangsi and Kweichow, at altitude 1700 meters.

4. **Stauntonia chinensis** De Candolle

A large climber; 7-foliated; leaflets oblong-lanceolate, acuminate at apex, obtuse at base; sepals 6 arranged in two whorls, outer 3 larger, inner 3 smaller; flowers white, fragrant; anthers long, connected below; filament free, cylindric, united at base.

Distribution: Kwangtung, Kwangsi, Hainan and Hongkong, at altitude of 2600 m.

5. **Stauntonia hebandra** Hayata

A climbing shrub, 3 meters long; 5-foliated; leaflets elliptic-obovate, 9 cm long, 5.5 cm broad, rotundate at base and apex; sepals 6, arranged in two series ovate-lanceolate, 10 mm long, 3.5 mm wide, obtuse; flowers white.

Distribution: Taiwan, at altitude 2200 meters.

Family 28. Magnoliaceae St. Hill.

(See orig. text pages 457-458)

Genus (1) Magnolia Linn. (See orig. text page 459)

1. **Magnolia amoena** Cheng

Tree 8-12 m high; leaves deciduous, membraneous, oblanceolate, lanceolate- oblong, long acuminate at apex, cuneate, rounded, slightly oblique at base, 10-15 cm long, 3.5-5 cm wide, glabrous on both surfaces, pilose along the midrib beneath; petioles 8-13 mm long, glabrous; flowers cup-shaped, 6 cm in diameters, very fragrant; pedicels 4.5 mm long; petals 9, similar, oblong lanceolate, subspathulate, apex acute or rotundate, 5-5.5 cm long, 1.5-1.8 cm wide, rose colored; stamens numerous, 9-10 mm long; filaments 3.5 -4 mm long; carpels numerous; stigma 1 mm long; aggregate fruits cylindrical, 4-6 cm long, 9-12 mm in diameter.

Distribution: Chekiang Tien Mo Shan, at altitude 700-1000 m.

2. **Magnolia biondii** Pamp. (See orig. text pages 459-460)
3. **Magnolia campellii** Hook. f. et Thoms. (See orig. text page 460)
4. **Magnolia cylindrica** Wilson (See orig. text pages 460-461)
5. **Magnolia dawsoniana** Rehd. et Wilson (See orig. text page 461)
6. **Magnolia duclouxii** Hu

Glabrous small tree, branches annulate at the apex; leaves lanceolate to lanceolate-obovate, tapering at the base, acuminate at the apex, glabrous, coriaceous, pale below, 13 cm long, 3.5–4 cm broad; petioles subterete, grooved above, 10–12 mm long; sepals fleshy, granulate when dry, 3 cm long, 1.5–2 cm broad; petals purple to rose, obovate, clawed, 2.5–3 cm long, 1.5 cm broad; claw thickened and transversely striate at the base; stamens numerous, mucronate, 10–12 mm long, mucro 2 mm long; filaments broad, short, connective, thick, produced at the apex into triangular appendages; gynophore villose, sessile, 2.3 cm long; gynaecium ovate, 1.5 cm long, 7 mm broad; carpels fusiform, hirsute, tapering into style at the apex, 7–8 mm long; style glabrous, 2–3 mm long; ovules 2–5 seriate.

Distribution: Yunnan.

7. **Magnolia delavayi** Franch. (See orig. text pages 461–462)

8. **Magnolia denudata** Desrouss (See orig. text pages 462–463)

      Var. 1. **M. denudata** var. **elongata**

      Var. 2. **M. denudata** var. **purpurascens** (See orig. text page 464)

9. **Magnolia fordiana** Oliv.

     Manglietia fordiana Oliv.

Tree 8–10 m tall, glabrous; leaves lanceolate, oblanceolate, 10–14 cm long, 2.5–3 cm wide, acute or obtuse at apex, cuneate at base, entire margin, very thick, coriaceous; petioles long, 2–3 cm long, stout, glabrous; flowers solitary, terminal, pedunculate; sepals and petals elliptic, obtuse at apex, concave; carpel 24–300; aggregate fruit ovoid, capitate.

Distribution: Hongkong, Fukien, Kiangsi, Chekiang and Anhwei.

10. **Magnolia globosa** Hook. f. et Thoms.

     Magnolia tsarongensis Sm.

     Magnolia globosa var. *sinensis* Rehd. et Wils.

Shrub or a small tree; branchlets at first rufous-hairy; leaves deciduous; stipules to a greater part of the petiole, rufous-hairy outside; petioles up to 9 cm long, but usually shorter, rufous-hairy especially when young; lamina ovate or broadly elliptic to elliptic-oblong, cordate to rounded or sometimes obtuse at the base, obtuse to acute or occasionally rounded at the apex and often more or less mucronate, up to about 26 cm long, 14 cm broad, glabrous above or at first rufous-hairy along the midrib, somewhat glaucescent beneath and densely rufous-to grayish-hairy on the midrib and more or less densely so elsewhere when young, particulary on the lateral veins; lateral veins 9–16 pairs, conspicuous beneath; flowers fragrant, appearing after the leaves; bud enclosed in a single spathaceous bract inserted at an interval below the flower, glabrous or rufous-hairy outside towards the base; peduncles straight or almost so, 3–6 cm long, rufous-hairy; sepals 9–12, 3-merous, similar, glabrous, white or creamy-white, outer 3 obovate or elliptic to obovate-oblong, 4–7 cm long; stamens 12–17 mm long, purple red; anthers obtuse often retuse at the apex, introrsely dehiscent; carpels numerous, glabrous; aggregate fruit 3.5–7 cm long.

158

Distribution: Eastern Himalaya to South-Eastern Tibet and Northwest extreme of
Yunnan, at altitude 2300–3400 m.

11. **Magnolia henryi** Dunn   (See orig. text pages 464–465)

12. **Magnolia liliflora** Desr. (See orig. text page 465)

13. **Magnolia mollicomata** Sm. (See orig. text pages 465–467)

14. **Magnolia nicholsoniana** R. et W. (See orig. text page 467)

15. **Magnolia nidita** Sm. (See orig. text pages 467–468)

16. **Magnolia obovata** Thunb.

Magnolia hypoleuca S. et Z.

A large tree 17–30 meters high, trunk 1 m in diameter; branches widely spreading, long silky-hairy on young growth; bark smooth, brown, with conspicuous lenticels; leaves deciduous, usually crowded at the ends of the branchlets, shortly petioled, obovate to elliptic-obovate, frequently 24–40 cm long, glaucous green below, more or less pilose apex, rounded, or more rarely shortly cuspidate, cuneate or rounded at base; lateral veins 18–24 pairs; flowers creamy-white, fragrant, 18–24 cm in diameter; sepals and petals obovate-spathulate, leathery, rounded, or slightly cuspidate; filaments bright-reddish-purple; aggregate fruits cone-like, ellipsoid, 15–24 cm long, erect, red when matured; carpels more than a hundred, truncate.

Distribution: Kiangsu and Japan.

17. **Magnolia officinalis** R. et W. (See orig. text page 468)

Var. 1. M. officinalis R. et W. Var. *biloba* R. et W. (See orig. text pages 468–469)

18. **Magnolia paenetalauma** Dandy

Small tree; 3 meters tall; bark reddish brown; branchlets slender; flowers creamy-white or white, terminal, 5 cm broad, fragrant; leaves elliptic-lanceolate, 16–24 cm long, 3–5 cm wide, acuminate apex, cuneate-acute at base, entire and incurved margin, thick coriaceous, lustrous dark green, pale green below, brownish pubescent along the midrib on lower surface; petioles 1 cm long, brownish rugose; aggregate fruits puberulouse, dehiscent; seeds red with funicles.

Distribution: Hainan at altitude 500–1400 m.

19. **Magnolia parviflora** Sieb. et Zucc.

Magnolia sieboldii Sieb. et Zucc. (See orig. text page 469)

20. **Magnolia rostrata** W. W. Sm. (See orig. text pages 469–470)

21. **Magnolia sargentiana** Rehd. et Wilson

Var. 1. M. sargentiana var. **robusta** R. W. (See orig. text page 472)

22. **Magnolia sinensis** (R. et W.) Stapf

23. **Magnolia sprengerii** Pampanini   (See orig. text pages 472–473)

24. **Magnolia taliensis** W. W. Smith

Shrub or tree 3–7 m tall; flowers creamy color; branchlets rufous-pilose; leaves broadly oblong, 4–9 cm long, 2–4 cm wide, obtuse to subobtuse apex, subrotundate at base, membraneous, sparsely rufo-pilose; peduncles 5–15 mm long, uniflora, rufo-pilose; flowers 8-9 cm in diameter; sepals 3, ovate obtuse, 3 cm long; petals 6, ovate-oblong, 4 cm long; stamens numerous; anthers 8 mm long; filaments 2 mm long; carpels glabrous, rostrate, 2-ovulate.

Distribution: Yunnan, Dail, at altitude 2300-2800 m.

25. **Magnolia wilsonii** Rehder (See orig. text page 473)

26. **Magnolia zenii** Cheng

Tree 5-7 meters high; branchlets lenticelled, purple; leaves deciduous, membraneous, oblong-obvate to oblong, 7-16 cm long, 3-7 cm wide, abruptly acuminate apex, broadly cuneate or rounded at base, shining glabrous above, pale green, pilose below; flowers fragrant, 12 cm in diameter; pedicels 2-3 mm long, densely pilose; sepals and petals 9, similar, subspathulate, rounded apex, subacute at base, 7-8 cm long, 3-4 cm wide; stamens numerous (60), 11 mm long; filaments 4 mm long; aggregate fruit cylindrical, 5-7 cm long, 1-1.5 cm in diameter.

Distribution: Kiangsu, Pao Hua Shan, at altitude 250-300 m.

27. **Magnolia championii** Benth. (See orig. text page 474)

28. **Magnolia coco** (Lour.) DC.

Genus (2) **Manglietia** Blume (See orig. text page 474-475)

1-10. (See orig. text pages 474-479)

11. **Manglietia wangii** Hu

Tree 8 meters tall; branchlets stout, pubescent, glabrescent when old; leaves thin, coriaceous, elliptic-lanceolate, short acuminate at apex, broadly cuneate and decurrent at base; glabrous, reticulate with stout midrib above, glabrescent with very stout striate midrib and elevated secondary veins and promounced reticulation beneath, to 41 cm long, 14.5 cm broad, secondary veins about 18 pairs, very distant, alternate, divergent at wide angles, curving up and forming loops near the margin; petioles stout, glabrous, striate to 5.5 cm long; flower solitary, white, 10 cm in diameter, on a stout more or less recurved, sparsely villose peduncle 1 cm in diameter; perianth 3-cyeled. 3-merous; petals 9, thick, fleshy, glabrous, outer 3 oblong-ovate, rounded at apex, 6 cm long, 3 cm broad, inner smaller, narrowed at base; stamens numerous, 11 mm long; gynaecium ovoid; carpels numerous, glabrous. Fruit unknown.

This species is allied to *M. Kwangtungensis* Dandy, *M. hainanensis* Dany, and *M. forrestii* W. W. Sm., in the 3-cycled flowers, but differing from all in much larger leaves and glabrescent lower surface of the leaves.

Distribution: South Yunnan, Nan-Chio, mixed forest in ravine.

Genus (3) **Kmeria** (Pierre) Dandy

1. **Kmeria septentrinalis** Dandy (See orig. text pages 479-480)

Genus (4) **Michelia** Linn. (See orig. text pages 480-481)

1. **Michelia alba** DC. (See orig. text page 481)

2. **Michelia balansae** (A. DC.) Dandy

Tree 6-10 m tall; stems 25 cm in diameter; bark smooth, whitish gray; leaves brownish pubescent below; young fruit fulvous pubescent; leaves oblong-lanceolate, 18 - 22 cm long, 6-8 cm wide, acute apex, cuneate at base, lustrous deep green above, brownish vilose along the midrib and veins beneath; midrib and veins highly elevated densely vilose; veins curving upward and forming loops near the margin, margin entire, very coriaceous and thick; branchlets dark brownish rufous; petioles stout, 3-4 cm long, densely brownish pubescent; buds axillary, densely brownish hairy, subsessile; pedicels thick, stout, cylindrical, densely brownish hairy.

Distribution: Kwangtung and Hainan, at altitude 300-700 meters.

3. **Michelia bodineri** Finet et Gagnep. (See orig. text pages 481-482)

4. **Michelia champaca** Linn.

5. **Michelia chingii** Cheng

Tree 15 m tall; branchlets glabrous, sparsely lenticellate; leaves oblong-lanceolate, 16-19 cm long, 5.7-7.7 cm wide, obtuse-acuminate apex, obtuse-acute at base, coriaceous, prominently reticulated beneath, glabrous above, papilloso-glaucescent; lateral veins 12-14 pairs; petioles 2-27 cm long; peduncle glabrous, 18-24 mm long; gynaecium glabrous; carpels numerous, glabrous; sparsely lenticellate aggregate fruit 6.5-8 cm across, dehiscent, sessile.

This species is closely related to *Michelia paypetala* Hand.-Mazz. (*M. fallax* Dandy) from which it differs by its glabrous habit, less reticulated leaves, which are sometimes oblanceolate, by its sparse and inconspicuous lanticels.

Distribution: Chekiang, at altitude 650 m.

6. **Michelia compressa** (Maxim.) Sarg.

Tree up to 11 m tall, 60 cm in diameter; bark smooth, gray; flowers whitsh, fragrant; branchlets slender, gray, smooth; leaves oblanceolate, 10-14 cm long, 2-3 cm wide, obtuse-acute at apex, narrowly cuneate at base, entire margin, thick coriaceous, lustrous dark green above, pale green, slightly pubescent along the midrib and veins below; petioles 1-2 cm long, glabrous; flowers solitary, axillary, white, fragrant, 4 cm in diameter, short pedicelled; pedicels 8 mm long, thick, glabrous.

Distribution: Arisan, Taiwan, at altitude 1360-2370 meters.

7. **Michelia dandyi** Hu

Shrub to 4 m high, covered with adpressed copper-brown indumentum; branchlets tomentulose when young, at last glabrescent; leaves oblanceolate, cuneate or slightly oblique at base, obtuse shortly obtuse-cuspidate at apex, to 8 cm long, 3 cm broad, very coriaceous, upper surface lustrous and glabrous at maturity, lower surface adpressedly copper-brown tomentose when young, glaberscent as aged, both sides densely reticulated; lateral veins 6-10 pairs; petioles 6 mm long; stipules free from the petioles, tomentose outside; flower-bud ovoid, acute; peduncles 5 mm at anthesis, tomentose, 1 cm long; perianth dicyclic, segments 6 subsimilar, white, oblong-lanceolate, glabrous, 2 cm long; stamens 9 mm long, connective, produced into short acute appendix above the anther cells; aggregate fruits apocarpous, including the stipe to 7 cm long; carpels 8-10 to 13 mm long when matured, glabrous, 1–3–seeded.

Distribution: South Yunnan, at altitude 2000 m.

8. **Michelia dolstopa** Buch.–Ham. (See orig. text pages 482–483)

9. **Michelia fallax** Dandy

10. **Michelia figo** (Lour.) Spreng. (See orig. text pages 483–484)

11. **Michelia floribunda** Finet et Gagnep.

12. **Michelia formasana** (Kaneh.) Masamune et Suzuki

Large tree, branchlets smooth and gray; leaves elliptic-lanceolate, acute apex, cuneate at base, entire margin, dark green above, pale green below, thick, glabrous, chartaceous, 8–10 cm long, 2 cm wide; petioles 1.5–2 cm long, glabrous; aggregate fruit solitary, axillary, white, 3–4 cm in diameter, pod–like, dehiscent into 2 parts; pedicels stout, short, 5 mm long, glabrous.

Distribution: Taiwan, An Ma Shan, at altitude 2100–2400 m.

13. **Michelia foveolata** Merr. (See orig. text page 485)

14. **Michelia fulgens** Dandy

Tree 25 m high; leaves ovate lanceolate – oblong, oblong – elliptic, cuneate–obtuse oblique at base, acuminate–acute at apex, coriaceous, thick, pubescent when young ultimately glabrescent, densely tomentose along the reticulated midrib and veins; lateral veins 14–20 pairs, inconspicuous; petioles 3.5 cm long, tomentose; perianth 3–cycled, 3–4–merous; tepals 9–12, sub–similar; ovules numerous (10 more); carpels 2 cm long, dehiscent.

This species is closely related to *M. foveolata* Merr. but best distinguished from each other by the shapes of leaf-bases; in *M. folgens* it is cuneate to obtuse and subsymmetrical, whereas *M. foveolata* has subcordate to rounded base often somewhat oblique.

Distribution: Kwangtung and Hainan, at altitude 1500 meters.

15. **Michelia lanceolata** Wilson

Small tree with robusty branchlets with purplish-brown lenticels and dense rufous villose; leaves lanceolate or oblong-lanceolate, 10–20 cm long or 11–20 cm long, 2.5–5.5 cm broad, acute apex, abruptly rounded cuneate at base, prominently elevated reticulation, sparse villose along the midrib and veins beneath, entire; flowers creamy white, elongated oblong-ovoid, pendiculate; peduncle 1.2–1.5 cm long; bracts densely rufo-brown villose; sepals and petals subequal, 15–18, oblong-spathulate, 3.5–4 cm long, 5 mm wide, rotundate–acute; stamens 1–2 cm long; filaments 2 mm long; anthers acuminate.

A very distinct species being closely related to the Himalayan *M. lanuginosa* Wall. which has broader and larger leaves, and tomentose shoots, leaves and flowers; flowers sessile.

Distribution: Yunnan.

16. **Michelia lanuginosa** Wall. (See orig. text page 485)

17. **Michelia leveilleana** Dandy

A small tree; leaves coriaceous, 15 cm long, 5 cm broad; branchlets fulvo-tomentos
when young and glabrous when adult; petioles black; carpels glabrous, 20-28 cm long
black, long spiked; stamens as long as the carpels.

Distribution: Kweichow.

18. **Michelia maclurei** Dandy (See orig. text page 486)

Var. 1. **Michelia maclurei** var. **sublanea** Dandy

19. **Michelia magnifica** Hu

Tree 15 m tall; 18 cm in diameter; young branches stout, terete, sparsely tawny
pilose, marked by the annular scars of the stipules and with scattered elevated whi
elliptic lenticels; older branchlets striate, tawny gray glabrescent; leaves thin cor
aceous, oblanceolate, acuminate or acute at apex, subcuneate and decurrent at base
slightly revolute along the margins, glabrous on both surfaces, shining green with im
pressed midrib and elevated secondary veins and reticulation above, opaque with sto
midrib and elevated secondary veins and reticulations beneath, to 17 cm long and 6 c
broad; lateral veins 20 pairs, arching and forming loops near the margins, much mor
prominent than the reticulations; stipules lanceolate densely tawny-pilose, 3.5 cm long
petioles channelled above, glabrous, free from the deciduous stipules, 2.5-3 cm long
flowers large, white, paniculate at the apex of the branchlets, with stout pedicels tawny
pilose at the nodes and to 12 mm long; buds at first included in 2 deciduous spatho
bracts tawny-pilosulous outside; tepals 9 in 3-series, obovate-spathulate, clawed, gla
brescent outside, to 6 cm long, 2.5 cm broad on the upper part, innermost 3.5-5 c
long, 1 cm broad; stamens numerous, 23 mm long, mucronate at apex; anthers 20 r
long, filaments 3 mm long, gynophore 2.5 cm long, minutely pilosulose; gynaecium to
mm long, with about 12 lanceolate, glabrous lenticelled carpels to 4 mm long, sty
elongated, recurved; stigmas pilose; ovules 10 in each carpel, biseriate.

This species is closely allied to *M. maudiae* Dunn in the large sized flowers, differi
in the tawny-pilose branchlets, in leaves being not glaucescent and with more promine
secondary veins beneath, in longer stamens and gynophors and gynaecium. *M. foveola*
Merr. and *M. maclurei* Dandy differ from the species in the copper-colored indumentu
and smaller flowers. *M. mediocris* Dandy differs in much smaller leave and flowers.

Distribution: Southwestern Yunnan, at altitude 1550 m.

20. **Michelia manipurensis** Watt.; 21. **M. maudiae** Dunn (See orig. text page 487)

22. **Michelia martini** Dandy; 23. **M. mediocris** Dandy (See orig. text page 488)

24. **Michelia microthricha** Hand.-Mazz.

Tree 3-20 m tall; branchlets glabrous, brownish, lenticellate; leaves lanceolate,
16 cm long, 3-4 cm broad, obtuse-acuminate at apex, cuneate at base, rigid, coriaceou
densely papillosorufo-brown pubescent; lateral veins 8-14 pairs, prominently retic
lated; petioles 2-3 cm long; aggregated fruit solitary, axillary; pedicels 5-8 mm lon
sepals 3.5-3.9 cm long, obtuse-ovate; petals 12, 3.5-4 cm long, obovate-oblong; fil
ments 1-1.5 cm long; anther 6-9 mm long; carpels 25-40 densely spiked.

Distribution: Yunnan.

25. **Michelia platypetala** Hand.-Mazz.

Tree 6 m tall; branchlets gray, smooth; leaves lanceolate, 9-21 cm long, 2.5-3.5 cm broad, rotundate-acuminate at apex, obtuse at base, papilloso-glaucescent below, very coriaceous; lateral veins 8-14 pairs, reticulated beneath; petioles 1.5-2.5 cm long; flowers axillary; sepals ovate, 4 cm long; peduncles 7-10 mm long; petals 9 obovate, elliptic-lanceolate, acute, white; filament 2 mm long;' ovules 8, style 3 mm long, glabrous; follicles lateral, 1-2.5 cm long, rectangular obovate.

Distribution: Hunan, at altitude 950 meters.

26. **Michelia sinensis** Hemsl. et Wils.

A tree, 15 m high; bark pale gray; leaves obovate-oblong or oblanceolate, narrowed into a short petiole, 10-15 cm long, 5 cm broad at the greatest width, abruptly obtusely acuminate, strongly reticulate, glaucous beneath, at length quite glabrous; midrib somewhat tuberculate; petioles rather under 1.5 cm long; stipules caducous, narrowly oblong-acuminate, 3 times the length of the petiole; flowers solitary, axillary, shortly pedunculate, 5-7.5 cm across, ivory-white, strongly aromatic; peduncles stout, 8 mm long, annular, pubescent; bracts covered with brown hairs; sepals and petals 10, spathulate to linear-oblong, rounded or acute; stamens very caducous, 1.2 cm long; filaments shorter than the anthers; anthers mucronate; carpels when young minutely glandular pubescent; stigmas red; fruits 15-20 cm long; carpels woody, subsessile, ovoid, lenticellate, shortly beaked.

Distribution: Western Szechuan, at altitude 1000 m.

27. **Michelia skinneriana** Dunn

Large tree; branchlets glabrous, leaves subsessile, lanceolate, 6-10 cm long, 25-30 mm broad, chartaceous, glabrous, base acute, apex caudate; veins 8-10 pairs, obscured reticulated; flowers axillary, solitary, pedunculate, 6-8 mm long, glabrous, reddish; sepals ovate, 18-20 mm long, glabrous, rotundate at apex; stamens 5-6 mm long; ovary densely pubescent.

Distribution: Hongkong.

28. **Michelia szechuaniana** Dandy (See orig. text page 489)

29. **Michelia tsoi** Dandy

Tree 10 m high; branchlets glabrous with puberous nodes; leaves obovate, 12 cm long, 5.5 cm broad, obtuse-cuneate at base, acuminate-subacuminate at apex, inequilateral, coriaceous; veins 10-15 pairs, conspicuously reticulated; petioles 2 cm long, puberulous when young, glabrous when old, bracts 3-4, deciduous, spathulates; perianth 2-cyclic, 3-merous; tepals 6, tomentose; carpels numerous, free; ovules 6.

This species is closely allied to *M. chapensis* Dandy. It is distingiushed by having however, smaller leaves and broader in shape than *M. chapensis.*

Distribution: Kwangtung.

30. **Michelia wilsonii** Finet et Gagnep. (See orig. text page 489)

31. **Michelia yunnanensis** Franchet

Genus (5) Liriodendron Linn. (See orig. text page 490)

1. **Liriodendron chinense** (Hemsl.) Sargent (See orig. text pages 490–492)

Genus (6) Illicium Linn.

Evergreen aromatic shrubs or small trees; leaves quite entire, pellucid–dotted; flowers bisexual or unisexual, solitary or fascicled, yellow or purplish; sepals 3–6; petals 9 or more, 3–many–seriate; stamens indefinite, filaments thick; anthers adnate, introrse; ovaries indefinite, 1–seriate, 1–ovuled; recurved; fruit of spreading compressed hard follicles; seeds compressed, testa hard, shining; albumen fleshy.

Distribution: North America, China, and Indo–Malaya. Species about 6.

1. **Illicium angustisepalum** A. C. Sm.

Small tree with grayish and brown bark; leaves in clusters in nodes elliptic–lanceolate, 6–10 cm long, 3–4 cm wide, narrowly acute at apex, cuneate at base, entire, recurved along margin, thick coriaceous, glabrous, dark green above, pale green pubescent along the midrib and veins veneath; petioles 1.5–2 cm long; flowers terminal; carpels 12–13.

Distribution: Hongkong.

2. **Illicium arborescens** Hayata

Tree 6–13 m tall; bark gray and rough; leaves subopposite, petiolate, lanceolate or oblanceolate, 8–10 cm long, 2.5 cm broad, acuminate apice, acute at base, chartaceous–coriaceous, finely serrate at margin; petioles 1 cm long; flowers terminal or axillary, solitary; peduncles 1–2 cm long; bracts depressed, 8 mm long, 10 mm wide, cordate; flower 1–1.5 cm in diameter; stamens numerous, 2–seriate, 2–3 mm long; filaments variable in sizes; carpels 10–14, 1–seriate, verticillate, compressed, ovate – caudate apex; fruit brownish red, flattened–radiated head formed by 8–12 dehiscent follicles; peduncles 3–4 cm long, glabrous.

Distribution: Taiwan, at altitude 300–1000 m.

3. **Illicium anisatum** Linn.

Illicium religiosum Linn.

Tree 4–8 m tall; leaves alternate, oblong–lanceolate, oblong, attenuate–obtuse at base, acute–acuminate at apex, thick; petioles 6–10 mm long; flowers axillary, glabrous, sub–sessile; bracts imbricate, deciduous; petals 12, tri–seriate; sepals lanceolate, 10–22 mm long; stamens 18–21, 6–7 – seriate; filaments dilated, connective; carpels connected; follicles green, 8–carpellate, poisonous.

Distribution: Korea, Japan, China, Taiwan, Indo–China, Borneo and India, at altitude 300–1300 meters.

4. **Illicium brevistylum** A. C. Sm.

Tree 12–18 m tall; bark smooth, dark gray; branchlets slender, gray smooth; leaves elliptic–oblong, 8–12 cm long, 3–4 cm wide, acute acuminate at apex and base, entire, thick coriaceous, dark green, glabrous above, pale green, somewhat brownish pubescent along the midrib and veins below; petioles 1.5-2 cm long, brown, glabrous; flowers axillary, solitary, pedicelled; pedicels stout, long, 3-5 cm glabrous; fruit light yellow, edible.

Distribution: Kwangtung, Kwangsi and Hunan.

5. **Illicium henryi** Diels

Bush 2 meters tall; branchlets gray, smooth, glabrous; leaves elliptic-lanceolate, 8 cm long, 2.5 cm wide, acuminate apex, cuneate at base, entire, thick, coriaceous, glabrous on both surfaces; petioles 1-1.5 cm long, grooved above; flowers 1-2 cm in diameter; fruit 1-6, axillary, long pedicelled; pedicels 4 cm long.

Distribution: Hongkong.

Var. 1. **Illicium henryi** var. **multistamineum** A. C. Sm.

This variety is distinguished by having more numerous stamens, occurring in Hongkong.

Var. 2. **Illicium henryi** var. **typicum** Diels

Bush 0.5-2 meters tall; flowers creamy-red, strictly glabrous; leaves oblanceolate, oblong-obovate, acute-acuminate at apex and base; flowers axillary, long peduncled; peduncles minutely bracted; sepals ovate-triangular; petals obtuse-ovate; petioles 1-1.5 cm long; leaves 10-15 cm long, 2-6 cm broad.

Distribution: Hupeh, I-Chang, at altitude 100-700 meters.

6. **Illicium lanceolatum** A. C. Sm.

Evergreen shrub, 5 m tall, 15 cm in diameter; bark brownish gray, smooth; branchlets slender, smooth; leaves oblanceolate, 9 cm long, 2.5 cm wide, acute-acuminate at both ends, entire, glabrous, light green above, pale green below, coriaceous; petioles 1-1.5 cm long; flowers solitary, axillary; pedicels 4-5 cm long, glabrous; perianth greenish; petals purplish red spreading.

Distribution: Fukien, Kiangsu, Kiangsi, Chekiang and Anhwei, at altitude 200-1000 meters.

7. **Illicium philippinense** Merr.

Illicium leucanthum Hayata

Small bush with dark gray bark; branchlets rough, dark gray; leaves oblanceolate, 6-8 cm long, 4 cm wide, acute at apex, cuneate at base, enitre margin, thick, coriaceous, dark green above, pale brownish below, glabrous on both surfaces; petioles 1-2 cm long; fruit solitary, axillary, long peduncled; follicles 8, dehiscent forming a star-like head, brownish red; peduncle 4-6 cm long, glabrous.

Distribution: Taiwan and the Philippines.

8. **Illicium macranthum** A. C. Sm.

Illicium yunnanense Finet et Gagnep.

Tree 4-7 m tall; bark whitish gray, smooth; branchletd slender, whtish gray; leaves elliptic-oblong, 10-12 cm long, 4-6 cm wide, acuminate at apex, cuneate at base, entire, coriaceous; petioles 2-3 cm long, glabrous; flowers axillary and terminal, solitary, in clusters of several, white.

Distribution: Yunnan, at altitude 3000 meters.

9. **Illicium majus** Hook. f. et Thoms.

Illicium griffithii Hook. et Thoms.

Tree 8–12 m tall, 10–30 cm in diameter; bark dark reddish brwon; leaves oblance-late, 12–16 cm long, 4–6 cm wide, acuminate at apex, cuneate at base, entire, thick coriaceous, glabrous above, pubescent along the midrib and veins below; petioles 2 cm long, glabrous; fruit reddish green; follicles 6–8, reddish, dehiscent; peduncle 5–7 cm long, glabrous; flowers light green, fragrant.

Distribution: Kwangtung, Kwangsi, Yunnan, Kweichow, Szechuan and Hunan, altitude 550–1300 meters.

10. **Illicium merrilleanum** A. C. Sm.

Illicium henryi Diels

Small shrub, bark grayish brown; branchlets slender, smooth; leaves oblanceolate, acute-acuminate at apex, cuneate-acute at base, entire, thick, dark green glabrous above, brownish pubescent below; petioles 1–2 cm long, brownish pubescent; flowers axillary, solitary, long pedicelled.

Distribution: Yunnan.

11. **Illicium micranthum** Dunn

Illicium wangii Hu

Small tree 2.5 m high; branchlets slender, flattened, striate, glabrous; leaves small crowed at the apex of the branchlets, thin coriaceous, obovate-lanceolate, elliptic lanceolate, to obovate, short acuminate, cuneate to sub-rounded at base, slightly re-volute and entire along the margins, glabrous, olive green with impressed midrib and slightly elevated secondary veins above, paler glabrous except with sparse and scattered long hairs along the prominent midrib and along the impressed secondary veins beneath to 5 cm long, 1.5 cm broad, sometimes to 1.5 cm long, 7 mm broad; petioles channelled above, glabrous, to 5 mm long; flowers very small, solitary, axillary, with glabrous pedicels, 5 mm long; sepals 5 unequal, suborbicular, acute, ciliate along the margin, puberulous outside, to 6.5 mm long and broad; inner petals thicker, unequal, elliptic oblong or lanceolate acute, 2.5 mm long, 1.5–3 mm broad; stamens 12, 1-seriate, 4 mm long; filaments glabrous; carpels 8, 2 mm long, glabrous; fruit unknown.

This species differs from all the others in the very small leaves and flowers.

Distribution: Southestern Yunnan, at altitude 1520 m.

12. **Illicium modestum** A. C. Sm.

Small bush 3 m tall, 8 cm in diameter; bark dark gray, rough; leaves elliptic lanceolate, 5 cm long, 2.5 cm wide, acute-acuminate at both ends, dark green above brownish pubescent below; petioles 5 mm long; flowers solitary, axillary, greenish-white 2 cm across; peduncles 3 cm long, glabrous; fruit green, 8-carpellate.

Distribution: Yunnan.

3. **Illicium oligandrum** Merr. et Chun

Tree 8–10 m tall, 24 cm in diameter, grayish brown; leaves obtuse in terminal verticels of 4 or 5 each, oblong, oblong–elliptic, 4–8 cm long, 1.5–3 cm wide, obtuse at apex, cuneate at base, entire incurved margin, dark green above, brownish pubescent below, thick; petioles 1 cm long; flowers greenish yellow, solitary, axillary; peduncles 2–3 cm long; fruit 8–carpellate, dehiscent follicles.

Distribution: Hainan.

4. **Illicium pachyphyllum** A. C. Sm.

Shrub 3 m tall; flowers purplish red, fragrant; leaves lanceolate, 8 cm long, 2 cm wide; acute apex, acuminate at base, entire incurved margin, coriaceous, brownish pubescent below; petioles 5–10 mm long; flowers shortly pedicelled or sub-sessile; fruit dry dehiscent follicle, edible.

Distribution: Kwangsi, Yao Chan

5. **Illicium tashiroi** Maxim.

 Illicium randaiense Hayata

 Illicium leucanthum Hatata

Small shrub, 1–2 m tall; bark dark gray, smooth; leaves elliptic, 5–6 cm long, 3–4 cm wide, acute at both ends; petioles 1 cm long, glabrous; flowers subsessile, axillary.

Distribution: Taiwan.

6. **Illicium simmonii** Maxim.

 Illicium griffthii K. et Thoms.

Small tree 8 m tall; bark reddish brown; branchlets stout, reddish pubescent; leaves aromatic, oblanceolate, unequal, acute apex, cuneate at base, somewhat undulate along margin, thick coriaceous, dark green above, pale green below; petioles thick, 1–2 cm long; flowers axillary, yellow, fragrant.

Distribution: Yunnan, at altitude 2800–3300 meters.

7. **Illicium ternstroemioides** A. C. Sm.

Tree 9 m tall; bark dark gray; leaves oblanceolate, 9–12 cm long, 4–5 cm wide, acute apex, cuneate at base, thick, glabrous, light green, brownish pubescent below; petioles flattened, 2 cm long; flowers solitary, axillary; fruit 8–valved follicle, reddish brown; peduncle 3–4 cm long, brown.

Distribution: Hainan.

8. **Illicium tsangii** A. C. Sm.

A swampy bush, 3 m tall; bark reddish brown, rugose; leaves elliptic–oblong, 8–10 cm long, 3–3.4 cm wide, acute–acuminate at apex, cuneate–acute at base, entire revolute at margin, thick, lustrous dark green above, pale green below, glabrous on both surfaces; petioles 1–1.5 cm long, glabrous; flowers purplish red, solitary, axillary, fragrant.

Distribution: Kwangtung and Kwangsi, at altitude 100–1600 m.

9. **Illicium verum** Hook. f.

Tree 3–10 m tall; branchlets brownish tomentose; leaves elliptic-lanceolate, oblong, lanceolate, obtuse-acuminate at both ends, entire, thick, glabrous; petioles fleshy, flattened, 1 cm long, glabrous; flowers lavender, fragrant; fruit 8-carpellate follicle solitary, axillary, edible; pedicels 3–5 cm long, brownish yellow.

This is the true Anise of China, the spieces being produced from this species. It closely related to *Illicium anisatum* Linn. and the characteristics are more like it.

Distribution: Kwangtung and Kwangsi, at altitude 1500 meters.

Genus (7) Tetracentron Oliv. (See orig. text page 493)

1. **Tetracentron sinense** Oliv. (See orig. text pages 493–494)

Family 29. Calycanthaceae Lindl.
(See orig. text page495)

Genus (1) Chimonanthus Lindl.

Meratia Loisel (See orig. text page 495)

1. **Chimonanthus praecox** (L.) Rehd. et Wilson (See orig. text page 495)

Var. 1. **C. praecox** (L.) Rehd. et Wilson var. **grandiflora** R. et W.

2. **Chimonanthus nitens** Rehd. et Wilson (See orig. text page 496)

3. **Chimonanthus salicifolius** Hu

Small shrub, bark purplish red; branchlets slender, purple, lenticellate, smooth, leaves lanceolate, 6–8 cm long, 2 cm wide, acute-acuminate at apex, cuneate at base, entire, thin, dark green above, pale green below, glabrous on both surfaces; petiole 5 mm long; flowers small, axillary, subsessile, solitary, purplish white.

Distribution: Kiangsi, Lu Shan.

4. **Chimonanthus yunnanensis** (W. W. Sm.) Hu

Small shrub 5–10 m high; branchlets angulate, pilosulous to glabrescent; leaves persistent at the time of flowering, opposite, ovate to sub-elliptic, obtuse to sub-obtuse at the apex, rounded at base, entire, coriaceous, bristlered scabrulous above, glabrous except sparsely pilosulous along the ribs and veins beneath, 4–7 cm long, 3–4.5 cm broad; petioles sparsely pilosulous, 5 mm long; flowers axillary, solitary, scarsely peduncled, dull yellow; bracteoles many-seriate, ovate to rounded, minutely pilosulous and ciliate, upper ones gradually larger, up to 5 mm long; sepals 2-seriate outer rounded, about 7 mm long, inner elliptic, obtuse, 10–12 mm long; petals broad ovate to sub-orbicular, about 5 mm long, with claws about 1 mm long; fertile stamens 5; fruit unknown.

Distribution: Yunnan.

Family 30. Lauraceae Lindley
(See orig. text page 496)

Keys to the sub-family of lauraceae (See orig. text page 497)

Genus (1) **Cinnamomum** Blume (See orig. text page 498)

1. **Cinnamomum applianum** Schowe. (See orig. text page 498)

    Var. 1. Cinnamomum applianum var. **tripartitium** Yang

        Tree 7 meters tall. It resembles the type typical form of the species in appearance but differs in its large petiole, longer panicles and oblong-ovate perianth lobes (broadly obovate in type), of which the inner side is densely coverd with long hairs, and in its 3-lobed stigma (cap-like in type). It may be a distinct species, without seeing the fruit it is temporary placed here.

2. **Cinnamomum bodineri** Levl.

    Tree 15-16 m high, 80 cm in diametel; leaves alternate, ovate elliptic-ovate, acuminate apex, acute-rotundate at base, glaucous pubescent beneath, dark green above, pale green below, 8-17 cm long, 3-10 cm wide; veins 4-6 pairs; petioles 2-3 cm long; panicles 10-15 cm long, terminal; racemes di-tri-chotomous; pedicels small, 2-4 mm long; drupe globose, 7-8 mm in diameter.

    Distribution: W. Hupeh, at altitude 300-1000 meters.

3. **Cinnamomum baurmannii** Blume (See orig. text pages 498-499)

    Var. 1. Cinnamomum baurmannii var. **angustifolium** (Hemsl.) Allen

        Small tree with linear leaves, linear-lanceolate, 13-14 cm long, 1.5 cm wide, penninervous; petioles 1 cm long, glabrous; panicles axillary, 5-9 cm long; pedicels 10-12 cm long; perianth 6, bi-seriate; fertile stamens 6, non-glandulous; stamino-filaments 3, triangular, stipitate; stigma peltate.

        Distribution: Kweichow and Hupeh.

4. **Cinnamomum camphora** (L.) Sieb.

    Var. 1. Cinnamomum camphora var. **glaucescens** (A. Br.) Liu et Liao

        Cinnamomum nominale Hayata

        Cinnamomum camphoroides Hay.

        Cinnamomum camphora var. *nominale* (Hay.) Kamikoti

        This variety is very near to the typical one of the species except that the leaves are more rounded, longer acuminate at apex, cuneate at base, more glaucescens beneath.

        Distribution: Fukien, Taiwan, Chekiang, Hunan, and Kwangtung.

5. **Cinnamomum caryophyllus** (Lour.) Moose

    Tree 6. m tall; bark gray; leaves obovate, 5-7 cm long, 4-5 cm wide, acute at apex, rounded and 3-nerved at base, revolute at margin, lustrous deep green above, glaucous beneath, coriaceous; petiole 5 mm long; flowers greenish yellow.

    Distribution: Taiwan.

6. **Cinnamomum cassia** Blume (See orig. text page 500)

7. **Cinnamomum chinensis** N. et E.

This species is closely related to *Cinnamomum camphora*. It differs in leaves being 6 cm long and 2.5 cm wide, the lateral veins 4–6 pairs, sub-opposite instead of 3-nerved, in acute base and acuminate apex, and in branchlets more terete, and more pubescent.

Distribution: Central China provinces.

8. **Cinnamomum chingii** Metcalf (See orig. text page 501)

9. **Cinnamomum granduliferum** Meissn.

10. **Cinnamomum ilicioides** A. Chevalier

Tree 20 m tall, 45 cm in diameter, with large rounded crown; bark grayish deeply fissured; branchlets dark gray; leaves obovate, elliptic-oblong, 6 cm long, 5.5 cm wide, acute apex, cuneate at base, sub-3-nerved or sub-opposite primary veins, incurved at margin, coriaceous; lustrous dark green above, light green below; petioles 1.5–2 cm long; fruit deep purple, ellipsoid, 1/3 enclosed by a cup-like green perianth tube.

Distribution: Hainan, at altitude 700 meters.

11. **Cinnamomum hupehanum** Gamble   (See orig. text page 502)

12. **Cinnamomum iners** Rainwardt (See orig. text pages 502–504)

13. **Cinnamomum insulari-montanum** Hayata (See orig. text page 504)

Cinnamomum acuminatifolium Hayata

C. macrostemon Hay. var. *pseudo-loureirii* (Hay.) Yam.

C. pseudo-loureirii Hay.

Tree; leaves oblanceolate, 5–6 cm long, 1.5–2.5 cm wide, acute-acuminate at apex, narrow cuneate at base, entire, membraneous, lustrous yellow brown above, purple brown beneath, glabrous on both sides, 3-nerved and sub-opposite; petioles 5–8 cm long.

Distribution: Taiwan.

14. **Cinnamomum inunctum** Meissn.

Var. 1. **Cinnamomum inunctum** var. **alboericeum** Gamble

Var. 2. **Cinnamomum inunctum** var. **longe paniculatum** Gamble

15. **Cinnamomum jenserianum** Handel-Mazz. (See orig. text page 506)

16. **Cinnamomum kotoensis** Kaneh.

Tree with whitish gray bark; branchlets terete glabrous; leaves subopposite, coriaceous, ovate or ovate-oblong, 10–14 cm long, 6–9 cm wide, obtuse apex, round at base, glabrous, shining green above, pallid beneath, distinctly 3-nerved; veins prominently elevated on both surfaces; petioles 1.5 cm long; cymes terminal, 23 cm long, stout, few-flowered; perianth cyathiform; drupe ellipsoid, 10 mm in diameter, 14 mm long; pedicels 10 mm long.

This species is characterized by its large ovate leaves and ellipsoidal drupes.

Distribution: Botel Tobago, Taiwan.

17. **Cinnamomum kwangtungense** Merr.

Tree 3 m tall; branchlets terete, glabrous; leaves elliptic oblong, 9 cm long, 3–4 cm wide, acute-acuminate at apex, obtuse at base, distinctly 3-nerved, incurved along margin, lustrous dark green above, brownish red pubescent beneath; midrib and 2 lateral primary veins thick; leaves coriaceous petioles thick, stout, 1–2 cm long, dark purple; inflorescences racemose, sub–axillary, few–flowred, flowers brownish green.

Distribution: Kwangtung.

18. **Cinnamomum mairei** Levl. (See orig. text page 506)

19. **Cinnamomum japonicum** Sieb.

Cinnamomum macrostemon Hayata

C. pedunculatum Nees

Tree 10–17 m tall; bark smooth, brownish gray; branchlets reddish brown, glabrous, lenticellate; leaves oblanceolate, 8–11 cm long, 3–4 cm wide, entire, incurved margin, distinctly 3–nerved, acute apice, cuneate at base, lustrous dark green above, pale green glabrous beneath; petioles 8 mm long; flowers in axillary racemes, greenish.

Distribution: Taiwan, Tainan.

Var. 1. Cinnamomum japonicum var. **angustifolium** (Hemsl.) Liu

20. **Cinnamomum micranthum** (Hay.) Hay.

Cinnamomum kanehirai Hayata

Tree with slender glabrous branchlets; leaves obovate, elliptic–ovate, 6.5–7.5 cm long, 2.8–3.8 cm wide, acute apex, obtuse, cuneate at base, entire, coriaceous, dark green above, pale green and pubescent below; petioles slender, 1 cm long, dark purple; fruits in terminal panicles.

Distribution: Taiwan, Hsin–Chu Hsien.

21. **Cinnamomum obtusifolium** Kaneh.

Tree 10–15 m tall; branchlets reddish brown, glabrous; leaves oblanceolate, 15 cm long, 6.5 cm wide, distinctly 3–nerved on both surfaces, obtuse at apex, rounded to cuneate at base, incurved entire margin, thick coriaceous, lustrous dark green above, pale green brownish beneath; petioles 1–2 cm long, purplish brown, glabrous; flowers in long spreading panicles, axillary; peduncles 20–25 cm long, glabrous.

Distribution: Hainan and Yunnan.

22. **Cinnamomum osmophloeum** Kaneh.

Tree 10 meters tall, 20 cm in diameter; branchlets very slender; leaves ovate 8.5 – 10.5 cm long, 4–5.5 cm wide, acuminate apex, broadly cuneate at base, entire, coriaceous, lustrous dark green above, brownish gray below, glabrous on both sides, 3–nerved but in opposite arrangement; petioles 1 cm long, brownish yellow.

Distribution: Taiwan.

23. **Cinnamomum parthenoxylon** Meissn. (See orig. text page 507)

24. **Cinnamomum pittosporoides** Hand.–Mazz.

25. **Cinnamomum randaiensis** Hayata

Cinnamomum bartheifolium Hay.

C. longicarpum Kaneh.

Tree 13–15 m tall; brancelets reddish brown; leaves elliptic–lanceolate, 6.5–9 cm long, 1.8–3.5 cm wide, acuminate at apex, cuneate at base, 3–nerved, entire, incurved at margin, lustrous dark green above, pale green, brownish yellow pubescent along the midrib and veins below, coriaceous; petioles 2 mm long; fruits in loose, few–flowered, slender, axillary and sub–terminal racemose panicles.

Distribution: Taiwan, Randai Shan, at altitude 660–2300 m.

26. **Cinnamomum recurvatum** (Roxb.) Wight   (See orgi. text page 508)

27. **Cinnamomum reticulatum** Hayata

Shrub, leaves obovate, 5.5 cm long, 2–3 cm wide, acute or obtuse at apex, cuneate at base, entire margin, 3–nerved, coriaceous; petioles 8 mm long, brownish yellow.

Distribution: Taiwan.

28. **Cinnamomum sancurium** (Hayata) Allen

Tree; branchlets slender, smooth reddish; leaves oblanceolate, 12 cm long, 4 cm wide, attenuate–acuminate at apex, narrowly cuneate at base, 3–nerved, entire, incurved margin, lustrous pale green above, light green and slightly whitish pubescent along the midrib and veins below, coriaceous; petioles 5–8 mm long, red, glabrous.

Distribution: Yunnan, lowland occurring.

29. **Cinnamomum sericeum** Hance

Tree 10 m tall; bark dark reddish brown; branchlets brownish pubescent; leaves oblanceolate, prominently 3–nerved on both surfaces, 24 cm long, 9 cm wide, entire margin, lustrous dark green glabrous above, grayish green, silky pubescent below, coriaceous; petioles short, stout, grayish pubescent; flowers in sub–terminal panicles, grayish pubescent; panicles 16–20 cm long; fruit green.

Distribution: Yunnan.

30. **Cinnamomum szechuanensis** Yang

Small tree 6 m tall; branchlets terete, glabrous; leaves sub–opposite, alternate, elliptic–oblong to elliptic–lanceolate, 10–16 cm long, 2–6 cm wide, long acuminate apex, sub–rounded at base, 3–nerved; petioles 1 cm long; flowers white; perianth lobed, oblong–ovate, 4–6 mm long, pubescent; stamens 9; ovary ovoid, glabrous; perianth truncate.

This species is closely related to *Cinnamomum wislonii* Gamble for both species have truncate perianth and subopposite leaves, and conspicuous hairs on the lower surface. However, *C. szechuanensis*, differs in its veins being impressed on its upper surface, short petiole and pubescent pedicels, glabrous filaments, cordate glands and pubescent peduncles.

Distribution: Szechuan Pa Hsien.

31. **Cinnamomum tamala** Nees et Ebermaier

Shrub; branchlets glabrous; leaves opposite or alternate, coriaceous, acute at the base, ovate–oblong, ellitpic–oblong, or lanceolate–oblong attenuate–acuminate, 3–nerved, shinny green and sparsely and obscurely reticulated beneath, 7.5–16 cm long; panicles axillary or termimal, many–flowered, minutely puberulous; cymose branches 3–5 flowered; calyx equal the length of the pedicels, slightly silky hairy; lobes ovate-obtuse; glabrescent, divided to beyond the middle.

This species is closely related to *C. burmanii* Blume, from which it can not be satisfactorily distinguished.

Distribution: India, Hupeh, Szechuan and Yunnan.

32. Cinnamomum tri-nervatum Yang

Small tree 15 m tall; leaves opposite, coriaceous, ovate to elliptic to elliptic-lanceolate, persistent, 6.5-15 cm long, 3-8.5 cm wide, prominently 3-nerved, acute apex, cuneate at base, entire margin, lustrous dark green above, pale green, densely brownish yellow hairy along the midrib and veins beneath; petioles 1.5-3 cm long; fruit sub-globose, 7 mm in diameters.

Distribution: Kweichow.

33. Cinnamomum tsangii Merr.

Samll tree; branchlets terete, glabrous; leaves opposite or alternate, lanceolate or oblong-lanceolate, 5-8 cm long, 2-4.5 cm wide, acute-acuminate at apex, cuneate rounded, 3-nerved at base, entire, thick coriaceous, lustrous dark green above, pale brownish pubescent along the midrib and veins below; petioles 1-1.5 cm long, dark brown; flowers small, in axillary racemes, yellow, fragrant.

Distribution: Kwangtung and Hunan.

34. Cinnamomum tsoi Allen

Small tree with slender and glabrous branchlets; leaves opposite, oblanceolate, 9 cm long, 3 cm wide, acute-acuminate at apex, entire, prominently 3-nerved, pale green glabrous on the lower surface, petioles 1 cm long, brown; flowers in loose few-flowered racemes, axillary; fruit yellowish green.

Distribution: Hainan.

35. Cinnamomum validineri Hance (See orig. text page 509)

36. Cinnamomum wilsonii Gamble

Var. 1. Cinnamomum wilsonii var. multiflorum Gamble

37. Cinnamomum zeylanicum Nees

Small handsome evergreen tree to 15 m tall; young branchlets slightly quadrangular with grayish outer bark variegated with whitish patches, and cinnamon or dark brown inner bark with strong cinnamon taste and odor, buds silky pubescent; leaves usually opposite, coriaceous, shiny, ovate to ovate-lanceolate, apex acuminate, base acute, 3-5-nerved, conspicuous pitted in the axils of the veins, reticulated, glaucous and glabrous beneath, 8-20 cm long; young foliage pink; inflorescences in silky pubescent panicles as long as the leaves, mostly clustered in the axils of the leaves; flowers in Jauary to March, numerous, small, yellowish, perfect or polygamous, about 6 mm high, grayish hairy on the out side; fruits 10-15 mm long, ovoid, black, dry or slightly fleshy surrounded by the much enlarged perianth cup with acutish lobes.

Distribution: India, Vietnam, Kwangtung, cultivated for the cinnamon bark of commerce.

Genus (2) Machilus Nees (Nan Mu.) (See orig. text page 510)

Key to the Species of Machilus

A. Leaves glabrous beneath; branchlets glabrous.

  B. Fruit oblong, 12 mm long; inflorescence 8 cm long; sepals glabrous ------------------ -- (25) *M. odoratissima*

BB. Fruit globose.

    C. Leaves thickly coriaceous.

      D. Inflorescence axillary or lateral; perianth hairy; leaves gray-green, not gla-
ucous beneath; fruit 1 cm across -------- (38) *M. thunbergii*

     DD. Inflorescence terminal.

       E. Leaves obovate-oblong, or oblong-lanceolate

        F. Leaves 5-8 cm long, slightly glaucous beneath; inflorescence paniculate,
6-10-flowered; perianth segments oblong-lanceolate --------------------
------------------------------ (7) *M. chinensis*

        FF. Leaves 4-5 cm long, narrower, more glaucous; inflorescence almost
umbellate; flowers more numerous; perianth segments ovate to obtuse--
------------------------------ (5) *M. breviflora*

      EE. Leaves oblong, glaucous beneath, 12-18 cm long; inflorescence umbellate-
fascicled, few-flowered ------------ (19) *M. leveinei*

    CC. Leaves papery, oblong lanceolate to lanceolate; inflorescence 3-5.5 cm long; per-
ianth silky pubescent outside ---------------- (14) *M. inchangensis*

AA. Leaves more or less hairy beneath.

  B. Branchlets and leaves densely hairy.

    C. Leaves obovate to obovate-oblong, short aucminate.

      D. Leaves rounded at the base; petioles 7-18 mm long ------------------------
----------------------------------- (10) *M. grijsii*

     DD. Leaves cuneate at the base; petioles 10-25 mm long ------------------------
----------------------------------- *M. hainanensis*

    CC. Leaves elliptic-oblong, 7.5-13 cm long; nerves more numerous; inflorescence
terminal, shorter. -------------------------(39) *M. velutina*

  BB. Branchlets, when mature, and leaves slightly hairy and glacuescent.

    C. Leaves narrow, lanceolate, caudate-acuminate.

      D. Leaves 5-8 cm long, lanceolate or oblong-lanceolate, lateral veins 8-10, gla-
ucous beneath; flowers almost racemose ---(23) *M. microcarpa*

     DD. Leaves larger, over 12 cm long, narrow lanceolate; lateral veins about 12.

       E. Leaves 12-18 cm long; branchlets reddish-yellow tomentose --------------
------------------------------ (26) *M. oreophila*

EE. Leaves about 20 cm long; branchlets grayish hairy ---------------------
-- *M. henryi*

CC. Leaves broader, oblong-lanceolate, long acuminate, 5-10 cm long, lateral veins numerous, conspicuously reticulated; flowers paniculate. ----------------------
-- *M. bournei*

1. **Machilus acuminatissima** (Hayata) Kaneh.

    Cinnamomum acumintissimum Hayata

    Cinnamomum caudatifolium Hayata

    Tree; leaves obovate lanceolate. or lanceolate, 6-7 cm long, 1.7-2.3 cm wide, acute to acuminate apex, cuneat at base, entire, slightly undulate margin, coriaceous, dark green above, pale green, glabrous below, brownish hairy along the midrib and veins beneath; lateral veins 30-40 degrees in divergence turning upward to the tips; petioles slender, 1.5 cm long, glabrous.

    Distribution: Taiwan.

2. **Machilus arisanensis** Hayata

    Tree up to 28 meters tall and 1 meter in diameter; branchlets dark gray, lenticellate, slender, smooth; leaves oblong-lanceolate, 7.5-9 cm long, 2-3 cm wide, acute-acuminate at apex, cuneate at base, dark green, glabrous above, pale green brownish pubescent below, entire and incurved at margin; petioles 1.5 cm long; flowering buds terminal, solitary.

    Distribution: Taiwan, at altitude 900-2300 meters.

3. **Machilus bracteata** Lecomte (See orig. text page 511)

4. **Machilus brachybotrya** Merr. (See orig. text page 521)

5. **Machilus breviflora** Hemsl.

6. **Machilus cavalerirei** Levl.

    This species is very different from any known *Machilus*. The leaves are dull, very prominently reticulated and obtuse to emarginate at the tip. The inflorescence is larger and open. It resembles *Beilschmiedia*, but the floral structure is typical *Machilus*. The perianth lobes are very rough, gray, pubescent on the outside.

    Distribution: Kweichow.

7. **Machilus chinensis** Hemsl. (See orig. text page 512)

8. **Machilus chunii** Cheng

    Small tree with dark brown bark; branchlets slender, dark gray, glabrous; leaves lanceolate, varying in sizes, 8-15 cm long, 3-4.5 cm wide, alternate, acuminate apex, cuneate at base, entire, undulate and incurved at margin, lustrous deep green above, pale green below, glabrous on both surfaces; petioles 2-3 cm long, glabrous; fruits globular, 1 cm high and broad, clustered in loose, racemes, long peduncles; with bracts; pedicels 1 cm long, brownish, glabrous.

    Distribution: Szechuan Mt. Omei.

9. **Machilus fragrans** Kaneh.

Small tree or shrub 2–15 m tall; bark whitish to brownish gray; leaves oblong-lanceolate, 10–14 cm long, 4–6 cm wide, acute apex; long cuneate at base, entire, lustrous pale green above, light green with brownish prominent reticulations below, thick coriaceous; petioles 1–1.5 cm long, brown; flowers green in terminal loose racemes.

Distribution: Hainan.

10. **Machilus grijsii** Hance (See orig. text page 513)

11. **Machilus hemsleyii** Nakai

Tree 17 m high, bark dark gray; branchlets dark gray roughly lenticellate, glabrous; leaves oblanceolate, 6–8 cm long, 2–4 cm wide, acute–acuminate at apex, acuminate at base, lustrous deep green above, brownish pilose along the midrib and veins below, coriaceous; petioles 1.5–3 cm long, glabrous; flowers in terminal clusters of loose racemes, 7 cm long, forming large panicles, small, white; tepals 6 oblong, sub-equal, 4 mm long, 1.5 mm broad, persistent; stamens 9, anthers 4-celled; ovary glabrous; fruit globular, 10 cm long and broad.

Distribution: Hupeh.

12. **Machilus holadena** Nees

Tree; leaves lanceolate elliptic, 10–11 cm long, 3.5–4.5 cm wide, lateral veins 10 pairs, attenuate at base; inflorescence in dense racemose panicles, terminal, axillary; bracts caudate; pedicels glabrescent; perianth 1–2 mm long and broad; stamens 9; pistil glabrous, 4.5–5 mm long; stigma tri-lobed.

Distribution: Yunnan.

13. **Machilus ichangensis** Rehder et Wilson (See orig. text pages 513–514)

Var. 1. Machilus ichangensis var. **leiophylla** Hand.–Mazz.

Small tree 6 m high; branchlets slneder, reddish brown, smooth; leaves elliptic lanceolate, 18–20 cm long, 4.5 cm wide, acute–acuminate at apex, cuneate at base, entire, dark shining green above, pale green, brownish red pubescent along the midrib and veins below, thick, coriaceous; petioles 2–3 cm long; flowers in loose, few-flowered racemes; peduncles 15–20 cm long, purple glabrous.

Distribution: Hunan, Hupeh, Kwangsi and Kweichow, at altitude 850–1000 meters.

Var. 2. Machilus ichangensis var. **synechothrix** Hand.–Mazz.

Small tree; leaves persistent, puberulous and prominently reticulated beneath.

Distribution: Yunnan at altitude 2400 m.

14. **Machilus japonica** Sieb. et Zucc.

Machilus pseudolongifolia Hay.

15. **Machilus kurzii** King

16. **Machilus kwangtungensis** Yang

Tree 10 m tall, 18 cm in diameter; branchlets densely ferruginous, purplish tomentose lenticellate; leaves oblanceolate, 6–11 cm long, 2–4.5 cm wide, acuminate apex, obtuse attenuate at base, glabrous above, pubescent below; veins 10–12 pairs, coriaceous; petioles 1 cm long; flowers subglobular, 6–7 mm in diameter, glaucescent; perianth lobes persistent, linear oblong, 4 mm long, 1–1.5 mm wide; pedicel 5–8 mm long, glaucescent pubescent.

Distribution: Kwangtung.

17. **Machilus kusanoi** Hayata

Large tree up to 33 m tall, 1.2 m in diameter; bark grayish brown; branchlets thick, stout, rough, brownish; leaves oblanceolate, elliptic-lanceolate, 12–18 cm long, 3–6 cm wide, acute-acuminate at apex and base, entire margin, thick coriaceous, lustrous dark green above, pale green, whitish purple pubescent beneath, glabrous, 3-nerved prominent at both surfaces; petioles 2–3 cm long, purplish brown, glabrous; flowers yellow, small, in long racemose panicles.

Distribution: Taiwan, at altitude 330–660 meters.

18. **Machilus leveinei** Merr. (See orig. text page 515)
19. **Machilus leptophylla** Hand.–Mazz.
20. **Machilus longipedicellata** Lecomte (See orig. text page 522)
21. **Machilus mekongensis** Diels (See orig. text pages 515–516)
22. **Machilus microcarpa** Hemsl.
23. **Machilus obovatifolia** (Hayata) Kaneh. et Sasak.

Machilus suffrutescens Hayata

Small tree; bark brownish gray; branchlets short, crooked; leaves obovate, 3–4 cm long, 2–3 cm wide, acute apex, acuminate at base, entire, thick coriaceous, lustrous dark green above, pale green beneath; petioles 5 mm long, glabrous; fruit solitary, globular, 1–2 cm long and broad; pedicels long, brownish pubescent.

Distribution: Taiwan.

24. **Machilus odoratissima** Nees (See orig. text page 516)
25. **Machilus phoenices** Dunn

A medium-sized tree; bark brown; leaves ovate-lanceolate, 10–13 cm long, acuminate apex, cuneate at base; lateral veins 8–10 pairs; petioles 1.3–1.9 cm long; flowering panicles 5–8 cm long; perianth segments sub-equal, oblong, 6–8 cm long.

Distribution: Eastern Kwangtung, near Swatow.

26. **Machilus platyphylla** Diels (See orig. text page 518)
27. **Machilus viridis** Hand.–Mazz. (See orig. text page 517)
28. **Machilus oreophila** Hance
29. **Machilus pauhoi** Kanehira
30. **Machilus pingii** Cheng

Tree 20 m tall; branchlets cinnamon color, glabrous; leaves elliptic, elliptic-ovate elliptic-lanceolate, 5–10 cm long, 2–4 cm wide, acute-acuminate at apex, cuneate at base, glabrous above, minutely puberulous below; veins inconspicuous; petioles glabrous, 10-15 mm long; panciles sub-terminate; peduncles 5 cm long, flowers 4-5 mm in diameter; pedicels 5-7 mm long; pedicels 5-7 mm long; perianth 6-lobed, lobes oblong, 3-5-nerved; stamens 9; anthers 4-celled; filaments glabrous, hirsute at base; ovary ovoid, rounded, 1 mm long; style 1-1.5 mm long, glabrous.

Distribution: Szechuan and Sikang, at altitude 400-1600 m.

31. **Machilus platyphylla** Diels   (See orig. text page 518)

32. **Machilus rehderi** Allen

Small tree; branchlets glabrous; purplish gray, rugose; leaves lanceolate, 9-12 cm long, 1.5-3 cm wide, long-acuminate at apex, attenuate at base, coriaceous; lateral nerves 7-8 pairs, inconspicuous, 45 degrees in divergence; petioles 15-20 mm long, glabrous; flowers in racemose panicles, 10-11 cm long, glabrous; bracts rubrofous-tomentose, deciduous; peduncle 3-5 cm long; pedicels 7-13 mm long; flowers 8-9 mm in across; perianth segments 6, free, 6-7 mm long, reflexed, externally obtuse-lanceolate, internally pubescent; stamens 9; filaments 1-1.5 mm long; glands 2; staminodes triangular, auriculate; ovary subglobose, minutely apiculate, 7-8 mm in diameter, glabrous; perianth purplish red, reflexed at base.

Distribution: Kweichow, at altitude 130 meters.

33. **Machilus rimose** Blume

Tree with reddish brown bark; leaves lanceolate, broadest above the middle, 8-12 cm long, 4.5 cm wide, obtuse or acute at apex, narrowly cuneate at base, margin revolute, dark green and smooth above, brownish pubescent along the midrib and veins below; lateral veins 9-10 pairs, very prominently elevated, coriaceous; petioles 3-4 cm long, glabrous; flowers in racemose panicles, purple, in terminal clusters.

Distribution: Hongkong.

34. **Machilus robusta** W. W. Smith (See orig. text pages 518-519)

35. **Machilus salicina** Hand.-Mazz. (See orig. text page 522)

36. **Machilus shweliensis** W. W. Smith

Tree 9-12 m high; branchlets glabrous; leaves lanceolate, elliptic-lanceolate, 11-18 cm long, 2.5-4 cm wide, long acuminate at apex, cuneate at base, coriaceous; lateral veins 16-20 pairs, reticulated; flowers in racemose pancicles of 7-9 cm long, glabrous; pedicels 3-5 mm long; perianth segments 4-5 mm long, lanceolate; stamens 9, 3 mm long; filaments villous; ovary subglobose, 1.5 mm in diameter; fruit globose, 2.5 mm in diameter; perianth segments reflexed.

Distribution: Yunnan, Shweli Valley.

37. **Machilus thunbergii** Sieb. et Zucc. (See orig. text page 519)

Var. 1. **Machilus thunbergii** var. *ducloxii* Lecomte

Tree 17-20 m tall; branchlets reddish brown, glabrous; leaves ob-ovate, 8-10 cm long, 2-4.5 cm wide, acute apex, obtuse or rounded at base, entire, incurved margin, coriaceous, lustrous light green above, brownish pale green and glabrous beneath; petioles 1-2 cm long, brown, glabrous; fruit in loose racemose panicles, 1-1.5 cm long and broad, glabrous; sepals 6, persistent, oblanceolate, 1-1.5 cm long; peduncles 5-8 cm long; pedicels 1 cm long.

Distribution: Yunnan, at altitude 1980 m.

38. **Machilus velutina** Champ. ex Benth.

39. **Machilus yunnanensis** Lecomte (See orig. text page 521)

40 **Machilus zuihoensis** Hayata

> Var. 1. **Machilus zuihoensis** Hay. var. **zuihoensis**
>
> Small tree; bark dark gray; branchlets dark gray, rougose, slender; leaves lanceolate, oblong-lanceolate, broader above the middle, 7-9 cm long, 2-3 cm wide, attenuate, acuminate at apex, cuneate at base, entire incurved at margin, lustrous dark green above, slightly pubescent along the middle rib and veins below, coriaceous; petiole slenders, 3-4 cm long, glabrous; flowers in terminal clusters of loose racemose panicles; peduncle 5 cm long, dark purple.
>
> Distribution: Taiwan.

> Var. 2. **Machilus zuihoensis** Hay. var. **longipaniculata** (Hay.) Liu et Liao
>
> *Machilus longipaniculata* Hayata
>
> Large tree 24-33 m high, 1 meter in diameter; bark brownish gray; branchlets thick, stout, glabrous; leaves lanceolate, elliptic-lanceolate, 15-20 cm long, 5-6 cm wide, acute apex and at base, entire, thick, coriaceous; petioles 1-2 cm long; flowers in terminal and in axillary racemose panicles, yellow, small, fragrant; pedicels 1-2 cm long; peduncle 10-15 cm long.
>
> Distribution: Taiwan, at altitude 660-1300 m.

nus (3) **Phoebe** Nees (See orig. text pages 522-524)

Key to Species of the genus Phoebe

. Leaves glabrous or glabrescent beneath when mature.

  B. Fruit ovoid or oblong.

    C. Petioles 2.5-4 cm long; leaves somewhat crowded lanceolate, oblanceolate or oblong-lanceolate, 17-28 cm long---------- (10) *Ph. hainanensis*

    CC. Petioles 2.5 cm or less long; leaves scattered:

      D. Flowers cymose; leaves leathery------- (18) *Ph. neurantha*

      DD. Flowers in umbullate panicles; leaves chartaceous -------------------------
---(1) *Ph. angustifolia*

BB. Fruit globose;

  C. Leaves sparsely scattered on the branch, large, about 22 cm long; petioles 2-4 cm long ----------------------------------- (6) *Ph. chinensis*

    CC. Leaves crowded near the apex of the shoots, smaller, 8–15 cm long; petiole

    about 12 mm long ------------------------ (7) *Ph. faberi*

AA. Mature leaves distinctly hairy beneath.

    B. Leaves usually 5–10 cm long, 2–4 cm broad, broadly lanceolate or obovate; fruitin

    perianth small; peduncle slender ---------------(17) *Ph. nanmu*

    BB. Leaves large, usually 22 cm long and 8 cm broad, broadly oblanceolate or obovate

    fruiting perianth on a thickened stout pedicel ----------*Ph. attenuata*

1. Phoebe angustifolia Meissner

Shrub or small tree, glabrescent; leaves chartaceous, very aromatic, pale green
linear lanceolate, long tapering at both ends, 15–24 cm long; secondary nerve
slender, arching, minutely reticulated; petioles 6–25 mm long; inflorescence axillary
long pedunculate, 5–12 cm long; flowers greenish, umbellate at the ends of the panicl
branches; perianth glabrous, segments about 3 mm long, appressed, rigid, and almos
horny in the fruit; fruiting calyx straw-yellow, shiny, about 7 or 8 mm long; fruit ovoid

    Distribution: From India to Yunnan, in swampy places along the banks of streams

2. Phoebe attenuata Nees

Phoebe sheareri Gamble

Tree 9 m tall, 45 cm in diameter; branchlets brownish, roughly lenticellate; leave
elliptic-lanceolate, 12–15 cm long, 4–5 cm wide, acute apex, cuneate at base, incurve
at margin, lustrous dark green above, pale green pubescent below; midrib and vein
prominently elevated in reticulations; lateral veins 10 pairs, 45 degrees divergent angl
curving upward and forming loops along the margin, thick, coriaceous; petioles 1–2 c
long, reddish brown; flowers greenish and hairy; fruits in loose sparse racemose pani
cles; capsules cylindrical, 1–2 cm long and 1/2 cm in diameter, pointed at both end
sepals 6, 2-seriate, tubular, brownish pubescent, green when young.

    Distribution: Hainan.

3. Phoebe blepharopus Hand.-Mazz.

Small tree or shrub; leaves persistent, lanceolate, 8–12 cm long, 4–4.5 cm wide
acuminate at apex, attenuate sub-rounded at base, entire margin, coriaceous; petio
4.5–11 mm long, glabrous above, white ciliated below; veins 12 pairs, prominently r
ticulated; fruits cylindrical, small, in racemose panicless; peduncles 2–3 cm long; p
dicels 3–5 mm long; calyx 5 mm long; lobes obtuse ovate.

    Distribution: Kwangtung, at altitude 800 meters.

4. Phoebe chienii Cheng

Shrub; leaves lanceolate, 7–10 cm long, 2–2.5 cm wide, attenuate acuminate at ape
cuneate unequal at base, entire incurved at margin, lustrous green above, pale browni
below; midrib and veins prominently elevated, slightly yellowish pubescent, coriaceou
petioles 2–3 cm long, glabrous; flowers yellow in long racemose panicles, axillar
5–6 cm long, pubescent; fruits ellipsoid 8 mm long, 5 mm broad; sepals 6, 2-seriate.

Distribution: Szechuan Mt. Omei

5. **Phoebe bournei** (Hemsl.) Yang

Machilus bournei Hemsl.

Tall densely leafy tree 15-30 m tall, trunk 1 to 1.5 meter in diameter; mature leaves coriaceous, oblong-lanceolate, acuminate at the apex, tapering to the cuneate base, 5-10 cm long, 1.2-4 cm wide; young shoots and leaves distinctly tomentose or puberulent, becoming glabrous and bright shining green on the upper surface, finally pale and pubefulent below; lateral veins numerous, the ultimate veins conspicuous reticulated; flowers small, creamy white or yellowish white, the flower bud, perianth and pedicels pubescent with short gray or brown hairs; perianth segments broadly oval-oblong; filaments hairy, stigma large, capitate.

Distribution: Hupeh, Szechuan, Fukien, and Kweichow commom as a forest tree in Western China particulary abundant in the Chengtu Plain and is much planted around temples and in gardens.

6. **Phoebe chinensis** Chun (See orig. text page 524)

7. **Phoebe faberi** (Hemsl.) Chun

Machilus faberi Hemsl.

Tree to 16 meters tall, entirely glabrous; branchlets thickish, black or nearly so, the foliage borne near shoot apex; leaves crowded, slender petioled, thick, coriaceous, narrowly oblong-lanceolate, acuminate, usually narrow at base, pale or glaucous below, shining above, 8-15 cm long, lateral veins numerous, inconspicuous, ultimate veins minutely reticulated; petioles 12 mm long; flowers yellow, small, spreading, about 5 mm in diameter, glabrous, narrowly cymose-paniculate, many from the apex of the shoots, slightly shorter than the leaves; pedicels slender scarcely equal the length of the flowers, perianth segments very nearly equal thickish, oval-oblong, sub-acute, ciliate hairy inside; ovary glabrous; fruit globose, 8-10 mm in diameter; perianth segments closely appressed around the base on a slightly thickened pedicels.

Distribution: Hupeh and Szechuan.

3. **Phoebe formosana** Hayata

Machilus formosana Hay.

Tree 12-30 m tall, 1.5 meter in diameter; bark yellowish brown; leaves oblanceolate, 12-15 cm long, 5-7 cm wide, broadest above the middle acute-acuminate at apex, narrow cuneate at base, dark green glabrous above, glaucous below; midrib and veins prominently elevated and reticulated, brownish pubescent beneath, coriaceous; petioles brown, 1 cm long; flowers in racemose few-flowered panicles; sepals 6, 2-seriate; peduncle 8-12 cm long; pedicels 5 mm long.

Distribution: Taiwan, at altitude 1200-1500 m.

. **Phoebe forestii** Sm. (See orig. text page 524)

'. **Phoebe hainanensis** Hand.-Mazz.

. **Phoebe henryi** (Hemsl.) Merr.

Machilus henryi Hemsl.

Small tree; flowering branchlets thickish, grayish, pubescent; leaves crowded at the shoot apices, petiolate, coriaceous, narrowly lanceolate, usually about 20 cm long, caudate acuminate, base narrowly cuneate, glabrous above, slightly pubescent at first, inconspicuous minutely reticulated with about 12 lateral veins beneath; flowers cymose-paniculate, panicles numerous, narrow on long peduncles, slightly shorter than the leaves; pedicles scarsely as long as the flower; perianth lobes 6, distinctly 2-seriate, almost free, valvate, subequal, thick, broadly oval, appressed hairy.

Distribution: Hainan.

12. **Phoebe hui** Cheng

Tree 25 m tall, 65 cm in diameter; bark gray, nearly smooth; leaves obvate, acuminate at apex, cuneate at base, incurved margin, coriaceous; petioles 1.5 cm long, glabrous; fruit dark blue, glaucous.

This species is closely related to *Phoebe bournei* Yang but differs in its shape, size and pubescence of the leaves, with lateral veins usually slightly elevated above and in its broader fruits. It is closely related to *Phoebe nanmu* (Oliv.) Gamble, but differs in its smaller leaves discoid stigma, sessile glands and hairy perianth lobes.

Distribution: Szechuan Mt. Omei, and Sikang, at altitude 1500 m.

13. **Phoebe hunanensis** Hand.-Mazz. (See orig. text page 525)

14. **Phoebe kwangsiensis** Liou

Tree; branchlets terete, lenticellate, 12-21 cm long, 2.5-5 cm wide, acuminate at apex; petioles 12-20 mm long; lateral veins 10-13 pairs; panicles 13-18 cm long; bract linear 3-4, racemose panicles with 3-5 flowers each; flowers small, 5 mm across; pedicles 8-9 mm; perianth tubular, 6-lobed, persistent; staminodes 3; pistil 12 mm long, glabrous; ovary globular, as long as the style.

Distribution: Kwangsi.

15. **Phoebe lanceolata** Nees

Small tree 4 m tall; leaves elliptic-lanceolate, 12-15 cm long, narrowly acuminate at apex and base, entire margin, lustrous dark green above, pale greensih brown beneath, glabrous on both surfaces, thin, coriaceous; lateral veins alternately running out from the midrib, prominently elevated, not reticulated, straight curving upward at 45 degree to the margin; petioles 1-1.5 cm long, glabrous; fruits in sub-terminal racemose panicles; perianth 6-lobed, persistent; peduncles 12-15 cm long; pedicles 1 cm long.

Distribution: Yunnan and Szechuan.

16. **Phoebe legenderi** Lecomte.

Tree 6-10 m tall; bark brownish gray, smooth; branchlets dark brown, slender; leaves lanceolate, 8-12 cm long, 1.5-2.5 cm wide, acuminate at apex, narrow cuneate at base, entire, lustrous dark green above, pale brownish below, slightly brown puberscent along the midrib and veins, prominently elevated, coriaceous; petioles 1 cm long, reddish brown; fruit globular, 1 cm across, tinged purple; calyx greenish, red flexed; peduncles axillary 10 cm long; pedicels 1 cm long; glabrous.

Distribution: Kweichow and Yunnan, at altitude 900–2000 m.

17. **Phoebe nanmu** Gamble (See orig. text pages 525–527)

18. **Phoebe neurantha** Gamble

19. **Phoebe sheareri** Gamble

Genus (4) Notaphoebe Blume (See orig. text page 523)

1. **Notaphoebe cavaleriei** (Levl.) Yang

Lindera cavaleriei. Levl.

Machilus mairei Leveille

Machilus cunniana Leveille

Aleseodaphne omeiensis Gamble

Notaphoebe omeiensis (Gamble) Chun

Small tree; leaves oblanceolate; perianth lobes unequal; fruits globose on thickened pedicels, drupaceous and berry-like; leaves glaucous whitish below.

Distribution: Kweichow, Szechuan Mt. Omei, and Sikang, at altitude 1300–1500 meters.

2. **Notaphoebe fargesii** (Blume) Liou

Tree 6 m tall; branchlets angular, puberulent, annulary; leaves alternate oblanceolate, attenuate-acuminate at base, acute-caudate at apex, 7–9 cm long, 1.5–2 cm wide, glabrous above, finely pubescent below, penninerved; veins 10–15 pairs; petiole 3–5 mm long; peduncles 3–7 cm long, perianth lobes reflexed; staments 9; anthers ovate-obutse; pistile glabrous, 2–7 mm long; ovary subspherical; style as long as the ovary.

Distribution: Szechuan, at altitude 1000 meters.

3. **Notaphoebe konishii** Hayata

Tree; leaves elliptic-lanceolate to lanceolate, 6–8 cm long, 2.2–2.8 cm wide, acute-acuminate apex, acute-cuneate at base, entire, incurved along margin, coriaceous, dark brown above, purple brown beneath, densely hairy along the midrib and veins beneath; midrib and veins prominently elevated; petioles purplish black with light brownish hairs, grooved above, 8 mm long.

Distribution: Taiwan, Yui Shan, at altitude 2520 m.

4. **Notaphoebe omeiensis** (Gamble) Chun (See orig. text pages 528–529)

5. **Notaphoebe duclouxii** Lecomte

Tree, branchlets glabrous, striate; leaves alternate, sub-coriaceous 12–14 cm long, 5–6 cm wide, long attenuate apex, narrowly long acuminate towards the base, entire incurved margin, dark green above, brownish green and slightly pubescent along the midrib and veins beneath; veins 5–6 pairs, elevated below and depressed above; petioles 5–10 mm long, purplish black, grooved; panicles axillary, few-flowered, bracts triangular villose; perianth lobes 6, yellow, outer 3 smaller, inner 3 large, 3–4 mm long, villose inside; fertile stamens 9; anthers 4-celled flattened, inner 3 with globose, stipitate glands; rudimentary stamens 3, triangular; ovary globose; style slender;

stigma peltate.

Distribution: Yunnan.

6. **Notaphoebe tsoongii** Cheng

Tree; leaves elliptic-lanceolate, lanceolate, 8-10 cm long, 2-3 cm wide, acuminate apex, cuneate at base, entire, slightly incurved at margin, lustrous green glabrous above, brownish and slightly pubescent below; lateral veins 6-7 pairs, prominently elevated, curving upwards forming loops near the edge margin, coriaceous; petioles 2-3 cm long, brown, slightly pubescent; peduncles short, slender, axillary, few-flowered; perianth 6, 2-seriate.

Distribution: Kweichow.

Genus (5) **Sassafras** Nees et Ebermaier   (See orig. text page 530)

1. **Sassafras randaiensis** (Hayata) Nakai

   Lindera randaiensis Hatata

   Sassafras randaiensis Hayata

   Yushunia randaiensis Kamikoti

   Pseudosassafras laciflora var. *randaiensis* (Hay.) Nakai

   Tree up to 26 meters tall, 1 meter in diameter; bark deeply fissured; leaves obovate to elliptic-ovate, 15 cm long, 8 cm wide, 2-3-lobed, entire or undulate, acute apex, cuneate at base, 3-nerved, lustrous green above, pale green below; midrib and veins prominently elevated hairy and reticulated, thick, coriaceous; petioles thick, stout, 3-5 cm long, brown; perianth segments 6, sub-equal, lanceolate; stamens 9; glands stipitate; stminodes 3; anthers 3-4-celled; ovary ovoid.

   Distribution: Taiwan, throughout the island, at altitude 1600-2500 m.

2. **Sassafras tzumu** Hemsl. (See orig. text pages 530-531)

Genus (6) **Actinodaphne** Nees (See orig. text page 532)

Key to the species of Actinodaphne

A. Fruting perianth cup-shaped; leaves verticillate; young part puberulous.

   B. Leaves acuminate, 7.5-15 cm long; petioles 8-12 mm long; fruits 12-15 mm high. -- (20) *A. reticulata*

   BB. Leaves acute, 5-13 cm long; petioles very short, thick; fruit about 12 mm long -- (3) *A. cupularis*

AA. Fruiting perianth not cupuliform.

   B. Pedicels of fruit dilated at the apex into a flattened disk; leaves alternate; young parts excepting the branchlets glabrous.------- (7) *A. hongkongensis*

   BB. Pedicels of fruit scarsely thickened; perianth wholly deciduous; leaves pseudo-verticellate; young parts wholly glabrous

      C. Leaves triplinerved --------------------- (2) *A. confertiflora*

CC. Leaves penninerved;

   D. Fruit pubescent ———————————— (22) *A. trichocarpa*

DD. Fruit glabrous:

   E. Leaves obovate:

      F. Leaves 10 cm long or less ———(12) *A. magniflora*

     FF. Leaves over 10 cm long:

        G. Fruit globose, 4 mm or less in diameter; inflorescences racemose; leaves 15–20 cm long ———— (19) *A. pilosa*

       GG. Fruit elliptic, 2.5 cm long, 1 cm broad, inflorescences of numerous umbels; leaves 50 cm long ——(16) *A. obovata*

  EE. Leaves never obovate.

    F. Largest leaves less than 10 cm long.

      G. Fruit subtended by cupules, 4–5 mm long ——————————————————————————————— (3) *A. cupularis*

     GG. Fruit subtended by shallow disk nearly flat

        H. Leaves obtuish at apex, dull on upper surface ———————————————(Japan and Taiwan)——(11) *A. lacifolia*

       HH. Leaves acutish at apex, more shining on upper surface, usually smaller than those of the typical form of the species ————————————————————————(11–1) *A. lancifolia* var. *sinensis*

    FF. Largest leaves over 10 cm long.

      G. Inflorescences racemose, cupule densely pubescent —————————————————————————————(5) *A. henryi*

     GG. Inflorescences not racemose.

        H. Leaves alternate.

          I. Young branches and lower leaf-surface ferrugineous-tomentose ——————————— *A. ferruginea*.

         II. Young branchlets, midrib and secondary veins brown-pubescent, lower surface glaucous ————————————————————————————————————(10) *A. litseaefolia*

       HH. Leaves verticillate or pseudo-verticillate.

          I. Leaves caudate-acuminate at apex; stamens exserted ————————————————————————— *A. tsaii*

         II. Leaves never caudate-acuminate.

           J. fruit globose.

             K. Leaves narrowly lanceolate, up to 50 cm long ————————————————————— *A. sesquipedalis*

            KK. Leaves smaller, more pubescent —————————————————————————— *A. sesquipedalis* var. *cambodiana*

KKK. Leaves not narrowly lanceolate, less then 30 cm long.

L. Leaves broadly elliptic, dark and shining above, pale beneath ------------------------ -----------------*A. perlucida*

LL. Leaves not broadly elliptic.

M. Fruits not more than 1 cm in diameter, not apiculate---- *A. glaucina*

MM. Fruits more than 1 cm in diamter, definately apiculate ---------------------- ------(17) *A. omeiensis*

JJ. Fruits ovoid, oblong-ovoid or obovoid

K. Fruit ovoid.

L. Leaves linear or oblong-lanceolate, shining above ----(21) *A. szechuanensis*

LL. Leaves elliptic-lanceolate, reticulate above -- ---------(20) *A. reticulata*

LLL. Leaves entirely glabrous --------------------- --------- (20-1) *A. reticulata* var. *glabra.*

KK. Fruit oblong or ovoid.

L. Lateral veins in numerous pairs, ascending, conspicuous on lower surface; lower sruface of leaves light brown, pilose-pubescent, glaucous when young; fruit oblong.--------------- --------- (20-2) *A. reticulata* var. *forestii*

LL. Lateral veins obscure; lower surface of leaves glaucous when young; fruit obovoid --------- --------- (9) *A. lecomtei*

1. **Actinodaphne acuminata** Meissn.

Large tree producing very valuable timbers, 18-20 m tall, trunk 20 cm or more in diameters; branchlets yellowish brown; leaves long lanceolate, up to 20 cm long, 3 cm broad, long acuminate-attenuate at apex, cuneate at base, entire incurved along margin, penni-nerved; lateral veins 20-24 pairs, coriaceous, dark green above, pale green and slightly brownish pubescent along the midrib and veins beneath, petioles 2-3 cm long; grooved, glabrous, brown; inflorescences few - flowered, racemose, axillary; fruit cylindrical, 1/4 inserted in the calyx tube; pedicels 5 mm long, glabrous.

Distribution: Chekiang, at altitude 460 m.

2. **Actinodaphne confertifolia** (Hemsl.) Gamble (See orig. text page 532)

3. **Actinodaphne cupularis** (Hemsl.) Gamble

4. **Actinodaphne diversifolia** Merr. (See orig. text page 534)

5. **Actinodaphne henryi** Gamble   (See orig. text pages 534–536)

6. **Actinodaphne hookeri** Meissn.

Shrub; branchlets yellowish rufous hairy; leaves oblanceolate, 15–20 cm long, 5–7 cm wide, acuminate at apex, cuneate, 3-nerved at base, entire incurved margin, thick, lustrous dark green above, pale brownish hairy below; midrib and lateral veins prominently elevated, densely hairy and runing out horizontally; petioles 1–2 cm long, stout, densely yellowish hairy.

7. **Actinodaphne hongkongensis** Chun (See orig. text page 535)

8. **Actinodaphne hypoleucophylla** Hayata

Tree 8–10 m tall, 20 cm in diameter; bark dark gray; branchlets stout, lenticellate, reddish gray; leaves elliptic-oblong, 6–9 cm long, 2–4 cm wide, acute apex, cuneate at base (some leaves unequal at base), entire, slightly incurved at margin, coriaceous, lustrous shining green above, pale green below, penni-nerved; lateral veins 10 pairs almost 80 degrees in divergence; petiole 5–10 mm long, brown.

Distribution: Taiwan.

9. **Actinodaphne lecomtei** Allen

Small tree 10 m tall, 50 cm in diameter; branchlets terete, greenish black, pubescent; leaves lanceolate, 10–15 cm long, 14–26 mm wide, long acute apex, cuneate at base, entire incurved margin, penni-nerved, membraneous, chartaceous, lustrous light green above, pale green glaucous below; petioles slender, 2–3 cm long; flowers numerous; perianth tubes 6-lobed, elliptic-lanceolate, fruits obovoid, 7 mm long, 5 mm broad, glabrous.

Distribution: Szechuan Mt. Omei, Kweichow and Kwangsi, at altitude 1800 meters.

10. **Actinodaphne litseaefolia** Allen

Shrub, bark deep brown; branchlets slender, brownish gray, rough; leaves obovate lanceolate, 15–18 cm long, 7–8 cm wide, blunt-acute apex, cuneate-acute at base, entire incurved margin, coriaceous; lustrous deep green above, pale green pubescent below, penni-nerved; petioles 1 cm long, brownish pubescent; fruits ovoid, borne on short racemes.

Distribution: Hainan.

11. **Actinodaphne lancifolia** (S. et Z.) Meissn. (See orig. text pages 535–536)

Var. 1. **Actinodaphne lancifolia** var. **sinensis** Allen

The leaves of the variety are for the most part, smaller more acute at the apex and more shining on the upper surface. In some cases, they are less oboviously glaucous. In working over the material of *Litsea rotundifolia* var. *oblongifolia* (Nees) Allen, which was under *Actinodaphne* or *Litsea chinensis* in the herbarium, it was found a goodly portion being not *Litsea rotundifolia* var. *oblongifolia*, but a species different in leaf shape, petiole lenght and infructescence. It resembles *Actinodaphne lancifolia* (S. et Z.) Meissn., from Japan, but differs slightly in leaf characters. The infructescence is similar. Although the difference is slight, I propose the above new variety of the species, because of the geographical separation.

Distribution: Chekiang, Kiangsu and Anhwei.

Var. 2. Actinodaphne lancifolia var. villosa S. Y. Hu

Tree 10 m tall; leaves elliptic-ovate, 5-8 cm long, 2-4 cm wide, acute at apex, cuneate at base, entire incurved margin, coriaceous, lustrous dark green above, pale green, whitish villose below; fruit red to black; petioles 1 cm long, whitish villose.

Distribution: Hunan and Kwangsi, at altitude 680 meters.

12. Actinodaphne magniflora Allen

Small tree 3 meters tall; branchlets terete, striate, densely tomentose; leaves oblanceolate-elliptic, 6-10 cm long, 2.5-4 cm wide, abruptly acuminate at apex, cuneate at base, entire incurved at margin, thick coriaceous, lustrous green above, reddish brown hairy below, penni-nerved, veins 8-10 pairs; petioles 9-12 mm long, thick, reddish hairy; flowers in terminal racemes, reddish hairy; pedicels pubescent, 2-4 mm long; perianth 6-lobed; stamens 9, 3 internal, 6 external, filaments 5-7 mm long; the internal ones stipitate and bi-glands; staminodes triangular.

Distribution: Kwangtung and Hongkong.

13. Actinodaphne morrisonensis Hay.

Tree; leaves oblanceolate to lanceolate, 12-14.5 cm long, acuminate at apex, cuneate at base, entire incurved along margin, slightly coriaceous, lustrous dark green above pale green glaucous and along the midrib and veins whitish hairy beneath; veins 10 pairs elevated and reticulated; petioles purple-black, 1.5-18 cm long, grooved.

Distribution: Taiwan, Hin Kao Shan, at altitude 2300 m.

14. Actinodaphne mushaensis (Hay.) Hayata

Litsea mushaensis Hayata

Tree 10-15 m high, 35 cm in diameter; leaves obovate-lanceolate, 7-10.5 cm long, 2-3.5 cm wide, acute apex, cuneate at base, entire incurved margin, slightly coriaceous, lustrous deep green above, dark brownish pubescent below; midrib and veins densely hairy; petioles 1 cm long, purplish black, hairy.

Distribution: Taiwan, at altitude 1300-2300 m.

15. Actinodaphne nantoensis Hayata

Tree up to 20 m high, 80 cm in diameter; bark brownish gray; branchlets stout short; leaves oblanceolate, 12-16 cm long, 2-4 cm wide, acuminate apex, cuneate base, entire incurved at margin, lustrous green above, pale whitish hairy beneath, coriaceous; petioles slender, 2-3 cm long, glabrous; flowers in axillary racemes; panicle short, 1 cm long; fruit globular, 1/4 inserted in a tubular perianth; pedicels 2-3 mm long.

Distribution: Taiwan, Nanto, at altitude 330-1360 m.

16. **Actinodaphne obovata** Blume

Small tree or shrub; branchlets thick stout, densely reddish yellow hairy; leaves extremely large, obovate shape, 50-60 cm long, 25-30 cm broad, oboval, 3-nerved, entire, slightly incurved at margin, acute apex, obovate-cuneate at base; midrib, lateral veins and veinlets prominently elevated, yellowish hairy, sub-coriaceous, dark green above, pale green and glaucous beneath; petioles 8-10 cm long, reddish hairy; flowers reddish brown, axillary, short pedicellate and short pedunculate, clustered on the branchlets, reddish hairy.

Distribution: Yunnan.

17. **Actinodaphne omeiensis** (Liou) Allen

Small tree 2-8 m high; branchlets glabrous; leaves oblong - lanceolate, elliptic-lanceolate, 15-24 cm long, 3.5-4.5 cm wide, acuminate at apex, cuneate at base, entire incurved margin, thick leathery, lustrous dark green above, pale slightly villose along the midrib and veins beneath, petioles 1.5-2 cm long, brown; fruits solitary, globose, yellowish green, subtended by cup-like persistent calyx.

Distribution: Szechuan, in thickets, at altitude 1000-1100 m.

18. **Actinodaphne pedicellata** Hayata

Shrub 3 m high; bark dark gray; branchlets slender, smooth, glabrous; leaves elliptic-lanceolate, 7 cm long, 3 cm wide, entire, acute apex, narrow cuneate at base, lustrous dark green above, pale green glabrous beneath, coriaceous; petioles 5 mm long; fruit in axillary small racemes, sub-sessile; calyx tube short; peduncles 5 mm long.

Distribution: Taiwan, at altitude level -700 m.

19. **Actinodaphne pilosa** (Lour.) Merr.

A. hainanensis Merr.

Shrub or small tree; branchlets, inflorescences and undersurface of leaves rusty pubescent; branchlets rounded, 4-5 mm in diameter, rusty hairy or glabrescent, young branchlets densely pubescent; leaves slightly crowded, leathery, ovate to oblong-obovate 10-15 cm long, 4-9 cm wide, short acuminate, narrowed toward the acute base, shiny olive green and glabrous or pubescent along the veins above, paler and densely rusty pubescent beneath, lateral veins 5-6 pairs, ascending, sharply defined; petioles densely rusty pubescent, 1-2.5 cm long; inflorescence in axillary panicles, usually about 7cm long, densely rusty pubescent, many-flowered; flowers in umbellate clusters; perianth segments elliptic, rounded, 4 mm long, pubescent; filaments densely hairy, as long as the anthers; anthers 2 mm long; glands sub-sessile; ovary hairy.

This species is closely allied to *Machilus velutina* Champ. ex Benth, from which it is distinguished by the much longer inflorescence, less pubescent leaves with fewer veins on longer petioles, obovate not elliptic on outline.

Distribution: Hainan, at altitude 100-330 meters.

20. **Actinodaphne reticulata** Meissn. (See orig. text page 536)

21. **Actinodaphne szechuanensis** (Gamble) Allen

Lindera setchuenense (Gamble) Rehder

Benzoin szechuanensis (Gamble) Rehder

Tree 18 m tall; branchlets slender, brownish, conspicuously lenticellate; leaves petiolate, papery, linear-oblong, apex and base acuminate, olive green above, grayish and minutely pubescent especially along the veins beneath, 15-17 cm long, 2-3 cm wide, veins slightly impressed above, conspicuously elevated and reticulated beneath, usually 17 pairs; petioles slender, about 7 mm long; pistillate inflorescences 1 or 2 in the axils of the leaves, on short peduncles, surrounded by nearly orbicular bracts, glabrous and about 3 mm long; staminodes 9, those of the first and the second whorls, clavate, 0.75 mm long, hairy at the base, the third whorl slightly shorter, obtuse, 2-glandular at the base; ovary ovoid; style curved, stigma capitate; berry ovoid, 1 cm long, on an enlarged cup-shaped perianth tube; pedicels thickened, about 5 mm long.

Distribution: Western Szechuan, at altitude 900 meters.

22. **Actinodaphne trichocarpa** Allen.

Tree 8 m high; branchlets terete, brownish pubescent; leaves verticillate, coriaceous, oblanceolate, elliptic-lanceolate, 8-13 cm long, 2-3 cm wide, acuminate at apex, cuneate at base, entire margin, lustrous dark green above, pale green beneath, glabrous on both surfaces, penni-nerved; lateral veins 6-10 pairs, inconspicuous, midrib prominently elevated; petioles 5-8 mm long, adpressed pubescent; inflorescences sub-umbellate, axillary, solitary, sub-sessile; fruit globose 12-15 mm long and broad, brown, adpressed, tomentose.

Distribution: Szechuan Mt. Omei, and Yunnan, at altitude 2200 m.

Genus (7) Neolitsea Merr. (See orig. text pages 536-537)

1. **Neolitsea acuto-trinervia** (Hayata) Kaneh. et Sasak.

Tetradenia acuto-trinervia Hayata

Tree 13-20 m tall, 30-40 cm in diameter; branchlets slender, dark gray; leaves oblong-lanceolate, 7-8.5 cm long, 1.8-2.5 cm wide, short acuminate at apex, cuneate at base, finely serrate or undulate at margin, sub-coriaceous, lustrous dark green above, brownish green below, trinerved; petioles 1-2 cm long, dark purple pubescent; inflorescences sub-umbellate; peduncles alternate and axillary on the branchlets, yellowish purple.

Distribution: Taiwan, at altitude 1300-2500 m.

2. **Neolitsea aurata** Hayata (See orig. text pages 537-538)

Var. 1. **N. aurata** var. **chinensis** Gamble

3. **Neolitsea aciculata** (Blume) Koidz.

Small tree, 4 m tall, 6 cm in dia.; bark smooth, black; branchlets very slender grayish glabrous; leaves oblanceolate, 8-12 cm long, 2-3 cm wide, acuminate at apex cuneate, 3-nerved at base, entire incurved undulate margin, glossy dark green above brownish glaucescent below, coriaceous; petioles 1 cm long, brown, glabrous; flower in alternate sub-umbels on branchlets; fruits bluish black, glabrous, globular, 1 c long and broad; pedicels 2 mm long.

Distribution: Hainan.

4. **Neolitsea acuminatissima** (Hay.) Kaneh. et Sasak.

Tetradenia acuminatissima Hayata

Tree 17 m tall, 40 cm in diameter; bark reddish brown; branchlets slender, reddish, glabrous; leaves elliptic-oblong, 6-10 cm long, 2-3 cm wide, acuminate at apex, cuneate 3-nerved at base, entire, slightly incurved and undulate at margin, lustrous dark green above, pale green glaucescent below, coriaceous; petioles slender, 1 cm long, brownish glabrescent; fruit berry-like, globular, 5 mm broad and high, solitary; pedicels 2 cm long, reddish, glabrescent.

Distribution: Taiwan, at altitude 1800-2800 m.

5. **Neolitsea buisanensis** Yamamoto et Kamikoti

Small tree with verticillate and slender branchlets; leaves elliptic-obovate, 8-10 cm long, 2-4 cm wide, acute at apex, cuneate at base, entire, thick, coriaceous, lustrous dark green above, pale green glabrous below, crowded at the shoot apex or around the nodes of the second year's growth; petioles slender, about 1 cm long.

Distribution: Taiwan.

6. **Neolitsea chekiangensis** Chun

Small shrub; leaves alternate; petioles 4-10 mm long, purplish tomentose; lanceolate to oblanceolate leaves of 29-65 mm long, 9-24 mm wide, acuminate apex, acute at base, trinerved, glabrous shining green above, whitish tomentose below; fruit globular, drupaceous, axillary; pedicels glabrous, 6-9 mm long, 1 mm thick; fruit a drupe, 6-9 mm long, 5-6 mm broad and long.

This species is closely related to *Neolitsea aurata*, but is distinguished by its purplish branchlets.

Distribution: Chekiang.

7. **Neolitsea chinensis** (Gamble) Chun

Neolitsea lanuginosa var. *chinensis* Gamble

Tree to 9 m tall; buds large; leaves pseudo-verticillate, or rarely alternate, oblanceolate, 15-20 cm long, 4.5-5.5 cm broad, acuminate, thinly coriaceous, glabrous and shining green above, very glaucous and densely brownish tomentose along the veins beneath, veins and transverse veinlets prominent on the lower surface; petioles 15-20 mm long; flowers fascicled; staminate flowers with 4 ovate-tomentose perianth segments, and 6 fertile stamens on filiform filaments with large oblong introrse 4-celled anthers; the pistillate flowers smaller than the staminate, with ovate-lanceolate lobes, 6 staminodes and a small ovary surmounted by a more or less 2-fid stigma; fruit globose, black, 12 mm long, seated on a small entire, circular, concave perianth attached to a recurved pedicel.

Distribution: Hupeh and Szechuan, at altitude 1700 m.

8. **Neolitsea ellipsoidea** Allen.

Large tree 30 m high, 2 m in diameter; branchlets terete, rugose, glabrous; leaves elliptic oblong, 6-10 cm long, 2-4.5 cm wide, acute-acuminate at apex, obtuse-acute at base, entire margin, coriaceous, triplinerves; petioles 2-3 cm long, glabrous, longitudinally rugose; inflorescences umbellate, 2-5-flowered, solitary, minutely pedunculate; peduncles 1-2 mm long, glabrous; pedicels ferrugino-pubescent, 3-4 mm long, corolla 4-5 mm long; perianth tube 4-lobed, elliptic-ciliate; stamens 6; filaments 6, pubescent; staminodes 6; ovary ovoid, glabrous; stigma discoid; fruit ellipsoid, 15-17 mm long; pedicels 8 mm long, 2 mm thick.

Distribution: Hainan.

9. **Neolitsea cambodiana** Lecomte.

Neolitsea ferruginosa Merr.

Tree 10 m high; bark dark brown; branchlets with dirty reddish indumentum, tawny; leaves oblanceolate, 12-15 cm long, 3-4.5 cm wide, short acuminate or acute apex, cuneate at base, incurved at margin, thick, coriaceous, lustrous dark green above, pale brownish green, tawny indumentum below; petioles 1 cm long, tawny; flowers in clustered umbels; fruits drupaceous, globular, 2 mm long and broad, reddish brown; pedicel 3 mm long.

Distribution: Kwangtung, Kwangsi, Hainan and Fukien, at altitude 600 meters.

Var. 1. **Neolitsea cambodiana** var. **glabra** Allen

Small tree 7 m tall. Difference between the variety and the typical form of the species is in the leaves. They are more attenuate at the base and apex, are concolorous and glabrous, and everywhere reticulate.

Distribution: Kwangtung.

10. **Neolitsea confertifolia** (Hemsl.) Merr.

Actinodaphne confertifolia (Hemsley) Gamble

*Litsea confertifolia*Hemsley.

Fiwa confertifolia (Hemsley) Nakai

Shrub or small tree almost wholly glabrous; flowering branches radiate, upright, leafy only at the apex and folks, leaves crowded, pseudo-verticillate, spreading, very short-petioled, leathery narrowly lanceolate, 5-13 cm long, acute, undulate, pale shining green above, glaucous beneath, midrib slightly elevated, ultimate veins inconspicuous; flowers densely fasciculate, appearing on the leafless part of the branch below the leaves, subtended by involucral bracts, the bracts deciduous, glabrous on the outside; pedicel long, silky-hairy; perianth segments 4, petaloid, broadly ovate, pelucid punctate; stamens 6, filaments almost filiform, hairy at the base, anthers large; fruit black, ovoid, to 10 mm long, pedicel scarsely thickened, perianth tube wholly deciduous.

Distribution: Hupeh and Szechuan.

11. **Neolitsea chuii** Merr.

Neolitsea subfoveolata Merr.

Tree 12 m tall; bark grayish brown, smooth; branchlets reddish brown, slender, glabrous; leaves elliptic-oblong, 10-12 cm long, 5-7 cm wide, short acuminate at apex, cuneate, 3-nerved at base, incurved undulate at margin, thick-coriaceous, lustrous dark green above, pale glaucous beneath; veins 4 pairs, prominent on both surfaces; petioles 3-4 cm long, glabrous, brown; flowers in axillary clusteres of many subumbels; pedicels 1 cm long; peduncles 1 mm long, brownish pubescent; fruit globular-ovoid, 1 cm long and broad, reddish black.

Distribution: Kwangtung, at altitude 700-1200 m.

Var. 1. Neolitsea chuii var. brevipes Yang

Tree 10 meters tall, 32 cm in diameter; leaves glaucous beneath; flower pale yellowish green. This variety differs from the typical form of the species in its less prominent foveolate and shorter pedicel and shining on the upper surface of the leaves.

Distribution: Yunnan, at altitude 1800 m.

12. Neolitsea homilantha Allen.

Tree, branchlets glabrous, striate, terete; leaves elliptic, 7-10 cm long, 2.5-4 cm wide, sub-caudate acuminate apex, cuneate, rounded, 3-nerved at base, incurved undulate at margin, lustrous dark green above, pale glacuous below, coriaceous; petioles 10-14 mm long, glabrous, rugose; inflorescence sub-umbellate, multiflora, axillary, sub-sessile; pedicels pubescent, 2 mm long; corolla 3-4 mm long, 4-lobed; stamens 6, bi-glandulous; staminodes and ovary glabrescent.

Distribution: Yunnan.

13. Neolitsea hongkongensis (Chun) Allen

The species stands out on account of the oblong-lanceolate to elliptic leaves, heavily and coarsely reticulate (not sub-foveolate) above and below, brown, glabrous above and very pale brown-pubescent below. The specimens from Gray, cited as possibly the iso-type of *Actinodaphne angustifolia* of Bentham is in fruit. It differs from *Actinodaphne angustifolia* of Nees in its smaller, oblong-lanceolate, leaves not glaucous below, and the flat disc subtending the fruit. However Hongkong No. 4633, which matches Wilford's specimens as to the leaf structure and other characters, is a male branch with the typical *Neolitsea* flower structure.

14. Neolitsea konishii Hayata

Tetradenia konishii Hayata

Tree up to 30 meters tall, 1.3 meter in diameter; bark dark brown; leaves oblong lanceolate, 11-14 cm long, 3.5-4.5 cm wide, long acute at apex, narrow cuneate at base, 3-nerved, incurved margin, coriaceous, lustrous dark green above, pale green, glaucous, pubescent below; primary veins prominently elevated; leaves clustered on the tips of the branchlets; petioles 1-2 cm long, dark purple; flowers in alternate clusters of umbels, brownish green, sub-sessile.

Distribution: Taiwan, at altitude 330-700 meters.

15. **Neolitsea kotoensis** (Hayata) Kaneh. et Sasak.

Small tree; leaves oblong-lanceolate to lanceolate, 9.5-15 cm long, 4.5-5 cm wide, acute-acuminate at apex, cuneate, 3-nerved at base, slightly coriaceous, lustrous dark green above, pale green whitish glaucescent below; petioles 8-15 mm long, brownish hairy.

Distribution: Botel Tobago, Taiwan.

16. **Neolitsea kwangsiensis** Liou

A tree; leaves ovate or obovate-oblong, glabrous, up to 20 cm long and 10 cm broad, triplinerved, with conspicuous parallel veins; the petioles up to 4 cm long; the large spherical fruit 1.5-1.8 cm in diameter.

Distribution: Kwangtung.

17. **Neolitsea lanuginosa** (Nees) Gamble

Tetradenia lanuginosa Nees

Litsea lanuginosa Nees

Small tree; leaves elliptic-oblong, 10-14 cm long, 3-4 cm wide, acuminate-rotundate at apex, cuneate at base, prominently 3-nerved, other veins inconspicuous, lustrous dark green above, bluish glaucous below, subcoriaceous; petioles stout, 1-2 cm long, reddish brown pubescent; flowers in alternate clustered subumbels, sub-sessile, reddish yellow.

Distribution: Yunnan.

18. **Neolitsea levenei** Merr. (See orig. text page 538)

19. **Neolitsea oblongifolia** Merr. et Chun

Tree 8-10 m tall, 30 cm in diameter; branchlets ferrugineo-pubescent; leaves pseudo-veiticellate, oblong, oblong-lanceolate, 5-10 cm long, 1-2 cm wide, acute-acuminate at apex, acute-acuminate at base, entire, incurved margin, 4-6-nerved, subcoriaceous, strictly penni-nerved; petioles 3-7 mm long, pubescent, male flowers numerous, axillary fascicled; bracts elliptic-ovate, concave, 3.5-4 mm long, pubescent; pedicels 5 mm long, ferrugineopubescent; perianth 4-lobed, ovate, pubescent, 1.5 mm long; stamens 6; anthers 4-celled; filaments 3 mm long, glabrous; fruit globular, 8 mm in diameter.

Distribution: Hainan.

20. **Neolitsea obtusifolia** Merr.

Tree 8 m tall; leaves oblong-lanceolate to oblong-obovate, triplinerved, 4.5-7 cm long, 2-2.5 cm wide. The species is well characterized by its faintly nerved, obtuse, relatively narrow leaves, although the leaves are distantly triplinerved, yet the lower nerved which leave the midrib at from 7-12 mm above the base do not differ materially from the upper nerves except in being somewhat longer. All the lateral veins are very oblique, sharply ascending, and very obscurely anastomosing. The leaves might with almost equal property, be described as penni-nerved.

Distribution: Hainan.

21. **Neolitsea parvigemma** (Hayata) Kaneh. et Sasak.

Tetradenia parvigemma Hayata

Tree 17-25 meters tall; branchlets slender, gray, terete, rusty; leaves elliptic-oblong, 7-9 cm long, 2-3.5 cm wide, acute at both ends, entire, undulate at margin, thin coriaceous, dark green above, pale below, glabrous, 3-nerved; petioles 1.8 cm long, glabrous, brown; flowers in sessile clusters of small sub-umbels.

Distribution: Taiwan.

22. **Neolitsea phanerophlebia** Merr.

Small tree 5 meters tall. It is manifestly allied to *Neolitsea subfoveolata* Merr. differing in its indumentum on the leaves, branchlets, and petioles, and in its leaves being more or less glaucous beneath, not at all sub-foveolate, and distinctly appressed-pilose with scattered hairs.

Distribution: Kwangtung, and Hainan, at altitude 730 meters.

23. **Neolitsea pulchella** (Meissn.) Merr. (See orig. text page 539)

Var. 1. Neolitsea pulchella f. glabra Liou

Small tree, 5 m tall; leaves much smaller than the typical form of the species, glaucescent below; basal lateral veins prominently triplinerved.

Distribution: Kwangtung and Kiangsi.

24. **Neolitsea sieboldii** Nakai (See orig. text pages 539-540)

25. **Neolitsea sutchuanensis** Yang

Small tree, 10 m high; leaves elliptic-oblong to oblong-lanceolate, 7.5-13 cm long, 2.5-4.5 cm wide, acute-acuminate at apex, cuneate, at base, triplinerved; veins 3-5 pairs irregularly distributed; petiole 1-2 cm long, glabrous; fruit ellipsoid, 5-6 mm across; peduncle 2-4 mm long.

This species is related to *N. chuii*, Merr. f. *anamensis* Liou which differs in its reticulated leaves, schorter pedicels, and larger rugulose fruit.

Distribution: Szechuan, Hung-Ya Hsien.

Var. 1. Neolitsea sutchuanensis var. longipedicellata Yang f.

This variety is very similar to the type, but differs in its longer pedicels and in the leaves not glaucous on the lower surface.

Distribution: Yunnan.

26. **Neolitsea umbrosa** (Nees) Gamble (See orig. text page 540)

27. **Neolitsea undulatifolia** (Levl.) Allen.

Litsea undulatifolia Levl.

Small tree or shrub; leaves small (less than 9 cm long), narrowly elliptic with an undulate margin, penni-nerved, the midrib very prominent, with numerous pairs of more inconspicuous lateral veins. The fruiting inflorescences consists of sessile umbels. An individual fruit is borne on an enlarged pubescent pedicel which flares into a shallow, more or less crenulate, somewhat pubescent cupule. The fruit is ovoid-ellipsoid, black, approximately 12 x 18 mm, apiculate, rugose on drying. The young branchlets are appressed-pubescent.

Distribution: Kweichow.

28. **Neolitsea variabillima** (Hayata) Kaneh. et Sasak.

Tree 8–15 m tall, 40 cm in diameter; branchlets dark gray; leaves oblanceolate, 3-nerved, 9 cm long, 4 cm wide, acute at apex, ovate rotundate at base, incurved margin, coriaceous, lustrous dark green above, pale, slightly pubescent along the midrib and veins below; petiole 1.15 cm long, brown, glabrous; fruit globular, berry-like drupe, 8 mm long, 5 mm broad, clustered, axillary; pedicel 6 mm long, brown, glabrous.

Distribution: Taiwan, at altitude 1200–2300 meters.

29. **Neolitsea wushanica** (Chun) Merr.

Small tree, 4–10 meters high; branchlets terete, glabrous; leaves 7 cm long, 2.5 cm wide, elliptic, acute.

Family 44. Aceraceae Lindley
(See orig. text page 738)

Acer [Tournefort] Linnaeus
Key to sections

Genus (1) Acer Linn.

A. Leaves simple, undivided, or palmately lobed; leaves or lobes entire or serrate.

  B. Flowers andro-polygamous or andro-monoecious, in terminal inflorescences of leafy-branchlets; nutlets flat or convex but not ridged (except in *Acer giraldii*)

    C. Flowers andro-polygamous, in corymbose or paniculate inflorescences; disk extrastaminal (except in *Acer decandrum*)

      D. Leaves deciduous, usually palmately lobed, chartaceous; inflorescences long-paniculate or coymbose.

        E. nutlets much flattened, smooth; lobes of leaves usually not serrate -- Sect. Platanoidea

        EE. Nutlets convex, veined; lobes of leaves serrate or serrulate.

          F. Leaves 7–13 lobed; inflorescences corymbose and consisting of few flowers ------------------------ Sect. Palmata

          FF. Leaves 3–7-lobed; inflorescences usually long-paniculate rarely short-paniculate or corymbose, mostly consisting of numerous flowers ----------------------------- Sect. Spicata

      DD. Leaves mostly persistent, usually undivided, coriaceous, inflorescences short-paniculate. -------------------------- Sect. Integrifia

    CC. Flowers andro-monoecious, in simple racemes, disk intrastaminal -- Sect. Mcrantha

  BB. Flowers dioecious; staminate flowers from lateral leafless buds; nutlets strongly convex or ridged.

C. Winter buds with 2 valvate outer scales; flowers 4-merous; stamens 4-6; pistillate inflorescences terminal on leafy branches; (leaves undivided or 5-lobed) -- Sect. Arguta

CC. Winter-buds with numerous imbricate outer scales; flowers 5-merous; stamens 8-10; pistillate inflorescences, like the staminate, from the lateral leafless branchlets; (leaves 3-5-lobed)----------------- Sect. Lithocarpa

AA. Leaves pinnately compound, 3-7-foliate; leaflets entire or coarsely serrate.

B. Winter-buds with numerous imbricate scales; flowers few in corymbose inflorescences; disk large, extrastaminal; (leaves 3-foliate, but 7-foliate in Acer pentaphyllum) --Sect. Trifoliata

BB. Winter-buds with 2 valvate scales; flowers numerous in long racemes; disk wanting; (leaves 3-5-foliate) ------------------------- Sect. Negundo

Section I. Platanoidea Pax
Key to the species

A. Leaves deeply 3-lobed; lobes narrow, parallel and of equal length. ------------------ -
-- A. stenolobium

AA. Leaves undivided or shallowly 3-5-7-lobed; if lobed the lobes wide, ovate, not parallel and not of equal length.

B. Wings of fruits 1-2 times as long as nutlets.

C. Leaves usually truncate at base; wings of fruits usually as long as nutlets ---
------------------------------------- (97) A. truncatum

CC. Leaves subcordate or cordate at base; wings of fruits usually 1.5-2 times as long as nutlets.

D. Leaves usually 5-lobed; wings including nutlets 3-3.5 cm long, within 1 cm broad --------------------------------- A. mono

DD. Leaves usually 7-lobed; wings including nutlets 4-4.5 cm long, 1.5-1.8 cm broad --------------------------------- A. okamotoanum

BB. Wings of fruits 2-4 times as long as nutlets.

C. Peduncles of inflorescences 1-2 cm long.

D. Leaves large (7-14 cm long, 7-12 cm broad) with acuminate or caudate lobes; inflorescence large and loose (5-8 cm long)

E. Leaves glabrous, with acuminate lobes.

F. Leaves cordate at base, usually 5 or 7 lobed, rarely 3-lobed (in f. tricaudatum); wings broad usually spreading at obtuse angles ----
---------------------------- (11) A. cappadocicum

FF. Leaves rounded at base, distinctly 3-lobed; wings narrow spreading at acute angles ----------------- A. bodinieri

EE. Leaves pubescent below, with caudate lobes.

F. Leaves slightly rufous-pubescent below; fruits with nutlets and wings 2.5-3 cm long -------- (31) *A. fulvescens*

FF. Leaves densely yellowish gray pubescent below; fruits with nutlets and wings 3.5-4cm long ----- (92) *A. tibetense*

DD. Leaves small (4-6 cm long, 3-6 cm broad) with obtuse or acutish lobes; inflorescences small (3-4 cm long)----(90) *A. tenellum*

CC. Inflorescences sessile or subsessile.

D. Leaves densely grayish pubescent below; wings of fruit spreading at acute angles----------------------------(52) *A. longipes*

DD. Leaves glabrous or nearly so when matured; wings of fruit usually spreading at obtuse angles (at acute angles in *Acer acutum*).

E. Leaves undivided or rarely with 1 or 2 obsolete lateral lobes.

F. Leaves large, 9-20 cm long, 4.5-13 cm broad, acuminate; wings of fruit widest at the middle, usually 3 times as long as the nutlets ------------------------- (12) *A. catalpifolium*

FF. Leaves small, 6-9 cm long, 2.5 - 5.5 cm broad, long-caudate-acuminate; wings of fruit parallel, 2 times as long as nutlets ----------------------------(17) *A. chunii*

EE. Leaves distinctly 5-7-lobed, rarely 3-lobed.

F. Leaves densely grayish pubescent on the nerves of lower surface while young, scarcely so when matured; flowers small, 10 mm in diameter, with sepals and petals about 3 mm in length; wings of fruit parallel, spreading at acute angles -- (1) *A. acutum*

FF. Leaves glabrous except axillary tufts of hairs on the lower surface while young; flowers large, 15 mm in diameter, with sepals and petals about 5 mm in length; wings of fruit widest at the middle, spreading at obtuse angles --(4) *A. amplum*

Section II. Palmata Pax
Key to the species

A. Petioles and peduncles glabrous or nearly so; ovary glabrous.

B. Fruit with nutlets and wings, 1-2.5 cm long, spreading at obtuse angles ---(65) *A. palmatum*

BB. Fruit with nutlets and wings 3.5-4 cm long, spreading horizontally ---(77) *A. robustum*

AA. Petioles and peduncles pubescent, at least while young; ovary villose.

B. Leaves 9-13-lobed.

C. Leaves 9–11–lobed.

    D. Wings of fruit oblong or obovate, not widest at the middle.

        E. Flowers large, 14 mm in diameter, ovary and nutlets densely villous–– ------------------------------------ *A. japonicum*

       EE. Flowers small, 8–10 mm in diameter, ovary and nutlets slightly pubescent.

           F. wings of fruits inwardly curved. ---- *A. nudicarpum*

          FF. wings of fruit straight, not inwardly curved -------------------- -------------------------- (71) *A. pseudosieboldianum*

    DD. wings of fruit elliptic–oblong, widest at the middle ---------------------- -- *A. ishidoyanum*

CC. leaves 13–lobed ----------------------------- *A. takesimense*

BB. Leaves 5–7–lobed.

    C. Leaves truncate or subcordate, 7–lobed; lobes ovate–oblong, acuminate.

        D. Wings of fruit oblong, not contracted at base, spreading at obtuse angles; leaves doubly serrate ----------------------*A. microsieboldianum*

       DD. Wings of fruit obovate, contracted at base, spreading horizontally; leaves simply serrulate --------------------- (14) *A. cerciferum*

    CC. Leaves cordate, 5–lobed, lobes obvate, acuminate or acute.

        D. Petioles 2.5–3.5 cm long; leaves deeply lobed, argute–serrate sinuses reaching four–fifth of the blade ------ (73) *A. pubipalmatum*

       DD. petioles 1 cm long; leaves shallowly lobed, doubly–serrate, sinuses reaching to two–third of the blade ---------(66) *A. pauciflorum*

Section III. Spicata Pax

A. Leaves 5–7–lobed.

    B. Inflorescences corymbiforum; leaves 5–lobed.

        C. Leaves deeply lobed, lobes nearly entire; fruits slender, small, 1.8 cm long, with wings spreading at acute angles ----- (15) *A. chingii*

       CC. Leaves shallowly lobed, lobes crenate–serrate with obtuse teeth; fruits stout, large, up to 5.5 cm long, usually erect or spreading at acute angles --------- -------------------------------------- (33) *A. giraldii*

      CCC. Leaves deeply lobed, lobes serrulate with acuminate teeth; fruits slender, medium–sized, 2–2.5 cm long, spreading nearly horizonally ---------------- --------------------------------------(64) *A. oliverianum*

   BB. Inflorescences elongated paniculate; leaves usually 7–lobed rarely 5–lobed.

    C. Panicles loose.

        D. Ovary and disk hairy.

           E. Ovary and disk white pilose; leaves glabrescent.

    F. Leaves coriaceous or subcoriaceous ----------------------------

      -------------------------- (84) *A. sinense*

   FF. Leaves membranaceous ------ (80) *A. schneiderianum*

  EE. Ovary and disk densely yellowish pubescent; leaves perulous below --

   ------------------------------ (37) *A. heptolobum*.

 DD. Ovary and disk glabrous ------------ (28) *A. flabellatum*

CC. Panicles compact, cylindric.

 D. Leaves glabrescent or more or less whitish or yellowish pubescent below, sharply serrate with acute or acuminate teeth.

  E. Sepals broadly ovate, glabrous outside, densely villose inside; petals obovate; ovary densely villose; fruit with strongly veined, globose and ridged nutlets, and with wings spreading horizontally ----------

   ------------------------------ (26) *A. erianthum*

  EE. Sepals ovate-lanceolate, slightly pubescent outside, glabrous inside; petals linear-oblong or linear-oblanceolate; ovary densely pubescent; fruit with slight veined and subglobose nutlets and with wings usually erect or spreading at acute angles ----------------------------------

   ------------------------------ (13) *A. caudatum*

 DD. Leaves densely yellow tomentose below, coarsely serrate with broad acute or obtusish teeth; fruits with smooth, flat nutlets and slender usually erect wings ----------------------------------- *A. ukurunduense*

AA. Leaves usually 3-lobed (rarely with 2 basal lobes or undivided)

B. Inflorescences distinctly elongated paniculate or racemose.

 C. Inflorescences racemose; lobes of leaves elongated, caudate-acuminate, argute-serrulate; stamens inserted at the middle of the disk ------------------

  --- (99) *A. wardii*

 CC. Inflorescences paniculate; lobes of leaves not elongated, caudate-acuminate, entire or rarely serrulate; stamens inserted at the inner side of the disk.

  D. Inflorescences 5-6 cm long; lobes of leaves acuminate; flowers 5-merous; wings of fruits nearly horizontally spreading ----------------------------

   ---------------------------------- (100) *A. wilsonii*

  DD. Inflorescences 3-4 cm long; lobes of leaves acute or shortly acuminate, flowers 4-merous; wings of fruits spreading at obtuse angles ------------

   ---------------------------------- (96) *A. tucheri*

BB. Inflorescences corymbiform.

 C. Leaves membranaceous, with incisively serrate lobes --------------------

  ---------------------------------- (32) *A. ginnala*

 CC. Leaves coriaceous or subcoriaceous, rarely membranaceous, with entire o: sparingly serrate lobes.

  D. Lower surface of leaves green or yellowish but not glaucous.

E. Branchlets and inflorescence densely tomentose; petioles stout, densely tomentose; leaves shallowly 3-lobed, with lateral lobes forwardly directed ------------------------------ *A. fenzelianum*

EE. Branchlets and inflorescences glabrous; petioles slender, glabrous except puberulous near the apex; leaves deeply 3-lobed, with lateral lobes sidewise directed --------- (101) *A. yuii*

DD. Lower surface of leaves white or whitish glaucous.

E. Leaves membranaceous; sepals and petals within 2 mm long; fruits with slender usually erect wings ---- (8) *A. buergerianum*

EE. Leaves coriaceous; sepals and petals about 4 and 8 mm long respectively; fruits with stouter wings spreading usually at right or obtuse angles ------------------------ (67) *A. paxii*

Section IV. Integrifolia Pax

A. Leaves with basal and lateral nerves distinctly prominent.

B. Leaves usually cuneate at base, glaucous below, entire or rarely lobed but not serrate.

C. Leaves, petioles and inflorescences usually glabrous (in some species rarely pubescent while young)

D. Fruits small with nutlets and wings usually 2-3 cm long; petioles not over 3 cm long.

E. Leaves ovate or oblong, broad, (usually more than 2 cm broad); petioles short (usually not over 2 cm long); fruits large (over 2 cm long).

F. Leaves coriaceous or chartaceous, oblong or oblong-lanceolate, conspicuously veined above --(63) *A. oblongum*

FF. Leaves thick, coriaceous, usually ovate, inconspicuously veined above ---------------------- (54) *A. lucidum*

EE. Leaves lanceolate, (not over 2 cm broad); petioles long (2-2.5 cm long); fruits small (not over 2 cm long) ---------------------------
-------------------------------- (48) *A. lanceolatum*

DD. Fruits exceptionally large, 6-7 cm long; petioles 5-8 cm long ----------
----------------------------------- (23) *A. decandrum*

CC. Leaves, petioles, and inflorescences persistently pubescent.

D. Leaves lanceolate-oblong, slightly or moderately pubescent below; wings of fruit upright or spreading at an obutse angle

E. Wings of fruit 2.8-3.2 cm long, upright, spreading ------------------
--------------------------------- (18) *A. cinnamomifolium*

EE. Wings of fruit spreading at an obtuse angle.

F. Leaves green, tomentose below; fruit large, with nutlets and wings 2-2.2 cm long ----------(20) *A. coriaceifolium.*

FF. Leaves white woolly below; fruit small, with nutlets and wings not over 1.7 cm long ------------(41) *A. hypoleucum*

DD. Leaves ovate, usually with 2 small lateral lobes densely pubescent below; wings of fruit spreading at an acute angle -------------------------------- -------------------------------------- (86) *A. sycopseoides.*

BB. Leaves usually rounded to cordate at base, serrate or dentate especially toward the apex.

C. Leaves coriaceous, deep green above, white glaucous below, rounded or sub-cordate at base, remotely dentate and usually 3-lobed near the apex ---------- -- (24) *A. discolor*

CC. Leaves cartaceous or cartaceous-coriaceous, both surfaces brownish green, not glaucous below, cordate at base, sparingly serrulate near the apex ------ -------------------------------------(20) *A. cordatum*

AA. Leaves with basal and lateral nerves more or less raised but not prominent.

B. Both surfaces of leaves greenish, not glaucous below.

C. Leaves smooth, not distinctly reticulate above.

D. Leaves cuneate at base, entire, shining and deep green above, pale green below ------------------------------ (27) *A. faberi*

DD. Leaves cordate at base, usually serrulate near the apex, brownish on both surfaces ---------------------------- (20) *A. cordatum*

CC. Leaves distinctly reticulate on both surfaces.

D. Leaves cartaceous, not shiny, sepals glabrous ----------------------- ---------------------------------- (47) *A. laevigatum*

DD. Leaves coriaceous, shiny, sepals ciliate ------------------------------ ---------------------------------- (75) *A. reticulatum*

BB. Leaves glaucous below.

C. Leaves elliptical or oblanceolate, with pale green undersurface.

D. Wings of fruit spreading at an acute angle; leaves elliptical or elliptical-oblong ----------------------------- (85) *A. sino-oblongum*

DD. Wings of fruit spreading at an obtuse angle; leaves oblanceolate --------- ---------------------------------- (51) *A. litseaefolium*

CC. Leaves lanceolate, with whitish purple undersurface ----------------------- ---------------------------------- (2) *A. albo-purpurascens*

Synopsis of the species of Acer in section Integrifolia of Southeastern China

A. Leaves 3-nerved at base (series *Trinervium*)

B. Leaves whitish or glaucous beneath, usually not cordate.

C. Leaves whitish beneath, usually oblong or oblong-lanceolate

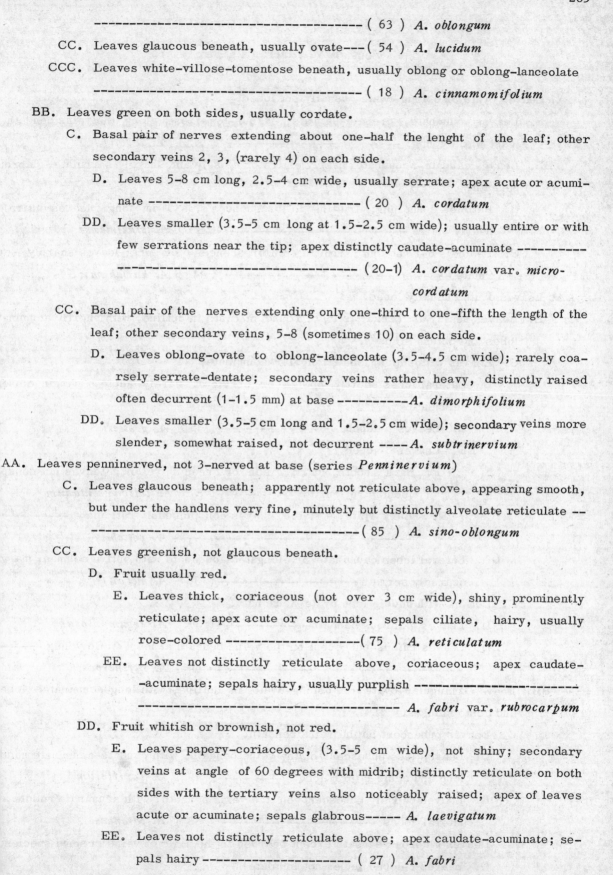

-- (63) *A. oblongum*

CC. Leaves glaucous beneath, usually ovate---(54) *A. lucidum*

CCC. Leaves white-villose-tomentose beneath, usually oblong or oblong-lanceolate

-- (18) *A. cinnamomifolium*

BB. Leaves green on both sides, usually cordate.

    C. Basal pair of nerves extending about one-half the lenght of the leaf; other secondary veins 2, 3, (rarely 4) on each side.

        D. Leaves 5-8 cm long, 2.5-4 cm wide, usually serrate; apex acute or acuminate ------------------------------- (20) *A. cordatum*

        DD. Leaves smaller (3.5-5 cm long at 1.5-2.5 cm wide); usually entire or with few serrations near the tip; apex distinctly caudate-acuminate -- (20-1) *A. cordatum* var. *microcordatum*

    CC. Basal pair of the nerves extending only one-third to one-fifth the length of the leaf; other secondary veins, 5-8 (sometimes 10) on each side.

        D. Leaves oblong-ovate to oblong-lanceolate (3.5-4.5 cm wide); rarely coarsely serrate-dentate; secondary veins rather heavy, distinctly raised often decurrent (1-1.5 mm) at base ----------*A. dimorphifolium*

        DD. Leaves smaller (3.5-5 cm long and 1.5-2.5 cm wide); secondary veins more slender, somewhat raised, not decurrent ----*A. subtrinervium*

AA. Leaves penninerved, not 3-nerved at base (series *Penninervium*)

    C. Leaves glaucous beneath; apparently not reticulate above, appearing smooth, but under the handlens very fine, minutely but distinctly alveolate reticulate --

--(85) *A. sino-oblongum*

    CC. Leaves greenish, not glaucous beneath.

        D. Fruit usually red.

            E. Leaves thick, coriaceous (not over 3 cm wide), shiny, prominently reticulate; apex acute or acuminate; sepals ciliate, hairy, usually rose-colored --------------------(75) *A. reticulatum*

            EE. Leaves not distinctly reticulate above, coriaceous; apex caudate-acuminate; sepals hairy, usually purplish ------------------------

---------------------------------- *A. fabri* var. *rubrocarpum*

        DD. Fruit whitish or brownish, not red.

            E. Leaves papery-coriaceous, (3.5-5 cm wide), not shiny; secondary veins at angle of 60 degrees with midrib; distinctly reticulate on both sides with the tertiary veins also noticeably raised; apex of leaves acute or acuminate; sepals glabrous----- *A. laevigatum*

            EE. Leaves not distinctly reticulate above; apex caudate-acuminate; sepals hairy --------------------- (27) *A. fabri*

Section V. Macrantha Pax

A. Leaves ovate or oblong-ovate, usually not lobed.

    B. Leaves acuminate, crenate-serrate, rufous-tomentose along the veins beneath at least while young ------------------------ (22) *A. davidii*

    BB. Leaves caudate-acuminate, nearly entire or closely and sharply serrulate, glabrous beneath.

        C. Petioles 2 mm long; fruiting inflorescences 13-15 cm long; leaves entire or nearly entire -------------------------- (83) *A. sikkimense*

        CC. Pedicels 6-7 mm long; fruiting inflorescences 6 cm long; leaves sharply serrulate ------------------------------ (44) *A. kawakamii*

AA. Leaves ovate, usually lobed.

    B. Leaves nearly as broad as long, roundish-ovate in outline, with shortly acuminate lobes and obtuse sinuses.

        C. Leaves with middle lobe triangular-acuminate.

            D. Lateral lobes shortly obtuse or obsolete, rarely acute, margin closely serrulate.

                E. Leaves 5-lobed -------------------(35) *A. grosseri*

                EE. Leaves 3-lobed.

                    F. Bark smooth, dark green or greenish yellow; leaves not conspicuously reticulate -----------(87) *A. taiton-montanum*

                    FF. Bark white, striated; leaves conspicuously reticulate ------------ ----------------------------------- *A. veitchii*

            DD. Lateral lobes cauminate or elongated acuminate with entire acumen; margin coarsely serrate --------------------(58) *A. metcalfii*

        CC. Leaves with middle lobe ovate-acuminate.

            D. Leaves glabrous beneath --------------(89) *A. tegumentosum*

            DD. Leaves rufous-pubescent on the veins beneath at least while young ------- --- *A. rufinerve*

    BB. Leaves triangular-ovate or oblong-ovate in outline, with long-acuminate lobes and acute sinuses.

        C. Leaves pubescent on the veins beneath.

            D. Leaves less pubescent on the veins beneath, with caudate-acuminate middle lobe and acute lateral lobes ---------- (49) *A. laxiflorum*

            DD. Leaves densely pubescent on the veins beneath, with acuminate middle and lateral lobes ----------------------- (88) *A. taronense*

        CC. Leaves glabrous beneath except bearded in the axils of veins in some species.

            D. Leaves 3-lobed (lobes not lobulate)

                E. Lateral lobes acuminate.

F. Middle lobe caudate–acuminate, lateral lobes acuminate or shortly acuminate; flowers with ovate–oblong sepals and obovate petals ————————————————————————————————— (29) *A. forrestii*

FF. Leaves with elongated caudate–acuminate middle and lateral lobes; flowers with linear–oblong sepals and petals ———————————————————————————————————— (99) *A. wardii*

EE. Lateral lobes usually shortly acute or obsolete.

F. Lateral lobes small, obtuse or obsolete ———————————————————————————————————— (87) *A. taiton-montanum*

FF. Lateral lobes comparatively larger, acute or obtuse —————————————————————————— (60) *A. morisonense*

DD. Leaves 5–lobed.

E. Leaves deeply lobed; lobes sharply serrulate and lobulate.

F. Middle lobe acuminate or caudate–acuminate; lateral lobes acuminate; basal lobes acute, reaching one–third to the middle of the blade; margin doubly serrate; pedicels 6 mm long ——————————————————————————— (57) *A. maximoviczii*

FF. Middle lobe and lateral lobes acuminate; basal lobes usually acute; sinuses deeply and narrowly acuminate, reaching two – third or four–fifth to the middle of blade; margin sharply serrulate; pedicels 8-12 mm long ———————————— *A. tschonoskii*

EE. Leaves shallowly lobed; lobes comparatively coarser serrate but not lobulate ——————————— (76) *A. rubescens*

Section VI. Arguta Rehder

A. Leaves undivided, densely pubescent below; fruits usually in long fruiting racemes —— (81) *A. staphyophyllum*

AA. Leaves more or less lobed, slightly pubescent below while young, glabrescent or glabrous when matured; fruits usually on short fruiting racemes.

B. Leaves distinctly 5–lobed, coarsely biserrate; petals obovate, clawed at base ———————————————————————————————————— (7) *A. barbinerve*

BB. Leaves slightly lobulate, incisively serrate, petals elliptical-oblong, not clawed at base ————————————————————————— (91) *A. tetramerum*

Section VII. Lithocarpa Pax

A. Leaves deeply 3–lobed, lobes oblong-ovate, nearly entire or rarely toothed with a few obtuse teeth; flowers in fascicle ————————————(70) *A. pilosum*

AA. Leaves shallow 3-5–lobed, lobes ovate or triangular-ovate, remotely serrate with coarse teeth or nearly entire; flowers in raceme or corymbose-raceme.

  B. Flowers yellow green; fruit usually with deciduous style ---------------------- --- (30) *A. franchetii*

 BB. Flowers purple; fruits usually with persistent style --------------------------- --- (82) *A. sino-purpurascens*

Section VIII. Trifoliata Pax

A. Leaves usually with 4–7 leaflets on each petioel; leaflets narrowly lanceolate 1–2 cm broad, entire ------------------------------------(68) *A. pentaphyllum*

AA. Leaves usually with 3–leaflets on each petiole; leaflets ovate or ovate-lanceolate, usually 3–6 cm broad, serrate.

  B. Inflorescence glabrous; nutlets glabrous.

    C. Inflorescence compound, containing many flowers; stamens nearly two times longer than the petals, exserted ---------------- *A. sutchuanensis*

   CC. Inflorescence simple, containing few flowers; stamens nearly as long as petals, not exserted (ex Maximowicz). ----------- (56) *A. manschuricum*

 BB. Inflorescence pubescent; nutlets pubescent.

    C. Leaves slightly pilose on the midrib below, occasionally papillose ----------- --- *A. trifolium*

   CC. Leaves with whole lower surface pubescent, not papillose

      D. Leaflets oblong-lanceolate, 7–14 cm long; nutlets with wings usually 5–6 cm long, less pubescent --------------(62) *A. nikoense*

     DD. Leaflets elliptic-oblong, 4–6 cm long, distinctly toothed with 2–3 bluntish teeth; nutlets with wings 3–3.5 cm long, densely pubescent ------------- ------------------------------------- (34) *A. griseum*

1. **Acer acutum** Fang

    Tree usually up to 10 meters high; bark brownish or brownish gray, smooth o slightly fissured; branchlets smooth, glabrous, those of the present years red or red dish green, those of the more than one year old brown or dark brown, lenticels ovate c rounded; winter buds brown ovate, outer 6 scales ciliate on the margin, inner 4- accrescent scales villose outside; leaves deciduous, chartaceous, cordate or subcor date at the base, ovate or ovate-oblong, 9–12 cm long, 6–20 cm broad, 5–7-lobed; lobe broadly ovate, or triangular; middle lobe and lateral lobes usually acuminate; bas lobes acute or obsolete; sinuses open, broadly obtuse; upper surface deep green, gla rous; lower surface yellowish green or pale green, reticulate, pubescent, especial densely grayish pubescent on the nerves while young, then glabrescent; petioles 4–12 long, puberulous near the apex while young then glabrous; flowers andro-monoeciou yellowish green, in puberulous terminal corymbs, on peduncles 3–5 mm long, from lea branchlets, appearing while developing of leaves; sepals 5, oblong, obtuse, ciliat slightly pilose outside, 2.8–3.2 mm long, 1.8–2 mm broad; petals 5, linear-oblanceolate or obovate, obtuse, glabrous, 3–3.5 mm long, 0.5–1 mm broad; stamens 8, in staminate flower as long as the sepals, in pistillate flower about 1.5 mm long, filaments glabrous; anther yellow; disk glabrous, extrastaminal; ovary glabrous, style glabrous, stigma incurved. Fruit glabrous, pale brown; nutlets compressed, 9–11 mm long, 7 mm broad; wings oblong, parallel-margined with nutlets 3–3.5 cm long, 9–10 mm broad, spreading at acute angles.

Distribution: Chekiang, Tien Mu Shan.

2. **Acer albo-purpurascens** Hayata

Small tree; branchlets slender, those of the present year red-purplish, pubescent, those of more than one year old dark purple or dark red, glabrous; leaves persistent, chartaceous-coriaceous, entire or slightly undulate, elongate-lanceolate, 10 cm long, 3 cm broad; actuminate or long-acuminate at apex; cuneate or broadly cuneate at base; upper surface green, lower surface whitish purple, glaucous, densely greenish pubescent while young; nerves 3 at the base, lateral nerves 7 pairs, more or less raised, diverging at acute angles; petioles 1.5 cm long, slender; flowers and fruits the winter never found.

Distribution: Taiwan.

3. **Acer amoneum** Hu et Cheng

Small tree 4–12 m high; Leaves ovate, 3.5–5 cm long, 1–1.3 cm wide, 7-lobed at base with 7 prominent veins, lobes acuminate, serrate at apex; flower andro-monoecious in corymbs, pubescent; peduncles 3 mm long; sepals linear-oblong or linear-lanceolate, rarely oblong, 3.5–4.3 mm long, apice obtuse, glabrous; petals and sepals similar sub-unequal, extrastaminal; ovary villose; style erect 2; samara 1.8–2 cm long, glabrous, sparsely pubescent.

This species is characterized by its thick coriaceous-ovate-3-nerved leaves, which are entire obscurely lobed above the middle, pale glaucescent on the lower surface, by its terete petioles, and by its yellowish pubescent inflorescence.

Distribution: Yunnan, at altitude 700–1000 m.

4. **Acer amplum** Rehder (See orig. text page 741)

5. **Acer angustilobum** Hu (See orig. text page 742)

6. **Acer bodinieri** Leveille

Tree usually 10–15 m high, rarely up to 20 meters high; bark brown or grayish brown, with conspicuous rounded lenticels; branchlets stout, glabrous, those of the present year purple or greenish purple, smooth, those of the more than one year old brown or yellowish brown, rarely deep brown; winter-buds subglobose, glabrous outside, slightly ciliate on the margin; leaves deciduous chartaceous, rounded at base, usually longer than broad, 10–16 cm long, 8–13 cm broad, 3-lobed, occasionally small entire leaves found in the same tree; middle lobes triangular-ovate, acuminate; lateral lobes obtuse or triangular-ovate, acuminate, forwardly directed; sinuses obtuse, reaching one-third to the middle of blade; upper surface deep green, glabrous, lower surface pale green, reticulate; primary nerves 5, glabrous, or sparingly whitish pubescent along the nerves while young; petioles 7-12 cm long, slender, glabrous; fruit purple while young, then greenish yellow, 3-5 in glabrous terminal corymbose fruiting inflorescences, about 5 cm long, on peduncles 1-2 cm long; nutlets oblong, compressed, flat, 1-1.5 cm long, 6 mm broad; wings sub-parallel or slightly broader near the apex, including the nutlets 3-3.5 cm long, 7-9 mm broad, spreading at acute angles; pedicles 2-2.5 cm long.

Distribution: Szechuan, Kweichow and Yunnan, at altitude 3000-3300 m.

7. **Acer barbinerve** Maxim.

Shrub or small tree usually about 5 m high; bark smooth, grayish yellow or grayish brown; branchlets slender, those of the resent year greenish or greenish purple, sparingly pubescent, those of more than one year old greenish yellow, or greenish brown, glabrescent; leaves deciduous, membranaceous, roundish ovate in outline, 8-10 cm long, 6-8 cm broad, cordate or subcordate at base, 5-lobed, middle lobe and lateral lobes acuminate, forwardly directed, basal lobes acute, doubly serrate, with coarsely obtuse teeth, sinuses acute, reaching one-half to the middle of blade; flowers yellowish green, dioecious, in racemes; pistillate flower in nodding racemes with small caducous bracts on puberulous peduncles; staminate flowers in short and simple racemes, usually 5 or 6 flowers forming a subsessile fascicle; sepals 4 oblong, petals 4 obovate-elliptical, 4-5 mm long, contracted at base; stamens 4 glabrous, slightly longer than petals; fruit greenish yellow, usually 5 or 7 in pendulous racemes fruiting inflorescence about 5 cm long on peduncles about 2 mm long; nutlets subglobose 1 cm long, 8 mm broad, strongly veined, rugose; wings introrse falcate, slightly contracted at base, 3-3.5 cm long, 1 cm broad, spreading at obtuse angles; pedicles 1-2 cm long, slender, glabrous.

Distribution: Machuria, at altitude 660-800 meters.

8. **Acer buergerianum** Miq. (See orig. text page 742)

> Var. 1. **Acer buergerianum** var. **nipponense** Rehd. (See orgi. text pages 742-743)
>
> Var. 2. **Acer buergerianum** var. **trinerve** Rehd.
>
> Var. 3. **Acer buergerianum** var. **formosanum** Sasaki
>
>> This variety differs from the type in the very short obtuse or obtuish lobes of the leaves, mostly broader than high, the middle lobe 1-1.5 cm long and about 2 cm broad, the upper side of the lateral lobes diverging horizontally from the middle lobe and forming a right angle with the outer margin, and in the diverging wings of the fruit.
>>
>> Distribution: Taiwan.
>
> Var. 4. **Acer buergerianum** var. **horizontalis** Metcalf
>
>> A shrub 5 meters tall; leaves 3-lobed and some are undivided into lobes but all 3-nerved at base, 5 cm long and 4 cm wide, entire margin;

petiole very slender, 2 cm long, dark green above, pale glaucous below; flowers greenish; fruit wings tinged; fruit purple along the inner margin.

Distribution: Chekiang, at altitude 1180 m.

Var. 5. Acer buergerianum var. kaiscianensis (Pamp.) Fang

This variety differs from the type chiefly in its more rounded and deeply 3-lobed leaves, glabrous beneath, and in its small fruits which have wings 18 mm long, 7 mm broad, spreading at obtuse angles.

Distribution: Hupeh.

9. **Acer caecium** Wall. (See orig. text page 743)

10. **Acer campbelli** Hook f. et. Thoms.

Small tree 5 meters high; leaves 5-lobed, 14–16 cm long and broad, the middle lobe obovate, long acuminate and coarsely serrate from the middle toward the apex; sinuses are half as long as the leaf-blade, coriaceous, dark green above, light green below; petioles 4 cm long; fruit brown.

Distribution: Kwangsi and Szechuan, at altitude 2330 m.

Var. 1. **Acer campbelli** var. **yunnanensis** Rehd. (See orig. text pages 743–744)

11. **Acer cappadocium** Gleditsch (See orig. text page 744)

Var. 1. A. **cappadocium** var. **indicum** (See orig. text page 745)

Var. 2. A. **cappadocium** var. **sinicum**

Var. 3. A. **cappadocium** var. **tricaudatum**

Var. 4. A. **cappadocium** var. **serrulatum** Metcalf

Large tree; bark reddish green, smooth; branchlets slender nodded; leaves distinctly 5-lobed, 15 cm long and broad in outline, 5-nerved at base, middle lobe oblong-lanceolate; sinuses more than half of the length of the leafblade, almost 45 degrees in diverging, lobes shallowly and minutely serrate long-acuminate at apex, dark green above, pale green below, coriaceous; fruit wings horizontally opened, in long terminal racemes; leaves densely serrulated on both surfaces, epsecially along the midribs and veins.

Distribution: Kwangsi.

12. **Acer catalpifolium** Rehd. (See orig. text page 745)

13. **Acer caudatum** var. **georgei** Fang

Var. 1. – 2. (See orig. text page 746)

14. **Acer cerciferum** Rehd. (See orig. text page 747)

15. **Acer chingii** Hu

16. **Acer chienii** Hu

Tree 17 m high; branchlets purplish black; leaves chartaceous, ovate-oblong, 8–13 cm long, 4–7.7 cm broad, tri-lobed; lobes caudate-acuminate, base cordate, 5–7-nerved, margin unequal doubly serrulate; petiole 2.5–5 cm long, purplish fruits in racemes 8–11 cm long.

Distribution: Yunnan.

17. **Acer chunii** Fang

Tree 7 m tall; glabrous; branchlets slender, dull brown, minutely lenticellate; leaves long slender petioled, deciduous, chartaceous, 3-nerved, ovate, rounded at the base, abruptly long-acuminate, with a long slender caudate falcate acumen minutely aristate at the apex, entire, unlobed at the same time variously 1-3-lobed on the same branch, lateral lobes equal or unequal, blade variable in size, larger ones 7-9 cm long and 4-5 cm wide, upper surface green, lower surface paler, minutely reticulated on both surfaces. three principal veins slender; inflorescences corymbose few-branched; nutlets flattened, not reticulate, ovate-oblong, 10 mm long, 6 mm broad.

Distribution: Kwangtung.

18. **Acer cinnamomifolium** Hayata (See orig. text pages 747-748)

19. **Acer confertifolium** Merr.

Small shrub about 1 m high, with rather densely much branched stems; bark brown or grayish, smooth, shining; leaves numerous, compactly arranged, 3-lobed, general outline ovate, blade 4 cm long and wide, base cordate 3-nerved, acute-acuminate apex, fruit wings widely divergent, wings obtuse slightly falcate, about 5 mm wide, twice as long as the seed-bearing part, glabrous, few.

Distribution: Kwangtung.

20. **Acer cordatum** Pax (See orig. text page 748)

Var. 1. A. **cordatum** var. **microcordatum** (See orig. text page 748)

Var. 2. A. **cordatum** var. **subtrinervium** (Metcalf) Fang

Tree 15 m high; leaves subcoriaceous, entire, lanceolate, 8-10 cm long and 2-3 cm wide, caudate-acuminate, cordate to round, at base, rarely broad obtuse, 3-nerved at base, extending only one-fourth of the leaf length, other veins penni-nerved, inserted at 60 to 85 degrees angle, usually 5-8 on one side, entire or rarely with few serrations at tip, petiole 1.3-2 cm long; inflorescences corymbose-paniculate, glabrous; fruit 5 cm long, wings wide spreading, 150 degrees, about 2.5 cm long, nutlets ridged.

Distribution: Fukien, at altitude 1280 m.

20. **Acer coriaceifolium** Leveille

Tree usually about 10 meters high, rarely up to 15 m; bark blackish gray or blackish brown; branchlets slender, those of present year brownish purple or brownish yellow, tomentose, those of more than one year old brownish yellow, glabrescent, lenticels ovate or oblong-ovate; winter-buds brown, shortly conical; scales ovate, tomentose on the margin; leaves leathery, persistent, ovate-oblong, oblong-lanceolate or rarely lanceolate, 8-11 cm long, 2.5-4.5 cm broad, broadly cuneate or cuneate or rarely obtuse at base, apiculate on the apex, margin entire; upper surface deep green, lower surface pale green or yellowish green, grayish green tomentose, less so when matured, lateral nerves 5-6 pairs, slightly impressed above, prominent below; petioles 1.5-3 cm long, slender, purple, tomentose; fruit brownish yellow, tomentose while young, slight so when matured, on tomentose corymbose fruiting inflorescence; nutlets strongly convex, 7 mm long, 6 mm broad; wings with nutlets 3-3.5 cm long, 7 mm broad, spreading at obtuse angles; pedicels 1 cm long, slender, tomentose.

Distribution: Hupeh, Kweichow and Szechuan, Mt. Omei.

. **Acer crassum** Hu et Cheng

Tree 10 m high. branchlets lenticelled; leaves coriaceous, elliptic oblong-elliptic, rarely oblong-obovate, 7.5-12.5 cm long, 3.2-3.3 cm wide, small petioled, apex obtuse-acute, obtuse-acuminate, base cuneate, penninerved; flowers monoecious, 5-merous, in terminal panicles, villose; sepals linear-oblong, oblong-obovate, apice rotundate, villose; petals linear or linear-lanceolate; ovary villose; samaras 2.7-3.3 cm long, locule convex, villose, 6 mm high, 7 mm wide.

Distribution: Chekiang, at altitude 1000 m.

. **Acer davidii** Franch. (See orig. text page 749)

Var. 1. **Acer davidii** var. **acuminifolium** Fang

Tree; leaves ovate-oblong, angust-serrulous, acuminate apex, 2-5 cm long, caudate-acuminate. It differs from the type species in its narrower ovate-oblong leaves, sharply serrulate with adpressed acute teeth and by the very long tip, which is up to 25 mm in length. It is closely related to *Acer laxifolium* Pax. var. *integrifolium* Fang

Distribution: Szechuan.

Var. 2. **Acer davidii** var. **glabrescens** Pax

Tree, bark dark gray; branchlets gray, glabrous; leaves obovate-oblong, 10 cm long, 5 cm wide, long-acuminate at apex, truncate at base irregularly dentate-serrate at margin, lustrous dark green above, pale green below, coriaceous, glabrous on both surfaces; fruits in terminal panicles; wings of fruit widely opened; pedicels 1 cm long, slender, glabrous.

Distribution: Szechuan.

Var. 3. **Acer davidii** var. **horizontale** Pax

Tree 20 m high; bark gray, stripped, whitish; leaves oblong, 10 cm long, 5.5 cm wide, attenuate-acuminate at apex, truncate base, ir-regularly-serrate margin, lustrous dark green above, light green below, coriaceous; fruits in terminal racemes; wings widely opened horizontally, greenish, pendulous.

Distribution: Chekiang, Hunan, and Anhwei, at altitude 700 m.

Var. 4. **Acer davidii** var. **integrifolium** Fang

Tree, 8 m high; bark green, smooth; branchlets glabrous, slender;

leaves oblanceolate, 6 cm long, 3 cm wide, long-acuminate at apex, cordate-truncate at base, serrate margin toward the tip of leaves, glossy green above, pale green and 6-paired nerves, glabrous below; petiole 5 cm long, reddish, glabrous; fruits in terminal, pendulous, slender, reddish racemes; samara red, widely opened; peduncles 6-10 cm long, red, glabrous.

Distribution: Sezchuan, Mt Omei. at altitude 2000 m.

Var. 5. Acer davidii var. trilobata Fang

This variety differs from the type chiefly in having a triangular distinctly 3-lobed leaves 4-5 cm in outline.

Distribution: Hunan.

23. **Acer decandrum** Merr.

Tree usually 6-8 meters high, rarely up to 12 m; bark brownish gray or blackish gray. Branchlets stout, glabrous, those of the present year purple or purplish green, those of more than one year old brownish purple; winter-buds brownish, globose; scales pubescent on the margin; leaves persistent, coriaceous, entire, elliptic-ovate or oblong-ovate, 8-15 cm long, 4-7 cm wide, apex acuminate or short-acuminate, base cuneate or broadly cuneate, upper surface pale green or brownish green, slightly reticulate, lower surface whitish or yellowish green, nerves slightly impressed above prominent below, basal nerves usually from one-third to one half as long as the blade petiole 5-7 cm long; flowers purplish, yellowish, dioecious, in glabrous racemes, cm in length, on glabrous peduncle about 1 cm long, from axillary buds, appearing after the development of leaves; sepals 5, ovate, glabrous, 2 mm long, petals 5, shorter than sepals; stamens 8-12; disk slightly pubescent, intrastaminal; fruit green or purplish green while young, brown or brownish yellow when matured; nutlets convex; wing falcate widest near the apex, with nutlets 6-7 cm long, 2 cm broad, occasionally only each pair developing, spreading at acute angles; pedicles 2-3 cm long, glabrous.

Distribution: Kwangtung, at altitude 500 m.

24. **Acer discolor** Maxim. (See orig. text pages 749-750)

25. **Acer duplicato-serratum** Hayata

Tree; 6-10 meters high; bark greenish gray, smooth; leaves obovate in general outline, 5-lobed, caudate at base acuminate at apex, sinuses widely opened, doubly serrate margin, midrib and veins prominently elevated, glabrous, glossy, dark green above, pale green glabrous below; petioles 6 cm long, glabrous; samara brown, wings with narrow base, 3 times as long as the seeds; nutlets 6 mm long, 1.5 mm broad, reticulated.

Distribution: Taiwan.

26. **Acer erianthum** Schwerin (See orig. text page 750)

27. **Acer faberi** Hance (See orig. text pages 750-751)

Var. 1. A. **faberi** var. **rubro-carpum** (See orig. text page 751)

Var. 2. A. **faberi** var. **megalocarpum** Hu et Cheng

This variety differs from the typical form in the large samaras, which are prominently reticulated, usually only one of each pair developing, about 4 cm long with the wings are up to 1.3 cm broad, somewhat incurved at apex. The samaras of the present variety resemble those of *Acer decandrum*, but the latter species has axillary inflorescence, longer (5–8 cm), petioles and larger samaras.

Distribution: Yunnan, at altitude 700 m.

28. **Acer flabellatum** Rehd.

29. **Acer forrestii** Diels

Var. 1. (See orig. text pages 751–752)

30. **Acer franchetii** Pax

Var. 1. **Acer franchetii var. majus** Hu

This variety differs from the type species in the leaves to 19 cm long, 17 cm broad; petioles to 15 cm long, and nutlets 1.5 cm long with upright wings to 7 cm long and 2–3 cm broad on the upper part.

Distribution: South Yunnan, at altitude 1780 m.

31. **Acer fulvescens** Rehder (See orig. text page 753)

32. **Acer ginnala** Maxim.

33. **Acer giraldii** Pax

34. **Acer griseum** Pax (See orig. text page 755)

35. **Acer grosseri** Pax

Var. 1. **A. grosseri var. hersii** (See orig. text pages 755–756)

36. **Acer henryi** Pax (See orig. text page 756)

Var. 1. **Acer henryi var. intermedium** (See orig. text page 756)

Var. 2. **Acer henryi var. serratum** Champ.

Tree 8–10 m high. It differs from the typical form by having all the leaflets coarsely toothed.

Distribution: Honan, Hupeh, Kiangsu and Chekiang, at altitude 360–500 m.

37. **Acer heptolobum** Diels (See orig. text pages 756–757)

38. **Acer hersii** Rehd.

Tree 8 m tall, belonging to the section Macranthae Pax. and is closely related to A. *davidii* Fr. and *A. laxiflorum* Pax. The first species is easily distinguished from it by the unidivided, generally oblong-obovate leaves, rounded or subcordate at the base and more densely pubescent furous-pubescent beneath and on the petioles when young, and in the usually larger fruits on slender pedicles. The second species, *A. laxiforum* Pax, differs from it chiefly in the caudate-acuminate, more closely and finely serrate leaves with acuminate teeth, glaucescent and glabrous beneath even when young and in the purplish and bloomy branchlets. Specimens of *A. henryi* with larger more prominently lobed leaves have some resemblance to *A. tegmentosum* Maxim. But the leaves of that species generally larger and broader with larger lateral lobes and a shorter middle lobe more sharply and doubly serrate with acuminate teeth and glabrous when young and the anthers are suborbicular.

Distribution: Honan and Hupeh, at altitude 1200–2000 m.

39. Acer hookeri Miq.

Tree 9 m tall; bark greenish gray, smooth; branchlets slender, glabrous, green; leaves obovate, 12 cm long, 7 cm wide, not lobed but pseudo–5–nerved at base, irregularly doubly serrate at margin, short acuminate apex, truncate at base, veins 7–9 pairs, lustrous dark green above, pale green glabrous beneath, subcoriaceous; petiole 4–5 cm long, green, glabrous; flowers yellowish green in mixed forests.

Distribution: Yunnan, at altitude 2300–2500 m.

40. Acer hilanense Hu et Cheng

Tree 10 m high. This species seems to be related to A. oblongum Wall. but differs from it in the thinner, oblong leaves with pubescent midrib and reticulate lower surface, rounded at base, caudate at apex, lateral veins more pairs, and in the larger samaras with oblong wings and subglobose nutlets cuneate at base, truncate at apex.

Distribution: Yunnan, at altitude 2500 m.

41. Acer hypoleucum Hayata

Small tree; bark dark; branchlets slender, those of the present year tomentose, those of the more than one year old, dark brown glabrous; leaves persistent, chartaceous, coriaceous, entire or slightly undulate, oblong or elliptic–oblong, 8 cm long, 3.5–4 cm broad; apex obtuse or acutish, base rounded or obtuse, upper surface glabrous, green or reddish green, lower surface whitish glaucescent, densely tomentose; nerves more or less raised above, distinctly prominent below, 3–nerved at base, lateral nerves 5–6 pairs, divergent at angles of 50–60 degrees; petioles 2–3 cm long, slender, tomentose; fruits in pubescent cymose inflorescence terminal on leafy branchlets; nutlets convex, 5 mm in diameter; wings with nutlets 17 mm long, 6 mm broad, spreading at angles of 80 degrees; pedicels 1.5 cm long, pubescent.

Distribution: Taiwan.

42. Acer johnedwardianum Metcalf

This species is closely related to A. oliverianum var. serrulatum Rehder

It has smaller, 3–lobed leaves with short ovate appressed serrulate lobes narrowed into a short obutish acumen, glabrous on both sides, reticulate beneath 2.5–4 cm long and 3.5–5.5 cm broad; corymb small and few–flowered.

Distribution: Fukien.

43. Acer kuikiangense Hu et Cheng

Tree 13 m tall; branchlets brownish black, pubescent; leaves chartaceous, oblong rarely oblong–ovate or oblong–elliptic, 7–10.2 cm long, 2.1–4.4 cm broad, apic caudate–acuminate, long–acuminate, margin remotely serrulate; nerves 7–9 pairs; petiol 1–1.8 cm long; fruits in terminal panicles, 5–7 cm long and 4 cm wide; samaras 2.5 c long, sparsely pubescent; wings horizontally in divergence.

Distribution: Yunnan, at altitude 1700 m.

44. **Acer kawakamii** Koidz.

Tree about 12 m high; branchlets slender, glabrous, those of the present year green or purplish green, those of the more than one year old green or dark green; leaves deciduous, chartaceous, ovate or ovate-oblong, 6–10 cm long, 3–4.5 cm broad, closely serrulate with sharp and appressed teeth, caudate-acuminate apex, rounded base, 5-nerved at the base and with 7–8 pairs of lateral veins, upper surface deep green, lower surface slightly pubescent on the nerves at first, then glabrous; petiole 3–4 cm long; stamens 8, shorter than sepals; flowers andro-polygamous in slightly pubescent racemes about 5 cm long on peduncles about 2 cm long, appearing while developing leaves; sepals 5, purple, oblong or obovate-oblong, obtuse, 2–2.5 mm long; petals 5, white, spathulate, emarginate, 3.5–4 mm long; disk glabrous, slightly lobed, intrastaminal; ovary purple, glabrous, style short, stigma revolute; fruits yellowish brown, nutlets covexed, 5 mm in dimaeter; wings introrsely falcate, spreading at obtuse angles; pedicels 6–7 mm long.

Distribution: Taiwan.

45. **Acer kwangnanense** Hu et Cheng

Tree 15 m high, 30 cm in diameter; branchlets angular, glabrous; leaves oblong, rarely elliptic-oblong, 8–14 cm long, 2.1–6.1 cm wide, obtuse-acuminate apice, rounded, rarely broadly cuneate at base, triplinerved; nerves 7–10 pairs; inflorescence corymbiformis; samaras 4.5–4.8 cm long, 8–9 mm wide.

Distribution: Yunnan, and Kwang-Nan, at altitude 1550 m.

46. **Acer lactum** C. A. Mey. var. tomentosum Rehder

Small tree; bark greenish gray, smooth; branchlets green, slender; leaves 3–5-lobed, 8 cm in outline, long-acuminate apex, undulate margin somewhat cordate at base, lustrous dark green above, pale green, reticulated below, coriaceous; petiole 7 cm long, slender glabrous; samaras few, in terminal small panicles, widely opened; wings 3 times longer than the seeds; pedicles 1 cm long; peduncles 5–7 cm long.

Distribution: Hupeh.

47. **Acer laevigatum** Wall. (See orig. text page 758)

48. **Acer lanceolatum** Molliard

Small tree with slender stem; bark darkish; leaves opposite, simple, coriaceous, entire, slightly undulate, oblong, 8–10 cm long, 1.7–2 cm broad, apex attenuate-acuminate and with incurved tip, base cuneate, lower surface glaucescent, nerves fine, distinctly 3-nerved at base, lateral nerves divergent at more than acute angles; petiole 2–2.5 cm long, slender; flowers 10 in glabrous terminal corymbs; disk extrastaminal; stamens 8, fairly developed; fruits with small nutlets 6–7 mm long, 3.5–4 mm broad; wings 2 cm long, 7 mm broad, spreading at angles of 80 degrees; pedicles long, slender, glabrous.

Distribution: Kwangtung, Kwangsi, and Sikang.

49. **Acer laxiflorum** Pax (See orig. text page 758)

50. **Acer liquidambarifolium** Hu et Cheng

Tree 15 m high, 30 cm in diameter; branchlets purplish black; leaves chartaceous, medium 3-lobed, lobes triangular-ovate, apice acute to acuminate and oblong-ovate, base cordate, rarely rounded or truncate, 8.5-14 cm long, 9.5-12.5 cm wide, glabrous; flowers andro-monoecious, 5-merous, in panicles, glabrous, 8-10 cm long, 2-2.5 cm wide; sepals small, triangular ovate; petals profundly 4-rarely 3-lobed, lobes lanceolate; stigma 2-lobed.

Distribution: Yunnan, at altitude 700-1000 m.

51. **Acer litseaefolium** Hayata (See orig. text page 759)

52. **Acer longipes** Franch. (See orig. text page 759)

53. **Acer longicarpum** Hu et Cheng

Tree 25 m high, 60 cm in diameter; branchlets glabrous, lenticelled; leaves oblong-ovate, oblong, 8-12.5 cm long, 3.8-5.7 cm wide, coriaceous, apice obtuse-acuminate, base rotundate trinerved; petiole 2.2-3.2 cm long; fruit in racemes 2-6 cm long; pedicles pubescent; samaras 6.2-7.6 cm long, densely pubescent.

Distribution: Yunnan, at altitude 1300 m.

54. **Acer lucidium** Metcalf

Tree 7 meters high; leaves distinctly coriaceous, 3-nerved, ovate to ovate-lanceolate, 6.5-8.5 cm long, 2-3 cm wide, apex acuminate to long-acuminate, base obtuse to rounded, glabrous, smooth and shiny above with veins inconspicuous, glabrous beneath, with secondary veins of 4-7 pairs, but not reaching the margin; petiole 10-15 mm long. Inflorescence axillary or terminal on short branches, 1, 2, or 3 together, sparsely pubescent; fruits with wings somewhat spreading about 70 degrees, each samara, 2-2.5 cm long and 9 mm wide; young branches reddish brown, older ones more grayish.

Distribution: Northern Kwangtung, and Kwangsi.

55. **Acer machilifolium** Hu et Cheng

Tree 16 m high, branchlets terete, glabrous, lenticellate; leaves coriaceous, glabrous, long-petiolate, elliptic-oblong, rarely oblong or elliptic, penni-nerved, base broadly cuneate obtuse or rounded; apex caudate-long-acuminate, 8-15 cm long, 3-7 cm wide; lateral nerves 10-13 pairs; petiole 1-6 cm long, glabrous; flowers monoecious, in panicles, axillary, 16 cm long, sessile, pubescent; sepals linear-oblong; petals linear-ligulate, rarely oblanceolate, ciliate at apex; stamens 8; disk extrastaminal, pubescent; samaras glabrous, 2-3 cm long, locules compressed, 12 mm long, 5 mm wide,

Distribution: Yunnan, at altitude 1800 m.

56. **Acer manchuricum** Maxim. (See orig. text pages 759-760)

57. **Acer maximoviczii** Pax

58. **Acer metcalfii** Rehder

59. **Acer mono** Maxim.

Acer mono is a variable species. It varies considerably in the size, shape, and lobing of the leaves and in the direction of the samaras which may be nearly horizontal to upright and connivent. As in other species of the genus, the extremes of these characters are connected by numerous intergrading forms, and the varieties even the species base on these characters are best considered as representing only forms, particularly as they do not show any clear geological segregation. Several new varieties have been transferred recently to *Acer mono* Maxim. The name *Acer pictum* under which this species has been generally known is invalidated by *Acer pictum* Thunberg of 1783, which is not an *Acer*, but belongs to the *Araliaceae* and is *Kalopanax pictus* (Thunberg) Nakai.

> Distribution: Shansi, Shantung, Kiangsu, Honan, Hopei, Manchuria, Chekiang Kiangsi, Shensi, Szechuan, Sikang, Anhwei, Hunan, Hupeh and Yunnan.

60. **Acer morrisonense** Hayata

Tree 10–20 m high, branchlets stout, glabrous; leaves pseudo–5–lobed, but 5–nerved at base, obovate in outline, 8 cm long, 6 cm wide, long–acuminate apice, coarsely serrate margin, lustrous green above, light green below, slightly cordate at base, coriaceous; petioles 6 cm long, glabrous; fruits in long pendulous panicles, wings broadly opened; pedicels 2 cm long, slender, glabrous.

> Distribution: Taiwan, at altitude 2300 – 3000 m.

61. **Acer negundo** L.

Tree to 20 m high; branchlets glabrous; leaves pinnate; leaflets 3–5, rarely 7 or 9, ovate to lance–oblong, 5–10 cm long, acuminate, coarsely serrate or the terminal ones 3–lobed, bright green, lighter green below and slightly pubescent or nearly glabrous; petioles 5–8 cm long; flowers yellowish green, before the leaves; the staminate ones corymbose, on slender pendulous pubescent stalks 2–3.5 cm long; the pistillate ones slender pediceled, in pendulous racemes; fruit glabrous; wings diverging at an acute angle and usually incurved, with the thick nutlets, 2.3–3.5 cm long.

> Distribution: Chekiang.

62. **Acer nikoense** Max. var. **megalocarpum** Rehd. (See orig. text page 761)

63. **Acer oblongum** Wall. (See orig. text pages 761–762)

> Var. 1. **Acer oblongum** var. **biauritum** Sm.
>
> Var. 2. **Acer oblongum** var. **concolor** Pax
>
> Var. 3. **Acer oblongum** var. **latialatum** Pax (See orig. text page 763)
>
> Var. 4. **Acer oblongum** var. **macrocarpum** Hu
>
> > Tree 17 m tall, bark gray, smooth; leaves lustrous green above, glaucous beneath, fruit not fully grown, rare. This variety differs from the type species chiefly in the large fruits; the persistent pubescence on the branchlets, the lower surface of the leaves and inflorescence is also found in the typical form as noted above.
>
> > Distribution: Kwangsi, at altitude 330 m.

Var. 5. **Acer oblongum** var. **trilobum** Henry

Tree 7 m tall, with 3-lobed leaves and the margins of leaves are remotely and sharply serrate; flowers are tiny, yellow, blooming in March, half way up to the mountains.

Distribution: Hupeh near I-Chang.

64. **Acer oliverianum** Pax (See orig. text page 763)

Var. 1. **Acer oliverianum** var. **serrulatum** Dunn (See orig. text page 764)

Var. 2. **Acer oliverianum** var. **nakaharai** Hayata

Tree up to 20 m high and 1 meter in diameter; branchlets slender, greenish gray, glabrous; leaves simple, 5 or 7-lobed and 5-7-nerved at base, long-acuminate apice, cordate at base, dentate-serrate margin, shiny green above, pale green below, sub-coriaceous; petioles 6 cm long; flowers in terminal panicles; samaras with broad wings, spreading nearly horizontally; nutlets compressed, globular, 1 mm in diameter; flowers yellow.

Distribution: Taiwan, at altitude 1333-2100 m.

Var. 3. **Acer oliverianum** var. **nakaharai** Hay. subvar. **formosanum** Koidz.

This sub-variety differs from the variety and the type species by having more shallowly sinuses and the spreading of nutlets in more smaller angles, and the fruiting petioles much shorter.

Distribution: Taiwan.

65. **Acer palmatum** Thunberg (See orig. text page 764)

66. **Acer pauciflorum** Fang (See orig. text pages 764-765)

67. **Acer paxii** Franch. (See orig. text pages 765-766)

68. **Acer pentaphyllum** Diels (See orig. text page 766)

69. Acer **pinnatinervum** Merr.

Tree 10-13 m high; leaves simple, not lobed, oblanceolate, 11 cm long, 5.5 cm wide acuminate at apex, cuneate at base, entire and incurved margin, lustrous dark green above, glaucous below; veins 14 pairs, prominently elevated beneath and depressed above; petioles strong, thick, round, 4 cm long, glabrous; fruits in axillary panicles wings broad, 2-3 cm long, 1.5-2 cm broad, diverging in about 30 degrees angle; fruiting pedicles 3-4 cm long, brown, glabrous; samara reddish green.

Distribution: Yunnan.

70. **Acer pilosum** Maxim. (See orig. text pages 767-768)

71. **Acer pseudosieboldianum** (Pax) Kom. (See orig. text page 768)

72. Acer **pubescens** Rehd.

Small tree 4-7 m tall; branchlets gray, rough; leaves 3-lobed but 5-nerved at base so some leaves look to be 5-lobed, the middle lobes 4 cm long, 3 cm wide, acute acuminate apice, deeply cordate at base, undulate and minutely serrate margin, dark green above, pale green with whitish hairs along the midrib and veins beneath, mem branaceous; petioles slender, purplish, white hairy, 4–6 cm long, clustered at tips of the spur –branchlets.

Distribution: Hupeh, at altitude 1850 m.

73. **Acer pubipalmatum** Fang

Tree usually 10–13 cm high,; bark gray or blackish gray, slightly longitudinally fissured; branchlets slender, those of the present year green or purplish green, densely white tomentose, those of the more than one year old greenish gray, or brownish gray, glabrescent, rough; buds purple; scales acutish ciliate on the margin; leaves deciduous, membranaceous, 4.5–5 cm long, 5–7.5 cm broad, truncate or sub–cordate, deeply 5–lobed, rarely 7–lobed; lobes lanceolate, acuminate, doubly serrate with argute teeth; sinuses acute or acuminate, reaching to four–fifth to the middle of the blade; upper surface deep green, lower surface densely white villose; petiole 2–4 cm long, densely villose when young; flowers purple, andro–monoecious, usually 5–8 in terminal corymbs, on villose peduncles 2–3 cm long, appearing after the developing of leaves; sepals 5, purple, ciliate on the margin, petals 5, yellowish white; stamens 8, glabrous; fruits purple brown; nutlets globose, 4 mm in diameter; anthers yellow; ovary densely villose; wings spreading at obtuse angles.

Distribution: Chekiang, at altitude 600–1000 m.

74. **Acer pubipetiolatum** Hu et Cheng

Tree 5–10 m tall; leaves oblong and oblong-lanceolate 6–9.6 cm long, 2–3.5 cm wide, base rotundate, truncate or subcordate, margin serrulate, 3–nerved at base, nerves 8–10 pairs; petioles 4–10 mm long; Flowers andro–monoecious, 5–merous; stamens 8; samaras 3.2–3.8 cm long.

Distribution: Yunnan, at altitude 1900–2600 m.

75. **Acer reticulatum** Champion   (See orig. text page 769)

76. **Acer rubescens** Hayata

Tree 10–20 m high; bark smooth, yellowish grey or dark gray. Branchlets slender, glabrous, those of the present year green or greenish purple, those of more than one year old greenish yellow or grayish black; leaves deciduous, chartaceous, roundish ovate in outline, 8–10 cm long, 6–8 cm broad, nearly truncate or subcordate at base, doubly serrate with coarser acute teeth, shallowly 5–lobed, middle lobe shortly ovate, acuminate or caudate–acuminate, lateral basal lobes, small, acute, obtuse, sinuses acute, obtuse, reaching one–fifth to the middle of blade, 5–nerved at base, nerves 5–6 pairs; petiole 5–7 cm long; fruits yellowish brown in small racemes; wings spreading at obtuse angles; pedicles 7–10 mm long, slender, glabrous.

Distribution: Taiwan, at altitude 2330–3000 m.

77. **Acer rubustum** Pax (See orig. text page 769)

78. **Acer salweenense** W. W. Sm. (See orig. text pages 769–770)

79. **Acer schoenermarkiae** Pax var. **oxycolpum** Handel– Mazz.

Small tree 5 m high; leaves 5–nerved, 3–lobed, sinuses acute, one–third deep as the length of the leaf, acuminate apice, rounded or truncate at base, remotely coarse serrate, margin, membranaceous, glabrous; petioles 10 cm long, glabrous; flowers very small in terminal panicles.

Distribution: Yunnan, at altitude 2300 m.

80. **Acer schneiderianum** Pax et Hoffm. (See orig. text page 770)

81. **Acer staphyophyllum** Hieronymus

Small tree, 5-10 m high, rarely up to 15 m; bark darkish or yellowish brown, smooth; leaves deciduous, chartaceous, ovate, 8-11 cm long, 5-6 cm broad, usually rounded or rarely slightly cordate at base, caudate-acuminate, cuspidate on the apex, coarse-serrate with appressed, obtuse or acutish teeth, 5-nerved at base, lateral nerves 4-5 pairs, densely whitish pubescent especially on the nerves when young, occasionally less pubescent when matured; petiole 3-8 cm long; flowers dioecious, in racemes; staminate flowers yellowish green; sepals 4, oblong, obtuse, 3-4 mm long, 3 mm broad; petals 4, slightly shorter than sepals, linear-oblong; anthers yellow and ovate; disk glabrous, lobed, exstrastaminal; fruit purple when young, yellowish brown when matured; nutlets oblong, convex, strongly rugose, 1.3 cm long, 1 cm broad; wings including nutlets 4-5 cm long, 1.5 cm rarely 2 cm broad, spreading usually erectly or rarely at obtuse angles; pedicels 2-2.5 cm long, slender, glabrous.

Distribution: Hupeh, Szechuan, Sikang, Yunnan and Tibet, at altitude 3700-4000 m.

82. **Acer sino-purascens** Cheng (See orig. text page 770)

83. **Acer sikkimense** Miq. var. **serrulatum** Pax. (See orig. text page 771)

84. **Acer sinense** Pax.

Var. 1. Acer sinense var. **concolor** Pax

Var. 2. Acer sinense var. **jatrophifolium** Diels (See orig. text page 772)

Var. 3. Acer sinense var. **pubinerve** (Rehd.) Fang

Var. 4. Acer sinense var. **brevilobum** Fang

Tree 15 m high; leaves small, 5-lobed; closely related to *A. sinense* Pax. but differs in the broad leaves being truncate or nearly rounded at base, shallowly 5-lobed, and remotely and shallowly serrulate. The oblong-ellipsoid nutlets are 8 mm long and 3 mm broad, with falcate wings, 3-3.5 cm long, and 1.4 cm broad, widest near the apex and very contracted at base.

Distribution: Szechuan, at altitude 1600-2000 m.

Var. 5. Acer sinense var. **longilobum** Fang

This variety differs from the type in the deeply 5-7-lobed leaves with much longer and narrower lanceolate, caudate-acuminate middle and lateral lobes, which are 6-8 cm long, 3 cm broad, coarsely and remotely serrate with appressed teeth and small basal lobes usually bending downward, as well as in the slender fruit which have globos nutlets with their wings spreading horizontally.

Distribution: Szechuan.

5. Acer sino-oblongum Metcalf   (See orig. text page 772)

6. Acer sycopseoides Chun

Small tree about 6 m high; bark grayish white, branchlets slender, those of the present year brownish yellow, densely pilose with yellowish hairs, those of more than one year old black; leaves persistent, coriaceous, ovate to triangular ovate, 5–7 cm long, 2–3.5 cm broad, 3-nerved; the veins impressed above, margin revolute, apex usually acuminate, base rounded or obtuse, usually with 2 obsolete lateral lobes, upper surface yellowish green, glabrous; lower surface pubescent and glaucous; petiole 1–2.5 cm long, stout, densely yellowish pubescent; fruit purple; nutlets 5 mm long, 4 mm broad, convex; wings with nutlets 1.8–2.2 cm long, 4 mm broad, spreading at obtuse angles; pedicels 5–10 mm long, yellow pubescent, in corymbose fruiting inflorescence.

Distribution: Kwangsi, at altitude 540 m.

7. Acer taiton-montanum Hayata

Tree usually 7–12 m high; bark smooth, dark green or grayish yellow; branchlets with small lenticels; leaves deciduous, chartaceous, triangular-ovate, acuminate or long-acuminate, lateral lobes small, 5–7 cm long, 4–5 cm wide, cordate or rounded at base, upper surface deep green, glabrous, lower surface pale green glabrous; lateral nerves 8–9 pairs; petiole 2–3 cm long; fruit greenish yellow or yellowish brown in fruiting racemes up to 4 cm long; nutlets convex, 1 cm long, 5 mm broad; wings 2.5–3 cm long, 8 mm broad, slightly introrsely falcate, spreading at right angles; pedicels 6–7 cm long, glabrous.

Distribution: Taiwan, at altitude 330–1000 m.

8. Acer taronense Handel-Mazz. (See orig. text page 774)

9. Acer tegmentosum Maxim. (See orig. text pages 774–775)

0. Acer tenellum Pax.

1. Acer tetramerum Pax.

Vars. 1–5 (See orig. text pages 776–777)

2. Acer tibetense Fang

A medium-sized tree; leaves deciduous, chartaceous, 6–9 cm long, 5–8 cm wide, base rotundate, 5-lobed, lobes triangular-ovate, acuminate, caudate-acuminate, aristate, sinuses acute, obtuse quadrantum; petiole 5–7 cm long; flowers in corymbs 5–6 cm long, 6 cm wide, subsessile; sepals 5, oblong; petals 5 obovate; fruits purplish.

Distribution: Tibet, at altitude 2000–2700 m.

3. Acer tonkinense Lecomte

Shrub with purplish branchlets; leaves 3-lobed but 5-nerved, lobes with acute apex, undulate entire margin, primary nerves prominently elevated and densely covered with white hairs, 12–15 cm long and 10–13 cm broad in outline, sinuses to one-third deep of the leaf-blade, acutely angled, lustrous dark green above, nearly glaucous below, base rounded; petioles 4 cm long thick, brownish, pubescent; fruits in terminal panicles, purplish; nutlets open widely nearly horizontally spreading.

Distribution: Kwangsi, at altitude 1150 m.

94. **Acer trifidum** Hook. et Arn.

Tree 20 m high, bark gray, smooth; leaves minutely 3-lobed and 3-nerved at base; sinuses very shallow and obtuse angled; lobes with acute apex; leaf-base rounded or broadly cuneate, entire margin and finely serrate on the middle lobe-margin, bright green and glabrous above, glaucous and glabrous beneath, 7 cm long, and 4.5 cm wide in general outline, thick, coriaceous; fruits in axillary racemes, nutlets closed, not spreading much, almost in 90 degrees angle.

Distribution: Kiangsu and Chekiang, at altitude 50 m.

95. **Acer triflorum** Komar. (See orig. text page 777)

96. **Acer tutcheri** Duthie

Tree usually 5-10 m high; bark brown or dark brown; branchlets slender, glabrous, those of the present year green or purplish green, those of more than one year old grayish brown or yellowish brown; leaves deciduous, membranaceous, rounded or rounded-truncate at the base, broadly ovate in outline, 6-9 cm long, 8-13 cm borad, usually 3-lobed, rarely 5-lobed, lobes usually irregularly-ovate, rarely ovate-oblong acute or acuminate, rarely caudate-acuminate, serrate, with argute teeth, entire near the base, rarely only with few small serrations near the apex; sinuses acute, reaching to two-third of the blade, upper surface deep green, lower surface pale green, glabrous, rarely with barbate hairs at the axils of the nerves; pedicels 2-3 cm long, slender, glabous; flowers andro-monoecious, in short panicles of 2-3 cm long, on pendulous 3 cm long, from terminal leafy branchlets, appearing the full developing of the leaves; sepals 4, yellowish green, ovate-oblong, obtuse, 2.5 mm long; petals 4, yellowish white, obovate, 2 mm long; disk slightly villose, slightly lobed, extrastaminal; ovary densely white pilose. stigma recurved; fruit yellowish; nutlets convexd, veined, about 6 mm in diameter; wings including the nutlets 2-2.5 cm long, 8-10 mm broad, spreading at obtuse angles.

Distribution: Kwangtung, Hongkong and Szechuan, at altitude 1000-1200 m.

Var. 1. Acer tutcheri Duthie var. **shimadai** Hayata

Small shrub with very slender branchlets; leaves 3-lobed; lobed with acuminate apex, rounded or truncate base, irregularly serrate margin, small; petioles slender, glabrous, 3-4 cm long, greenish red fruits in axillary and terminal panicles; wings spreading in about 45 degrees angles.

Distribution: Taiwan.

97. **Acer truncatum** Bge. (See orig. text pages 777-778)

98. **Acer villosum** Wall.

Tree 6-10 m high; bark purplish gray; branchlets stout, thick, dark gray, rathe rough, lenticelled; leaves large, 3-lobed, middle lobes obovate or oblong-ovate, short acuminate, caudate at base, irregularly dentate-serrate margin, 14 cm long and 16 cm broad in general outline, sinuses acute, 1/3 deept to the length of the lobes, lustrous dark green above, brownish pubescent with very prominently elevated and densely veined and 5-nerved at base beneath,coriaceous or subcoriaceous;fruits large, in few-flowered axillary racemes, nutlets rounded, reticulated, 12 mm in diameter, wings spreading in acute angles, including nutlets 4.5 cm long, 1.5 cm broad; pedicels of the fruit 2 cm long.

Distribution: Yunnan, at altitude 2800 m.

99. **Acer wardii** W. W. Smith (See orig. text page 778)

100. **Acer wilsonii** Rehder (See orig. text pages 778-779)

Var. 1. **Acer wilsonii** var. **chekiangense** Fang

This new variety differs from the type in having the leaves distinctly 5-lobed, sparsely pubescent on the lower surface, serrate almost to the base of the lobes, truncate or slightly cordate at base, with pubescent petioles. The leaves and petioles will not likely become glabrescent when fully matured. This variety is related to *Acer angustilobum* Hu, but the latter has narrower leaves, with narrower, larger and long caudate-acuminate lobes, cuneate and rounded at base and glabrous on the lower surface and petioles.

Distribution: Chekiang, at altitude 1180 meters.

Var. 2. **Acer wilsonii** var. **kwangtungense** Chun

This variety differs from the type in being conspicuously pilose with yellowish hairs on the branchlets, petioles, on both surfaces of the leaves along the veins and throughout the under surface.

Distribution: Kwangtung, Anhwei and Kweichow. Tree 8-15 meters high.

101. **Acer yui** Fang

Tree about 7 m high; bark brownish gray or blackish gray, longitudinally slitting; branchlets lenticelled; leaves deciduous, chartaceous, nearly rounded or broadly obtuse at the base, broadly ovate in outline, 5-7 cm long, 3.5-5.5 cm broad, 3-lobed, the margin of the lobes entire or slightly sinuate; middle lobes ovate, oblong-lanceolate or lanceolate., acute, below the middle of the blade the two sides of the margins usually parallely; lateral lobes usually triangular-ovate, obtuse;sinuses obtuse, reaching from 3/5 to 1/3 of the blade; upper surface deep green, glabrous, smooth, lowers surface yellowish or yellowish green, reticulate, grayish or yellowish pubescent at the axils of the nerves; primary nerves 3, inconspicuous above, prominent below, secondary nerves 5-7 pairs, elevated below; petiole 3-4 cm long, purplish or purplish green, slender, near the apex slightly pubescent, below glabrescent; fruit yellowish brown, 3-5 in cor-ymbose fruiting inflorescences, on peduncles 5-7 mm long; nutlets 7 mm long, 5 mm broad, convex, veined, slightly puberulous; wings including nutlets 2.3 cm long, 1 cm broad, obovate, obutse, spreading at obtuse angles; pedicels slender, 3-5 mm long.

Distribution: Szechuan, at altitude 1905 m.

Family 45. Hippocastanaceae D C.

(See orig. text page 779)

Genus (1) Aesculus Linn. (See orig. text pages 779-780)

1. **Aesculus assamica** Griffith

Tree 10-12 m high; bark grayish brown. Branchlets slender, stout, yellowish brown, glabrous. Leaves digitate, leaflets 7, oblanceolate, 18 cm long, 7 cm wide, abruptly acuminate apex, cuneate at base, finely serrate margin, lustrous dark green above, pale brownish and glabrous below; subcoriaceous; petioles 1-2 cm long, somewhat grooved above. Flowers in large terminal panicle, white, with orange yellow strips, companulate, 5-toothed, 5-lobed; sepals 5-lobed.

Distribution: Yunnan, at altitude 1500 meters.

2. **Aesculus chinensis** Bunge (See orig. text page 780)

3. **Aesculus wilsonii** Rehder (See orig. text pages 480-482)

Genus (2) Bretschneidera Hemsley (See orig. text page 783)

1. **Bretschneidera sinensis** Hemsley (See orig. text page 783)

Family 46. Sapindaceae Juss.

Key to the genera (See orig. text pages 783-784)

Genus (1) Sapindus Linn. (See orig. text pages 784-785)

1. **Sapindus delavayi** (Franchat) Radlk. (See orig. text page 785)

2. **Sapindus mukorossi** Gaertn. f. (See orig. text pages 785-786)

3. **Sapindus oligophyllus** Merrill et Chun

Tree 10 m high. Leaves 12-18 cm long, 1-4-foliated; petiole 1.5-2 cm long. This species in general resembles *Sapindus mukorossi* Gaertn. f. but with smaller fruits, shorter leaves, and much fewer leaflets, most of the leaves have but a single pair of leaflets and these sometimes reduced to 1, occasionally there being 3 leaflets, rarely 4.

Distribution: Hainan, at altitude 570 m.

4. **Sapindus tomentosus** Kurz.

Tree 3-10 m high, close related to *Sapindus delavayi* Radik., but this species differs in having tomentose leaves.

Distribution: In Yunnan, at altitude 1800 m.

Genus (2) Euphoria Comm. (See orig. text page 787)

1. **Euphoria longana** Lamark (See orig. text page 787)

Genus (3) Litchi Sonnerat (See orig. text page 787)

1. **Litchi sinensis** Sonnerat (See orig. text pages 788-789)

Genus (4) **Koelreuteria** Laxm. (See orig. text page 789)

1. **Koelreuteria apiculata** Rehd. et Wilson (See orig. text page 789)

2. **Koelreuteria bipinnata** Laxm. (See orig. text page 790)

3. **Koelreuteria formosana** Hayata

Tree up to 17 m high; bark reddish gray. Branchlets slender, reddish purple, densely lenticelled, glabrous; leaves bipinnate, leaflets 11-15 alternate, leaflets oblong 5 cm long, 2.5 cm wide, abruptly acuminate, obtuse and asymmetrical at base, deeply doubly serrate at margin, dark lustrous green above pale green somewhat whitish pubescent along the midrib below, coriaceous; petioles 1 mm long, red, with whitish hairs; fruits solitary in an orbiculary bladdery 4 cm long and 5 cm broad, papery, slightly notched on the top, reticulated, sessile; peduncles 1 cm long, glabrous. Flowers yellow.

Distribution: Taiwan, Heng-chun.

4. **Koelreuteria paniculata** Laxm. (See orig. text page 790)

Var. 1. **Koelreuteria paniculata** var. **apiculata** (R. et W.) Rehd.

It is distinguished by the usually bipinnate leaves, the suborbicular to broad-oval sepals with erose or lacerate margin.

Distribution: Kwangsi and Kweichow.

5. **Koelreuteria integrifolia** Merr. (See orig. text pages 791-792)

6. **Koelreuteria minor** Hemsl.

Tree 20 m high; bark grayish brown, longitudinally stripped. Branchlets stout grayish brown, rough. Leaves simple compound, alternate; leaflets 15-19, alternate, 2.5 cm long, 1 cm wide, oblong, acute at apex, obtuse asymmetrical at base, dark green above, pale green glabrous below, subcoriaceous; flowers reddish in large terminal panicle; fruit a 2-lobed bladdery and a thin walled capsule, purplish, 18 mm long and across, notched at apex; pedicles 3 mm long; peduncles 1 cm long, slightly pubescent.

Distribution: Kwangsi.

Genus (5) **Xanthoceras** Bunge (See orig. text page 792)

1. **Xanthoceras sorbifolia** Bunge (See orig. text pages 792-793)

Order VII. Rhamnales
Family 47. Rhamnaceae Lindl.

Key to genera of Rhamnaceae (See orig. text pages 793-794)

Genus (1) **Paliurus** Mill. (See orig. text pages 794-795)

1. **Paliurus hemsleyana** Rehd. (See orig. text page 795)

2. **Paliurus hirsutus** Hemsley

3. **Paliurus orientalis** (Fr.) Hemsley (See orig. text page 796)

4. **Paliurus ramosissimus** (Lour.) Poir.

Genus (2) **Zizyphus** Mill. (See orig. text page 797)

1. **Zizyphus fungii** Merr.

Tree 14 m high, half a meter in diameter; branchlets slender, with short hooked spines; and densely lenticelled leaves elliptic-oblong, 7 cm long, 3.5 cm wide, acute apice, and unequal at base, finely serrate margin, pseudo-3-nerved at base, lustrous dark green above, pale glaucous below, coriaceous, brownish pubescent along the midrib and veins beneath; petiole 5 mm long. Flowers in lateral panicles; petals 4 in creay white color; fruit globular 2 cm in diameter, brown, berrylike.

Distribution: Hainan, at altitude 230 meters.

2. **Zizyphus funiculosa** Hance

A climber. Branchlets with small climbing hooks. Leaves oblanceolate, 9 cm long, 4.5 cm wide acute apice, caudate and unequallateral at base, light green, glabrous above, pale green with prominently elevated and brownish pubéscent pseudo-5-nereves underneath, finely serrate margin, coriaceous; petiole 6 mm long, brown; fruit oblong-cylindrical capsule, 2 cm long, 1.5 cm in diameter, brownish gray. The trunk with spines.

Distribution: Yunnan, at altitude 1100-1500 m.

3. **Zizyphus glabrata** Heyne

Shrub; stem and branches with long sharp spines, with dense spreading branches ascending. Branchlets slender, 8 m in height; leaves obovate, 4 cm long, 2.5 cm wide, 3- nerved at base, blunt to acute apice, obtuse equallateral at base, crenate serrate margin, dark green above, pale green, glabrous beneath, coriaceous; petiole 5 mm long; flowers yellowish in lateral panicles.

Distribution: Kwangsi, at altitude 600 m.

4. **Zizyphus incurva** Roxb.

Tree 14 m high. Branchlets with minute sparse spines, gray. Leaves oblong, 8 cm long, 4.5 cm wide, long acute apice, unequallateral obtuse at base, finely crenate serrate margin, dark green above pale green, glabrous, with 3-nerves brownish and prominently elevated below, coriaceous; petiole 1 cm long, stout, reddish brown; fruit a yellow berry.

Distributinn: Kwangsi, and Yunnan, at altitude 2200 m.

5. **Zizyphus jujuba** Mill. (See orig. text page 789)

    Var. 1. **Zizyphus jujuba** var. **inermis** (Bge.) Rehd.

6. **Zizyphus laui** Merr.

A scandent shrub 2 meters high. Leaves sub-membranaceous, oliver green, 4-5 cm long, 2.5 cm wide, sub-rhomboidal-ovate, distantly inequallateral on both sides of the leaf-blade, broadly acute end, 3-nerved at base, obtuse rotundate at apex, minute obscure apiculate-serrate margin, sub-coriaceous; petiole 4-6 mm long, pubescent inflorescence axillary, solitary, in subumbellate-cymose; flowers 3-5 mm in diameter green; calyx lobes ovate-acute to acuminate, 1.3 mm long; petals oblong-ovate, rotundate.

Distribution: Hainan.

7. **Zizyphus mauritiana** Lam.

8. **Zizyphus montana** Sm. (See orig. text page 779)

9. **Zizyphus oenoplia** Miller

A straggly shrub. Leaves oblong, 6 cm long, 3 cm wide, acute apice, obtuse inequallateral, pseudo-5-nerved at base, minutely serrate margin, dark bluish green and pubescent above, reddish brown hairy along the midrib and veins beneath; flowers white; bark reddish brown, thorny; fruits globular, small, 1 mm in diameter, mucronate, brown, axillary, solitary or in two's; fruiting pedicles 2 mm long brownish pubescent.

Distribution: Kwangsi, at altitude 200-700 meters.

10. **Zizyphus pubinervis** Rehd.

Tree; leaves chartaceous, oblong-lanceolate, 5-9 cm long, 2-3 cm wide, acuminate at apex, obliquely cuneate and broadly subrotundate at base, minutely apiculate-serrate margin; petiole 2-4 mm long, pilose; drupe ovoid-subglobose, 10-11 mm long, 9-10 mm wide; flowers 2-4 in umbeliformis cymes. Fruiting exocarp rugose, monosperma.

Distribution: Kwangsi and Kweichow.

11. **Zizyphus rugosa** Lam.

Shrub 2 m high. Leaves obovate, 15 cm long, 10 cm wide, acute at apex, cordate pseudo-5-nerved at base, finely crenate serrate margin, lustrous dark shining green above, brownish pubescent and densely wooly along the midrib and veins and primary veins very prominently elevated below, subcoriaceous; petioles thick, stout 7 mm long, brownish hairy; flowers pale yellow; stamens yellow, pistil pale green. Inflorescence in lateral umbellate cymes. Branches sparsely thorny.

Distribution: Hainan, Yunnan and Kwangsi.

12. **Zizyphus yunnanensis** Schneider (See orig. text page 799)

Genus (3) Rhamnus Linn. (See orig. text page 800)

1. **Rhamnus acuminatifolia** Hayata

Small shrub 1-2 meters tall. Branchlets terete, slender, grayish brown. Leaves lanceolate to oblong-lanceolate, 5-10 cm long, 1-4.5 cm wide, short acuminate at apex, cuneate at base, distantly fine serrate margin, dark shining green above, pale brownish pubescent and hairy along the midrib and veins below; veins 5-10 pairs prominently elevated beneath and distinctly deppressed above, subcoriaceous; petioles 5-15 mm long; fruits in axillary umbels, round, 2 mm in diameters, 2-seeded, brown.

Distribution: Taiwan, at altitude 2330 m.

2. **Rhamnus aurea** Heppler

Erect shrub 1-2 meters tall. Flowers white.

Distribution: Yunnan.

3. **Rhamnus arguta** Maxim.

4. **Rhamnus blinii** (Level.) Rehder

Small tree 7 m tall. Branchlets gray, smooth, glabrous. Leaves oblanceolate 12 cm long, 4 cm wide, acute or long-acuminate at apex, obtuse to base, irregularly crenate-serrate or finely serrate margin, lustrous olive-green above, pale green and slightly pubescent along the midrib and veins below; secondary veins 10-13 pairs very prominently elevated beneath; petioles 2 mm long; fruits globular, 1.5 mm in diameter, 2-seeded, solitary, axillary, lateral; brownish black; fruiting pedicels slender, 1 cm long.

Distribution: Szechuan, at altitude 1500 m.

Var. 1. Rhamnus blinii var. sargentianus (Schneider) Rehd.

Tree or shrub 12 m tall. Leaves elliptic-oblong, 7 cm long, 4 cm wide, short-acuminate, obtuse or cuneate at base, finely serrate margin, dark green above, pale green slightly brownish pubescent along the midrib and veins beneath, subcoriaceous; petiole 5 mm long; fruits soliatry, globular, 1.5 mm across, 2-4-seeded, black; pedicles slender 1 cm long.

Distribution: Szechuan, at altitude 2000-3300 m.

5. **Rhamnus hemsleyanus** Schneider (See orig. text page 801)

6. **Rhamnus bodinerei** Levl.

7. **Rhamnus coriophylla** Handel-Mazz.

Shrub 5 m tall. Leaves elliptic-oblong to ovate elliptic, 3.5 cm long, 2-4 cm wide, acuminate apex, cuneate at base, remotely dentate, serrate margin; flowers singular, axillary, racemose, 10-flowered; calyx tubular, sepals 5; stamens abortive 5; style 3.

Distribution: Kwangsi and Taiwan at altitude 870 m.

8. **Rhamnus chlorophorus** Decne. (See orig. text page 801)

9. **Rhamnus crenatus** S. et Z.

10. **Rhamnus davurica** Pall.

11. **Rhamnus dumetorum** Schneider

12. **Rhamnus esquirolii** Levl. (See orig. text page 802)

13. **Rhamnus formosanus** Matsum.

Shrub 2-5 m tall. Branchlets slender, gray, glabrous. Leaves ovate to oblong-ovate, 5 cm long, 3 cm wide, bluntly acute apex, obtuse at base, doubly serrate margin, dark green above, pale green, glabrous beneath coriaceous; petiole 1.5-2 cm long, glabrous; flowers in axillary racemes; fruits small, globular, 1 mm in diameter, 2-seeded, brown; fruiting pedicels 5 mm long.

Distribution: Taiwan, at altitude 600-1100 m.

14. **Rhamnus forrestii** Sm.

Shrub 4 meters tall; flowers light yellow; leaves elliptic, 4 cm long, 2.5 cm wide, acuminate apex, obovate at base finely serrate margin, light olive green above, pale green below, subcoriaceous.

Distribution: Yunnan.

15. **Rhamnus fulvotinctus** Metcalf

Shrub 2.5 meters tall, unarmed; leaves alternate typically elliptic to lanceolate-elliptic, 5–6 cm long, 1.5–2.2 cm wide, apex acuminate, base cuneate; nerves 4–5 pairs; margin entire, revolute; petiole 3–4 mm long; fruits 1–2, rarely 3–4 in each axil, globose to ovoid; seeds 5.5 mm long, smooth.

Distribution: Kwangtung.

16. **Rhamnus globosus** Bge.

17. **Rhamnus hainanensis** Merr. et Chun

Scandent shrub. Leaves oblong, 10 cm long, 5 cm wide, acuminate at apex, obtuse at base, finely serrate margin, subcoriaceous; Flowers green, Fruits green, globular, 2 mm in diameter, mucronate.

Distribution: Hainan, and Kwangtung.

18. **Rhamnus hamatidens** Levl.

Shrub 2 m tall; leaves lanceolate elongate, 4–10 cm long, 8–25 mm wide; acuminate apex, margin denticulate or irregularly distantly dentate; flowers 5–7 in fascicles, petals wanting.　　　　　　　　　　Distribution: Kweichow.

19. **Rhamnus henryi** Schneider　(See orig. text page 802)

20. **Rhamnus heterophyllus** Oliv.

21. **Rhamnus hupehensis** Schneider

22. **Rhamnus iteinophyllus** Schneider

23. **Rhamnus lamprophyllus** Schneider

24. **Rhamnus leptocanthus** Schneider

25. **Rhamnus leptophyllus** Schneider　(See orig. text page 803)

　　　　Var. 1.　**Rhamnus leptophyllus** var. **milensis** Schneid.

　　　　Var. 2.　**Rhamnus leptophyllus** var. **scabrellus** Rehd.

26. **Rhamnus leveillianus** Fedde

27. **Rhamnus libanotica** Boiss.

Shrub 2 m tall. Branchlets slender, whitish gray, glabrous. Leaves oblong- obovate or elliptic-oblong, 7 cm long, 3.5 cm wide, short acuminate at apex, cuneate unequal at base, irregularly crenate-serrate margin, dark green above, pale green slightly pubescent below; fruit solitary, axillary, globular, 1 mm in diameter; pedicels 1 cm long, whitish hairy.

Distribution: Chekiang.

28. **Rhamnus longipes** Merr. et Chun

Erect shrub; leaves oblong-lanceolate, acute-acuminate apex, acute at base, margin distantly crenate-serrate, dentate, incurved-apiculate, subcoriaceous. Inflorescences axillary subumbellate; fruits singular, 2 or 3, globose-obovoid, red, chestnut brown, 6 mm in diameter.

Distribution: Hainan, at altitude 1800 m.

29. **Rhamnus meyeri** Schneider (See orig. text page 803)

30. **Rhamnus nakaharai** Hayata

Shrub or small tree 10 m tall. Branchlets reddish gray, lenticellate. Leaves oblong or elliptic-oblong, 5-8 cm long, 3-4 cm wide, short acuminate or acute at apex, cuneate or rounded at base, finely serrate margin, lustrous dark green above, pale green, slightly brownish pubescent below, veins 6 pairs; midrib and veins prominently elevated, subcoriaceous. Fruits in axillary racemes, globular, 1 mm in diameter, dull red to black; pedicels slender 6 mm long, pubescent.

Distribution: Taiwan, at altitude 1000 m.

31. **Rhamnus nepalensis** Wall. (See orig. text page 803)

32. **Rhamnus obovatilimbus** Merr. et Metcalf

Shrub 2.5 m tall. Leaves oblong-ovate, 5 cm long, 3.5 cm wide, rounded at top, broadly cuneate at base, irregulary crenate dentate margin; fruits green, globular 2 mm in diameter 2-4-seeded; pedicels slender, 5 mm long.

Distribution: Kwangtung.

33. **Rhamnus oiwakensis** Hayata

Bush 2-3 m tall. Leaves small, oblanceolate 3.5 cm long, 2 cm wide, clustered at tips of the spur branchlets.

Distribution: Taiwan, at altitude 1660 m.

34. **Rhamnus paniculflorus** Schneider (See orig. text page 803)

35. **Rhamnus parviflorus** Bge. (See orig. text page 804)

36. **Rhamnus persica** Boiss.

37. **Rhamnus rosthornii** Pritz. (See orig. text page 805)

38. **Rhamnus rugulosus** Hemsley

39. **Rhamnus sargentiana** Schneider

Shrub. Branchlets dark gray, rough; leaves oblanceolate, 11 cm long, 3.5 cm wide, bluntly acute at apex, obtuse at base, finely serrate margin, lustrous dark green above, pale green glabrous below, coriaceous.

Distribution: Szechuan, Mt. Omei, at altitude 2500 m.

40. **Rhamnus schnerei** Levl.

41. **Rhamnus serpyllifolius** Levl.

Spinous shrub. Leaves obovate to obovate-oblong, entire, coriaceous, 4-10 mm long, 2.5-4 mm wide, apex rotundate, emarginate, base cuneate.

Distribution: Yunnan, at altitude 2550 m.

42. **Rhamnus velutinus** Anth.

Shrub clinging closely to the limestone cliffs and on rocky slopes; flowers chocolate red, 2-3 in fascicles. Leaves reddish purple beneath; fruit a black berry.

Distribution: Yunnan, at altitude 3300 m.

43. **Rhamnus tinctorius** W. et K.

Shrub, branchlets dark gray, glabrous. Leaves obovate, 6 cm long, 4 cm wide, rounded and emarginate at apex, cuneate, inequallateral at base, irregularly serrate margin, light green above, pale green below, membranaceous; petiole 1.5-2 cm long, whitish pilose; flowers in axillary clusters of 5 or 6, small, purplish.

Distribution: Hupeh

44. Rhamnus utilis Decne.

Shrub 3-4 m tall. Branchlets thick, stout, reddish gray. Leaves elliptic-lanceolate, 7 cm long, 3 cm wide, acute-acuminate at apex, cuneate inequallateral at base, irregularly crenate serrate margin, subcoriaceous; fruit a blackberry, 1 cm in diameter, globular; pedicels very slender, 1.5 cm long.

Distribution: Hupeh, Szechuan, Kweichow, Kwangtung, Fukien, Kwangsi, Kiangsu, Chekiang, Taiwan, and Hunan, at altitude 300-1000 m.

45. Rhamnus virgatus Benth.

46. Rhamnus wilsonii Schneider

Genus (4) Hovenia Thunb. (See orig. text page 805)

1. Hovenia acerba Lindley

Tree 33 m tall. Branchlets slightly zigzag, lenticelled, dark gray. Leaves obovate, 8 cm long, 6 cm wide, short-acuminate, ovate, 3 - nerved at base, crenate serrate margin, lustrous dark green above, pale green, glabrous beneath, subcoriaceous; petioles 2-3 cm long, flattened, brown, glabrous; flowers in axillary cymes, petals 5; fruits small, globular, 1 mm in diameter, fruiting pedicels 2 mm long, slender, not supported by a fleshy stalk or peduncle; calyx disk persistent, slightly peltate.

Distribution: Kwangsi and Kwangtung, at altitude 400 meters.

2. Hovenia dulcis Thunberg (See orig. text pages 806-807)

3. Hovenia tomentella Nakai

Tree bark dark gray, branchlets dark purple, lenticelled; Leaves obovate or rounded, 10 cm long, 8 cm wide, acute-acuminate at apex, cordate, 3-nerved at base, irregularly crenate-dentate-serrate margin, lustrous dark green above, pale green, glabrous, with prominent midribs and veins beneath, subcoriaceous; petiole 2 cm long, flattened, brown, glabrous, flowers whitish yellow, in terminal racemes, slightly brownish pubescent; peduncles short brownish pubescent.

Distribution: Chekiang, at altitude 300 m.

4. Hovenia trichocarpa Chun et Tsiang

Tree 12 m tall; bark gray, longitudinally fissured. Leaves oblong-ovate to broadly-ovate, 15-20 cm long, 10-15 cm wide, apex minutely - acuminate, base subrotundate, cordate, margin crenate-dentate-serrate deep green above, light green covered with brown hairs beneath, 3-nerved at base, 2 lateral nerves curving upward, secondary nerves 6-10 pairs; petiole 2-5 cm long, glabrous; flowers in terminal and axillary cymes; fruits matured with the pedicels, 6-10 mm long, globose, brown.

Distribution: Kwangtung, Kwangsi, Kiangsi, Chekiang, Anhwei, and Hunan, at altitude of 600-1350 meters.

Order XVIII Malvales

Family 48. Tiliaceae Juss.
(See orig. text page 807)

Genus (1) Tilia Linn. (See orig. text pages 807–808)

1. **Tilia amurensis** Rup. (See orig. text page 808)

2. **Tilia chenmoui** Cheng

Tree 17 m tall, 50 cm in diameter. Leaves ovate to broadly ovate, 6–12 cm long 5–5.7 cm wide, base oblique, truncate or rarely semi-cordate, apex acuminate or short-acuminate, margin remotely serrate, or serrulate-dentate, minutely mucronate at apex, dark green minutely stellate-pubescent above, dense stellate-whitish-tomentose beneath, nerves 7–10 pairs; petiole 3–4 cm long, densely tomentose; peduncles and pedicels slightly angular, dense stellate-tomentose; bracts linear-oblanceolate, slightly stellate-cinereo-tomentose, base oblique, long, stipitate, apex rotundate or rarely obtuse, 12.5–16.5 cm long, 2 cm broad; fruits obovoid, 8 mm long, 7 mm broad, obscure 5-toothed, acute or apiculate, densely stellate-tomentose.

Distribution: Yunnan, at altitude 1600 m.

3. **Tilia chingiana** Hu et Cheng

Tree 8–15 cm tall, 35 cm in diameter, undivided or divided into 2–4 trunks at base, bark gray, smooth; branchlets glabrous to sparsely puberulous, glauscent in autumn. Leaves broadly ovate, acuminate to abruptly acuminate, obliquely truncate to cordate at base, sharply serrate, teeth erectly aristate-acuminate to mucronate-acuminate, 5–10 cm long, 4.5–9.5 cm broad, upper surface deep green, glabrous, lower surface sparsely stellate-pubescent to nearly glabrous, lateral veins 8–9, elevated; petiole slender, 3–5 cm long, glabrous; cymes 4–10-flowered; peduncles and pedicels angular, peduncle glabrous, pedicels sparsely stellate-pubescent; bracts oblong – lanceolate to oblong, adnate to the peduncle at or above the middle, upper surface sparsely stellate-pubescent, lower very sparsely so; sepals concave, elliptic-ovate, acuminate, 5 mm long, 1.5–2 mm broad, shortly stellate-pubescent outisde, pilose at apex and base inside; petals concave, oblanceolate-oblong to oblong-elliptic, about 7 mm long and 3 mm broad, obtuse to rounded and slightly erose at apex, cuneate at base; staminodes 5, petaloid, spathulate, slightly shorter than petals, about 6 mm long; stamens 40–50, glabrous, half as long as petals; pistils 5 mm long, ovary globose, obtusely angulate, tomentose, style about 3 mm long, stigma simple. Fruit subglobose to subovoid, 9–11 mm long, 7–9 mm broad, apiculate, verrucose, densely appressedly tomentose.

This speicies is allied to *Tilia tuan* Szyszyl. but differs in the sharply serrate leaves with sparse stellate-pubescence or near glabrous on the lower surface and not bearded in the axils of veins, in few-flowered cymes, in flowers with oblong – lanceolate or oblong-elliptic petals acute at base, in spathulate staminodes and more numerous stamens.

Distribution: Kiangsi, Lushan, Kuling, at altitude 1300 m.

4. **Tilia chinensis** Maxim. (See orig. text page 809)

    Var. 1. Tilia **chinensis** var. **investita** (Engler) Rehd.

5. **Tilia croizatii** Chun et Wong

   Tilia begoniifolia Chun et Wong

  Tree 20 m tall. Branchlets stout, at first stellate-pubescent, finely glabrous, and dull black. Leaves subcoriaceous, long-petiolated, ovate-oblong, very unequal sided, 12-18 cm long, 8-11 cm wide, apex gradually acuminate with a short broad obtuse acumen, base oblique, semi-cordate and truncate, usually rounded on one side and truncate on the other, margin crenate-dentate above the middle with 3-6 large, somewhat distant, mucronate teeth, upper surface deep green, glabrous, drying brown, lower surface paler, closely but tinly whitish stellate-pilose and with barbate hairs in the axils of the veins, lateral veins 6-9 on each side of the midrib, elevated on both surfaces, strongly so beneath, joined by somewhat distant transverse veinlets with close but rather indistinct reticulation; petiole terete, stellate-pilose at least toward the apex, 5-6 cm long; cymes stellate pubescent, including the peduncles 12-15 cm long, few-branched, divericate; bracts shroter than the cymes, adnate only to the base of the peduncle, broadly oblong, 10-12 cm long, 3.5 cm wide at the abruptly dilated cordate base, 2.5 cm wide towards the middle, obtuse at apex, rarely emarginate, margin sinuate, strongly veined; fruit ellipsoid, 1 cm long, scarsely costate, rounded at apex, densely but thinly pilose, with minute scale-like hairs; epicarp thin, separating into 5-valves.

    Distribution: Kwangtung and Kwangsi.

6. **Tilia dictyoneura** Engl. (See orig. text page 810)

7. **Tilia endochrysea** Handel-Mazz.

8. **Tilia eurosinica** Croizat

  Tree; leaves ovate orbicular, apex acuminate, base obliquely-rotundate or cordate, serrate glandulous-mucronate coarsely toothed margin, glaucous below, 9-11 cm long, 5-8 cm wide; fruit ellipsoid, subglobose, 8 mm long, 5 mm broad; corymb-bracts (including free base) 8 cm long, 1 cm or less broad.

    Distribution: Chekiang, and Anhwei.

9. **Tilia henryana** Szys. (See orig. text pages 810-811)

    Var. 1. Tilia **henryana** var. **subglabra** Engl.

      This variety differs from the typical form by having all parts of the plant being glabrous.

    Distribution: Kiangsi and Kiangsu.

0. **Tilia hypoglauca** Rehd.

1. **Tilia intonsa** Wilson

2. **Tilia lactevirens** Rehd. et Wilson (See orig. text page 812)

3. **Tilia lepidota** Rehd. (See orig. text pages 812-813)

14. Tilia leptocarya Rehd. (See orig. text page 813)

Var. 1. Tilia leptocarya var. triloba Rehd.

This variety differs from the type chiefly in the leaves being furnished with lateral tooth or short lobe on each side and having thier underside more distinctly glaucous with ramnants of a fluccose-stellate pubescence near the base.

Distribution: Kiangsi, Anhwei and Chekiang.

15. Tilia kwangtungensis Chun et Wong

Tree; branchlets thick, at first densely fulvous floccose-stellate-tomentose, finely glabrous, dull brown and striate minutely; buds ovoid, obtuse, the outer scales lustrous, glabrous except the margin, about 6 mm long. Leaves ovate, apex gradually acutely acuminate, base oblique, rounded, truncate or sometimes subcordate, subcoriaceous margin near to the base minutely closely denticulate with mucronulate, incurved teeth, glabrous above, whitish beneath with densely matted, adpressed stellate hairs, lateral veins 7-10, slightly impressed on the upper surface, strongly elevated on the lower surface joined by slender, subparallel, slightly elevated, transverse veinlets; petiole somewhat slender, stellate tomentose, 3-4 cm long; cymes 10-15- flowered, including the peduncle 5.5-9.5 cm long, 4-6 cm wide, peduncle and pedicels thickish, fulvous stellate-tomentose; pedicles 4-5 mm long; bracts oblong, obtuse, sessile, adnate to the flower half of the peduncle, 7-10 cm long, 1.5-2 cm wide, both surfaces stellate pilose, densely so on the back. Flowers large, somewhat approximated; sepals thick, narrowly ovate-oblong, cymbiform, 6-7 mm long, 3-mm wide, stellate tomentose outisde, silky pilose inside; petals oblong-lanceolate, cymbiform, membranous, pale yellow, glabrous, 8 mm long, 2 mm wide; staminodes spathulate, glabrous, apex dilated, contracted below the middle into a thick stipe; stamens 30-40, somewhat unequal; ovary ellipsoid, 3 mm long, densely pilose; style cylindric pilose; stigma shortly 5-fid.

Distribution: Kwangtung, and Kwangsi, at altitude 650 m.

16. Tilia mofungensis Chun et Wong

Small tree 5 m tall; branchlets glabrous, at first pale, at length blackish, leaves oblong to oblong-ovate, shortly acuminate, base oblique, semicordate, 7-11 cm long, 4-6 cm wide, subcoriaceous, entire, margin somewhat thickened and slightly revolute, upper surface dark green, lower surface paler, softly silky pilose with scattered few-branched spreading stellate hairs on the blade and with stellate and simple hairs intermixed on the midrib and veins, lateral veins 7-10 pairs on each side of the midrib; petiole glabrous, subterete, 2-2.5 cm long; cymes slightly longer than the bracts; bracts linear-oblong, obtuse, 8-10 cm long, about 1 cm wide, sessile, both surfaces at first stellate pilose, becoming glabrous and purplish at fruiting time. Fruit subglobose, apex conical-umbonate, densely adpressed stellate tomentose, 8-10 cm long, brownish when mature.

This species is distinguished by having oblong, entire leaves, stellate silky pilose on the under surface and by the narrow, linear, purplish, sessile bracts.

Distribution: Kwangtung.

17. **Tilia manchurica** Rupr. et Maxim. (See orig. text pages 813-814)

18. **Tilia mongolica** Maxim.

19. **Tilia nobilis** R. et W.

20. **Tilia oblongifolia** Rehd. (See orig. text pages 815-816)

21. **Tilia oliveri** Szys.

      Var. 1. **Tilia oliveri** var. **cinerascens** R. et W. (See orig. text pages 816-817)

22. **Tilia orocryptica** Croizat

    Tilia chingiana Hu et Cheng

Small shrub. Branchlets slender glabrous, Leaves obovate, 8 cm long, 6 cm wide, acute-acuminate apex, base oblique cordate, margin serrate, membranaceous; petioles 4-6 cm long, slender, glabrous; fruit globular, 1 mm in diameter, slightly mucronate; fruiting pedicels 1 cm long, glabrous.

Distribution: Kiangsi.

23. **Tilia paucicostata** Maxim. (See orig. text page 817)

    Var. 1. **Tilia paucicostata** var. **yunnanensis** Diels

Small tree 7 m tall. Branchlets purplish brown, glabrous; leaves obovate, 6 cm long, 5 cm wide, attenuate-acuminate at apex, oblique cordate or truncate at base, coarsely serrate margin, dark green above, pale green glabrous below, 3-nerved at base, coriaceous; flowers in lateral panicles, white; bract lanceolate, 6 cm long, 1.8 cm wide, obtuse apex, cuneate at base, pale green, reticulated, adnated to the middle of the peduncle; peduncle 8 cm long, glabrous.

Distribution: Yunnan.

24. **Tilia pumila** Cheng

Small shrub and is distinguished by its glabrous habit, small broadly ovate leaves which are truncate rarely broadly cuneate or subcordate at base, sharply serrate, acuminate apex, without tufts of axillary hairs on the lower surface, a few-flowered cymes with stalked bract, small flowers with suborbicular-obovate staminodes, and about 20 stamens, and short and stout style.

It seems to be related to *Tilia mongolica* Max. but they are differing in many respects.

Distribution: Sikang.

25. **Tilia tuan** Szys. (See orig. text pages 817-818)

    Var. 1. **Tilia tuan** var. **chinensis** R. et W. (See orig. text pages 818-819)

    Var. 2. **Tilia tuan** f. **divaricata** V. Engl.

Tree; branchlets slender purplish brown, slightly lenticelled; leaves oblong 10 cm long, 7 cm wide acute apex, obliquely cordate at base, finely serrate margin, subcoriaceous; petiole 10 cm long, slightly whitish pubescent; flowers in terminal panicles; bract oblanceolate, 13 cm long, 2.5 cm wide, pubescent on the lower surface, reticulated; peduncles 11 cm long, reddish brown, lenticellate.

Distribution: W. Hupeh.

26. **Tilia yunnanensis** Hu

Tree; branchlets purplish-brown, glabrous. Leaves membranaceous, obliquely-ovate, long-acuminate at apex, broadly cordate and oblique at base, closely and finely setose-serrate, upper surface glabrous except sparsely stellate along the reddish brown midrib and veins, shining green, reticulate, lower surface densely tawny-stellate-lanuginose-tomentose, especially along the midrib and veins and veinlets, bearded in the axils, to 7.5 cm long, 4.5 cm broad at base; petiole slender, 3.5 cm long, stellate-pilosulouse; bract subsessile, spathulate, rounded at apex, densely stellate-tomentose on both surfaces, obscured veined, 4.5 cm long, 8 mm broad; peduncle as long as the bract, and attached half of its length to it, stellate-tomentose; cymes 3-flowered, each flower bud enclosed by 2 caducous unequal sized membranaceous bracteoles, the larger one obovate, rounded at apex, 5.5 mm long, 4 mm broad, smaller ones spathulate, 4.5 mm long, 1 mm broad, minutely stellate-pilosulose outside; flower inmature, calyx and pedicel grayish stellate-tomentose.

Distribution: Yunnan, at altitude 3000 m.

Family 49. Elaeocarpaceae

Mostly tropical trees with showly flowers. Leaves simple, usually alternate, 15-20 meters in height. Flowers perfect or polygamous, in axillary racemes; sepals distinct, 4 or 5, cut or fringed (rarely entire), attached about a thickened torus; stamens many (rarely 8-12), with long-awned anthers, opening by a slit at the apex; ovary 2-5-celled; fruit a drupe, with a large and bony stone, sometimes one-celled by abortion. This family was included in Tiliaceae and separated as independent family recently. About 100 species distributed in the old-world tropics and some of them distributed reaching. The fruit pulp in some sepcies are edible.

Genus (1) Elaeocarpus Linn.

Tree or shrubs. Leaves simple, alternate, rarely opposite, entire or serrate; Flower hermaphrodite, polygamous, small in racemes, usually fragrant, regular; sepals 4-6; petals 5, toothed or fringed, valvate with 5-10 glands; anthers long aristate obtuse, dehiscent from one terminal pore; stamens yellow; fruit a drupe, oblong or globose. Inflorescence axillary in racemes or in corymbs, containing 2-5 flowers.

About 50 species distributed in Tropical and Subtropical Asia.

1. **Elaeocarpus alatus** Kunth

Small tree; leaves oblanceolate, 15 cm long, 4.5 cm wide, base acute, apex cuspidate, acutish, margin finely serrate-undulate, papery, brownish viridis below, glabrous above, lateral nerves 8–10 pairs, prominent; racemes 6.5 cm long, multiflorous, pedicels 5 mm long, glabrous; fruit oblong, rotundate–ovate, 17 mm long, 3–4 mm wide.

Distribution: Hupeh.

2. **Elaeocarpus apiculatus** Mast.

Tree 15 m tall, 45 cm in diameter. Leaves oblanceolate, broadest above the middle and tapering down to the base, 15 cm long, 8 cm wide, acute–apiculate at apex, acute–cuneate at base, crenate, serrate to undulate margin, coriaceous, lustrous dark green above, pale green, prominently veined and glabrous below; petiole 4 cm long, slightly flattened, glabrous. Fruits oblong, 4 cm long, 2.5 cm broad, brown, dehiscent, seeds black.

Distribution: Hainan, at altitude 3300 m.

3. **Elaeocarpus austro-yunnanensis** Hu

Tree 9 m tall, 60 cm in diameters; young branchlets stout, striate, erect, rufous–tomentose, soon glabrous, grayish brown; leaves chartaceous, ovate, elliptic to oblong–lanceolate, long acuminate at apex, acute to acuminate at base, obscurely setadeous crenulate with appressed or slightly incurved black setae along the margins, glabrous with slender elevated midrib and very fine but elevated reticulations above, densely rufous–tomentose but soon to glabrescent to glabrous with prominent midrib and veins and very fine reticulations beneath, 8–15 cm long, 3.5–6.5 cm wide, secondary veins 8–10 pairs, arching and branching near the margins and ending into teeth; petiole 2–4 cm long, glabrescent, bearing 2 to several black setae; inflorescence to 20 cm long; rachis slender rufous–tomentose; pedicels up to 40 in number, to 7 mm long, tomentulose; buds ovoid, 3.5 mm long; sepals 5, lanceolate, acuminate, gray–pubescent on both surfaces; petals 5, cuneate, irregularly divided into 30 segments half way, pendulous and ciliate along the margins, 6 mm long; stamens 40; filaments half as long as the anthers bearded at the apex; disk tawny–velutinous, with 2 distinct 3-lobed glands; ovary tawny–velutinous, style simple, glabrous; cells 3, with 2 collateral ovules in each cell.

Distribution: Southeastern Yunnan, at altitude 1380 m.

4. **Elaeocarpus brachyphyllus** (Merr.) Kunth

Shrub 1–3 m tall. Leaves lanceolate, 7 cm long, 2.5 cm wide, acute at apex, cuneate base, minutely acute–serrate margin, glabrous, nerves 12–15 pairs; petiole 0.5 cm long; flowers pseudo–umbellate; peduncles terminal; pedicels 1–1.5 cm long; bracteal ovate, irregularly 8–10 mm. long, pilose; petals 25–27 mm long; sepals 22 mm long, 2 mm wide at base, 2–4–flowered; stamens 15 mm long; anthers aristate, 5 mm long.

Distribution: Hainan.

5. **Elaeocarpus chinensis** (Gaertn. et Champ.) Merr.

Shrub 3 m tall. Leaves elliptic ovate, 6 cm long, 5 cm wide, abrupt–acuminate at apex, cuneate at base, undulate–serrate margin, lustrous dark green above, pale green, glabrous beneath, coriaceous; petiole 2–3 cm long; fruits in axillary racemes, globular, 1 cm long, 6 mm broad, bluish; pedicels 1 cm long; peduncles 2-3 cm long glabrous. Flowers blue-black. Fruits berrylike, edible.

Distribution: Hainan, Kwangtung, Fukien, Kwangsi, Kiangsi, Anhwie and Taiwa at altitude 130-600 meters.

6. **Elaeocarpus decurvatus** Diels

Small tree 3-5 m tall. Leaves oblong, 12-15 cm long, 5-8 cm wide, acute at apex broadly cuneate at base crenate-serrate margin, lustrous dark green above, pale green glabrous below, subcoriaceous; petioles slender, 4-6 cm long, flowers in racemes (8-12 cm long, robusty; sepals triangular-lanceolate margin serious pilose, 10 cm long base 3-3.5 cm wide; petals densely pilose, multifid at apex; stamens 20-30, 6-7 m long pilosous; ovary sericeo-tomentose, 3-4 locular; drupe ellipsoid, 18 mm long, 10 m broad, 1-loculary.

Distribution: Kwangsi, at altitude 300-350 meters.

7. **Elaeocarpus decipens** Hemsl.

Tree 8-13 m tall. Branchlets stout, thick, rough, dark gray. Leaves elliptic lanceolate, 6 cm long, 2.5 cm wide, acute apex, cuneate at base, crenate-irregularly serrate margin, dark green above, pale green, glabrous below, coriaceous; petio stout, 2-3 cm long, glabrous; flowers in axillary corymbs; fruits ellipsoid-ovoid, 1. 1.8 cm long, 1 cm broad.

Distribution: Taiwan.

8. **Elaeocarpus hayatai** Kaneh. et Sasak.

Large tree; leaves oblanceolate, 9 cm long, 4 cm wide, acute at apex, and at base irregularly crenate-serrate margin, lustrous dark green above, pale green, glabro beneath, subcoriaceous; petiole 2 cm long, glabous. Flowers in compound paincles fruits globular capsule, 2.5 cm long, 1.5 cm broad, rather tapering toward the ti glabrous, black.

Distribution: Taiwan.

9. **Elaeocarpus howii** Merr. et Chun

Tree 9-15 m tall. Leaves oblong-elliptic to elliptic, 10-15 cm long, 3.5-7 cm wid acute-acuminate at apex, base subrotundate-acute, serrulate-dentate margin, coriaceou lustrous dark green above, pale green glabrous below; nerves 10-12 pairs, ferruginu tomentose; petioles 1.5-6 cm long, ferruginous-pubescent; racemes axillary, numerou 5-8 cm long, 10-15-flowered, sub-ferruginous-tomentose; pedicels 5 mm long; flowe 5-merous, sepals oblong-ovate, 5-6 mm long, ferruginous-villose, ciliate pebescer petals obovate, glabrous, margin ciliate; ovary oblong-ovoid, densely ferruginou hirsute; fruits ellipsoid, 4.5 cm long, 3 cm broad, longitudinally, irregularly undualt carinate, densely ferruginous-hirsute.

Distribution: Hainan, at altitude 900 m.

10. **Elaeocarpus kobanmochii** Koidz.

Small tree; leaves oblanceolate, 12 cm long, 4 cm wide acute-acuminate at ape cuneate at base, irregularly crenate serrate margin, lustrous dark green above, pale green, glabrous below; nerves 4–6 pairs, prominent, coriaceous; petiole 4–6 cm long, glabrous; flowers in large terminal panicles.

Distribution: Taiwan.

1. **Elaeocarpus dubius** A. DC.

Tree 8 m tall; leaves clustered at current years' growth, elliptic-oblong to lanceolate 6 cm long, 3 cm wide, long-acuminate apex, narrowly cuneate at base, crenate distantly serrate margin, dark green above, pale green glabrous beneath, subcoriaceous; petiole 2–3 cm long, glabrous. Fruits globular, 1.5 cm long, 1 cm broad, blue; fruiting pedicels 15 mm long; peduncles 4–6 cm long brown, glabrous. Branchlets growing in whorls, whitish gray, smooth.

Distribution: Hainan, at altitude 800 m. Kwangtung and Kwangsi.

2. **Elaeocarpus duclouxii** Gagn.

Evergreen large tree, 20 m tall, 50 cm in diameter, bark gray, smooth; branchlets slender, dark gray, glabrous; leaves oblanceolate, 8–15 cm long, 3.5–6 cm wide, acute-acuminate at apex, narrow cuneate at base, crenate, irregularly dentate-serrate margin, lustrous shining green above, shining pale green glabrous below, nerves 8 pairs prominently elevated, coriaceous; petiole 5–20 mm long, stout, glabrous; flowers small, greenish, in lateral small racemes; fruits globular 1–2 cm long, 12 mm in diameter, slightly mucronate; fruiting pedicles 1 cm long; fruite edible, black.

Distribution: Hunan, Kiangsi, and Chekiang, at altitude 500–800 m. Kwangtung, Kwangsi, Yunnan and Kweichow.

3. **Elaeocarpus hainanensis** Oliv.

Tree or shrub, 3–4 meters tall. Leaves lanceolate-elliptic, 7–15 cm long, 2–4.5 cm wide, acute apex, base acute-acuminate, crenate, irregularly serrate margin, subcoriaceous; petiole 1.5 cm long; lateral veins 9–12 pairs. Flowers in lateral racemes, which with more or less persistent oblong - ovate, blunt, fleshy, denticulated, leafy bracts, 6–8 mm long, 2–7 mm wide; pedicels 1.5–3 cm long; sepals 12–13 mm more or less glabrous; petals 13–15 mm long, 9–10 mm wide; ovary adpressedly pubescent. Fruits narrowly fusiform, 3 cm long, 1.2 cm broad; stone 25 mm across.

Distribution: Hainan, Indo-China, and Malaya.

Var. 1. **Elaeocarpus hainanensis** var. **brachyphyllus** (Merr.) Kunth

Tree; leaves lanceolate, 7 cm long, 2.5 cm wide, acute at both ends, margin minutely acute-serrate, subcoriaceous; flowers pseudo-umbelliferae; peduncles terminal 1.5–2 cm long, 2–4-flowered; sepals 22 mm long; petals 25–27 mm long; anthers aristate, 5 mm long, capillary; stamens 15 mm long.

Distribution: Hainan.

4. **Elaeocarpus japonicus** Sieb. et Zucc.

Small tree 10 m tall. Leaves oblanceolate, 7 cm long, 3 cm wide, acute-acuminate at apex, cuneate at base, crenate irregularly acutely serrate, dark green above, pale green below, glabrous, subcoriaceous; petiole 5-6 cm long, slender, glabrous; flowers pubescent; sepals 5, lanceolate, acuminate, thin, membranaceous, puberulous, and keeled inside, appressed pubescent outside, 6 mm long; petals 5, thick, somewhat fleshy, oblong, slightly dilated upwards, apex shortly irregularly dentate, with 5-7 oblong teeth, densely appressed pubescent excepting the thin apex outside, strongly keeled and pubescent inside, 6 mm long, 2 mm wide; stamens about 18, not awned not barbate, puberulous, 3.2 mm long, sterile; ovary ovoid-globose, 1 mm long, puberulous, 3-celled; style 2 mm long.

Distribution: Kwangtung, Kwangsi, Kweichow, Yunnan, Szechuan, Fukien, Hunan and Chekiang, at altitude 1100-1200 m.

Var. 1. Elaeocarpus japonicus var. **euphlebius** Merr.

Small tree; branchlets dark brown, rough; leaves oblong, 8 cm long 4 cm wide, acute-acuminate at apex, obtuse at base, irregularly crenate-serrate margin, lustrous dark green above pale brownish below, coriaceous; petiole 4 cm long, glabrous; flowers in lateral racemes, purplish; pedicels 5 mm long; peduncles 5 cm long, stout, winged, brownish, glabrous.

Distribution: Hainan.

15. Elaeocarpus lantsangensis Hu

Tree 10 meters tall, 15 cm in diameter, branchlets stout, terete, striate, tawny-pilose, at last galbrous; leaves chataceous, lanceolate to oblanceolate, long acuminate at apex, acute at base, crisp with setaceous teeth along the margin, 8-13 cm long, 3-4 cm broad; veins 10 pairs; petiole 3-4.5 cm long, inflorescence in racemes, about 4 mm long, rachis puberulous; sepals 5, lanceolate, acute, 4 mm long; petals 5, obovate-oblong, slightly divided into 5 lobes at apex; disk with 5 distinct 2-lobed glands; stamens 15, filaments very short; anthers 2 mm long, pilosulose; drupe oblong, olive green, 17 mm long, stone verrucose.

Distribution: Yunnan, at altitude 2800 m.

16. Elaeocarpus limitanea Handel-Mazz.

Small tree 4 m tall. Leaves oblong, 9 cm long, 4 cm wide, acute apice, cuneate at base, irregularly, crenate-serrate margin, lustrous dark green above, pale brownish pubescent below, thick, coriaceous; petiole 2-3 cm long, slightly pubescent; flowers in lateral racemes, brownish pubescent. Fruits light blue, globular, 4 cm long, 2 cm broad, mucronate.

Distribution: Kwangtung, Kwangsi, Hainan and Yunnan.

17. Elaeocarpus lanceaefolius Roxb.

Tree 10 m tall. Leaves lanceolate, 9 cm long, 2 cm wide, acute at apex, acuminate-acute at base, irregularly crenate serrate margin, lustrous dark green above, pale bluish green below, subcoriaceous; petiole 1-2 cm long, flattened, glabrous. Flowers in lateral racemes; fruits globular, 3 cm long, 2 cm broad, black, longitudinally reticulated; pedicels 5 mm long; peduncle 5 cm long, stout.

Distribution: Kwangtung, Hongkong, Kiangsi, Fukien, Taiwan and Kwangsi, at altitude 450 meters.

18. **Elaeocarpus makinoi** Kaneh.

Shrub; branchlets slender, reddish black, lenticelled; leaves oblanceolate, acute at apex, cuneate at base, irregularly crenate denate margin, lustrous dark green above, pale green glabrous beneath, subcoriaceous; petiole 2-3 cm long, glabrous.

Distribution: Taiwan.

19. **Elaeocarpus nitentifolius** Merrill et Chun

Tree 12 m tall. Leaves oblanceolate, 10 cm long, 5 cm wide, abruptly acuminate at apex, narrowly cuneate at base, crenate-dentate undulate margin, lustrous dark green above, pale light green glabrous below, subcoriaceous; petiole 3-5 cm long; fruits in axillary racemes, black, globular, 1.5 cm long, 7 mm broad, tapering pointed towards the tip; fruiting pedicels 5 mm long, brown, glabrous; sepals subglabrous to sparsely pubescent, narrowly lanceolate, margin densely pubescent, especially on inside surface; petals slightly longer, about 5 mm with 4 or 5 shallow lobes, oblanceolate.

Distribution: Hainan, at altitude 3300 m.

20. **Elaeocarpus prunifolioides** Hu

Small tree 6 m tall. Branchlets terete, striate, glabrous; leaves chartaceous, recurved, elliptic to elliptic lanceolate, obtusely long-acuminate at apex, acuminate and decurrent at base, obscurely crenate-serrate along the margins, glabrous on both surfaces, midrib, secondary veins and reticulations with slightly elevated above, 6-8 cm long, 4-5 cm broad; petiole 1.5-2.5 cm long, glabrous; inflorescences racemose, about 5 cm long,; sepals 5, lanceolate, puberulous outside, tomentulose along the margins; petals 5, obovate-oblong, upper 1/5 divided into 10 segments, densely sericeous outside, tawny-villose and keeled inside; disk with 10 distinct globose, yellow villose glands; stamens 20-22.5 mm long, filaments filiform, 1 mm long; anthers 4 mm long, pilose, scabrous, mucronate; ovary ovoid, tawny pilose, 1.5 mm long, 3-celled, with 6 ovules in 2 series in each cell; style simple, pilosulose at base.

Distribution: Western Yunnan, at altitude 1200 m.

21. **Elaeocarpus petiolatus** (Jack.) Wall.

Shrub, 4 m tall. Leaves oblong, 9 cm long, 4 cm wide, acute at apex, broadly cuneate at base, crenate-undulate-serrate margin, lustrous dark green above, pale green glabrous below, with prominent veins and midrib, coriaceous; petiole very long, slender, 4-5 cm long, round, glabrous, brownish; flowers in lateral racemes, white, fragrant; peduncles 8 cm long; fruit globular, 1.5 cm long, 8 mm wide, mucronate, grayish brown; pedicels 1.5 cm long.

Distribution: Yunnan, and Hainan, at altitude 600 m.

22. **Elaeocarpus decurvatus** Diels

Large tree 7 m tall. Leaves oblong, 18 cm long, 8 cm wide, short-acuminate at apex, obtuse at base, irregularly coarsely serrate margin, lustrous dark green above, pale brownish green above, pale brownish green below, glabrous on both surfaces, coriaceous; petiole 4-6 cm long, brown, glabrous; fruits globular, 2 cm long, 1.5 cm broad; pedicels 2 cm long, brownish, glabrous; panicles axillary, 12 cm long.

Distribution: Kwangtung, Kwangsi and Yunnan, at altitude 1400 m.

23. **Elaeocarpus shunningensis** Hu

Tree 6 m tall. Leaves coriaceous, oblonglanceolate, to ovate oblong, short acuminate at apex, acute to rounded at base, remotely mucronate-serrate, shining green, glabrous with slightly elevated velutinous midrib and elevated reticulations above, ferrugineo-tomentulose especially along the prominent midrib, secondary veins and reticulations beneath, 11-16 cm long, 4-5.8 cm wide; secondary veins 10 - 13 pairs, distant and curving, forming loops neat the margins; petiole 3 cm long, geniculate at apex, brown tomentose; inflorescence 17 cm long; pedicels 8 m long, ferruginous velutinouse; flowers yellowish green, 1.5 cm in diameter; bracteoles pectinate, ferruginouse-velutinous, 3 mm long; sepals 5, ovate-lanceolate; petals 5, broadly cuneate, velutinous and tomentose, densely pubescent inside, 6 mm long, upper half irregularly divided into about 48 lobes; stamens about 40; filaments half as long as the anthers, puberulouse, without appendages; cells 3, with 2 collateral ovules in each cell; drupe oblong to subglobose, 3 cm long, 2 cm broad; stone oblong, subtriangular, 2 cm long, 1.5 cm broad; mesocarp bony, with 3 longitudinal satural grooves.

Distribution: Yunnan, at altitude 1600-3000 m.

24. **Elaeocarpus subglobosus** Merr.

Tree 10 m tall. Leaves oblong, acute at apex, cuneate at base, finely serrate or slightly incurved margin, 8 cm long, 4 cm wide, membranaceous, shining green above, pale green, glabrous below, veins 7 pairs; fruits globose or round, 1.5-2 cm long and broad, 5-clevage dehiscent, brown, woody; pedicels stout, 7 mm long; peduncles 6 cm long, glabrous.

Distribution: Yunnan, and Hainan, at altitude 750 m.

25. **Elaeocarpus sylvestris** (Lour.) Poiret

Tree 10 m tall; leaves elliptic-oblong, 7-10 cm long, 4-6 cm wide, acute at apex, narrow cuneate at base, irregularly crenate-serrate margin, subcoriaceous; flowers in lateral racemes, yellow; pedicels 3 mm long; peduncles 7-10 cm long; fruit solitary, globose, 1 cm long, 5 mm broad; pedicels 1 cm long, purplish brown, glabrous; flowers white; fruits edible.

Distribution: Yunnan, Hainan, Kwantung, Kwangsi, Fukien, Chekiang, Szechuan and Taiwan, at altitude 950-1000 m.

Genus (2) **Sloanea** Linn.

Trees or shrubs often with fascicled pubescence. Leaves simple, alternate, entire, deciduous; flowers perfect, sepals 5-lobed; stamens numerous; filaments filiformis;

fruits a capsule or nut-like or drupaceous, rarely a berry or separating into druplets.

There are about 20 species and several varieties distributed in tropical and subtropical Asia.

1. **Sloanea assamica** (Benth.) Rehder et Wilson

Large tree usually up to 40 meters high; bard dark gray, rough; branchlets thick, stout, dark gray, rough, lenticelled; leaves obovate or oblanceolate, 12 cm long, 5 cm wide, short acuminate at apex, narrowly cuneate at base, irregularly crenate dentate-serrate and incurved margin, lustrous dark green above, pale green, glabrous below, nerves 7 pairs prominently elevated, sub-coriaceous; petiole 5-10 mm long; flowers in terminal umbels, yellowish white; fruits a globular capsule, 2 cm long, 1.5 cm broad, densely covered with long bristles, brown, woody.

Distribution: Yunnan and Kwangsi, at altitude 1500 meters.

2. **Sloanea chingiana** Hu

Tree 14 m tall, 30 cm in diameter with gray smooth bark; branches glabrous with scattered lenticels. Leaves oblong-lanceolate to spathuate, long acuminate, cuneate at base, entire along the margins, 17 cm long, 5 cm broad, glabrous on both surfaces, dark green above, light green below; petiole 5 cm long. Fruits 5-7, umbellate, on a common peduncle to 6 cm long, pedicels to 3.5 cm long, glabrous; capsule globose, 1.5 cm long, valves 3-4, rather thin, woody, velvet, covered with dense brown bristles of 1 mm long; seeds oblong, shining brown, 8 mm long, 6 mm broad, arillate.

Distribution: Kwangsi.

3. **Sloanea dasycarpa** Hemsl.

Tree 14 m tall. Branchlets stout, dark purplish, rough, scattered lenticellate; leaves oblong, 14 cm long, 6 cm wide, acuminate at apex, narrowly cuneate at base, irregularly and distantly serrate margin, lustrous dark green above, light green, glabrous below, subcoriaceous; petiole 3-4 cm long, glabrous; fruits globose, 2 cm long, 1.5 cm broad, 4-velved capsule, covered with dense brownish bristles of 1 mm long.

Distribution: Taiwan, and Yunnan, at altitude 700 m.

4. **Sloanea elegans** Chun

Tree 7-8 m tall; branchlets, pedicels and peduncles densely pubescent. Leaves deciduous, petiolate, lanceolate or oblanceolate, or elliptic-lanceolate, 6-11 cm long, 1.5-3 cm wide, margin irregularly undulate, acute at apex, narrowly cuneate at base, chartaceous; petiole 3-4 cm long, pubescent; veins 7-8 pairs, irregularly and sparsely reticulated; flowers 1.8-2 cm across; sepals 5, ovate, deltoided-ovate, acute 4-5 mm long,; petals 5, imbricated, 10-12 mm long, obliquely cuneate, apice truncate, lobes linear-oblong; stamens numerous (about 80), 6-7 mm long; anthers 2.5 mm long, introrse; ovary 3 mm in diameter, conico-ovoid, densely pilose; fruits a capsule of 4-5-valved, woody.

Distribution: Kwangtung, Yunnan and Taiwan, at altitude 1650 m.

5. **Sloanea forrestii** W. W. Sm.

Tree or shrub, 6–15 m tall. Branchlets dark gray, rough, lenticelled. Leave oblong-obovate, 15 cm long, 7 cm wide, short acuminate at apex, cuneate at base, ir regularly undulate and teethed margin, lustrous dark green above, light green, glabrou below, coriaceous, thick; petiole 4 cm long. Fruits a large globular capsule, 3–4 cm i diameter, covered with dense and long brownish bristles of 1–3 cm long.

Distribution: Yunnan, and Tibet, at altitude 1700–2200 m.

6. **Sloanea hainanensis** Merr. et Chun

Tree 8–15 m tall. This species is characterized by its short petioled leaves whic are in general obovate to oblanceolate in outline, 6–15 cm long, 2–6 cm wide, obtus acuminate apice, abruptly obtuse at base, often prominently toothed, although occasi onally one observes entire leaves on the same branches as the toothed ones. Leave narrowed below the middle, normally 5–7 mm wide, being abruptly rounded or obtuse giving some leaves an almost pandurate appearance.

Its alliance seems to be with *Sloanea hemslyana* Rehd. et Wilson

Distribution: Hainan, at altitude 350 m.

7. **Sloanea hemsleyana** Rehd. et Wilson

Tree 16 m tall. Leaves oblanceolate or lanceolate, 10 cm long, 3.4 cm wide, acu minate at apex, cuneate at base, irregularly undulate serrate, lustrous dark gree above, pale green, glabrous below, coriaceous; petiole 1–2 cm long. Flowers in dens cymes, yellowish white; fruits globose, covered densely with brownish bristles of abo 2 cm long; fruiting pedicels 10 cm long, brownish, glabrous.

Distribution: Yunnan and Szechuan, at altitude 1430 m.

8. **Sloanea honkongensis** Hemsley

Tree 15 m tall. Leaves coriaceous, lanceolate or oblanceolate, 8 cm long, 3 cm wide long acute at apex, obtuse at base, entire margin, lustrous dark green above, pale gree glabrous below, veins about 7 pairs, irregularly distributed, rather prominently eleva ted; petiole 8–18 mm long, brown, glabrous; fruits globose, 3 cm long, 2 cm in diamete 5–6-valved, densely covered with strong and brownish bristles of about 7 mm long, t fruiting peduncles thick, stout, 8 cm long, 1.5 mm thick, glabrous.

Distribution: Hongkong.

9. **Sloanea siguma** (Bl.) K. Schum.

Tree 15 m tall. Branchlets whitish gray, smooth, glabrous. Leaves obovate, 7 long, 4.5 cm wide, acute at apex, rounded at base, entire, incurved margin, lustro dark green above, pale green, prominently reticulated with highly elevated midrib a veins beneath, coriaceous; petiole 3.5 cm long, glabrous; fruits solitary, globose, 5 long, 4 cm in diameter, densely covered with strong bristles of about 1 cm long, valved calyx and petals pale gree; stamens many, yellowish; flowering buds blui pubescent.

Distribution: Hainan, at altitude 800 m.

10. **Sloanea sinensis** (Hance) Hu

Tree about 10 m tall, with spreading branches and pithy inside; leaves oblanceolate, acuminate, obtusely or acutely cuneate at base, entire or remotely dentate above the middle, veins and reticulations not very prominnent, glabrous above, puberulent beneath especially along the veins, 10 cm long, 4 cm broad; petiole 1–3 cm long; flowers greenish white, about 1.5 cm wide; peduncle 6–8 cm long, gray-pubescent; sepals oblong, about 6 mm long, 4 mm broad, gray-pubescent; petals brader than long, deeply lobed, gray-pubescent; stamens numerous, crowded, anther apiculate, with straw-colored sericeous pubescence; ovary conical, gray-pubescent; fruits with 5–6 stellately spread woody valves lines with purple inside; setae rigid, slender, filiform, covered with straw-colored pubescence; seeds with yellowish arillus, solitary in each cell.

From *Sloanea hemsleyana* R. et W., this species differs in smaller flowers and generally paler pubescence in flowers and fruit.

Distribution: Kwangtung, Kwangsi, Kiangsi, Fukien, Chekiang and Kweichow, at altitude 150–600 m.

11. **Sloanea kweichowensis** Hu

Tree with gray and smooth branchlets. Leaves oblanceolate, acute at apex, obtuse at base, entire and crenate serrate above the middle margin, lustrous green above, prominently reticulated below, coriaceous; petiole 3–4 cm long, glabrous; inflorescence in terminal racemes; calyx ans petals 4-lobed, imbricated, densely pubescent; stamens numerous.

Distribution: Kweichow.

12. **Sloanea leptocarpa** Diels

Tree 20–30 cm high, 30 cm in diameters; leaves oblanceolate, 15 cm long, 5 cm wide, acuminate at apex, narrow cuneate at base, entire, undulate, irregulary serrate above the middle of the margin, lustrous dark green above, pale green, glabrous, with very prominently elevated and reticulated veins and midrib beneath, chartaceous; petiole 3–4 cm long, brownish pubescent; fruits, solitary, axillary, globular, 2 cm in diameter, covered with dense strawcolored bristles, fruiting pedicels 3–4 cm long, brownish pubescent.

Distribution: Kwangtung and Kwangsi, at altitude 1700 m.

13. **Sloanea tsiangiana** Hu

Tree 8–9 m high; branchlets slender, terete, striate, gray brown, glabrous; leaves deciduous, membranaceous, lanceolate to oblanceolate, long to short acuminate, acute at base, 5–12 cm long, 2–4 cm broad, margin entire, slightly undulate, glabrous, upper surface green, with immersed midrib, lower surface pale green, midrib elevated, veins 7–8 on each side; petiole slender, geniculate at apex to 3 cm long, glabrous; capsule solitary, ovoid globose, about 1.5 cm long, dehiscent into 4 valves; valeves thin, ligneous, purplish red iside, densely covered with short soft deciduous pale red spines outside about 2 mm long; seeds ellipsoid, shining purple-black, about 7 mm long, 4 mm broad.

Distribution: Kweichow.

14. **Sloanea tsinyunensis** Chien

Tree 30 m tall, 35 cm in diameter; leaves persistent, chartaceous, oblong-elliptic, oblong, or oblanceolate, acuminate at apex, base obtuse rotundate, undulate margin, 7-15 cm long, 2.3-3.2 cm wide 1-4-denticulate; nerves 5-7 pairs, sparsely puberulate on midrib above; petiole 6-25 mm long, densely puberulent, geniculately thickened at tip; stipule subulate 2 mm long; flowers solitary, axillary, nodding; pedicels 2.5 cm long, densely villose; calyx 4 mm long, 7 mm in diameter, lobes 4-5, triangular-ovate, acutish, tomentellous on both sides; petals 6-7, 6-7 mm long, unequal in width, the broader petals 2 or 3, broadly cuneate or obovate-elliptic, unequally bilobate beyond middle, lobes again divided into linear acute, 2-2.5 mm long lobulets, the narrower ones linear, 2-3-fid or dentate, rarely entire, all puberulent on both sides; stamens very numerous, inserted on a yellowish fleshy 4 mm in diameter puberulent disk, 3-4 mm long; filaments densely hirtellous, equal to the anthers in length, less hirtellous prominently produced at tip, dehiscent by terminal pores; pistils 6 mm long; ovary 3-4-celled; capsule globose 3-4 grooved, depressed at tip, 15-18 mm in diameter, densely covered with barbellate, purple-red, 0.5-2.5 mm long deciduous spines, valves 3-4, ovate, ligneous, purple inside, each tipped with a remnent style; seed one in each cell, oblong, 11 mm long, 7 mm in diameter, black and shining, except the upper third or fourth all inclosed in the orange-red fleshy aril.

Distribution: Sezchuan.

15. **Sloanea tomentosa** Rehd. et Wilson

Tree more than 10 meters tall. Branchlets of current years growth covered with densely yellowish hairs, those of last year growth glabrous, dark gray. Leaves oblong ovate, 22 cm long, 10 cm wide, actue at apex, obtuse at base, entire and irregularly shallowly serrate above the middle of the leaves margin, lustrous dark gray glabrous above, browrish tomentose along the midrib and veins and prominently reticulated beneath, coriaceous; petioles 3-4 cm long, densely yellowish hairy, stout, round. Fruits globular, 5 cm long, 4 cm in diameter, densely covered with brownish bristles of 5 mm long, 4-6-valved; fruiting peduncle stout, thick, 6 cm long, erect, brownish tomentose.

Distribution: Yunnan, at altitude 1600 m.

Family 50. Sterculiaceae Schott et Endl.

Key to genera of the family (See orig. text page 819)

Genus (1) Reevesia Lindl. (See orig. text page 820)

1. **Reevesia formosana** (Sprague) Hayata

Small tree with grayish bark; branchlets dark gray, smooth and slightly pubescent on current years growth. Leaves elliptic-lanceolate, 5 cm long, 1.5 cm wide, acute apex cuneate at base, entire margin, dark green above, pale green below, glabrous on both surfaces, membranaceous; petiole 1 cm long, slightly pubescent; flowers in terminal panicles; fruit an elongated woody capsule, 3 cm long, 1 cm broad, slightly curved, sessile; peduncle 2 cm long, stout, glabrous.

Distribution: Taiwan, the south cape.

2. **Reevesia lofauensis** Li

Tree 10-12 cm high, Leaves chartaceous, oblong-lanceolate, 8-12 cm long, 1.5-2.5 cm wide, apex long-acuminate, base acute, margin entire, somewhat undulate, lustrous dark green above, pale green, glabrous below; petiole 3-4 cm long, glabrous. Inflorescences stellate pubescent. Flowers in terminal panicles, stellate-pubescent, multiflorous; pedicels 6-8 mm long; calyx tube stellate-pubescent, 5-6 mm long, fruit obovoid-oblong, 5-lobed.

This species is much allied to *R. thyrsoidea* Lindl. differing in the much narrower lanceolate leaves.

Distribution: Hainan.

3. **Reevesia lancifolia** Chun

Tree 10 m high. Branchlets dark gray, rough, glabrous; leaves variable in size and in shape, obovate to oblong-lanceolate, 8-10 cm long, 4-5 cm wide, acute at apex, obtuse to rounded at base, lustrous dark green above, light green, glabrous below coriaceous; petiole 3-4 cm long, slightly brownish pubescent; flowers pale green, with white petals, interminal panicles, fragrant; fruits an oblong woody capsule, 6-valved, 5 cm long, 2.5 cm in diameter.

Distribution: Kwangtung, Loh Fou Shan and Hainan, at altitude 1000 m.

4. **Reevesia rotundifolia** Chun

Tree 16 m tall, 50 cm in diameter; bark grayish white; young branchlets densely with tawny stellate tomentose, about 3 mm in diameter, becoming soridid tomentose, finely glabrescent, gray-brown and closely striate. Leaves petiolate, thinly coriaceous, oribicular or obovate-rotundate, 6-11.5 cm long, as broad or slightly broader than long, rounded at apex, truncate or broadly obtuse at base, abruptly broadly and shortly triangular cuspidate and with 2-3 short, irregular sparse teeth on each side terminating as many as the upper most lateral nerves, upper surface deep green, lower surface slightly yellowish green, pubescent with stellate hairs along the midrib and veins; capsule, obovoid-oblong, 3.2-3.8 long, 2.3 cm broad, 5-lobed, apex rounded; seeds 2-3 cm long with wings of 1.6 cm long, 8 cm wide at the base, ovate-oblong, base truncate, apex obliquely obtuse, brown, terminating the base of the nutlets.

Distribution: Kwangtung.

5. **Reevesia longipetiolata** Merr. et Chun

Tree 8 m high. Leaves oblong-elliptic or oblong-obovate, 7-17 cm long, 3-6 cm wide, acuminate at apex, obtuse at base, entire incurved margin, lustrous dark green above, pale green glabrous below, coriaceous; petiole 1–3 cm long. Flowering cymes terminal, multiflorous, stellate pubescent; flowers white, calyx tube stellate–pubescent; petals unguiculate, oblanceolate, 2 cm long, 4 mm wide; ovary glabrous.

Distribution: Hainan.

6. **Reevesia pubescens** Mast.

Tree 12 m high. Leaves oblong, 9 cm long, 4 cm wide, acute at apex, obtuse or slightly cordate with 3–nerved at base, entire incurved margin, lustrous dark green above, brownish pubescent below, reticulated, coriaceous; petioles 3–4 cm long, brownish pubescent flowers in terminal racemes; pedicels 5 cm long, brownish pubescent.

Distribution: Kwangsi, at altitude 1150 meters.

7. **Reevesia siamensis** Hu et Wang

Tree 10 m high. Leaves oblong, 17 cm long, 8 cm wide, acute at apex, obtuse, 3–nerved at base, entire incurved margin, lustrous dark green above, midrib, nerves and reticulated pale green pubescent and prominently elevated beneath, subcoriaceous; petiole 3–4 cm long pubescent. Flowers in terminal panicles; fruits grayish yellow, globular 2 cm long, 1.5 cm broad.

Distribution: Yunnan, at altitude 1600 m.

8. **Reevesia sinica** Wilson (See orig. text page 820)

9. **Reevesia taiwaniana** Tsiang

Tree with grayish brak. Leaves oblanceolate, 8–10 cm long, 3–4 cm wide, acute at apex, cuneate at base, entire and incurved margin, subcoriaceous. Fruit a globular woody capsule, about 2 cm in diameter.

Distribution: Taiwan.

10. **Reevesia tomentosa** Li

Tree 12 m high. Branchlets stellate-tomentose. Leaves subcoriaceous oblong-ovate, 8–14 cm long, 3–6 cm wide, acute or obtuse at apex, rounded or subcordate at base, nerves 6–10 pairs, elevated below; petiole 1–3 cm long densely brown tomentose; fruits long-pedicelled, woody, 4 cm long, 3 cm broad, obovoid-oblong, apex rotundate depressed, base acute, stellate-tomentose; pedicels 2.5–3 cm long.

Distribution: Kwangsi.

11. **Reevesia thyrsoidea** Lindl. (See orig. text pages 820–821)

Genus (2) Sterculia Linn. (See orig. text pages 820–821)

1. **Sterculia bracteata** Gagn.

Small shrub 1 m tall. Branchlets slender, pithy, purplish, pubescent. Leaves oblanceolate 17 cm long, 5 cm wide, acute at apex, narrowly cuneate at base, entire margin subcoriaceous, dark green above, prominent midrib and veins, pale green, glabrous beneath; petiole 2 mm long; flowers light red, in lateral and terminal racemes.

Distribution: Yunnan, at altitude 800 m.

2. **Sterculia euosma** W. W. Sm.

3. **Sterculia foetida** Linn.

Tree 12 m high, 25 cm in diameter; fruits bright red.

Distribution: Kwangsi.

4. **Sterculia hainanensis** Merr. et Chun

Shrub 1 meter high. Leaves oblong or oblanceolate, 15–23 cm long, 2.5–4.5 cm wide, acute apex, acute or subobtuse at base, entire margin, chartaceous, nerves 13–18 pairs, distinct; petiole 1.5–2.5 cm long; stipule linear-lanceolate, acuminate, 5–7 mm long, hirsute. Inflorescence axillary, racemose, 5–8 cm long, sub-stellate-pubescent, mm long; sepals coherent, oblong to oblong-elliptic, subacute, 5–5.5 mm long, 2–2.7 mm wide, stellate-pubescent; androphore glabrous, curved, 4–5 mm long, anthers sessile, 1-series, petals cream-white; fruit a capsule, 4 cm long, 2 cm wide, 3-seeded, with a curved beak 6 mm long; seeds ellipsoid, 1 cm in diameter.

Distribution: Hainan and Kwangsi.

5. **Sterculia lanceaefolia** Roxb. (See orig. text page 823)

6. **Sterculia lantsangensis** Hu

Tree 10–15 m high; branchlets stout, pale gray, covered with stellate pubescence, glabrescent when old, inconspicuously lenticelled, with quite broad pith. Leaves palmately 3–5-lobed, broadly cordate at base, up to 17 cm long, 21 cm broad, middle lobe broadly ovate, caudate-acuminate, 8 cm long, 8 cm wide at base, lateral lobes similar, slightly smaller, basal lobes 3 cm long, especially tawny stellate-pilose, along the midrib and veins above, densely tawny-stellate-tomentose beneath, midrib, veins all thick and elevated beneath; petioles stout, stellate-tomentose, 16 cm long; stipules striangular, acuminate, tawny-stellate toemtnose, 1 cm long, 8 mm broad; fruiting panicle terminal, crowded, with rather stout tomentose pedicels to 2 cm long; fruits with 4–5 equal thick woody valves, shortly beaked at apex, to 5 cm long, 2.3 cm broad, densely tawny-stellate-tomentose with stinging hairs on both sides.

Distribution: Yunnan, at altitude 1300 m.

7. **Sterculia monosperma** Vent.

Tree, branchlets stout, yellowish brown, glabrous. Leaves obovate, 20 cm long, 11 cm wide, minutely acute at apex, broadly cuneate at base, entire incurved margin, shining dark green above, pale green, glabrous below, thin, membranaceous; petioles round, 5 cm long, glabrous; flowers small, in axillary panicles.

Distribution: Amoy, Fukien.

8. **Sterculia nobilis** Sm.

Small tree 7 m high; bark cinnamon brown. Branchlets stout, brownish gray, Leaves oblong-spathulate, 20 cm long, 9 cm broad, acute at apex, entire undulate margin, broadly cuneate at base, 3-nered, nerves 10 pairs, lustrous dark green above, pale green glabrous and slightly pubescent along the midrib and veins beneath, subcoriaceous; petiole 3–5 cm long, slightly pubescent. Flowers in lateral panicles, calyx tubular with 5 narrow lobes; fruit globose 7 cm long, 5 cm in diameter, opening from the tip, brownish hairy outside, solitary; fruiting pedicel thick, stout, 4 cm long, 3 mm thick, brownish. Fruit bright reddish yellow; seeds edible.

Distribution: Kwangtung, and Kwangsi, at altitude 1150 m.

9. **Sterculia henryi** Hemsl. (See orig. text page 824)

10. **Sterculia lanceolata** Cav.

11. **Sterculia pexa** Pierre

Tree 10 m high, 30 cm in diameter; bark chalky white. Leaves palmately compound, leaflets 9, oblong, 13 cm long, 6 cm wide, acute at apex, narrow-cuneate at base, undulate margin, lustrous dark green above, pale green, with yellowish pubescence along the midrib and veins beneath, veins conspicuous more than 20 pairs on each side of the midrib, subcoriaceous; petiole 1 mm long, rachis 25 cm long, brownish glabrescent; fruit globose 5 cm long, 4 cm in diameter, concaved on the top, 4-valved, brownish hairy outside; fruiting pedicels 5 mm long.

Distribution: Yunnan, and Kwangsi, at altitude 1000 m.

Genus (3) Firmiana Marsigli (See orig. text page 824)

1. **Firmiana colorata** (Roxb.) R. Br.

Tree 10-12 m high; bark whitish gray. Branchlets whitish gray, with large pith; leaves deciduous. Flowers deep sienna colored in axillary racemes, reddish pubescent; leaves simple, ovate, 15 cm long and wide, 5-nerved at base, bluntely acute apex, cordate at base, entire undulate margin, subcoriaceous.

Distribution: Hainan and Yunnan, at altitude 250 m.

2. **Firmiana simplex** (L.) W. Wight (See orig. text pages 825-826)

3. **Firmiana major** (Sm.) Handel-Mazz. (See orig. text page 827)

Order XIX Parietales

Family 51. Theaceae Mirb.
(See orig. text page 827)

Genus (1) Thea Linn. (See orig. text page 828)

1. **Thea assimiloides** Sealy.

Shrub 1-2 m high. Leaves simple, alternate, elliptic-lanceolate, 5 cm long, 2 cm wide, long-acuminate at apex, narrow-cuneate at base, irregularly and distantly serrate, shining dark green above, light green below, coriaceous; petiole 2 mm long; flowers in terminal racemes; sepals 5; petals 5, pubescent; stamens numerous.

Distribution: Hunan.

2. **Thea amplexifolia** Merr. et Chun

Camellia amplexifolia Merr. et Chun

Shrub 4 m high. Leaves oblanceolate, 18 cm long, 5 cm wide, strongly amplexicaul sessile, the narrow sinus quite embracing the stem, the rounded basal lobes free, as well as by its small flowers and fruits, apiculate glandulose, deep green above, pale green beneath, lustrous, coriaceous; flowers axillary, solitary, sessile; stamens 20; fruit globose, irregulary dehiscent, angular, 5 mm long.

Distribution: Hainan, at altitude 330 m.

3. **Thea caudata** Seem. (See orig. text pages 828–829)

4. **Thea cordifolia** Metcalf

Shrub 4 m high. Branchlets pilose. Leaves chartaceous, cordiform to ovate-lanceolate, 5.5–7.5 cm long, 2–2.5 cm wide, acuminate apex, base cordate to rounded, margin serrate, glabrous above except for slightly pubescent impressed midrib; flowers axillary, 1–3, usually sloitary, subsessile; sepals obovate to sub-round, silky-villose, 5 mm long; petals white, 10–12 mm obovate-oblong, somewhat hairy on back; stamens numerous, 2/3 united, densely hirsute.

Distribution: Kwangtung, and Kwangsi.

5. **Thea craprelliana** Tutcher

Tree 3–7 m high. Leaves 4–5 cm long, 1.5–2 cm wide, obovate, emarginate acuminate, serrate, revolute, glabrous, subcoriaceous; flowers solitary, sessile white, 3–4 cm in diameter; bracteae orbiculary; sepals orbiculary; petals 6–8, obovate; styles 3, distinctly glabrous. Fruit 10 cm in diameters.

Distribution: Hongkong.

6. **Thea crassipes** Sealy

Small tree with minutely petiolate leaves; leaves elliptic, 3.5–6.5 cm long, 1.5–2.2 cm wide, serrate, coriaceous, slightly hirsute below; petiole 2–3 mm long, hirsute; flowers solitary, small pedicelled; bracteoles 2 broadly ovate; sepals 5, unequal, 3–5 mm long, 5–6 mm wide, sparsely pilose; corolla white, 2 cm long, petals 2 exterior ones suborbicular, concave, pilose, 4 interior ones obovate or suborbicular; style 1.5–1.7 cm long.

Distribution: Yunnan.

7. **Thea banksiana** Lindl.

This species is allied to *Thea assimilis*, but differs from in having the style free from a greater distance, the capsule silky-hairy instead of glabrous, the flowers sweet-scented, and in the hairness of the stamens.

Distribution: Hongkong.

8. **Thea brevistyla** (Hay.) Coh. - Stuart

Small tree 3–8 m high. Branchlets very slender, glabrous. Leaves elliptic-oblong, 3.5 cm long, 1.5 cm wide, acute apex, acute at base, serrate margin, thick, lustrous dark green above, pale green, glabrous below, coriaceous; flowers solitary, terminal, white, 2 cm in diameter, subsessile; fruits round, 8 mm in diameter, black, mucronate, sessile, pubescent.

Distribution: Taiwan, Ari Shan.

9. **Thea costei** (Levl.) Rehd.

Shrub closely related to *Thea cuspidata* Kochs from which it is distinguished chiefly by the thinner leaves with the veins beneath slightly elevated and by the filaments being united about one half.

Distribution: Kweichow.

10. **Thea confusa** Craib

Shrub 2 m high. Leaves oblong, 8 cm long, 4 cm wide, acuminate at apex, cuneate at base, serrate margin above the middle; flowers, solitary, terminal, yellowish white.

Distribution: Kwangtung, Yunnan and Kwangsi, at altitude 840 m.

11. **Thea cuspidata** Kochs

Large shrub, 3–5 m tall. Branchlets slender, gray, smooth. Leaves elliptic-lanceolate, 5 cm long, 2.5 cm wide, long-acuminate, cuneate at base, serrate above the middle margin, subsessile, lustrous dark green above, pale green, glabrous below; flowers solitary, terminal, 3 cm across, white, glabrous; fruit round, 1.5 cm in diameter; receptacles persistent.

Distribution: Hupeh, Szechuan, Kweichow, Anhwei, Chekiang, Kwangtung, Kwangsi, Fukien, Taiwan and Kiangsu.

12. **Thea drupifera** Lour.

Shrub, 2 m high. Leaves elliptic or elliptic-lanceolate, 5 cm long, 2.5 cm wide, acute-acuminate at apex, cuneate at base, serrate margin above the middle; flowers 3 cm across, white, odorless, terminal, solitary; fruits globose, 2 cm long and broad, slightly ridged, hard drupe, reddish purple, glabrous.

Distribution: Anhwei, Chekiang, Kiangsu, Hupeh, Kweichow, Kwangtung, Kwangsi, Yunnan, Szechuan, Hunan, Kiangsi, Fukien and Taiwan, at altitude 550 m.

13. **Thea forrestii** Diels

Shrub 1–2 m high. It is closely allied to *T. euryoides* (Lind.) Booth., but differs from it by thicker, broader, more glabrous leaves, more glabrous sepals and emarginate petals; flowers creamy white.

Distribution: Yunnan, at altitude 2250 m.

14. **Thea gaudichaudii** (Gagn.) Sealy

Shrub 3 m high; bark whitish gray smooth. Leaves elliptic-oblong, 6 cm long, 3 cm wide, blunt apice, cuneate at base, incurved margin, glabrous on both surfaces, subcoriaceous; petiole 3 mm long. Fruit globose, 2 cm in diameter; seeds used for extracting oils for cooking.

Distribution: Hainan.

15. **Thea gracilis** Hemsl.

Shrub 3 m high. Allied closely to *T. assimilis* Champ. though it has much thinner leaves, smaller flowers; ovary trioculary.

Distribution: Taiwan.

16. **Thea henryi** (Gagn.) Sealy

Small tree; brak brown, smooth. Leaves lanceolate, 10 cm long, 3.5 cm wide, long-acuminate apex, cuneate at base. serrate above the middle, dark green above, pale green below, subcoriaceous; fruit a thin shelled capsule, 2 cm long, 1.5 cm broad.

Distribution: Kwangsi.

17. **Thea hongkongensis** (Pierre) Hu et Chun

Small, tree with oblong-lanceolate leaves, acute apex, narrow cuneate base, crenate serrate margin, thick, coriaceous; flowers solitary, red, terminal; petals 6, orbicular ovate; stamens numerous.

Distribution: Hongkong.

18. **Thea hozanensis** Hayata

Small shrub with elliptic-ovate leaves, acute apex, cuneate at base, entire margin; petiole 3-5 mm long, glabrous; flowers terminal.

Distribution: Taiwan.

19. **Thea lapidea** Wu

Shrub 3-6 m high. Leaves elliptic-lanceolate, 16 cm long, 3-4 cm wide, caudate-acuminate apex, base acute; flowers terminal, solitary, sessile, 6 cm in diameter; sepals 5, inequal, imbricated, seriated; petals 5, subrotundate; stamens numerous multiserious; ovary 3-locular, densely villose; capsule globose, 4.5 cm in diameter, lapidea, aspera, puberula or glabrescent, apex rostrate, 4-valved.

Distribution: Kwangsi, at altitude 800 m.

20. **Thea latipetiolata** Chi

Shrub characterized by large relatively thin oblong closely but indistinctly serrulate leaves, with a rounded or subrounded base and usually a broad rather short acumen; upper leaves subsessile, lower ones shortly petioled with a broad somewhat expanded petiole; stamens few; ovary pilose crowned by 3 free styles. Flowers white.

Distribution: Kwangtung.

21. **Thea fraterna** O. Kuntze

Shrub 5 m tall. Leaves elliptic or elliptic-oblong, 6 cm long, 3 cm wide, long-acuminate at apex, cuneate at base, serrate above the middle margin, glabrous on both surfaces, subcoriaceous; petiole 2 mm long, pubescent.

Distribution: Kwangtung, Fukien, Chekiang, Taiwan, Kiangsu, Anhwei, Hunan, Hupeh, Yunnan and Szechuan.

22. **Thea purpurecea** (Merr.) Coh.-Stuart

Shrub 4 m high. Leaves oblanceolate, 12 cm long, 5 cm wide, acute apex, narrow cuneate at base, serrate above the middle margin, subcoriaceous.

Distribution: Kwangtung, Hainan and Kwangsi, at altitude 1000 m.

23. **Thea grijsii** (Hance) Kochs

Shrub 2-3 m high. Leaves elliptic, 4 cm long, 3 cm wide, acuminate apex, cuneate at base serrate margin, lustrous dark green above, pale brown beneath, subcoriaceous; petiole 2 mm long, pubescent.

Distribution: Hupeh and Kweichow, at altitude 20-100 m.

24. Thea henryana Cohen-Stuart

Shrub 3-7 m high. Leaves elliptic-oblong, 5 cm long, 2.5 cm wide, short-acuminate apex, cuneate at base, serrate margin, subcoriaceous; petiole 2 mm long; fruit a woody globular capsule 3 cm in diameter, 3-thick-valved.

Distribution: Yunnan, at altitude 2800 m.

25. Thea japonica (L.) Nois. (See orig. text page 829)

26. Thea kissi Wall.

Tree 7 m high. Branchlets rather thick, stout, gray, smooth. Leaves elliptic ovate, 7 cm long, 3 cm wide, acute-acuminate apex, cuneate at base, simply serrate above the middle on the margin, lustrous deep green above, light green below, glabrous on both surfaces, subcoriaceous; petioles 3 mm long, slightly whitish pubescent; flower solitary, axillary, 5-parted, white; filaments yellowish, stamens numerous; style 3.5 mm long; fruit a woody capsule globular, 2 cm long, and broad, greenish yellow, dehiscent at apex, 3-thick-valves, exposing 2 seeds, glabrous; fruiting pedicel 1.5 mm long, whitish pubescent.

Distribution: Kwangtung, Hainan, Kwangsi and Yunnan, at altitude 2000 m.

27. Thea mairei (Levl.) var. **lepidea** Wu

Shrub 7 m high. Branchlets slender, grayish brown. Leaves oblong, oblanceolate, 11 cm long, 4.5 cm wide, acuminate at apex, cuneate at base, finely serrate margin above the middle, lustrous dark green above, pale green below, veins 10 pairs, prominent above, impressed above, coriaceous; flowers large, showy, 5 cm across, red, petals spathulate and notched at the top; stamens numerous, hairy, filaments half as long as the petals; fruits solitary, subterminal, globular, 2.5 cm across, glabrous, dehiscent from the top into 3 thick woody valves, brown, glabrous, 2-seeded.

Distribution: Kwangsi, at altitude 540-1500 m.

28. Thea melliana Handel-Mazz.

Shrub 1-2 m high. Leaves elliptic-lanceolate, 3 cm long, 12 mm wide, acute-acuminate at apex, cuneate at base, finely serrate margin, lustrous dark green above, pale green below, subcoriaceous; flowers white, fragrant, calyx pubescent.

Distribution: Kwangtung, at altitude 700-800 m.

29. Thea microphylla (Merr.) Chun

Shrub 1-2 m high. Leaves oblanceolate, 3.5 cm long, 1.5 cm wide, minutely acute and bluntely-spathulate at tip, acuminate at base, serrate above the middle of the leaf margin, evergreen, dark lustrous green above, pale and glabrous green below; petiole 1-2 mm long; flowers solitary, axillary; fruit, sessile, subovoid 1.5 cm long and i diameter, irregulary dehiscent, slightly pubescent; sepals deciduous.

Distribution: Anhwei at altitude 200 m.

30. Thea nidissima Chi

Small tree 6 m high. Leaves oblong, elliptic-oblong to ovate-oblong, 8-11 cm lor 3-4.5 cm wide, small acuminate at apex, obtuse cuneate at base, coarsely irregula serrate margin, lustrous olive-green above, with lateral veins diverging from the midrib at a wide angle; and by a large short peduncle; capsule coriaceous, brownish verruculous on the outside, on the short stalked glabrous fruit.

Distribution: Kwangtung, at altitude 1200 m.

31. **Thea nokoensis** Hayata

Shrub 5-8 m high. Leaves elliptic-obovate, 4 cm long, 1.5 cm wide, long acuminate at apex, cuneate at base, simply serrate margin lustrous dark green above, pale green below, subcoriaceous; petiole 1 mm long; flowers lateral, solitary, white.

Distribution: Taiwan.

32. **Thea pachyandra** Hu

Tree 10 m high; Branches terete, striate, yellowish brown; branchlets slender, subangular, striate, glabrous, dark brown, becoming whitish gray in age; leaves chartaceous, elliptic to obovate elliptic, caudate-acuminate at both ends, sharply glandulose-serrulate-denticulate along the whole margins, glabrous, and with elevated midrib, secondary veins and loose reticulations above, glabrous except pilose along the rather prominent midrib and with elevated secondary veins and midrib and reticulations beneath, to 10 cm long, 4 cm broad, cauda to 7 mm long; petioles channelled above, glabrous to 6 mm long; flowers solitary, small, white, with pedicels 1 mm long; bract coriaceous, broadly-ovate, keeled outside, glabrous to 4 mm long; sepals 4, coriaceous, suborbicular, with membranaceous margins, glabrous, 6 mm in diameter; petals 3-4, sometimes 8, ovate oblong, 9 mm long, 6 mm broad, connate into a short tube at base; stamens half connate into a ring and adnate to the petals at base, 6 mm long, filaments stout, glabrous; ovary 3-gonous, pilose; style 3-lobed, 1.5 mm long; capsule subglobose, to somewhat 3-gonous, 3.3 cm in diameter.

Distribution: Southwestern Yunnan, at altitude 1500 m.

33. **Thea parviflora** Merr. et Chun

Shrub 3 m high. Leaves elliptic-lanceolate, 5 cm long, 16 mm wide, acute-acuminate at apex, cuneate at base, entire incurved margin, lustrous dark green above, pale green glabrous beneath, coriaceous; petiole 1 mm long; flowers white, solitary, very small.

Distribution: Hainan, at altitude 1500 m.

34. **Thea parvilimba** Merr. et Metcalf

A small erect shrub 1-1.5 m high, with glabrous branches and slender shortly pubescent branchlets, the terminal part somewhat silky; leaves elliptic, 2-2.5 cm long, up to 10 mm wide, acute to obtusely acuminate, base acute to narrowly obtuse, dark greenish, shining and subglabrous above, or rarely with a few distinct, long appressed blackish hairs paler beneath, minutely papillose, and usually with scattered blackish hairs margin somewhat revolute, distinctly crenate to bluntly serrate, the lower 1/3 entire, lateral veins and reticulations obsolete. Fruits often pendulous, long-peduncled, the pedicels 10 mm long, glabrous, with scattered minute bracts below the insertion of the sepals; persistent sepals 5, ovate obtuse, somewhat silky within. Fruit yellowish, ovoid, glabrous, about 1 cm long, irregulary 3-valved, usually 1-seeded, valve somewhat woody, minutely verruculose; seed about 8 mm in diameter, brownish-black.

Distribution: Kwangtung, at altitude 530 m.

35. Thea paucipunctata Merrill et Chun

Tree 6 m high. Leaves oblong-obovate, 11 cm long, 6 cm wide, acute at apex, cuneate at base, simply serrate above the middle and entire 1/3 below the middle margin and revolute the whole margins, lustrous dark green above, light green, prominently reticulated beneath; petioles 6 mm long, channelled, coriaceous; flowers yellowish white; stamens numerous; fruit globular, 2 cm long, 1.8 cm across, 6-valved, 3-seeded, brown, sessile.

Distribution: Hainan, at altitude 500 m.

36. Thea polygama Hu

Shrub 4 m high, branchlets terete, dark-brown hirtellate, bark ashgray-purplish. Leaves thinly coriaceous, oval to ovate-elliptic-lanceolate, 2-4 cm long, 1.2-2.4 cm wide, subobtuse to shortly acuminate, broadly cuneate to subrounded and entire at base, serrate along the margins, upper surface glabrous except dark brown-hirtellate, along the elevated midrib above, lower surface glabrous excpet sparsely hirtellate along the midrib elevated to above the middle, lateral veins inconspicuous; petiole to 4 mm long, upper surface grooved, black, densely darkbrown hirtellate, lower surface red, brown-hirtellate. Flowers singular or paired, axillary, polygamo-dioecious (?), pedicels 4 mm long, covered by the crustaceous bracts; sepals broadly ovate, 3 mm long and slightly broader, crustaceous and broadly scariose along the margins, brown, glabrous; petals white, obovate, 8-10 mm long and narrower, glabrous; stamens about 30, glabrous, subequalling the corolla, sometimes all fertile, sometimes the inner 10-20 reduced into clavate sometimes forked staminodes; ovary glabrous; styles 2-3, cunnate nearly to the apex.

This species seems particularly different from other species in having stamens reduced into staminodes. Under this number two types of specimens are included; one type with larger leaves and larger flowers with all stamens fertile, one type with smaller leaves and smaller flowers with a portion of inner stamens reduced to staminodes. But the characteristic red petiole and other details prove these specimens belonging to the same species. It cannot be definitely ascertained whether these specimens belong to two plants or the same plant; wether these species is functionally polygamouse-dioecious. At any rate the presence of staminodes is a rare occurence in the genus Thea.

Distribution: Yunnan, at altitude 1800 m.

37. Thea punctata (Kudo) Coch. - Stuart

Shrub 4 m high. Leaves elliptic-oblong, 5 cm long, 3.5 cm wide, short acuminate at apex, narrow cuneate at base, serrate above the middle margin, lustrous dark green above, pale green, glabrous beneath, subcoriaceous; petiole 2 mm long; flowers white; ovary hairy; fruits a capsule, hairy, subsessile.

Distribution: Sezchuan, Kiatin, at altitude 500 m.

38. Thea pitardii (Stuart) Rehder

Tree 2 or 3 meters high. It is very variable in size and in the shape of the leaves, in the pubescence of the sepals and also in the color of the flowers, which vary from bright red to white. In the typical form the leaves are generally oblong, 5–10 cm long and acuminate to long acuminate with the veins above slightly raised and less so beneath; the sepals are densely silky outside and also the petals are more or less silky outside. As an extreme form the following may be distinguished. Generally flowers are purplish red, large and showy, 5–7 cm in diameter, many petalloid; stamens numerous.

Distribution: Yunnan, at altitude 1500–2300 m. Kweichow, Kwangsi, Hunan and Szechuan.

Var. 1. Thea pitardii Cohen-Stuart var. yunnanica Sealy

As originally described, has caudate or abruptly acuminate very prominently serrulate leaves. It comes from Kweichow, and has also been found near Mengtze, Southeastern Yunnan, and in Western Szechuan and adjacent Sikang. Widely distributed at moderate elevations throughout Yunnan and in the adjacent part of Southern Szechuan, are plants which greatly resemble the original *Thea pistardii* in most characetrs but which are readily distinguishable by the leaf-blades being relatively narrower and generally more attenuated both to the base and apex, and much less prominently serrulate. There is a considerable variations in the size of flowers while the floral perules vary from glabrous with a ciliate margin to very densely silky-tomentose. There is also variation in sized of leaves and though on some twigs the leaves approach those of *C. saluenensis* in size, they are generally much larger and agree with this repsect with those of *Thea pitardii*. Yunnan is famous for the numerous varieties of beautiful camellias ovary 70 varieties all of great beauty are cultivated in Yunnan-fu., the capital of the province. The majority of these cultivated Camellias "varieties" probably belong to *Thea* or *Camellia pitardii* var. *yunnanica* and to *C. saluenensis*.

Distribution: Yunnan, at altitude 300–1700 m.

Var. 2. Thea pitardii var. lucidissima (Levl.) Rehder

This variety differs from the type in the smaller leaves, usually 3.5–6 cm long, acute or even obtusish, of thicker texture and usually very lustrous with the veins above mostly impressed, and in the glabrescent bracts, sepals and petals; shrub 1–2 meters high. Flowers pinkish purple.

Distribution: Yunnan, at altitude 2700 m.

39. Thea rosthorniana Handel-Mazz.

Shrub 2 m high. Leaves small, elliptic, 3 cm long, 1 cm wide, long-acuminate at apex, cuneate at base finely serrate margin above the middle, lustrous shining green above, pale green below, glabrous on both surface, subcoriaceous; flowers white, terminal; petals obovate, 8–12 mm long; sepale obovate, 2 mm long, margins scariose brownish ciliate; ovary glabrous; style connate.

Distribution: Szechuan.

40. **Thea semiserrata** Chi

Tree 8–12 m high. Leaves persistent, oblong to elliptic oblong, 8–15 cm long, 3–6 cm wide, acuminate apex, broad cuneate at base, dentate–serrate on the upper part of margin and 1/3 lower part revolute margin, coriaceous. Flowers large 6.5 cm in diameter, occasionally terminal, solitary, erect, sessile; sepals bractea 11, coriaceous, deciduous, inaequal; petals 6–7, broad rotundate, 5 cm long, 4.5 cm wide, apice emarginate, base cuneate; stamens numerous, 5–series; ovary glabrous ovoid–globose 4.5 cm in diameter, loculicide dehiscent, valves 3–5, monosperma. This plant bears a local name of "Kwang–Ning–Cha". An economically important sepcies and has been cultivated for many years for Tea oil production, but the plantations should be greatly extended to meet the demands of commerce.

Distribution: Kwangtung Kwang–Ning Hsien.

41. **Thea sophiae** Hu

Shrub 2.5 m high. Leaves coriaceous, elliptic–lanceolate, long acuminate, subrotundate at base, glandulose–serrulate along the margins, glabrous except pilosulose along the midrib and veins above, midrib reticulated and veins prominent beneath, 6.5 cm long, 2.5 cm wide; petiole channelled, 4 mm long, serious–pilose; flowers solitary in leafy axils, crowded near the apex of the branchlets; sepals 5, unequal, 9 mm long, 13 mm broad, densely tawny outside; petals 5, white, obcordate, clawed and connate into a short ring at base, 3.5 cm long and broad, tawny serious outside style 3–lobed at apex,

Distribution: Yunnan, at altitude 1600 m.

42. **Thea speciosa** Pitard

Shrub 2 m high. Flowers rose–pink, on dry open chalky hill sides.

Distribution: Yunnan, at altitude 2600 m.

43. **Thea stenophylla** Kobuski

Shrub 3 m high. Leaves lanceolate, 5 cm long, 1.5 cm wide, long–acuminate apex, cuneate at base, serrate margin, dark green above, pale green below, glabrous on both sides, coriaceous; flowers light yellow.

Distribution: Hainan, on the stream sides.

44. **Thea stuartiana** Sealy

Tree 6 m high. Leaves broad–elliptic or oblong–elliptic, 7.2–10.5 cm long, 3–4 cm wide, serrulate dentate margin, sparsely villose; petiole 5–7 mm long; flowers axillary or terminally, solitary; bracteoles 5 imbricate, appressed, broadly triangular; calyx cupulary; petals 5–7, 2 exteriors free, suborbiculary, obovate or oblong–ovate, concave, coriaceous, dense villose; ovary 5–lobed; style attenuated, 1.7–1.8 cr long.

Distribution: Yunnan.

45.. **Thea szechuanensis** Chi

This species resembles *Camellia tuberculata* Chien in general appearance but may be easily distinguished by the strigose-hirsute petiole and the smooth, not tuberculate fruits. It is characterized by slenderly caudate-acuminate leaves with the midrib and principal veins sharply elevated and very prominent on the upper surface and nearly obsolescent on the lower surface when dry. The lateral veins are somewhat irregular and diverge from the midrib at a wide angle and joined by only a few sparse veinlets.

Distribution: Szechuan Hung-Chun-Ping, near Chi-Fung.

46. **Thea synaptica** Sealy

Small shrub, 3 m high. Leaves elliptic or broad elliptic, 4.5-9 cm long, 1.8-3.4 cm wide, caudate apex, serrulate-dentate, incurved margin, cuneate at base; petiole 3-4 mm long, puberulous. Flowers terminal or axillary, pedicels 5-7 mm long; bracteoles 4 or 5 broad triangular; sepals 5, rotundate; corolla white, 2-2.3 cm long; petals 5-6, exterior 1 or 2 suborbicular; ovary 1.5 mm long; style 13-18 mm long.

Distribution: Yunnan.

47. **Thea reticulata** Lindley

Small tree 5-7 m high. Branchlets gray and smooth. Leaves elliptic-oblong, 7 cm long, 4 cm wide, acute-acuminate at apex, obtuse-cuneate at base, finely serrate margin, lustrous dark green above, pale green glabrous below, thick, coriaceous; petiole 15 mm long, channelled, reddish pubescent; flowers scarlet red, terminal, and lateral about 6 cm across, calyx bracteoles obovate with dense whitish hairs outside; petals many, oblong-ovate, 5 cm long, 4 cm wide, narrowed at base and notched at top, whitish pubescent or hairy outside; fruit a large woody capsule, globular, 5.5 cm long, 4 cm broad, 1-seeded, brown, glabrous.

Distribution: Yunnan, at altitude 2100 m.

48. **Thea saluenensis** Stapf

Shrub 2-4 m high. Branchlets short, stout, gray, smooth. Leaves elliptic-lanceolate, 4 cm long, 2 cm wide, acute at apex, cuneate at base, finely serrate at margin, lustrous dark green above, pale green, glabrous, prominently reticulated beneath, coriaceous; petiole 1.5 mm long, brownish pubescent; flowers pink, terminal, solitary, calyx bracteoles broadly ovate, glabrous; stamens numerous, half as long as the petals; fruit round, 1.5 cm in diameter, 6-valved, somewhat mucronate-concaved at tip, brown, densely covered with brownish hairs, solitary, sessile, axillary.

Distribution: Yunnan, at altitude 2100 m.

49. **Thea salicifolia** Champion

Shrub 2 m high. Branchlets dark gray, brownish hairy when young, smooth when old; leaves lanceolate, 6 cm long, 2 cm wide, long-acuminate at apex, cuneate at base, finely serrate margin, shining green above, pale green, brownish hairy along the mdirib and veins beneath, subcoriaceous; petiole 1 mm long, brownish pubescent; flowers white, fragrant, solitary, axillary; sepals 5-7, exterior hairy, imbricated and subtended by imbricated hairy bracteoles; petals 5, white, oblong-ovate to obovate-gamopetalous at base; stamens numerous in 4-rows the outer rows united into a tube, 2 inner rows with nearly free filaments; style hairy, elongated simple; stigmas 1-3, filiform; ovary hairy, 2-3-celled, each with a double-rows of 3 anatropous ovules; capsule roundish-rostrate, usually by abortion, 1-seeded.

Distribution: Kwangtung, Kwangsi, Fukien and Taiwan, at altitude 2100 m.

50. **Thea sinensis** Linn.

Thea cantonienensis Lour.

Thea cochinchinensis Lour.

Camellia thea Link.

Thea chinensis Seem.

Shrub of 1-2 m high. The size of the leaves depends on good cultivation; on neglected plants the leaves are large and coarse and of comparatively little value and if the soil is fairy good and the plants grow freely the leaves assume the size and shape of those so-called Assam Tea plant. Close picking of the young shoots and leaves dwarfes the plants and reduces the size of the leaves. In general, the leaves of the wild plants are elliptic-ovate or elliptic-oblong in shape, about 4-6 cm long, 2-3 cm wide, blunt acute at apex, obtuse cuneate at base, serrate margin, lustrous shining green above, pale green, glabrous beneath, subcoriaceous; petiole 1 mm long, reddish; flowers white, solitary, axillary or terminal, sepals 5-lobed, petals 5, stamens numerous; fruit a globular woody capsule.

Respecting the variations of *Thea chinensis* that they are supposed to be much more marked than they really are. There is indeed a vast difference between the narrow-leaves forms of what is called *Thea bohea* Linn. in the Kew Garden, and the broad-leaved specimens of the wild Thea of Assam, but the transition from *Thea bohea* to *Thea viridis* Linn., and thence to *Thea assamica* Master, is so gradual, that is almost impossible to draw up any precise definition of these three great varieties. Besides, it must not be supposed that when we have finished characters for these principal varieties our labours have terminated. As in all cultivated plants, there are minor vaieties, and form of the highest agricultural and commercial values, that claim our atterntion. The belief so long entertained that *Thea bohea* yielded the black, *Thea viridis* Linn. the green tea of commerce, has long been exploded; but a slight doubt seems still to linger in some quarters whether the fact *Thea bohea* suffers less from frost, and begins to put forth its young leaves later than *Thea viridis*, does not approve a specific difference between them. The reply to this is, that *Thea viridis* of the gardens does not certainly begin to grow earlier than *Thea bohea*, and therefore is apt to suffer more from night frost than *Thea bohea*, but it does not follow that it must on that account be specifically distinct, as according to the same rule, we should have to make species of all the early and late sorts of our kitchen vegetables and of our fruit-trees. Thea plant was intro-duced from India by the Buddist priests, so that it is possible that we may term a species "Chinese" that is in reality "East-Indian" in the origin. The plant may be found wild yet in North-western China.

Distribution: Kwangtung, Fukien, Chekiang, Taiwan, Anhwei, Hupeh, Szec-huan, Kweichow, Yunnan, Kiangsi and Hainan, at altitude 750-2300 m.

Var. 1. Thea sinensis var. assamica (Mast.) Sealy

Tree or shrub 2-3 m high. Leaves oblong lanceolate, 8 cm long, 4 cm wide, acute at apex, cuneate at base, coarsely serrate margin, lustrous dark green above, pale green below, glabrous, coriaceous petiole 7 mm long, grooved, glabrous; flowers solitary, axillary, white; fruit rounded 2 cm in diameter, reddish, 6-valved.

Distribution: Yunnan, Kweichow, Hainan, Kwangutng and Kwangsi, at altitude 800-1200 m.

51. Thea tegmentosa (Koidz.) Mak.

Shrub 1 meter high. Leaves variable in size and shape, elliptic-lanceolate in general outline, 3-8 cm long, 1.5-3 cm wide, acute at apex, obtuse-cuneate at base, finely serrate margin, lustrous shining green above, pale green and glabrous beneath; petiole 3 mm long, slender, glabrous.

Distribution: Taiwan.

52. Thea tenii Sealy

Shrub 1 meter high. Leaves elliptic, 2.5-4.3 cm long, 1.2-2.2 cm wide, obtuse-acute at apex, broadly cuneate at base, serrulate-dentate margin, coriaceous, glabrous above, sparsely villose below; petiole 3-5 mm long, densely pubescent; flowers terminal of axillary, solitary, sessile; sepals 9-10, suborbicular, imbricated, cupulary, per-sistent; petals obovate-oblong, rounded, emarginate, 8-12 mm long, 5-8 mm wide, corolla white, petals 6.

Distribution: Yunnan.

53. Thea tenuiflora (Hayata) Coh.-Stuart

Shrub 1-2 m high. Leaves elliptic-obovate, 4-6 cm long, 1.5-3 cm wide, bluntly acute at apex, obtuse-acute at base, serrate margin, shining green above, pale green glabrous beneath, subcoriaceous; petiole 3 mm long.

Distribution: Taiwan.

54. Thea transarisaensis (Hayata) Coh.-Stuart

A small slender shrub of a few cm tall, with brownish hairy branchlets. Leaves elliptic, 2.5 cm long, 1.5 m broad, short acuminate at apex, obtuse at base, serrate margin, dark shining green above, pale green and glabrous beneath, subcoriaceous; petiole 1 mm long, reddish, pubescent. Fruit globose, 13 mm long, 10 mm broad, 3-valved capsule, brown, glabrous.

Distribution: Taiwan, at altitude 2300 m.

55. Thea tsingpienensis Hu

Shrub 3 m high; young branchlets slender, terete, dark-gray-pilose. Leaves chartaceous, ovate-lanceolate, caudate-acuminate at apex, rounded at base, closely and sharply serrulate along the margins, glabrous except scabid along the midrib above, glabrous except pilosulose along the elevated midrib beneath, veins, obscure, to 7 cm long, 2.5 cm broad, caudate to 1.5 cm long; petiole densely pilose, to 5 mm long; flowers solitary, small, white, 1.5 cm in diameter; pedicels 2 mm long; sepals unequal suborbicular, imbricate membranaceous along the margins, glabrous, to 5 mm long; petals ovate-oblong, 1 cm long, 6 mm broad; stamens numerous, connate to the middle, 8 mm long, filaments pilose; pistil equalling the stamens; ovary and style glabrous, 2-3-lobed at apex; fruit globose, 1 cm in diameter.

Distribution: Yunnan, at altitude 1800 m.

56. Thea tsofui Chien

Shrub 1-2 m high, branching; branchlets slender, yellow, densely and spreadingly hirsute, the hairs persistent in the third year's growth of branches, older branches yellowish-gray; bud cylindrical, acuminate, 4-6 mm long, outer scales 6, accrescent, rounded to broadly elliptic-oblong, rounded at apex, apiculate, serceous-ciliolate and sericeous outside. Leaves chartaceous, lanceolate or oblong-rarely ovate-lanceolate, rotundate or cuneate at base, obtusely caudate-acuminate, only in some very small leaves the acumen very short obtuse or acutish, 3-5.5 cm long, 1.2-1.7 cm broad, upper surface dark green, except the strigillose midrib glabrous, lower surface light green, sparsely sericeous or excpet the basal part of midrib glabrescent, serrulate on both sides, teeth 12-20 on each side, nerves 6-7 on each side, obsoletely impressed above, slightly elevated below; petioles 2-3 mm long, plane-convex, hirtellous, flowers terminal, single or two, white or purplish red outside when young, 2.5-3 cm in diameter; pedicels 5-6 mm long, slightly curved downward, hirtellous or glabrescent; bracts 4-6, broadly ovate, obtuse, margin and back puberulent, small; calyx cup-shaped, 2 mm long, lobes 5, like bracts in form, 1 mm long, ciliolate, puberulent on both sides; petals 5, unequal in size, 18 mm long, narrowly connate at base, 2 smaller broadly obovate, apex rounded, 6-7 mm long, 5 mm broad, 3 larger broadly obovate or almost orbicular, rounded or emarginate at apex, 13-15 mm long, 10-12 mm broad, all ciliolate, sometimes puberulent on back above; stamens dimorphous, 5 hypogynous, free, 11-12 mm long, 24-36 epipetalous, 12-18 mm long, lower third or fourth connate, the base also adnate to the corolla, filaments all sparsely pilose, anthers hardly 2 mm long, auriculate at base pistil slender, 22 mm long, glabrous; ovary globose, 1 mm in diameter, 3-celled, each cell containing 2 ovules, style filiform, stigma 3, 1 mm long.

Distribution: Szechuan.

57. Thea villicarpa Chien

Shrub 2.5 m high; young branchlets yellowish brown, straight, densely and spread ingly hirsute, hairs persistent even in the third year's branches, second year's branchlets brown, the bark of the older branches finely becomes fissured. Leaves chartaceous, elliptic, rarely ovate-lanceolate, mostly obtusely acuminate, rarely as narrowed as the base, mucronate, 2-3.5 cm long, 1-1.5 cm wide, light green and opaque above, paler below except the base serrulate on both sides, midrib prominently on both sides, densely hirtellose along the entire length above, strigillose toward the base below, nerves 7 on each side; petiole 1 mm long, broadly concave and hirtellose above. Flowers not seen. Fruit 1 or 2 attached at the apex of one year's growth of branchlets; pedicels 1-1.5 mm long, puberulent; bracts 4-5, ovate, acutish or rounded; calyx persistnet, 5 mm in diameter, lobes 5, broadly ovate; capsule globose 1.2 cm in diam., densely verruculose, sparsely covered with thin straight hairs, irregularly dehiscent, seed one in each fruit, about 1 cm long, smooth.

Distribution: Szechuan, at altitude 1000-1200 m.

58. **Thea wardii** Kobuski

Shrub 2 m high. Branchlets slender, terete, grayish brown, smooth; leaves oblong, 9 cm long, 4 cm wide, long-acuminate at apex, obtuse acute at base, simply serrate margin lustrous dark green above, pale green, prominently reticulate, glabrous beneath, subcoriaceous; petiole 12 mm long, glabrous, grooved; flowers axillary, solitary, sessile, white, pubescent.

Distribution: Yunnan.

59. **Thea wenshanensis** Hu

Shrub 4 m high; young branchlets slender, terete, densely gray-pilose. Leaves chartaceous, lanceolate, long caudate-acuminate, rounded at base, sharply serrulate along the margins, glabrous excpet pilosulose along the midrib elevated above, glabrous except long pilose along the elevated midrib beneath, veins impressed on both surfaces, to 5 cm long, 1.8 cm broad; petiole gray-pilose, 3 mm long; flowers axillary, solitary or in pairs, white short pedicelled; bracts and sepals rounded, densely white sericeous in the middle leaving broad glabrous margins on the outside; sepals to 7 mm long, persistent; petals obovate, 12 mm long, 6 mm broad, white sericeous in the middle leaving broad glabrous margins on the outside, ciliate along the margins; stamens numerous, highly connate, densely white-sericeous inside, slightly shorter than the petals; ovary hairy, style slender, pilose, 3-lobed at apex.

Distribution: Southern Yunnan, Wen-Shan Hsien, at altitude 2000 m.

60. **Thea taliensis** (W. W. Sm.) Melchier

Tree 13 m high. Leaves oblanceolate or obovate, 14 cm long, 4-6 cm wide, apex obtusish-acuminate, cuneate at base, serrate margin, lustrous olive-green above, pale green glabrous beneath except along the midrib and veins slightly white pubescent, papery; veins prominent above and inconspicuous beneath; petiole 12 mm long, brown, grooved; fruit sub-quadrangular-globose, green; flowers expand 5-6 cm in diameter; sepals orbicular, 5-10 mm in diameter; petals white, broad elliptic, 2 cm wide; ovary densely white villose; fruit 5-angulate pilosus.

Distribution: Yunnan, Tali Lake, at altitude 3000 m.

61. **Thea tsai** Hu

Tree to 5 m high; branchlets slender, terete, glandulose-hirtellate; leaves chartaceous, narrow lanceolate, long caudate-acuminate at apex, broadly cuneate to subrounded at base, closely and sharply serrate along the margins, glabrous on both surfaces except finely hirtellate along the elevated midrib above, secondary veins obscure above, midrib and secondary veins elevated beneath, to 8 cm long, 2 cm broad; petiole hirtellate, 5 mm long; flowers 1-3 in leaf-axils, white; pedicels nodding, to 3 mm long; bracts broadly cordate, 1.5 mm long, 2mm broad, pilosulose outside; petals 5, elliptic-obovate, rounded at apex, glabrous, 18 mm long, 8 mm broad; stamens numerous, unequal, slightly shorter than the petals; filaments almost free to the base, glabrous; pistil 16 mm long; ovary and style glabrous, stigma 3, very short.

Distribution: Yunnan, at altitude 1750 m.

62. **Thea tuberculata** Chien

Shrub 1-4 m high; glabrous except buds and flowers; new branchlets light yellow, striaght, to 19 cm long, slightly compressed, verrucose, middle internodes 3-4 cm long, older branchlets yellowish gray; buds cylindrical, acuminate, 6-10 mm long, outer scales 5, accrescent, broadly ovate or broadly oblong, apiculate, ciliolate, upper back pubescent. Leaves subcoriaceous, oblong-elliptic, sometimes obovate-oblong, abruptly acuminate at apex, broadly cuneate at base, 8-12 cm long, 3-4 cm broad, serrulate, dark green shining above, lighter beneath, narrowly white-membranaceous at margin, densely verrucose on both sides, midrib slightly raised above, prominently so below, nerves 8-9 on each side, slightly raised on both sides; petioles 9-13 mm long, sulcate above; flowers solitary, terminal, white, 4 cm in diameter; pedicels 4-5 mm long decurved, thick, strigillose, covered by bracts; bracts 5-6, accrescent, gradually passed into sepals; petals 7-8, broadly ovate-rotundate, rounded at apex, 10-12 mm long, coriaceous, fragil, ciliolate, densely appressedly sericeous on back, subspathulate, emarginate, 20-300 mm long, horizontally spreading, revolute toward the apex, glabrous; stamens about 90, equals to the petals in length; capsule depressed globose about 20 mm in diameter, conspicuously tuberculate, upper part villose, mostly 3-celled and 3-lobed, loculicidally dehiscent; pericarp lignose, 1 mm thick with persistent sepals at base, bracts rarely persistent; seed 3 in each fruit, oblong, 12 mm long, rather long villose.

Distribution: Szechuan, at altitude 500-1300 m.

63. **Thea yunnanensis** Pitard

Shrub 1-3 m high; Leaves small petiolate, papery, ovate or ovate-lanceolate 3-5 cm long, 1.7-2.5 cm wide, acuminate apex, rotundate at base, serrulate margin; flowers pedunculate, erect, expand to 5 cm in diameter; sepals margin scarious; petals white, elliptic, 2-2.5 cm long, 1-1.3 cm wide, emarginate; ovary glabrous, style free.

Distribution: Yunnan, at altitude 3000 m.

Genus (2) Gordonia Ellis (See orig. text pages 829-830)

1. **Gordonia axillaris** Szyszl. (See orig. text pages 830-831)
2. **Gordonia anomala** Spreng.

Tree, bark gray. Branchlets slender, gray, smooth, glabrous. Leaves oblanceolate 10 cm long, 3 cm wide, acute-emarginate at apex, cuneate at base, entire and revolute margin, shining deep green above, light bluish green and glabrous beneath, thick, coriaceous, secondary veins inconspicuous on both surfaces; petiole 2 mm long, reddish brown, glabrous; flowers terminal, solitary, white, calyx imbricated, bluish-white silvery outside, persistent; petals 5, obovate, glabrous, about 5-7 cm in diameter; stamens numerous, filaments 1/3 as long as the petals.

Distribution: Taiwan, low altitude.

3. **Gordonia balansae** Pitard.

Tree 15 m high. Branchlets whitish gray, smooth, glabrous. Leaves oblanceolate, 9 cm long, 3 cm wide, long-acute at apex, short-acuminate at base, irregularly dentate-serrate margin, glossy, shining green above, light green glabrous below, thick, coriaceous; petiole 5 mm long, reddish brown, glabrous; flowers white, terminal or axillary; capsule, woody cylindrical, 2.5 cm long, 1 cm in diameter, open from the tip, 5-valved, brown, with calyx persistent; fruiting pedicel 1 cm long, pubescent; seeds winged.

Distribution: Hainan, at altitude 700 m.

4. **Gordonia chrysandra** Cowan (See orig. text page 831)
5. **Gordonia yunnanensis** Hu

Tree 5 m high; branchlets slender, terete, glabrous, ashy gray. Leaves chartaceous, oblanceolate, acuminate at apex, cuneate and decurrent into the petiole at base, revolute and serrulate along the margins, glabrous, the reddish midrib and veins elevated on both surfaces, secondary veins 13-15 pairs, to 14 cm long, 5 cm wide; petiole flat, broad, reddish glabrous, to 1 cm long; flowers axillary, solitary, peduncled; peduncle 1 cm long; bracts very unequal, broadly ovate, glabrous, membranaceous along the margins, 9 mm long; sepals 5, unequal, imbricate, orbicular, glabrous outside, yellow sericeous inside, broadly membranaceous along the margins to 2 cm long and broad; petals obovate, white membranaceous, glabrous, 2.5 cm long, 1.8 cm broad; stamens very numerous, connate at base, and adnate to the base, 2 cm long; style sericeous, 5-lobed; ovary pentagonal, densely tomentose, 5-celled, ovules 4 in each cell, arranged in two rows.

Distribution: Yunnan, at altitude 1750 m.

Genus (3) Schima Reinw.

Evergreen trees; leaves alternate, coriaceous, serrate, crenate, rarely entire margins; flowers solitary, axillary, erect, with 2 bracts; in racemes; sepals 5, small, unequal; petals 5, connate at base, imbricate, external concave; stamens numerous; anthers turning round; ovary 5, rarely 4-6, 2-6-locular, lateral ones subpendular; capsule woody, depressed globose; locules dehiscent, columella persistent; seeds plane, reniform.

About 12 species distributed in Southern part of China.

1. **Schima argentea** E. Pritzel

A shrub or large tree, 2–20 m high, evergreen. Branchlets rather straight; bark dark purplish; lenticels very small and numerous. Innovations sericeous. Leaves rather narrowly elliptic–oblong to oblanceolate, 7–13 cm long, 2–4.5 cm wide, entire, base acute, apex acuminate, acumen very glaucous below with a skin of adpressed sericeous hairs (invisible without a lens), eventually glabrescent; midrib prominent below flat, and often reddish above; lateral nerves 10–12 pairs, slender, patulous not conspicuous epsecially below; veinlets immersed, reticulate; petiole 8–15 mm long, rather wide, flattened above, thinly sericeous. Flowers solitary, axillary, up to 9 from each innovation; bud globose, peduncle terete, 6–15 mm long, thinly sericeous, abruptly expanded at the apex, into a turbinate densely sericeous torus. Bracteoles immediately below torus, obovate–oblong, about 5 mm long, brown–membranaceous, falling in young bud, scars conspicuous; sepals from edge of torus, suborbicular, 2–3 mm long, 2.5–3.5 mm broad, glabrous within and without, or thinly sericeous on back towards the base, margin conspicuously long ciliate; petals suborbicular or obovate–orbicular, 1–2.5 cm long, 0.8–1.6 cm wide, rounded at apex, cuneate below into short tube, glabrous except the lowermost quarter or third without, which is densely adpressed sericeous firm in texture, creamy–white; stamens 50–60, about 1 cm long, adnate to the base of the petals, glabrous; ovary ovoid, sericeous below, glabrous above; style glabrous, 1–1.5 cm long; stigma small, capitate; capsule obovate–spherical, 0.8–1.2 cm long, 1–2 cm wide, thinly sericeous; seed flat, thin semicircular to subreniform, 6–8 mm long, 4–6 mm wide, pale brown, dull.

Distribution: Szechuan, Yunnan, Kweichow, Taiwan, Assam and E. Siam, at altitude 1500–2300 m.

2. **Schima bambusaefolia** Hu

Tree 5–7 m high. Branchlets reddish purple, lenticelled. Leaves lanceolate to oblanceolate, 8 cm long, 2 cm wide, long-acuminate at apex, narrowly cuneate at base, entire, deep shining green above, glaucous and minutely pubescent along the midrib below, veins inconspicuous, subcoriaceous; petiole 1 cm long, flattened. Flowers solitary, axillary in leaf axils, white, fragrant. Flowering pedicels thick, stout, 1.5 cm long, erect, brown, glabrous, racemose, 2.5 cm in diameter; sepals 5, subcoriaceous, reniform, brown, sericeous–ciliolose along the margins 2 mm long, 4 mm broad, receptacle sericeous–pubescent; petals 5, orbicular, glabrous, 1.5 cm in diameter; stamens numerous, 6–8 mm long, filaments connate and glandulose at base; ovary lanugilose, style clavate, articulate, 1 cm long, stigma capitate 5-lobed. Fruit globose, 1 cm in diameter, brownish punctate with white dots; pedicels thickish, 12 mm long; seeds reniform, slightly concave on one side, narrowly winged, 5 mm long, 4 mm broad.

Distribution: Kwangtung, Kwangsi, and Yunnan, at altitude 450 m.

3. **Schima confertiflora** Merr.

Tree 10 m high. When growing on an exposed slopes a shrub 1–3 m high. glabrous except the flowers and the tips of the young branchlets; branchlets dark brown, rugose, rather stout, terete, terminal bua-scales densely appressed pubescent with pale shining hairs; leaves numerous, crowded, thickly coriaceous, oblong-ovate to oblong-elliptic, 4–9 cm long, 2–3.3 cm wide, acute at base, shortly and obtusely acuminate at apex, margins distinctly crenate-serrate, when dry brown to brownish-olivaceous, shining; lateral nerves slender, not prominent, 8–10 pairs anastomosing, the reticulations distinct; petiole 1–1.5 cm long; flowers numerous, white, in the uppermost axils and racemosely crowded at tips of the branchlets, about 3 cm in diameter; their pedicels glabrous, about 1 cm long, stout, brown when dry; sepals suborbicular, rounded, subcoriaceous, about 5 mm in diameter, glabrous externally, internally densely appressed-pubescent, margins densely and prominently ciliate with pale hairs; petals obovate, glabrous except the sparingly ciliate margins; ovary ovoid, densely pubescent at the base, glabrous above; style stout, about 7 mm long; fruit globose or depressed globose, woody, about 1.2 cm in diameter, brown when dry, at first splitting into 2 or 3 valves, ultimately into 5, the persistent sepals very coriaceous, glabrous; seed somewhat reniform, rounded at both ends, about 7 mm long, 4.5 mm wide, somewhat rugose.

Distribution: Kwangtung, at altitude 950 m and Chekiang.

4. **Schima crenata** Korth.

Tree 27 m high; branchlets reddish purple, slender, smooth; leaves obovate to oblanceolate, 7 cm long, 3 cm wide, long-acuminate at apex, obtusely cuneate at base, irregularly crenate-serrate margin, shining dark green above, pale green, glabrous below, subcoriaceous; petiole 1.5 cm long, flattened; flowers white, solitary, leafy-axillary, calyx reddish brown, tubular, glabrous; petals 5, obovate-oblong, distinctly inserted in the calyx-tube; stamens numerous, unequal in length, half as long as the petals; flowering pedicels long and slender, 3 cm long, reddish brown, glabrous; fruit round, 12 cm in diameter, brown, glabrous.

Distributiom: Kweichow and Szechuan, at altitude 1100 m.

5. **Schima forrestii** Airy-Shaw

Tree 12–18 m high; branchlets robusty, subglaucous, lenticelled; leaves oblong-lanceolate, about 21 cm long, 6.5 cm wide, base angustish-rotundate, apex minutely acuminate, margin subcrenate-serrate, dark green above, subglaucous beneath; flowers expand 6–7 cm in diameter; pedicels rigid, 2–3 cm long, 3–4 mm in diameter; bracteoles sub-opposite, tomentolous; calyx cupulary-turbinate; petals obovate, 3–3.5 cm long, 2–3 cm wide; stamens numerous, 1.5–2 cm long; anthers oblong, 1–1.5 mm long; ovary broad ovoid, 5 mm in diameter.

Distribution: Yunnan, at altitude 1800 m.

6. **Schima kankonensis** Hayata

Tree 6 m high; branchlets slender, dark gray, glabrous; leaves elliptic-oblong,

7 cm long, 2.5 cm wide, apex long acuminate, base obtuse-cuneate, entire margin, dark shining green above, pale green glabrous below, subcoriaceous; petiole 2 cm long, flattened, reddish brown, glabrous; flowers white, 5 distinct petals, calyx cupular, purplish brwon; stamens numerous, unequal in length, half as long as the petals; pedicles 1 cm long, glabrous.

Distribution: National Taiwan University campaus, Taiwan.

7. Schima khasiana Dyer

Tree 10–20 m high; branchlets thick, stout, reddish purple, lenticelled; leaves oblong, 16 cm long, 6 cm wide, acute at apex, obtuse-cuneate at base, irregularly, coarsely, crenate-dentate-serrate margin, lustrous dark green above, pale shining green and light glaucous below, nerves 8–10 pairs, not very prominent on both surfaces, coriaceous; petiole 1.5 cm long, reddish brown, glabrous; flowers solitary, axillary; calyx 5 imbricated bracts, obovate, notched at tip and ciliated margin; fruit round, 2 cm in diameter, with persistent bracts, slightly pubescent; capsule woody, 5-valved; fruiting pedicels 5 cm long, stout, purplish brown, lenticelate, glabrous.

Distribution: Yunnan, at altitude 1500–2100 m.

Var. 1. Schima khasiana var. sericans Handel-Mazz.

Tree with dark gray branchlet; leaves oblong-obovate, 13 cm long, 6 cm wide, acute at apex, narrowly acute at base, irregularly crenate-serrate margin, lustrous dark green above, pale glaucous and sericeous hairy along the midrib and veins beneath, subcoriaceous; petiole 1.5 cm long, reddish brown, sericeous pubescent.

Distribution: Yunnan, at altitude 1900–2750 m.

8. Schima norohnae Reinw.

Tree 30 m high; branchlets dark gray, smooth, leticelled; leaves oblanceolate, 11 cm long, 4 cm wide, acuminate apex, cuneate at base, irregularly sharply serrate margin, lustrous dark green above, pale brownish green below, nerves inconspicuous on both sides, coriaceous; petiole 3 cm long, glabrous; flowers in terminal and lateral crowding on the tips of young branchlets; calyx cupulary, imbricated, ciliated, 5-parted; petals 5, obovate, 1.5 cm long and broad; fruit round, 2 cm in diameter, glabrous, 5-valved; pedicels 4 cm long, reddish brown, glabrous, solitary, axillary.

Distribution: Kwangtung, Chekiang and Yunnan, at altitude 2400 m.

9. Schima villosa Hu

Tree 7 m high; branchlets striate, terete, white-lenticelled, glabrescent, grayish black, young branchlets angular, densely, sericeously tomentulose; leaves coriaceous, elliptic-lanceolate, lanceolate to oblanceolate, acuminate at apex, cuneate at base, entire and slightly revolute along the margins, glabrous, except tomentulose along the stout and slightly elevated flat midrib and slightly reticulate above, densely sericeous-villose especially along the prominent midrib and elevated secondary veins and fine reticulations beneath, up to 18 cm long, 6 cm broad, secondary veins 14–16 pairs, lower arching from the midrib and divergent at 45 degrees, upper divergent at about 60 degrees, forking and anastomosing near the margins; petiole stout, flat above, terete beneath, sericeous-tomentulose; sepals rounded, 7 mm long, densely sericeous outside; flowers solitary in leaf-axils, white, 3 cm in diameter; pedicels stout, recurved, to 2 cm long, sericeous-tomentulose; sepals rounded to 7 mm long, densely sericeous outside, minute inside; petals suborbicular, 2.5 cm long, densely sericeous on the lower part outside; stamens numerous, 1 cm long, filaments glabrous; ovary globose, densely sericeous-tomentulose; style rather stout, very sparsely pilosulose, 11 mm long, 5-lobed at apex; fruit subglobose, 1.5 cm in diameter, sericeous near the apex and base.

Distribution: South Yunnan, at altitude 1300 m.

0. **Schima sinensis** (Hemsl. et Wilson) Airy-Shaw

 Gordonia sinensis Hemsl. et Wilson

Tree 12 m high; leaves ovate-lanceolate, including petiole, 12-18 cm long, 5-6.5 cm broad, shortly acuminate, cuneate at base, crenate - serrate, coriaceous dark green above, often paler, brownish below; primary veins 12-14 on each side of the midrib, very prominent on both surfaces; petiole stout, rather under 1.5 cm long; flowers erect, solitary, axillary, pedunculate, bracteate, 5-6.5 cm across, white; peduncles stout, angular, 4-4.5 cm long; bracts 2, immediately below calyx, obovate, 8 mm long; sepals orbicular, 3-5 mm long, ciliolate, glabrous outside, silky-pubescent inside; petals ovate or obovate, 2.5-3 cm long, 1.5 cm broad, rounded, connate at base, glabrous save at base, which is silky-pubescent; stamens adnate to, and about 1/3 length of petals; filaments flattened, subulate; anthers nearly globular; ovary silky-pubescent, 5-lobed; style shorter than stamens; stigma large, capitate.

Distribution: W. Szechuan, at altitude 600-1000 m.

1. **Schima superba** Gardn. et Champ.

Shrub 5 to 20 m high; branchlets dark gray, rugose, glabrous; leaves elliptic-obovate, 8 cm long, 3.5 cm wide, attenuate-acuminate at apex, obtuse-cuneate at base, irregularly crenate-dentate-serrate margin, shining deep green above, paler brownish beneath, veins inconspicuous on both surfaces, thick, coriaceous; petiole 2 cm long, flattened, minutely pubescent; flowers solitary, white, axillary; petals 5, obovate; calyx green, imbricated; stamens numerous, filaments yellow, anthers brown; fruit brown, pubescent, round, 1.5 cm in diameter, 5-valved, pedicles stout, 4 cm long, brown, glabrous.

 Distribution: Hainan, Kwangtung, Fukien, Kwangsi, Kweichow, Szechuan, Hunan, Hupeh, Chekiang, Taiwan, Kiangsi, Anhwei, and Hainan at altitude 125m-1600m.

2. **Schima wallichii** Choisy

Tree 12-17 m high; branchlets dark gray, glabrous, terete; leaves oblanceolate to elliptic-obovate, 9-14 cm long, 4-6 cm wide, shortly acuminate at apex, obtuse-cuneate at base, entire incurved margin, dark green shining above, pale green, prominently veined and somewhat pubescent along the midrib and veins beneath, subcoriaceous;

petiole 2 cm long, flattened, slightly brownish pubescent; flowers white, solitary b⋮ crowding on the tips of young branches; calyx 5-lobed, imbricated, ciliated; fruit round 2 cm in diameter, slightly pubescent; pedicels thick, stout, 2.5 cm long, brown, glab⋮ rous.

Distribution: Yunnan, Kweichow and Kwangsi, at altitude 2450-2980 m.

Genus (4) Stewartia L. (See orig. text page 834)

1. **Stewartia gemmata** Chien et Cheng (See orig. text pages 834-835)

2. **Stewartia rubiginosa** Chang

Tree 15 m high; bark smooth, reddish brown; young branches glabrous, apical bud⋮ pubescent; leaves chartaceous, elliptic-ovate, 9-13 cm long, 5-6.5 cm wide, abrupt⋮ acuminate at apex, acumen 1.5 cm base round or obtuse, yellowish green above, glossy⋮ pale beneath, glabrous, lateral nerves 8-12 pairs, prominent above, elevate beneath⋮ margin serrate, teeth glandular; petiole 1-1.5 cm long, grooved above, glabrous⋮ flowers axillary, solitary; pedicels 4-7 mm long, glabrous; bracts 2, reniform, widt⋮ various, the smaller ones 5-6 mm long, 10-11 mm wide, apex almost cuneate, the large⋮ ones 5-6 mm long, 12-14 mm wide, glabrous on the back; sepals deltoid-ovate, siz⋮ varies, 5-6 mm long, 9-13 mm wide, the outside covered by sericeo-pilose, the insid⋮ glabrous; petals white, obovate, 3.5-5.4 cm long, 2-2.5 cm wide, attenuate at the base⋮ 4-5 mm wide, the outside covered by sericeous hairs, the margin glabrous, stamen⋮ numerous, unequal in length, the longer ones 2.2 cm long, the shorter ones 1 cm long⋮ the lower half of the filaments connate, the anthers dorsifixed, ovoid, 1.5 mm long⋮ ovary pilose, style 5-6 mm long, glabrous, stigma 5, reflexed.

Distribution: Kwangtung, at altitude 750 m.

3. **Stewartia peteropetiolata** Cheng

Tree 13-15 m high; bark gray; leaves thick, leathery, glossy green above, ligh⋮ green below, capsules greenish, sepals brown. The distinguished characters of thi⋮ species are the evergreen habit and conspicuously winged petioles. In *Stewartia gem⋮ mata* and *S. sinensis* the petioles are also winged although much narrower. As there ar⋮ no differences in floral, as well as fruiting structures between *Hartia* and *Stewartia*.

Distribution: Yunnan.

4. **Stewartia sinensis** Rehder et Wilson (See orig. text page 835)

Genus (5) Hartia Dunn (See orig. text page 835)

1. **Hartia cordifolia** Li

Tree 18 m high; branchlets slender, whitish gray, glabrous; leaves obovate, 6 c⋮ long, 4 cm wide, short acuminate apex, obtuse at base, irregularly serrate margin⋮ lustrous dark green above, light green below, glabrous on both surfaces, coriaceous⋮ petiole 2 cm long, flattened, minutely winged, reddish purple, slightly pubescent⋮ flowers leaf-axillary, short pedicelled; fruit a globular woody capsule, 4-valved, 1.⋮ cm in diameter, brownish, glabrous.

Distribution: Kwangsi, at altitude 1600-2000 m.

2. **Hartia micrantha** Chun

Shrub 1–2 m high; leaves coriaceous, angusti-oblong, 6–8 cm long, 1–3 (usually 2.5) cm wide, acute at apex, rotundate at base, margin remotely crenulate-serrate; flowers very small, with rounded sepals and very distinctive leaves, with obscure lateral veins and with lax almost obsolete reticulations.

Distribution: Kwangtung and Kwangsi, at altitude 1400 m.

3. **Hartia obovata** Chun et Chang

Tree 15 m high; young branches covered by hairs at the end; leaves oblong or obovate-oblong, 7–11 cm long, 3–4 cm wide, apex obtuse or subrotundate, emarginate, base obtuse, slightly oblique, dark green and glossy above, olivaceous-green beneath, entire or wavy towards the apex, glabrous; lateral veins 7–9 pairs, slightly visible above, elevate beneath; petiole 1–1.5 cm long, glabrous; wings 1.5 mm wide; capsule solitary, axillary, globose, slightly angular, 1.1 cm long, 5-locular, glabrous, persistent style 2 mm long, persistent sepals obovate-orbicular, 8–10 mm long, pubescent on the outside, glabrous inside.

Distribution: Kwangtung.

4. **Hartia robusta** Hu

Shrub 1.5 m high; branchlets stout, terete, resinous-glandulose-lepidote; leaves coriaceous, spathulate-oblong to obovate-spathulate-oblong, rounded apex, cuneate to rounded at base, entire and slightly revolute margins, upper surface glabrous and rugose with impressed midrib and secondary veins, lower surface glaucous, intermixedly resinous-glandulose and punctate throughout except being lepidote along the very thick and elevated midrib and veins, secondary veins 18 pairs, closely spased; petiole grooved, winged above, punctate and glandulose-lepidote to 2 cm long, flower racemose, on recurved pedicels, 3.5 cm long, sepals thick, membranaceous, imbricate, suborbicular, rounded at apex, glabrous and glaucous; capsule woody, oblong, acute apex, resinouse glandulose outside, 2.3 cm long, 1.3 cm in diameter, valves 5, thick; seeds very numerous, very slender, 2.5 mm long, tailed at both ends.

Distribution: Yunnan, at altitude 2000 m.

5. **Hartia serratisepala** Hu

Tree 8 m high; leaves thin, coriaceous, elliptic-oblong to elliptic-oblanceolate, obliquely acuminate at apex, rounded at base, callous-serrulate along the margin, glabrescent with impressed midrib and closely reticulate above, sericeous pilose along the elevated reddish midrib, secondary veins and reticulations, and glabrescent or sparsely appressed pilose on the rest of surface beneath, secondary veins 15–17 pairs; petiole boat-shaped, 17 mm long; flowers solitary; calyx open, receptacle densely white-sericeous-pilose, sepals ovate-oblong, acute or acuminate, serrulate along the margins, distinctly reticulate, with elevated midrib; petals white, obovate, densely white-sericeour outside, 2 cm long, 13 mm wide; stamens numerous, filaments highly connate; pedicels white-sericeous-pilose, 1 cm long; capsule 18 mm high, capitate.

Distribution: South Yunnan, at altitude 2500 m.

6. **Hartia sinii** Hu

Tree 10 m high; leaves elliptic, 11–18 cm long, 4.5 cm wide, apex acuminate, bas acute, dark olivaceous green above, pale green below; petiole 1.5 cm long, margin re motely serrate; inflorescence axillary, racemose, white, sessile; flowers subsessile 3 cm in diameter; bracts 2, sepals 5, petals 5, style 5, connate, capsule 5–locular.

Distribution: Kwangsi, at altitude 1200 m.

7. **Hartia sinensis** Dunn (See orig. text pages 835–837)

Var. 1. **Hartia sinensis** var. **chingii** Chun (See orig. text page 838)

8. **Hartia villosa** Merr.

Hartia kwangtungensis Chun

Tree 8–10 m high; leaves elliptic-oblong, 6–12 cm long, 2–4.5 cm wide, apex acut to minutely acuminate, base obtuse to rotundate, margin crenate-serrate, coriaceous lustrous dark green above, pale green, glaucescent and slightly villose below; flower white, 4 cm in diameter, solitary, axillary; sepals 5, imbricated; calyx cupulary adpressed villose; petals unequal, obovate-oblong, rotundate margin, involute, adpre ssed white-sericeous-pilose, obscure puberulose; ovary conical oblong, ovules 4 loculed; capusle brown, pubescent.

Distribution: Kwangtung, and Kwangsi.

Var. 1. **Hartia villosa** var. **grandiflora** Chun

This variety differs from the type in thinner much larger leaves me asuring from 15–21 cm long and 5.5–7 cm wide, with 13–14 pairs o distinct lateral veins; petiole 2 cm long, persistently pilose; capsule as in the type, with the valves measuring 1.5 cm long; tree 20 m hig and 30 cm in diameter; bark dark gray; branches hanging; capsul 5–valved, spreading.

Distribution: Kwangsi Man-ning, at altitude 830 m.

Genus (6) Eurya Thunberg (See orig. text page 838)

Evergreen shrub or trees; winter-buds naked; leaves alternate, serrate to crenate rarely entire, short-petioled, rarely subsessile; flowers dioecious, axillary, solitar or fascicled; pedicels usually short, with 2 small persistent bracts at apex; sepals 5 persistent; corolla companulate or urceolate, petals 5, united at base; staminate flower with many stamens shorter than petals and with or without rudimentary ovary; pistillat flowers without stamens; ovary 5–celled; style 3–5, more or less connate or free; frui a many-seeded berry; seeds albuminous.

More than 50 species in East Asia, India, and Malasia.

Key to the species of China, Indo-China, India and Ceylon

A. Terminal leaf-buds and young branchlets glabrous.

  B. Leaves sessile; base auriculate with lobes clasping the stem. -- (3) *E. amplexifolia*

 BB. Leaves petiolate; base entire.

   C. Young branchlets terete.

    D. Leaves entire or nearly so.

     E. Leaves tapering to an acuminate apex --- (29) *E. macartneyi*

      (*E. macartneyi* occasionally with some leaf serrations)

     EE. Leaves bluntaly obtuse at the apex ------------------------------------(11-1) *E. cuneata* var. *glabra*

    DD. Leaves sharply serrate ------------ (29-1) *E. macartneyi* var. *hainanensis*

   CC. Young branchlets angled.

    F. Branchlets 4-angled.

     G. Leaves up to 25 cm long, 6 cm wide, veins 20 or more pairs, deeply impressed on upper surface, highly raised (even to cross veins) on lower surface; style 5-6 mm long ------------------------------------- (31) *E. polyneura*

     GG. Leaves up to 10-11 cm long, 3 cm wide; veins raised on upper surface, inconspicuous; style short (1 mm long) ------------------------------- (37) *E. tetragonoclada*

    FF. Branchlets 2-angled.

     H. Leaves narrow, usually 0.5-0.8 cm wide, occasionally up to 1 cm wide; fruit oblong ------------------------------------- (40) *E. stenophylla*

     HH. Leaves usually much wider (Occasionally only 1.7 cm wide in *Eurya handeliana*); fruit globose.

      I. Veins on upper surface deeply impressed, as if etched ------------------------- *E. handeliana*

      II. Veins on upper surface raised or inconspicuous, nor impressed.

       J. Leaves tapering at both ends, oblong ------------------------- (30) *E. nitida*

       JJ. Leaves rounded at base, obtusely acuminate, wider because of rounded base ------------------------- (30-1) *E. nitida* var. *aurescens*

AA. Terminal leaf-buds and young branchlets pubescent.

  B. Ovary and fruit glabrous.

   C. Leaf-base oblique or lobed.

    D. Leaves 8–10 cm long, membranaceous, long attenuate at apex, margins flat, not revolute ――――――――――――――――*E. obliquefolia*

  DD. Leaves 4–6 cm long, coriaceous, apex blunt occasionally, shortly acuminate, margins revolute ――――――――― (19) *E. glandulosa*

CC. Leaf–base cuneate, occasionally somewhat rounded, never lobed or oblique.

    D. Leaves rounded at apex, emarginate, never acuminate ―――――――――――――――――――――――――――― (15) *E. emarginata*

  DD. leaves acuminate at apex.

    E. Margins entire, occasionally slightly undulate, never sharply serrate ―――――――――――――――― (11) *E. cuneata*

  EE. Margins sharply serrate, never entire.

    F. Leaves mostly small, less than 4 cm long.

      G. Leaves eventually elliptic –acuminate; veins deeply impressed on upper surface ――――――――――――――――――――― ―――――――――――――― (16) *E. fangii*

    GG. Leaves obovate, quite obtuse at' apex, sometimes nearly rounded; veins up–raised or nearly insignificant on upper surface ――――――――― (8) *E. chinensis*

  FF. Leaves considerably longer, 6–12 cm long.

    G. Leaves thick, coriaceous, margins revolute ――――――――― ――――――――――――――――――― *E. ceylanica*

    GG. Leaves membranaceous or nearly membranaceous, margins not revolute (In case of *E. symplocina,* the older leaves are occasionally quite coriaceous)

      H. Calyx pubescent; terminal leaf–bud and young branchlets pilose.

        I. Leaves narrowly lance–acuminate, usually 3 times as long as wide; veins not especially conspicuous on upper surface ――――――――――――――――――― ――――――――――(1) *E. acuminata*

        II. Leaves wide–lanceolate, up to 4 cm wide, veins conspicuously depressed on upper surface ―――――― ―――――――――(4) *E. cerasifolia*

      HH. Calyx glabrous; terminal leaf–bud and young branchlets minutely pubescent, sometimes appearing glabrous ――― ――――――――――― (28) *E. loquaiana*

BB. Ovary and fruit pubescent.

  C. Leaves auriculate at base, clasping stem――(13) *E. disticha*

  CC. Leaves cuneate or rounded at base, not auriculate or clasping.

    D. Calyx glabrous.

E. Fruit becoming glabrescent at maturity with only occasional hairs present; leaves delicately tapering at both ends; terminal-bud finely puberulent, at times appearing almost glabrous ---------------------- ----------------------------- (41) *E. trichocarpa* .

EE. Fruit pubescent at maturity, leaves although tapering somewhat, nearly rounded at base, terminal bud pilose ------------------------- ------------------------------ (14-1) *E. distichophylla* var. *henryi*

DD. Calyx pubescent.

E. Leaves huge, 10-14 cm long, 5 cm wide --------------------------- ------------------------------ (39) *E. velutina*.

EE. Leaves up to 10 cm long, narrow-lanceolate, seldom over 2 cm wide.

F. Calyx obtuse, with short pilose hairs, style trifid ---------------- --------------------------- (14) *E. distichophylla*.

FF. Calyx acuminate, densely covered with long yellow hairs; styles usually 4-fid ----------------- (9) *E. ciliata*

Key to the species of Taiwan, Korea and Ryukyu Islands

A. Ovary and fruits pubescent.

B. Leaves narrow-lanceolate, up to 14 cm long; strigillose-pubescent on stem as well as fruits. -------------------------------- (35) *E. strigillosa* (Taiwan)

BB. Leaves ovate-elliptic, up to 7 cm long; stem glabrous or nearly so, not strigillose ---(18) *E. gnaphalocarpa* (Taiwan)

AA. Ovary and fruit glabrous.

B. Largest leaves less than 4 cm long, usually 2-3 cm or less.

C. Leaves membranaceous, 2-3 cm rarely 4 cm long --------------------------- ------- --------------------------- (24) *E. leptophylla* (Taiwan)

CC. Leaves coriaceous, minute, usually less then 1 cm long, occasionally 2 cm long.

D. Leaves about as broad as long, less than 0.5 cm either way, seemingly entire, deeply emarginate, obcordate. --------------------------------- ------------------------------ (15-1) *E. emarginata* var. *microphylla* (Japan)

DD. Leaves longer than broad, although small, always found up to 1.5-2.0 cm long, serrate, never obcordate in shape.

E. Leaves elliptic, acute apex -----(10) *E. crenatifolia* (Taiwan)

EE. Leaves obtuse at apex, obovate --(23-1) *E. japonica* var. *microphylla* (Japan)

BB. Largest leaves up to 11-12 cm long, all considerably longer than 4 cm.

C. Entirely glabrous even to terminal bud.

D. Branches winged, stem zigzag from node to node.

    E. Twenty stamens, filaments twice as long as anthers. ——————————
—————————————————————————— *E. yaeyamensis* (Ryukyu)

    EE. Ten stamens, anthers twice as long as filaments ————————————
——————————————————————*E. zigzag* (Ryukyu)

DD. Branches perhaps slightly winged, zigzag growth absent.

    E. Leaves sharply toothed, evenly elliptic ——————————————————
—————————————————— (17) *E. glaberrima* (Taiwan)

    EE. Leaves nearly entire of undulate-serrate, never sharply toothed.

        F. Leaves nearly entire, very slightly serration ——————————
—————————————————— (20) *E. hayatai* (Taiwan)

        FF. Leaves always undulate-serrate, usually more noticeable at apex
—————————————————— (23) *E. japonica* (Japan)

CC. Pubescence found on stem as well as terminal buds.

    D. Leaves acuminate, attenuate apex.

        E. Leaves 3.5 cm wide, robust ————(34) *E. rengechiensis* (Taiwan)

        EE. Leaves less than 2 cm wide at broadest part ————————————
—————————————————— (1) *E. acuminata*

    DD. Leaves obtuse at apex.

        E. Leaves heavy-coriaceous, perfectly obovate, rounded at apex,
never acuminate, distinctly emarginate, slightly serrate ————————
——————————————————(15) *E. emarginata*

        EE. Leaves coriaceous, sometimes obovate, always acuminate, usually
not emarginate, distinctly serrate ——————————————————
—————————————————— (8) *E. chinensis* .

1. Eurya acuminata DC.

Bush or small tree 3–7 m high; branchlets slender, brownish gray, rough; leaves lanceolate, 7 cm long, 2 cm wide, acuminate apex, cuneate at base, finely serrate and slightly incurved margin, lustrous shining green above, lighter green glabrous beneath, lateral veins inconspicuous, coriaceous; petiole 2 mm long, glabrous, alternate; flowers small, axillary, solitary or 3 or 4 crowded in the axils of leaves, greenish white; fruit globular, 1 mm in diameter, slightly mucronate, black, 5-valved, subsessile, glabrous.

Distribution: Yunnan, Kwangtung and Taiwan, at altitude 1450–2440 m.

2. Eurya alata Kobuski

Shrub 2 m high; leaves linear-lanceolate, 6–8 cm long, 1.5–2.5 cm wide, apex obtuse, base cuneate, margin serrulate; petiole 2–3 mm long; flowers axillary, 2–3 aggregated; pedicels 2 mm long, glabrous; sepals 5, imbricated, subrotundate, obtuse-emarginate at apex, base minutely contracted; petals 5, white, connate at base, oblong-ovate, 2–2.5 mm long, 1 mm wide. An interesting feature of this species is outstanding winged condition on the very young branchlets with wings as much as 1 mm long, making the branchlet appears almost quadrangular, in the older branches, the wings are reduced to pronounced ridges, which seem to zigzag along the stem. *Eurya alata* because of its leaves texture and venation resemble *E. glaberrima* Hayata from Taiwan. However it can be separated by its winged stems, longer style, and delicate corolla.

Distribution: Kwangtung.

3. **Eurya amplexifolia** Dunn

Shrub 3–10 m high. This species is characterized by its larger (16 cm long 5 cm wide) amplexical leaves. The two auriculate basal lobes extend as much as 1–1.5 cm beyond and often overlap the other side of the stem. The younger branchlets 2–winged, glabrous even to the terminal bud. The fruit is oblong–ovate (7 mm long, 4 mm wide) with a short style (less than 1 mm) which is connate most its length. Fruit black.

Distribution: Kwangtung.

4. **Eurya cerasifolia** (D. Don) Kobuski

Shrub 3–5 m high; leaves oblanceolate, 9 cm long, 3.5 cm wide, acute–acuminate apex, cuneate at base, incurved margin and entire, lustrous dark green above, paler green with prominent secondary veins beneath, pubescent along the mdirib below, coriaceous; petiole 2 mm long, brown, glabrous; flowers axillary, solitary or 2–3 crowded in each axil of the leaves; fruit small globular 1 mm in diameter with persistent calyx, subsessile.

Distribution: Yunnan, at altitude 3000 m.

5. **Eurya chuekiangensis** Hu

Shrub 3.5 m high; branchlets terete, slightly winged, glabrous; leaves coriaceous, oblong–lanceolate, acuminate, rounded to subcuneate at base, close and doubly glandulose–serrate along the margins, glabrous, upper surface olive–green, with impressed midrib, secondary veins and reticulations lower surface with prominent midrib and elevated secondary veins and reticulations, and spasely nigro–punctate, to 8 cm long 3 cm broad; petiole channelled above, to 4 mm long; pistillate flowers small, solitary or in pairs in axils of leaves; bracts reniform, ovate, rounded at apex, ciliate; sepals 5, unequal, ovate; petals 5, oblong, acute, scarbid outside, glabrous inside, subequalling the sepals; ovary 3–celled, glabrous, 3–lobed; stigma 2–lobed; ovoid conical fruit to 13 mm long, 6 mm in diameter, verruculose; style 1.5 mm long; seeds numerous, chestnut–brown.

Distribution: North Yunnan, at altitude 3000 m.

6. **Eurya acuminata** DC. var. **groffi** (Merr.) Kobuski

Eurya groffi Merr.

A shrub or small tree; branchlets rather densely pilose, terete, glabrous, dark reddish brown; leaves numerous, lanceolate, chartaceous to subcoriaceous, greenish olivaceous and shining when dry, 3.5–6 cm long, 8–12 mm wide, margins denticulate, the upper surface glabrous, lower surface pilose, midrib impressed above, prominent beneath, lateral veins obsolete or subobsolete on the upper surface, distinct and some–

what projecting on lower surface, apex slenderly acuminate, the base obtuse and often minutely inequalateral cordate, sessile or subsessile; fruit axillary, glabrous, globose, or ovoid, 3-3.5 mm in diameter, smooth, their pedicels 1-1.5 mm long; sepals coriaceous, elliptic-ovate, 1.5-2 mm long, rounded, the outer ones somewhat pilose.

Distribution: Kwangtung, Hainan,Yunnan and Kwangsi, at altitude 4000 m.

7. **Eurya carvinervis** Vesque

Eurya handeliana Kobuski

Shrub 1-2.5 m high; leaves oblong, 4 cm long, 1.5 cm wide, apex acute and emarginate, base cuneate, margins serrate above the middle, sub-coriaceous., glabrous on both surfaces; a style is three-parted; fruit a berry greenish black, many-seeded.

The truly remarkable feature of this species is the pronounced veining on the upper surface of the leaves. The veins all, even including the small cross-veins, are deeply impressed, giving the effect of etching. The calyx lobes in both the male and female flowers are bluish green, at least in the herbarium specimens.

Distribution: Yunnan, at altitude 2900 m.

Var. 1. Eurya carvinervis var. strigillosa (Handel-Mazz.) Kobuski

Flowers white; fruit greenish black, many-seeded.

This variety is characterized by its shining coriaceous, dark-green leaves, with deeply impressed or channeled veins on the upper surface and raised on the lower, which all this variety to *E. carvinervis* rather than *E. nitida* as Handel-Mazzetti, had though. The pubescent character of stem and flower parts, together with the terete stem, are fextures which separate it from its species, *Eurya carvinervis*.

Distribution: Yunnan, at altitude 2300 m to 3300 m.

8. **Eurya chinensis** R. Brown

Shrub 1-2 m high; branchlets slender reddish purple, covered with white blooms; leaves small obovate, 2.5 cm long, 1.5 cm wide, acute apex, slightly emarginate cuneate at base, serrate margin, subcoriaceous; petiole 1 mm long, glabrous; flowers small, white numerous crowded along the axils of leaves; fruits solitary, globose, 1 mm in diameter, glabrous, mucronate, with persistent calyx; fruiting pedicels very slender, 1 mm long, glabrous; flowers white; fruit black.

Distribution: Kwangtung, Yunnan, Kwangsi,Fukien,Taiwan and Kiangsi,at altitude 660-2800 meters.

9. **Eurya ciliata** Merr.

Tree 10 m high, the young branchlets densely covered with long spreading silky yellowish hairs becoming glabrescent with age; leaves coriaceous, short petioled or subsessile, oblong-lanceolate, 5-9 cm long, 2-2.5 cm wide, round-oblique at the base minutely cordulate, gradually acuminate at the apex, densely long-pilose pubescent on the midrib with the veins obscure on both surfaces; fruits ovoid-globose, 4-5.5 mm long scattered pilose; style glabrous, 4 mm or more long, usually 4-fid, filiform, free calyx and ovary densely pubescent.

In comparing the types of *E. ciliata* and *E. potentipila*, no differences could be found to possibly distinguish them as separate species.

Distribution: Hainan, Kwangtung and Kwangsi, at altitude 1000 m.

10. **Eurya crenatifolia** (Yamamoto) Kobuski

Shrub 1–2 m high. The outstanding feature of this species was the pentandrous male flowers. This character is unusual perhaps for Formosan Euryas, quite prevalent in the genus throughout the Pacific Islands, especially in New Guinia and the Fiji Islands, and along is not worthy of generic status. The female flowers has very short styles and in fruit these persistent styles seem almost non-existent, the stigma curving immediately away from the fruit. It is closely allied to *E. leptophylla*. However, in the latter species the styles are longer and stamens number is 7–8. The leaves are generally larger, more membranaceous and attenuate at apex.

Distribution: Taiwan, at altitude 1330–1660 m.

11. **Eurya cuneata** Kobuski

Small tree, branchlets terete, pubescent; leaves oblong-obovate, 6–9 cm long, 2–3.5 cm wide, obtuse-acuminate at apex, cuneate at base, lustrous dark green above, pale green glabrous beneath, coriaceous; petiole 2 mm long, glabrous; flowers axillary singular, or in twos; pedicels 4 mm long, sepals 5, imbricated, obtuse 3 mm long; petals 5, connate at base, rotundate obtuse, 4–4.5 cm long; stamens 15, filaments gracilous, 1.5 mm long; anthers apiculate; ovary glabrous, 1.5 mm long, 1 mm wide, style connate, trifids.

Distribution: Hainan, at altitude 1300 m.

Var. 1. Eurya cuneata var. glabra Kobuski

This variety likes the type except that it is strictly glabrous even to the younger stems and terminal buds. As in the species the stamens number is 15 and the petals are united at the base.

Distribution: Hainan, at altitude 660 m.

12. **Eurya dasyclados** Kobuski

Shrub 1 meter high; leaves coriaceous, rigid, oblong-ovate, 7–10 cm long, 2.5–3.5 cm wide, yellowish and metallic green in color; veins appear to be impressed on the upper surface. On close observation one finds that veins are distinctly raised on both surface, pilose sparse on the lowers surface; corolla lobes very narrow, tapering, 0.75 mm at the base, to 0.25 mm near the acuminate apex, adnate for 1 mm ovary and fruit glabrous.

Distribution: Kwangtung, Kwangsi and Szechuan.

13. **Eurya disticha** Chun

Small shrub with distichous branches; branchlets slender, subterete, the youngest parts covered densely with long brownish silky, spreading hairs; leaves arranged in 2 ranks, numerous, contigeous, chartaceous, sessile, oblong, 2–3.5 cm long, 0.7–1 cm wide, base bi-auriculate and somewhat clasping the stem, the basal lobes rounded, unequal, apex broadly shortly acuminate, the acumen rounded or emarginate at the apex, margin distinctly crenate-serrulate from the base, not revolute, midrib deeply impressed above, elevated beneath, lateral veins about 12 on each side of the midrib, slender, indistinct, upper surface dull green, glabrous, lower surface pale yellowish green, glabrous except on the midrib which is sparsely pilose towards the base; petiole 1.5 mm long, tumid, puberulous; flowers 1-3 in the axils of the leaves, small, glabrous; sepals elliptic-oblong, glabrous, corolla 4 mm long, cylindric, base coalescent, lobes lanceolate acute, apex slightly reflexed, ovary narrowly conical, glabrous, about 2 mm high; style cylindric, about 2 mm long, apex divided into 3 recurved slender stigmas about 0.5 mm long; berry ovoid, dark blue, glabrous, 4.6 mm long; seeds about 12, angularly compressed and obliquely-ovoid, lustrous pale brown, densely foveolate, 1 mm long.

Distribution: Kwangtung.

14. **Eurya distichophylla** Hemsl.

Small tree characterized by having pubescent ovaries and fruit; in the flower the ovary is silky villose and possesses an elongated style which is connate for part its length. Upon the maturity of fruit, unlike its near relative, *E. tronchocarpa*, does not become glabrescent but possesses longish straggling hairs. Leaves are subsessile and arranged distichously on the stem. *Eurya distichophylla* was base on male flowers. The female flowers were described by Merrill under *E. swiglei* and at time though to belong to a new speices.

Distribution: Kwangung, Kwangsi, Kiangsi, Kweichow, Fukien, at altitude 400 m.

Var. 1. **Eurya distichophylla** var. **henryi** Kobuski

This variety is characterized by having more lanceolated leaves and more pubescent branchlets and more villose on the lowers surface of leaves; flowers purple.

Distribution: Yunnan, at altitude 2000 m.

15. **Eurya emarginata** (Thunb.) Makino

Shrub 1 m high. It is characetrized with thick coriaceous leaves, cuneate obovate oblong-obovate, emarginate, with revolute, crenate-serrate margins; young branchlet are clothed with a short, rufous-brown villose tomentum.

Distribution: Kwangtung, Fukien, Checkiang, Ryukyu, Japan and Korea.

Var. 1. **Eurya emarginata** (Thunb.) Mak. var. **microphylla**

16. **Eurya fangii** Rehd.

Shrub characterized by deeply impressed veins on the upper surface. Sharp point terminate the serrations on the leaves, also distinctive in hirsute branchlets and cililate sepals. This species is quite closely related to *E. hamdeliana* from which it differ especially in its smaller leaves and hirsute branchlets.

Distribution: Szechuan, Mt. Omei, at altitude 2600-2750 m.

17. **Eurya glandulosa** Hayata

Shrub characterized by probably one of the shortest styles in *Eurya*, being 0.25 mm long. The calyx, style, and stigma are purple in the pistillate flower; leaves are coriaceous, linear-lanceolate, 6-8 cm long, 1-2 cm wide, slightly emarginate, finely but sharply serrate. The whole plant is glabrous.

Distribution: Taiwan, at altitude 3100 m.

18. **Eurya gnaphalocarpa** Hayata

Shrub resembling *E. trichocarpa* in its pubescent ovary. This species differs in leaf characters and floral parts. In *E. trichocarpa* the leaves are somewhat narrower and taper off abruptly at first and then are drawn out more finely to an attenuate apex. In this species the apex is less attenuate and the tapering off is very gradual. In the male flowers, a rudimentary, pilose ovary is present.

Distribution: Taiwan and Philippine Islands, at altitude 1330-2660 m.

19. **Eurya glandulosa** Merrill

Shrub characterized by terete stems, auriculate coriaceous leaves, (4-6 cm long, 1.5-3 cm wide) with pronounced reticulate veining on the lowers surface. These veins are impressed above. Young stems, terminal buds, and calyx lobes are hirsute. Style approximately 1 mm long and connate for most its lengtth. It is closely related to *E. disticha* from which it can easily be separated by its coriaceous leaves, pronuonced reticulated veinings, leaf width, and short style. A second related species is *E. obliquefolia* (Yunnan) which differs from *E. glandulosa* in its larger (up to 10 cm) leaves, which are membranaceous rather than coriaceous, attenuate-acuminate at the apex, with serrated margins which are not revolute.

Distribution: Kwangtung, Kwangsi, Kweichow and Yunnan, at altitude 1000 m.

20. **Eurya hayatai** Yamamoto

The veining of leaves, except for the midrib, is obscure. This smooth, seemingly unveined leaf surface is one of the outstanding feature of the speices. Also on the revolute or near revolute margins, the serration is so finely crenate that the appearance of entirely is given in most cases. The whole plant, even to terminal bud, is glabrous.

Distribution: Taiwan, at altitude 2000-2830 m.

21. **Eurya huiana** Kobuski

Tree 2-7 m high; having pubescent leaf-buds, young branchlets and occasionally pubescent midribs, which immediately separate it from the strictly glabrous *E. nitida* The stem of this species is terete in contrast to the winged stems of *E. nitida*. Fruit black, globose, 7 mm in diameter, mucronate.

Distribution: Kweichow and Hunan, at altitude 400-650 m.

22. **Eurya impressinervis** Kobuski

Shrub or small tree; leaves membranaceous, glabrous ovate or obovate, 7-11 cm long, 2-3 cm wide, base cuneate, apex acuminate, margins serrulate, nerves impressive above, elevated beneath; petiole 2-5 cm long, glabrous; male flowers axillary, solitary or in twos; pedicels 2-2.5 mm long; bracts sepaloid; sepals 5, imbricate, inequal, suborbicular, concave, apiculate, margins glandulose; petals 5, basal connate, obovate, 5 mm long, 1.5–2.5 mm wide; stamens 15, filaments 2 mm long; ovary rudimentary; female flowers 2–4 in axils of leaves; pedicels glabrous; stigma 3; fruit globose 3 mm long; pedicels 3 mm long.

Distribution: Kwangsi, at altitude 1800 m.

23. Eurya japonica Thunberg

Shrub 1–2 m high; leaves oblanceolate, 4.5 cm long, 2 cm wide, acute and emarginate at apex, cuneate at base, finely serrate margin, lustrous dark green above, pale green beneath glabrous, coriaceous; petiole 2 mm long, glabrous; flowers small, white, solitary, axillary, fruit globose 1 mm in diameter, with persistent calyx; pedicels slender, 1 mm long.

Distribution: Taiwan, Ryukyu and Japan, at altitude 2300 m.

Var. 1. Eurya japonica Thunb. var. microphylla

24. Eurya leptophylla Hayata

The leaves are small for the genus being 3–3.5 cm long, 1–1.5 cm wide. At the same time they are quite membranaceous and oblong–lanceolate. The male flowers have 7–8 stamens and the styles in the female flowers are columniform; these may or may not split to near the base.

Distribution: Taiwan, at altitude 2300 m.

25. Eurya metcalfiana Kobuski

Small shrub, glabrous in all parts; leaves elliptic or oblong–elliptic, 2–3.5 cm long, 8–15 mm wide, base cuneate, apex obtuse acuminate, margin serrulate, nerves 7–10, profound impress above, elevated below; male flowers axillary, solitary, fragrant; pedicels 12 mm long; bracts 2, sepaloid; sepals 5, imbricate, concave, obtuse, unequal; petals 5, basal connate, white, obtuse; stamens 10, filaments 3 mm long; ovary rudimentary; fruit globose; style 0.25 mm long.

Distribution: Kwangtung, Hainan and Anhwei, at altitude 1400 m.

26. Eurya muricata Dunn

Shrub 2 m high; leaves oblong, 5 cm long, 2.5 cm wide, acute apex, cuneate at base, entire incurved margin, lustrous glaucous green above, pale brownish green below, glabrous, thick, coriaceous; petiole 1.5 mm long, reddish brown; flowers very small, axillary, solitary or in 2 or 3, sub–sessile.

Distribution: Near Hongkong.

27. Eurya obliquifolia Hemsl.

Tree 10 m high; this species is closely allied to E. glandulosa. It can be separated, however, by its larger leaves (up to 10 cm) which are membranaceous rather than coriaceous and attenuate–acuminate at apex. The leaves of E. glandulosa are decidedly revolute and from the upper surface appear entire. The leaf margins of E. glandulosa are not revolute and are decidedly serrate.

Distribution: Yunnan.

28. Eurya loquaiana Dunn

Shrub with styles, fruits glabrous. Branchlets very slender, minutely puberulent terminal leaf-buds pubescent; male flowers with sepals 5, slightly pubescent, 1.25 mm long, subtended by obtuse bracts; petals 5, lined at base, 4.5 mm long, slender, 2 mm wide, rounded; stamens 10, filaments 2 mm long; anthers 1.25 mm apiculate. Distinct veining on the under surface of the leaves. The veins are usually yellow and raised against the reddish-brown background of the leaf.

Distribution: Fukien, Kwangtung, Kwangsi, Kweichow, Kiangsi and Chekiang, at altitude 700 m.

29. Eurya macartneyi Champ. et Benth.

Small shrub; in most species of *Eurya*, one can find winged branchlets accompanying strictly glabrous terminal bud. This species is one of the few exceptions to this group, having terete branchlets with glabrous terminal buds. Branchlets are sturdy, as are the leaves, petioles and flowers bud. The large leaves have pronounced veining on the upper surface revolute margins and slight serration if any. The fruit is globose while the attached style is approximately 1 mm long and free its entire length. Flower white; fruit black.

Distribution: Kwangtung, Hainan, Kwangsi and Kiangsi, at altitude 1000 m.

Var. 1. Eurya macartneyi var. **hainanensis** Kobuski

Shrub or small tree, 10 meters high. Leaves obovate, 8 cm long, 4 cm wide, acute-attenuate at apex obtuse cuneate at base, serrate margin, lustrous dark shining green above, pale green, with brownish pubescence along the midrib below; veins 10 pairs prominent beneath, inconspicuous above, thick, coriaceous; petiole 6 mm long, grooved above; flowers axillary, solitary or in twos, greenish white; fruit dark purple.

Distribution: Hainan, at altitude 1000 m.

30. Eurya nitida Korthals

Shrub 1-3 m high. Branchlets slender, whitish gray. Leaves elliptic-oblong, 3-6 cm long, 1-3 cm wide, acute and slightly emarginate at apex, cuneate at base, serrate margins above the middle, lustrous shining green glabrous above, and glabrous below; veins incuspicuous on both surfaces, midrib deeply impressed above, elevated above; flowers small, dense along the young branchlets, greenish yellow, fragrant; fruit black, globose 1 mm in diameter, mucronate, with persistent calyx at base; pedicels slender, 1 mm long, axillary, solitary.

Distribution: Kwangtung, Kwangsi, Yunnan, Hainan, Kweichow, Fukien, Taiwan, Hunan, Chekiang, Anhwei, Kiangsu, Hupeh, Kiangsi, Szechuan and Sikang, at altitude 1900 m.

Var. 1. Eurya nitida Korthals var. **aurescens** (R. et W.) Kobuski

Shrub or tree 10-18 m high. Branchlets whitish gray, rough. Leaves oblong-lanceolate, 8 cm long, 3.5 cm wide, acute and slightly emarginate at apex, obtuse-cuneate at base, finely serrate and incurved margins, lustrous dark green glabrous above, pale green glabrous, except slightly pubescent along the midrib beneath, veins deeply impressed above, not very conspicuous below, coriaceous; petiole 8–12 mm long, rusty brown; fruits solitary, axillary, black, globose, 1 mm in diameter, mucronate, with persistent calyx at base, sessile, glabrous.

Distribution: Kwangsi, Kweichow, Hunan, Kiangsi, Anhwei, Kiangsu, Chekiang, Hupeh and Szechuan, at altitude 500–1200 m.

31. Eurya polyneura Chun

Shrub 4 m high, wholly glabrous; branchlets and branches stout, green, strongly angular, sharply rigid, internodes 1.5–2 cm long; leaves deep green, drying pale yellow green above and pale green beneath, not distichous, sub-coriaceous; apex shortly acuminate, margin densely minutely crenate-denticulate, midrib and lateral veins impressed on the upper surface, strongly elevated on the lower, lateral veins close, numerous, 25 or more on each side of the midrib (including intermediate ones 30–50), horizontally spreading, slightly curved, anastomsing and confluent 2–3 mm within the margin, veinlets laxly reticulate; petiole stout, 1.5–2 cm long, semiterete, deeply grooved above, shortly decurrent down the petiole and continuous with the ridges; fruits solitary or in pairs or several in a cluster on the lower part of the branches in the axils of fallen leaves, on glabrous pedicels of 2 mm long with several bracts and bracteoles at the base; berry oblong-ovoid, 11 mm long, about 5 mm wide, at first dull brownish red, turning black when mature, crowned by the remnant of the persistent, glabrous, slender style which in its entire is about 4.5 mm long, 3-fid about 2 mm above the ovary; calyx about 5 mm long and wide, glabrous, lobes oblong-ovoid, obtuse, margin sub-hyline seeds numerous, lustrous pale brown, densely foveolate, obliquely ovoid-reniform about 1 mm long.

Distribution: Kwangtung.

32. Eurya pseudocerasifera Kobuski

Tree 7 m high; leaves oblong-elliptic, decurrent, 9–13 cm long, 3–5 cm wide, apex acuminate, base cuneate, margin entire incurved, lustrous dark green above, pale green glabrous below. This species is characterized by the entire leaves, the pubescent ovary and the long style (5 mm), 3 or 4 parted, the branches free for one half the length. Also most unusually the size, recorded by Tsai (56882) as a big tree attaining a height a hundred feet, but none of the 3 specimens examines and cited is recorded as taller than 30 feet.

Distribution: Yunnan, at altitude 2300 m.

33. Eurya quenquelocularis Kobuski

Tree 3–10 m high; leaves membranaceous, oblong-ovate, 7–15 cm long, 2–4 cm wide apex acuminate, base cuneate, margin serrulate; petiole 2-3 mm long; female flowers 5-6, axillary, pedicels 5-6 mm long, pubescent; bracts 2, 1 mm long, pubescent, sepaloid; sepals 5, imbricate, pubescent inequal, concave, 2-2.5 mm long, 2 mm wide, orbicular; petals 5, orbicular, 3 mm long, 1.5 mm wide, base connate 1 mm; fruit globose, quequeloculary, 6 mm broad, nigrescent.

Distribution: Kwangsi and Kwangtung, at altitude 600 m.

34. **Eurya rengechiensis** Yamamoto

Shrub. This is the most robust species found in Taiwan. Leaves oblanceolate, 7-8 cm long, 2.5-3.5 cm wide; the widest leaf of the genus in Taiwan. The revolte margin is minutely serrulate, giving an entire appearance; veins 12-15 pairs which are attached to the midrib at an angle of 60 degrees, deeply impressed on the upper surface and raised on the lower surface.

Distribution: Taiwan.

35. **Eurya strigillosa** Hayata

Tree; in pubescence and leaf shape this species is very similar to *E. ciliata* of Hainan and Kwangtung. The ovary and fruit are invested in stiff hairs. It resembles also *E. gnaphalocarpa* and *E. trichocarpa*. However, unlike the last two species, whose stems are glabrous or nearly so, *E. strigillosa* has strong strigillose hairs along the branchlets and on terminal bud.

Distribution: Taiwan.

36. **Eurya subintegra** Kobuski

Shrub with robusty brown branchlets; leaves oblanceolate, 10 cm long, 4 cm wide, attenuate-acuminate apex, cuneate at base, entire undulate margin, thick, lustrous dark green above, pale green glabrous below; petiole 5 mm long, grooved, flowers solitary, axillary on the fallen leaves axils; pedicels slender, 6 mm long, glabrous, with persistent calyx.

Distribution: Kwangsi.

37. **Eurya tetragonoclada** Merr. et Chun

A small tree, glabrous; the older branches terete, brownish purple, branchlets elongated, up to 20 cm long, 2-3 mm in diameter, sharply and conspicuously 4-angled or narrowly or thickly 4-winged; the younger parts pale greenish, internodes 1-2.5 cm long; leaves coriaceous, shining, olivaceous, greenish beneath, oblong to oblong-elliptic or oblong-lanceolate, 4-9 cm long, 1.5-3.5 cm wide, rather prominently acuminate, base acute, margins crenulate-serrate except in lowers 1/4 which are entire, teeth small, mostly black glandular-apiculate, lateral nerves slender, not prominent, 8-10 on each side of the midrib; petiole 4-6 mm long; flowers few, axillary, mostly in pairs; pedicels 2 mm long; bracteoles 0.5 mm long; sepals rounded, suborbicular, coriaceous, glabrous, 1-1.5 mm long; ovary ovoid, glabrous; style stout, 1 mm long, glabrous or with few scattered spreading short hairs, the arms 3 or 2, not excceding 0.5 mm in length.

Distribution: Kwangtung.

38. Eurya tsingpienensis Hu

Shrub 3.6 m high; branchlets very slender, angular, slightly winged, minutely glandulose-pilosulose; leaves thin, chartaceous, narrow-oblong, lanceolate or ob-lanceolate, falcate-caudate-acuminate at apex, subrounded and slightly decurrent at base, slightly revolute and minutely crenate along the margins, glabrous and impressed midrib and elevated secondary veins and reticulations above, glabrous except pilose along the elevated midrib and with very slender secondary veins and reticulations beneath, 5.5-7.5 cm long, 1.8-2.8 cm broad, cauda to 1.8 cm long, secondary veins about 20 pairs; pistillate flowers 1-2, on puberulous pedicels; bracts broadly-ovate, 3 mm long, sepals suborbiculate, sericeous puberulous outside; fruit globose 3.5 mm in diameter.

Distribution: South Yunnan.

39. Eurya velutina Chun

Tree 12 m high; branchlets angular, stout, densely tomentose with yellowish silky villose hairs, becoming glabrous or subglabrous the second or the third year, older branches dark brownish purple; leaves persistent, scattered, short petioled, coriaceous 12-15 cm long, 4-5 cm wide, elliptic-oblong, base broadly cuneate, apex gradually caudate-acuminate, margin closely crenate-serrulate, when mature upper surface sublustrous, glabrous, drying yellowish green, with flattened or slightly impressed midrib, lower surface pale green, densely, softly, yellowish silky pilose on the strongly elevated midrib, shortly adpressed scattered pilose on the blade, lateral veins usually 16-20, slightly elevated on both surfaces, reticulate veinlets obsolete beneath; petiole 3-4 mm long, 2 mm broad, sordid, pendulous; berry 1-4 (immature) on stout silky pilose pedicels about 2 mm long in the axils of leaves or fallen leaves, ellipsoid, 6 mm long, 5 mm wide, densely silky pilose; calyx obovate-oblong to suborbicular, apex rounded, adpressed pubescent outside; style glabrous, about 4 mm long, 4-fid to below the middle or nearly distinct to the base; seeds about 1.2 mm long.

Distribution: Kwangtung.

40. Eurya stenophylla Merr.

Shrub, entirely glabrous; branches terete, reddish brown, the branchlets narrowly winged; leaves numerous, subcoriaceous, pale olivaceous, somewhat shining, crowded lanceolate, 2.5-5 cm long, 6-8 mm wide, base acute, apex obtuse acuminate, margins distinctly crenate-serrate, the basal 1/4 entire; nerves 10-12 on each side of the mid rib, slightly impressed on the upper surface, projecting on the lower surface, slender distinct; petiole 1 mm long or less; flowers axillary, solitary or in pairs; sepals coriaceous, elliptic, rounded or retuse, 2.5 mm long; the pedicels in fruit 4-5 mm long fruit oblong-ovoid, 5-6 mm long, about 4 mm in diameter, apiculate-acuminate by the persistent style.

Distribution: Kwangtung, at altitude 2100 m.

41. **Eurya trichocarpa** Korthals

Eurya acuminatissima Merr. et Chun

Shrub 1–4 m high; leaves oblanceolate, 7 cm long, 2.5 cm wide, long-acuminate at apex, cuneate at base, entire margin, lustrous dark green above, pale green glabrous beneath; midrib deeply impressed above, projecting below; veins inconspicuous on both surfaces, coriaceous; flowers solitary, axillary, white, fragrant, 2 or 3 in clusters; fruit globose, 1 mm in diameter, mucronate with pistillate remanant, blue black, sub-sessile.

Distribution: Kwangsi, Kwangtung, Kweichow, Szechuan and Yunnan, at altitude 500 m.

Family 52. Flacourtiaceae Dunn

Key to the genera of Flacourtiaceae (See orig. text pages 838–839)

Genus (1) Xylosma Forst (See orig. text page 839)

1. **Xylosma delicatum** Merr. et Metcalf

Xylosma controversum Clos

Shrub 1–3 m high; bark brownish gray; branchlets slender, brownish gray, somewhat lenticelled, smooth, glabrous; leaves oblanceolate, 11 cm long, 4 cm wide, acuminate at apex, obtuse cuneate at base, crenulate-serrate margin, dark green above, light green below, subcoriaceous; veins 5 pairs, conspicuous on both surfaces; petiole 12 mm long, reddish purple, glabrous; flowers greenish white, anthers yellow, in axillary racemes of the fallen leaves; fruit globose, 1.5 mm long, 1 mm broad, green, mucronate with pistillate remnant; pedicels very slender, 1 mm long, glabrous.

Distribution: Kwangtung, Hainan and Kwangsi, at altitude 1150 m.

2. **Xylosma congestum** (Lour.) Merr. (See orig. text pages 839–840)

Var. 1. **Xylosma congestum** var. **pubescens** Rehd. (See orig. text page 841)

Var. 2. **Xylosma congestum** var. **kwangtungensis** Metcalf

3. **Xylosma controversum** Clos

4. **Xylosma longifolium** Clos (See orig. text page 842)

5. **Xylosma racemosum** Miq.

Tree 7 m high; branchlets reddish brown; leaves simple, alternate, elliptic oblong, 7 cm long, 3.5 cm wide, long-acute at apex, obtuse cuneate at base, coarsely serrate margin, deep lustrous green above, light green below, subcoriaceous; petiole 15 mm long, brown, flattened, glabrous; flowers purplish yellow, in axillary racemes; fruits berry, round, 1 mm in diameter, gray; pedicels slender, 2 mm long, bearing persistent calyx on tops.

Distribution: Kwangtung, Kweichow and Hupeh, at altitude 1500–1600 m.

6. **Xylosma senticosum** Hance (See orig. text page 842)

7. **Xylosma subrhombea** Hance

    Caseria subrhombea Hance

Small tree; leaves coriaceous, rhombic-ovate, acuminate apex, cuneate at base, glandulose-serrate margin, glabrescent, subtri-penninerved veins, prominently reticulated, 6-8 cm long, 4-5 cm wide; petiole slender; racemes densiflorae; rachis tomentose; pedicels with small bracteoles; calyx lobes ciliate.

Distribution: Kwangtung.

8. **Xylosma trichophyllum** Merr. et Metcalf

Shrub 4 m high; branchlets gray, the younger branchlets covered with dense reddishbrown hairs; leaves oblanceolate to obovate, 10 cm long, 5 cm wide, short-acuminate at apex, obtuse cuneate at base, sub-trinerved at base, crenate dentate-serrate margin, lustrous dark green above, light green glabrous except brownish hairy along the midrib below, thick, coriaceous; petiole 17 cm long, brownish pubescent; fruits globular, black, 14 mm across.

Distribution: Kwangtung, Kwangsi, and Kiangsi.

Genus (2) Idesia Maxim. (See orig. text page 842)

1. **Idesia fargesii** Franch.

Shrub; branchlets brownish pubescent; leaves obovate, 11 cm long, 10 cm broad, acut-acuminate at apex, truncate and 5-nerved at base, coarsely sub-crenate serrate margin, lustrous dark green, above, pale green, glabrous below, sub-coriaceous; petiole 7-11 cm long, slender, glandular, covered with brownish hairs; flowers yellowish brown, in long terminal racemes; stamens numerous, filaments 3 mm long, purplish; sepals imbricate; fruits in axillary and terminal racemes, berry round, 1 cm in diameter, pedicels 2 cm long, slender, glabrous, yellowish brown; peduncle 12-15 cm long, brownish pubescent.

Distribution: Yunnan, Szechuan.

2. **Idesia polycarpa** Maxim. (See orig. text page 843)

    Var. 1. Idesia polycarpa var. **intermedia** Pamp.

Tree; leaves obovate, about 10 cm long, 7 cm wide, acute apex, subcordate and 5-nerved at base, irregularly serrate margin; petiole about 5 cm long; flowers in axillary racemes; pedicels and peduncles very slender, glabrous.

Distribution: Hupeh.

    Var. 2. Idesia polycarpa var. **latifolia** Diels

Shrub; branchlets slender, smooth, glabrous; leaves round to obovate, 10 cm long, 8 cm wide, acuminate apex, cordate and 5-nerved at base, irregularly finely serrate margin, dark green above, pale glaucous below; nerves conspicuous on both surfaces; petiole about 12 cm long, glabrous.

Distribution: Szechuan, Nan-Chuan Hsien.

Var. 3. **Idesia polycarpa** var. **pubescens** Diels

Large tree; 10 m high, 30 cm in diameter; bark whitish gray, smooth, tight; leaves like that of the type but pubescent.

Var. 4. **Idesia polycarpa** var. **vestita** Diels   (See orig. text page 843)

Genus (3) Poliothyrsis Oliv. (See orig. text pages 843–844)

1. **Poliothyrsis sinensis** Oliv. (See orig. text page 845)

Genus (4) Itoa Hemsl. (See orig. text page 845)

1. **Itoa orientalis** Hemsl. (See orig. text pages 845–847)

Genus (5) Carrierea Franchet (See orig. text page 847)

1. **Carrierea calysina** Franch.

2. **Carrierea dunniana** Levl.

Tree 10 m high, 25 cm in diameter; bark gray; branchlets lenticellate; leaves oblong, 10 cm long, 4 cm wide, long-acuminate at apex, broadly-ovate and 5-nerved at base, deep lustrous green above, light green and glabrous below, distantly crenate-serrate margin above the middle, subcoriaceous; petiole 6 cm long, slender, purplish, glabrous; flowers white, in terminal panicles.

It is allied to *C. calysina* Franch. but easily distinguished from it by the many-flowered paniculate inflorescence, the much smaller sepals not cordate at the base, and the ovate to oblong rahter long-acuminate leaves.

Distribution: Kweichow.

3. **Carrierea rehderiana** Sleumer

Small tree, dioecious; leaves broadly oblong, 2.5–4.5 cm long, acuminate at apex, rotundate at base, trinerved, 8–12 cm long, 6–7 cm wide, distantly serrate margin; inflorescence paniculate, 5-flowers, terminal, 5–6 cm long; pedicels 12–15 mm long, in upper part articulated; tepal 5 oblong, cordate at base; male flowers with stamens numerous, filaments glabrous, 4–6 mm long; style 3, bifid, subglabrous.

Distribution: Kweichow.

Order XX Myrtales

Family 53. Elaeagnaceae Lindley
(See orig. text page 848)

Key to the genera of Elaeagnaceae (See orig. text page 848)

Genus (1) Hippophae Linn. (See orig. text pages 848–849)

1. **Hippophae rhamnoides** Linn.

Var. 1. **Hippophae rhamnoides** var. **procera** Rehd.

Genus (2) Elaeagnus Linn. (See orig. text pages 849–850)

1. **Elaeagnus umbellata** Thunb. (See orig. text pages 851–852)

2–6. (See orig. text page 853)

7. **Elaeagnus delavayi** H. Lecte.

   Shrub 1 meter high.

   Distribution: Yunnan, at altitude 2700–3000 m.

8. **Elaeagnus difficilis** Servettaz

   Shrub 1 meter high.

   Distribution: Szechuan, Patung Hsien, Hupeh.

9. **Elaeagnus formosana** Nakai

   Shrub 1–4 m high.

   Distribution: Arisan, Taiwan, at altitude 833–1000 m.

10. **Elaeagnus fruticosa** (Lour.) Merr.

    Elaeagnus gaudichaudiana Schlecht.

    Scandent shrub on trees.

    Distribution: Hainan.

11. **Elaeagnus glabrata** Thunb.

12. **Elaeagnus grijsii** Hance

13. **Elaeagnus gussonii** Gasp. (See orig. text page 855)

14. **Elaeagnus gonyanthes** Bentham

    Shrub 4 meters high.

    Distribution: Hainan, at altitude 430 m.

15–20. (See orig. text page 854)

21. **Elaeagnus macrophylla** Thunb.

    Shrub 1–2 m high.

    Distribution: Japan, Ryukyu and Taiwan.

22. **Elaeagnus morrisonensis** Hayata

    Shrub 2–4 m high.

    Distribution: Arisan, Taiwan, at altitude 2500 m.

23. – 28. (See orig. text pages 854–855)

29. **Elaeagnus thunbergii** Servattaz

    Shrub 2–3 m high; scandent.

    Distribution: Arisan, Taiwan, at altitude 2700 m.

30. **Elaeagnus viridis** Serv. (See orig. text page 856)

31. **Elaeagnus yunnanensis** Servettaz

    Shrub 3 m high, leaves whitish tomentose beneath.

    Distribution: Yunnan and Szechuan, at altitude 720 m.

Family 54. Nyssaceae Endl.

Key to genera of Nyssaceae (See orig. text page 856)

Genus (1) Camptotheca Decne. (See orig. text pages 856–857)

1. **Camptotheca acuminata** Decaisne

Genus (2) Davidia Baill. (See orig. text pages 857–859)

1. **Davidia involucrata** Baill. (See orig. text pages 859–860)

      Var. 1. **Davidia involucrata** var. **vilmoriniana** Hemsl.

Genus (3) Nyssa Linn. (See orig. text pages 860–862)

1. **Nyssa sinensis** Oliv. (See orig. text pages 862–864)
2. **Nyssa javanica** (B.) Wang (See orig. text page 864)

Order XXI Umbellales

Family 55. Araliaceae Vent.
(See orig. text page 864)

Key to genera of Araliaceae. (See orig. text page 864)

Genus (1) Acanthopanax Miq. (See orig. text page 865)

Key to species and varieties of *Acanthopanax*

A. Styles 5, united throughout their whole length into a single column (Sect. I Eleutherococcus (Maxim.) Harms.

  B. Leaflets distinctly petiolate.

    C. Leaflets glabrous or pubescent, not sectose or only very slightly so.

      D. Branches usually densely covered with slender bristle-like prickles. ———————————————————————————— (12) *A. senticosus*

    DD. Branches unarmed or with few and usually with reflexed prickles.

      E. Branches glabrous; prickles slender; peduncles usually slender, glabrous, without prickles.

        F. leaflets 5-foliolate, rarely 3–4-foliolate.

          G. Leaflets glabrous ——————(9) *A. leucorrhizus*

          GG. Leaflets scabrous-pubescent above, fulvous-pubescent, along the veins beneath.

            H. Leaflets serrate or slightly double-serrate, without pristles ——————————(9-1) *A. leucorrhizus* var. *fulvescens*

            HH. Leaflets double-serrate, with sectose-acuminate teeth, pristly on the petiolules and the midrib beneath ——————————————————— (9-2) *A. leucorrhizus* var. *scaberulus*

        FF. Leaflets 3-foliolate, rarely 4–5-foliolate ———————————————————————————— *A. szechuanensis*

EE. Branches rough–pubescent at first, later glabrous, the prickles short, conical; peduncle stout and pubescent.

F. Leaflets pubescent along the veins beneath; pedicels glabrous or slightly pubescent ————— (6) *A. henryi*

FF. Leaflets glabrous beneath, pedicels very pubescent ——————————————————————— (6-1) *A. henryi* var. *faberi*

CC. Leaflets bristly or with setose hairs on both surfaces ———————————————————————————————————————*A. simonii*

BB. Leaflets very short–petiolulate or almost sessile.

C. Petiolulate short, 2–4 cm long; leaflets obovate to oblong small, 3.5–5.5, 1.5–2.3 cm the apex rounded to obtuse, the margins entire; umbels 1 or 2 ——————————————————————————— *A. brachypus*

CC. Petiolules long, 10–16 cm long; leaflets oblong-elliptic, large, 14–17, 5.5–8 cm the apex acuminate, the margins serrulate–dentate; umbels more than 2. ——————————————————————(10) *A. phanerophlebius*

AA. Styles 2–5, divided at least at the apex.

B. Branches prickly.

C. Flowers subsessile or on short pubescent pedicels, 3–10 mm long; style 2 (Sect. II Cephalophanax Baill.)

D. Styles united into a single column, bifid at tip only.

E. Leaflets usually 5, rough–pubescent benath; pedicels 3–10 mm long. —————————————————————————— *A. divericatus*

EE. Leaflets usually 3, glabrous or nearly so beneath; pedicels very short, almost wanting.

F. Leaflets obovate to oblong–lanceolate, large, 8–18 cm long; umbels 3.5 cm across; fruit 1–1.5 cm long ———*A. sessiliflorus*

FF. Leaflets elliptic, small, 5–9 cm long; umbels less than 3.5 cm across; fruit 1 cm or less long —————*A. sessiliflorus* var *parviceps*

DD. Styles 2, united at base or to middle only; pedicels 5–7 mm long; leaflets 3 ——————————————————————— (8) *A. lasiogyne*

CC. Flowers slender–pedicellate, the pedicels glabrous; styles 2–5.

D. Umbels usually solitary; styles more or less united into a column or to middle or only at base (Section III. Euacanthopanax Harms.)

E. Styles 3–5, free, or united to middle.

F. Style free or almost free—————(7) *A. cissifolius*

FF. Style united at base or to above middle.

G. Style united only at base or at most to middle.

H. Branches more or less densely prickly.

I. Prickles conical, reflexed, slightly broadened at base

---------------------(24) *A. yui*

II. Prickles bristle-like, spreading or reflexed, narrow at base.

    J. Branches densely prickly ---------------------- ------------------- *A. giraldii*

    JJ. Branches unarmed or nearly so.

        K. Leaflets obovate to obovate-oblong, glabrous, the margins irregularly double-serrate ------ ------------------*A. giraldii* var. *inermis*

        KK. Leaflets lanceolate to oblanceolate, sparingly scarbid above, short-villose-pilose beneath, margins simple-serrate --------------------- ---------------- *A. giraldii* var. *pilosulose*

HH. Branches unarmed or pirckly only at nodes.

    I. Branches glabrous, unarmed or only bristle-prickly at the nodes.

        J. Leaflets oblanceolate to oblong-lanceolate, 4-5.5 0.5-1.6 cm peduncles 1.5-5 cm long --------------- -------------- (23) *A. wilsonii*

        JJ. Leaflets narrowly lanceolate to oblanceolate, 2-6.5 0.4-1.5 cm peduncles 1 cm or less long. -------- ---------------------- *A. stenophyllus*

    II. Branches densely covered with bristles and with single prickle at the base of petiole ------------------------ ----------------------- *A. setulosus*

GG. Styles united to middle or above.

    H. Peduncles short, 1-2 cm long; styles united into a short conical column, their tips distinct and recurved --------- ------------------- (11) *A. rehderianus*

    HH. Peduncles slender, 5-10 cm long; styles connate into a slender column nearly to apex --------------------------- ------------------- (19) *A. sieboldianus*

EE. Styles 2, free or united at base.

    F. Leaflets glabrous or sometimes very slightly setulose ------------ -- *A. gracilistylus*

    FF. Leaflets pubescent to villose or scarbid.

        G. Leaflets glabrous above, pubescent especially along the nerves beneath ------------------ (3-1) *A. gracilistylus* var. *pubescens*

        GG. Leaflets glabrous to slightly setulose above, villose beneath

slightly setulose along the nerves ------------------------
-------------------- (3-3) *A. gracilistylus* var.
villosus

GGG. Leaflets scarbid-setulose above, scarbid to pubescent beneath
-------------------- (3-1) *A. gracilistylus* var.
nodiflorus

DD. Umbels usually 4-7 at ends of branches, rarely solitary; styles 2, united
to middle or only at base (Section IV. Xanthoxylopanax Harms.)

E. Prickles recurved at their tips; petioles scattered-prickly; peduncle
2-7 cm long; pedicels 1 cm long; fruit compressed.

F. Leaflets glabrous or very slightly setose along the midrib and
veins above; margins serrulate ----------------------------
-------------------------- (20) *A. trifoliatus*

FF. Leaflets more or less densely setose along the midrib and veins
above; margins double-serrate ---------------------------
--------------------------(20-1) *A. trifoliatus* |var. *setosus*

EE. Prickles more or less straight; petioles unarmed; peduncles 1-2 cm
long; pedicels 5-10 mm long; fruit very much compressed ------------
------------------------------ (22) *A. wardii*

BB. Branches unarmed; umbels several in a raceme or compound umbel; styles 2-4,
united at base or to middle (Section V. Evodiopanax Harms)

C. Leaflets glabrous, ferruginous-tomentose in axils of nerves beneath; peduncles
and pedicels glabrous.

D. Leaflets 3 umbels few to many-flowered; pedicels in fruit 1-3.5 cm long.
----------------------------------- (1) *A. evodiaefolius*

DD. Leaflets mostly 5; umbels few-flowered; pedicels in fruit 1-2.5 cm long.-
----------------------------------- (1-1) *A. evodiaefolius* var.
gracilis

CC. Leaflets ferriginous-tomentose on lateral nerves beneath; peduncles and
pedicels ferruginous-tomentose -----------(1-2) *A. evodiaefolius* var.
ferrugineus

1. **Acanthopanax evodiaefolius** Franch. (See orig. text page 865)

    Var. 1. Acanthopanax evodiaefolius var. **gracilis** Sm.

    Var. 2. Acanthopanax evodiaefolius var. **ferrugineus** Sm.

2. **Acanthopanax ricinifolius** Seem. (See orig. text page 866)

    Var. 1. Acanthopanax ricinifolius var. **maximoviczii** Schreider (See orig.
text pages 867-868)

3 - 5. (See orig. text page 868)

    Var. 1. Acanthopanax gracilistylus var. **nodiflorus** Li

        Acanthopanax nodiflorus Dunn

Shrub or climber, 2 m high; leaflets scabrid-setulos above, pubescent beneath.

Distribution: Kwangtung, Kwangsi, at level-land.

Var. 2. Acanthopanax gracilistylus var. **pubescens** (Pampanini) Li

Acanthopanax spinosus var. *pubescens* Pamp.

Shrub 2 m high. Leaflets glabrous above, pubescent along the nerves below.

Distribution: Hupeh.

Var. 3. Acanthopanax gracilistylus var. **villosulus** Li

Acanthopanax villosulus Harms.

Shrub 1-2 m high. Leaflets villose beneath.

Distribution: Hupeh, Szechuan, at altitude 1200-1800 meters.

6. **Acanthopanax henryi** Harms. (See orig. text page 869)

Var. 1. Acanthopanax henryi var. **faberi** Li

Shrub differing from type in leaflets being glabrous below, serrations often broad, umbels small; pedicels and calyx pubescent.

Distribution: Tien Mu Shan, Chekiang.

7. **Acanthopanax cissifolius** (Nakai) Li

Eleutherococcus cissifolius Nakai

Shrub 3 m high; branchlets unarmed or with scattered short prickles; leaves 5-foliated; umbels many-flowered; styles 3-5 almost entirely free.

Distribution: Yunnan, at altitude 3300 m.

8. **Acanthopanax lasiogyne** Harms. (See orig. text page 869)

9. **Acanthopanax leucorrhizus** Harms.

Var. 1. A. leucorrhizus var. **fulvescens** Harms. et Rehd.

Var. 2. A. leucorrhizus var. **saberulus** Harms. et Rehd.

10. **Acanthopanax phanerophlebius** Merr. et Chun

Shrub subscandens; leaves 3-4-foliated; leaflets inequalateral; inflorescence lax, castaneous indumentum on the younger parts of inflorescence.

Distribution: Kwangtung.

11. **Acanthopanax rehderianus** Harms. (See orig. text page 869)

12. **Acanthopanax senticosus** Harms.

13. - 18. (See orig. text page 870)

Var. 2. Acanthopanax stenophyllus var. **angustissimis** Rehd.

This variety differs from the type in the leaflets being more linear, only 3-5 mm wide, and minutely serrulate. A shrub 0.75-2.5 m tall; branches armed at the nodes with a few bristle-like erect prickles.

Distribution: Kansu, at altitude 2300 m.

19. **Acanthopanax sieboldianus** Makino

Shrub, 2 m tall, with arching branchlets, unarmed, or with few compressed prickles,

5-7-foliated leaves, solitary umbels borne on short lateral branches; leaves fascicled partly on short spurs; flowers dioecious; petals 5, greenish white; pedicels 1 cm long, glabrous; calyx glabrous, 5-dentate; stamens 5; ovary 5-celled; style 5, connate near to apex; fruit black, subglobose, 6-8 mm across.

Distribution: Anhwei, at altitude 1800-1900 m.

20. **Acanthopanax trifoliatus** (Lour.) Merr. (See orig. text page 871)

Var. 1. **Acanthopanax trifoliatus** var. **setosus** Li

A climbing shrub, differing from the species in having leaflets slightly sectose simple-serrate instead of double, sectose-serrate.

Distribution: Kwangsi, at altitude 1700 meters.

21. **Acanthopanax villosulus** Harms. (See orig. text page 871)

22. **Acanthopanax wardii** W. W. Sm.

Shrub 1-3 m high; leaves petiolate, 2-4 cm long, glabrous; leaflets 3, sessile, 3-5 cm long, 1.5-3 cm wide, ovate to oblong-ovate or obovate; apex obtuse-acute, base broadly cuneate, margin denticulated; umbels 4-6-florae; petals triangular, white; stamens 5; styles 2.

Distribution: Yunnan, at altitude 2600 m.

23. **Acanthopanax wilsonii** Harms. (See orig. text page 871)

24. **Acanthopanax yui** Li

Shrub 1 meter high. It relates to *A. giraldii* Harms. from which it may be distinguished by its stouter conical prickles, larger leaflets, and larger umbels. Some are densely armed and some sparingly so.

Distribution: Yunnan, at altitude 3250 m.

Genus (2) Aralia Linn. (See orig. text page 871)

Key to the woody species of genus Aralia.

A. Flowers distinctly pedicellate, umbellate (Section Arborescentes Harms)

  B. Plants always more or less armed with prickles or spines.

    C. Stems and branches densely prickly; petioles, rachises and partial rachises of leaves as well as inflorescences more or prickly.

      D. Leaves and inflorescences with long prickles and dense, long setose hairs, prickles 3-10 mm long ———————(11) *A. spinifolia*

      DD. Leaves and inflorescences with short prickles, glabrous or pilose, the prickles less than 4 mm long.

        E. Pedicels short, 1.5 cm long, pubescent ——————————————————————————————————(2) *A. armata*

        EE. Pedicels long, 2-5 cm long, glabrous or near so ——————————————————————————————(6) *A. foliolosa*

    CC. Stems and branches densely or sparingly prickly; petiole, rachis and partial rachises of leaves and inflorescences unarmed or occasionally with very few widely scattered prickles.

    D. Inflorescence corymbose-paniculate, the axis short, the branches sub-umbellately arranged.

        E. Leaflets undulate-mucronate ---- (13) *A. undulata*

      EE. Leaflets serrate, not undulate.

           F. Leaflets subchartaceous, glabrous to slightly pubescent along the veins; inflorecence pubescent-(9) *A. elata*

          FF. Leaflets coriaceous, fulvous-strigose-tomentose; inflorescence densely fulvous-strigose------(10) *A. searelliana*

    DD. Inflorescence paniculate, the axis long, the branches racemosely arranged

    E. Pedicels short, 4-6 mm long.

           F. Leaflets glabrous to slightly scabrid above, pubescent especially along the veins beneath ----- (3) *A. chinensis*

          FF. Leaflets glabrous above, glaucescent and glabrous benath except the sparingly pubescent midrib -- (3-1) *A. chinensis* var. *nuda*

         FFF. Leaflets densely yellow-strigose above, densely yellow-strigose tomentose especially along the veins beneath --- (3-2) *A. chinensis* var. *dasyphyllo ides*

      EE. Pedicels long, 0.8-3 cm long.

           F. Leaflets membranaceous to subchartaceous, glabrous ---(8) *A. echinocaulis*

          FF. Leaflets chartaceous to coriaceous, fulvous-tomentose.

              G. Umbels many (30-50) - flowered --- (5) *A. decaisneana*

            GG. Umbels fewer (15-20) - flowered -- (12) *A. thomsonii*

  BB. Plants completely unarmed.

    C. Leaves once or twice pinnate.

      D. Leaves usually once pinnate, 10-16 cm long, the leaflets ovate to orbicular --- (1) *A. apioides*

    DD. Leaves pinnate, 30-40 cm long, the leaflets oblong-ovate to ovate-lanceolate------------------------------------- (14) *A. wilsonii*

  CC. Leaves pinnate ------------------------- (7) *A. plumosa*

AA. Flowers sessile, capitate (Section Capituligerae Harms) --(4) *A. dasyphylla*

1. **Aralia apioides** Handel-Mazz.

  Shrub or a small tree, glabrous unarmed, with usually 1-pinnate leaves and terminal subsessile panicle; leaves 5–7–foliate, 10–16 cm long including petiole; petiole 2.5–7 cm long; leaflets often 3–foliate; calyx 5–dentate, lobes ovate; petal ovate–oblong, 2.5 mm long, reflexed; stamens 5; ovary 5–celled; style 5, distinct erect; fruit globose, 4–6 mm across, 5–angled.

Distribution: Yunnan, at altitude 3000 m.

2. **Aralia armata** (Wall.) Seem.

A sparingly prickly shrub, with large 3–pinnate leaves and prickly large paniculate inflorescences; prickles conical, short, often recurved, the bases broadened; leaves usually 3–pinnate, with a pair of leaflets at each division of the rachis and partial rachises; petiole prickly; the ultimate pinnules 5–9–foliate; calyx 5–dentae; petals 5 triangular–ovate, stamens 5; ovary 5–celled; styles 5, distinct, erect; fruit globose, 4 mm across, prominently 5–angular.

Distribution: South Yunnan, Kwangsi and Hainan, at altitude 1400 m.

3. **Aralia chinensis** Linn. (See orig. text page 872)

> Var. 1. **Aralia chinensis** L. var. **nuda** Nakai (See orig. text page 872)
> Var. 2. **Aralia chinensis** L. var. **dasyphylloides**

4. **Aralia dasyphylla** Miq.

A sparingly prickly shrub with pinnate leaves, large corymbose panicles; flowers sessile, capitate at ends of peduncles.

Distribution: Kwangtung and Kweichow, at altitude 200–700 m.

5. **Aralia decaisneana** Hance

A sparingly prickly and fulvous–tomentose shrub 3 m high, with large pinnate leaves and large terminal panicle; branches, petiole, and inflorescence densely fulvous–tomentose; prickles slender, short, straight.

> Distribution: Kwangtung, Hainan, Kweichow, Taiwan, Fukien, Kiangsi and Kwangsi, at altitude 1000 m.

6. **Aralia foliolosa** (Wall.) Seem.

A large prickly shrub, with 2 or 3 pinnate leaves and large lax panicles; prickles short, strong, spreading; leaves with a pair of leaflets at each division of rachis, the ultimate pinnules 5–9–foliate; stamens 5; styles 5.

Distribution: Yunnan, at altitude 1700 m.

7. **Aralia plumosa** Li

Shrub; leaflets scabrid on the upper surface, more or less tomentose beneath. In the compound leaves the lowest pairs of pinnae are usually subtended by an extra pair of smaller pinnae, the latter mostly 3–5–foliate, but often one of each pair reduced to a simple leaflet.

Distribution: Yunnan.

8. **Aralia echinocaulis** Handel–Mazz.

A small tree, 3 m high, with dense armed branches, large bi–pinnate leaves, and a long terminal panicle; prickles slender, 7–14 mm long, straight; leaves 35–40 mm long or more, glabrous, the pinnae 5-7-foliate, leaflets obovate to lanceolate 4-11.5 cm long, 2.5-5 cm wide, apex long-acuminate, base cuneate to rounded and lateral once oblique, margins remotely mucronulate to serrulate; inflorescence 30-50 cm long; flowers in umbels, 12-20-flowered.

Distribution: Chekiang, Kiangsi, Hunan, Kwangsi, Kwangtung and Anhwei, at altitude 1180-1250 m.

9. **Aralia elata** Seem.

Shrub with 1-2-pinnated leaves; flowers in umbels, in racemes or in panicles; calyx truncate or minutely 5-dentate; petals 5, imbricated; style 5 free; ovary 5-locular.

Distribution: Manchuria and Japan.

10. **Aralia searelliana** Dunn

Small tree 5 m high with pinnate leaves and large corymbose panicles; prickles short, conical, straight, leaflets 12-18 cm long, 7-9 cm wide, ovate, apex acuminate, base cordate, margin serrate; nerves 8-10 pairs; inflorescence to 2 m long, densely fulvous-strigose, the rachis prickly; flowers in umbels, many-flowered; calyx 5-dentate; petals 5, triangular-ovate; styles 4-5; ovary 5-celled.

Distribution: Yunnan, at altitude 1400 m.

11. **Aralia spinifolia** Merr.

Shrub 3 m high, with bipinnate, prickly, with setose leaves lax prickly setose panicles; leaves large, pinnae 5-9-foliate, about 30 cm long; leaflets membranaceous, oblong-ovate, 12 cm long, 4-6 cm wide; subglobose about 30 fruits; pedicels 10-15 cm long, setose; fruits ovoid, 5 mm long, prominently 5-keeled and deeply sulcate, the depression broad, rounded.

Distribution: Kiangsi, Kwangtung, Kwangsi and Fukien.

12. **Aralia thomsonii** Seem.

A large armed shrub, all parts fulvous-villose, with large 2 or 3 pinnate leaves and large paniculate inflorescence; pinnae 5-9-foliated; flowers in umbels, 15-20 flowered; peduncle 1.5 cm long; the bracts narrowly lanceolate, 6 mm long; stamens 5; styles 5, ovary 5-celled; fruit globose, 5-angled.

Distribution: Yunnan, at altitude 1900 m.

13. **Aralia undulata** Handel-Mazz.

A sparingly armed shrub, 3-6 m high, with large bipinnate leaves and large corymobse terminal panicle; leaves to 60 cm long, glabrous; inflorescence to 40 cm long; stamens 5; styles 5, calyx 5-dentate; petals 5 oblong and reflexed; ovary 5.

Distribution: Kwangsi, at altitude 2100 m.

14. **Aralia wilsonii** Harms.

Shrub, 2-3 m high; leaves bipinnate; leaflets 2-4 cm long; leaves 20-30 cm long; pedicels 12-18 mm long. It allied to *A. chinensis* L.

Distribution: Yunnan and Sezchuan, at altitude 1700-2100 m.

Genus (3) **Schefflera** R. et G. Forst.

Shrub or tree glabrous or tomentose, unarmed. Leaves digtately compound, the stipules connate within the petiole. Flowers in umbels, racemes or globose head, arranged in panicles or compound racemes, the bracts hairy, deciduous, persistent, the pedicels not articulated under the flowers; calyx-margin entire or 5-dentate; Petals 5-7, valvate; stamens as many as petals. The anthers ovate; ovary 5-7-celled, rarely less; style united into a column or none, the stigmas distinct, sometimes sessile. Fruit globose or ovoid, 5-7-deeded, angled or not; seeds laterally compressed; endosperm uniform or slightly ruminated.

Between 300 and 400 species widely distributed in the tropics of both hemisphers.

1. **Schefflera chinensis** (Dunn) Li

A tree about 10 m high, with 6-foliate leaves, ovate-oblong leaflets and a terminal panicle formed of pedunculate globose heads of short pedicellate fruits; leaves petiolate; petioles slender, glabrous, terete, 10-17 cm long; leaflets subcoriaceous, petiolulate, glabrous above sparsely stellate-tomentose beneath, ovate-oblong, 10-15 cm or more long, 3.5-5 cm or more wide, generally broadest below the middle, acuminate at apex, broad-cuneate to almost rounded at base, margin entire or sparingly serrulate, slightly revolute, lateral veins 10-12 pairs, slightly oblique, prominent beneath; inflorescence in a terminal panicle, 30 cm long, densely tomentose; flowers subsessile or short pedicellate; calyx densely tomentose, margin entire; petals 5, densely tomentose outside, glabrous inside; stamens 5; styles 5, erect, connate below; fruit subglobose, 5-celled.

Distribution: Yunnan, at altitude 1300 m.

2. **Schefflera diversifoliolata** Li

Tree 7 m high; leaves 7-foliolated; leaflets oblong – elliptic, with very unequal leaflets, 7-17 cm long, 3-10 cm wide, apex acuminate, base rotundate, margin entire.

Distribution: Yunnan.

3. **Schefflera elata** Harms.

Tree 10-13 m high; with 5-7-foliated leaves, leaflets elliptic-oblong, glabrous entire; inflorescence formed by umbels; panicles 30-40 cm long, slightly tomentose to glabrescent, the lower branches usually compound, the flowers in racemosely arranged umbels, which are 12-15-flowered, 2 cm in diameter; bracts ovate; stamens 5; ovary 5-celled; fruit globose, 4-5 mm across.

Distribution: Yunnan, at altitude 1700 m.

4. **Schefflera esquirolii** (Levl.) Rehd.

Acanthopanax exquirolii Levl.

It seems to be related to *S. octophylla* (Lour.) Harms. but is readily distinguished by the remotely serrulate leaflets. The slender-pedicelled flowers are borne in many flowered long-peduncled umbels which seem to form large panicles; the inflorescence is sparingly setellate-pubescent; the style is about 1 mm long, it may be new species, but the material is too fragmentary for a satisfactory description.

Distribution: Kweichow.

5. **Schefflera fargesii** (Franch.) Li

   Heptleurum fargesii Franch.

   Shrub glabrous; branchlets erect, rigid, lenticellate. Leaves 5-foliolate. Leaflets 10–14 cm long, base attenuate, apex acuminate, margin serrulate, lanceolate, inflorescence terminal in quasi corymbose, 15–25 mm long, umbels many-flowered; calyx dentate-deltoides, acute; petals viridis.

   Distribution: Szechuan, at altitude 1400 m.

6. **Schefflera fukienensis** Merr.

   Shrub, scandent, with 3-foliate leaves; leaflets elliptic, and with terminal panicles; flowers in umbels, racemosely-arrnged on the branches. Leaves petiolate, 12–14 cm long; leaflets petiolate, subcoriaceous, glabrous on both surfaces, elliptic, 7–9 cm long, 4.5–5.5 cm wide, apex short-acuuc, base broadly-acute to rounded, margins entire. Inflorescence in terminal loose panicles, about 15 cm long, the branches oblique, the lower ones to 8 cm long. Floweres in umbels, 6–10-flowered, 7–8 mm in diameter; calyx margins slightly dentate; Petals 5, ovate, acute; stamens 5; the filaments same length as the petals; ovary 5-celled, rarely 6-celled.

   Distribution: Fukien and Kwangtung.

7. **Schefflera glomerulata** Li

   Small tree 6–7 m high. Leaves 3–5-foliate; leaflets obovate-elliptic, 8–15 cm long, 3–7 cm wide, apex obtuse to acute, base cuneate, margin integrate revolute, nerves 8. Inflorescence in terminal panicles, 15–20 cm long, bract caudous; ovary 5-loculary, stigmas 5, sessile. Fruit elongate-ovoid, 5 mm long, 3 mm across, sessile.

   Distribution: Yunnan, at altitude 1000 m.

8. **Schefflera arboricola** Hayata

   A shrub, sometime scandent, about 3–4 m tall, with 7–9 foliate leaves, ovate-oblong, obtuse to acute, sometimes emarginate. Flowers in umbels racemosly arranged on the lateral branches of a terminal panicles. Leaves 12–15 cm long; leaflets petiolate, coriaceous, glabrous, obovate-oblong, 9 cm long, 4 cm wide, the apex obtuse to acute, base obtuse, margin entire, lateral nerves 5 or 6 on each side; leaflets sometimes emarginate. Floweres in umbels of 5–10-flowered; ovary 5-celled; stigmas 5. Fruits 5-angular, the disk conical, about the length of the fruits.

   Distribution: Taiwan, and Hainan, at altitude 3000 m.

9. **Schefflera bodinieri** (Levl.) Rehd.

   Shrub with 7–9-foliated leaves. Leaflets linear-lanceolate, membranaceous, glabrous, 8–15 cm long; leaflets unequal petiolulate, dark green above, glaucous beneath. Inflorescence in terminal panicles, 7–15 cm long, nearly puberulent. Floweres in racemosely-arranged umbels on the primary branches, bibracteolate; the bracteoles short, often inserted below the middle of the peduncle and often with abortive buds in the axils, the umbels many-flowered; calyx 5-dentate; Petals 5, oblong-ovate, reflexed.

Ovary 5-celled; fruit 5-angulary.

Distribution: Szechuan, Kweichow and Kwangsi, at altitude 800-1300 m.

10. **Schefflera delavayi** (Franch.) Harms.

Tree 5-8 m tall; general with 4-7-foilated leaves and acuminate, ovate-lanceolate leaflets, these densely tomentose beneath, subentire to distantly dentate or lobed; flowers sessile, densely arranged on the many lateral tomentose branches of the terminal inflorescences; Petiole, erect, tomentose soon become glabrescent; leaflets ovate-lanceolate, 12-124 cm long, 5-12 cm wide, apex acuminate, base obtuse, margins subentire to distantly and irregularly dentate or lobed, lateral nerves 7-13 on each side; calyx distinct 5-dentate, tomentose, teeth subhyaline, triangular acute to mucronate. Petals 5, thin, glabrous on both surfaces, 2 mm long; stamens 5; filaments slightly longer than the petals; ovary 5-celled. Fruits numerous, globose, 4-5 mm across, short pedicelled, the pedicels 1 mm long; the disk 3 mm across, the stigma capitate.

Distribution: Yunnan, Kweichow, Hupeh, Szechuan, and Hunan, at altitude 1500-2200 m.

Var. 1. **Schefflera delavayi** var. **ochrascens** Handel-Mazz.

Shrub 3-4 m tall. It differs from the type by having usually toothed leaves, closer and thinner pubescence and shorter racemes, and brown tomentum.

Distribution: Yunnan, Kwangtung and Kiangsi, at altitude 1700-2400 m.

11. **Schefflera dumicola** W. W. Sm.

Shrub 4-6 m high, with 5-9-foliate leaves. Lealets oblong, acuminate and with paniculate inflorescences; flowers racemosely arranged on the branches; the lower branches mostly compound. Leaflets coriaceous, glabrous, green above, glaucous beneath, narrow oblong to lanceolate, 15-24 cm long, 4-5 cm wide, apex acuminate, base cuneate, margin entire; calyx glabrous to sparsely tomentose, inconspicuously 5-dentate; petals 5, glabrous on both surfaces; stamens 5; ovary 5-celled. Fruit globose, 4-5 mm across, disk 2 mm across.

Distribution: Szechuan, Sikang and Yunnan, at altitude 2300-2500 m.

12. **Schefflera hainanensis** Merr. et Chun

Tree 10 m tall, characetrized by its long-petioled, multifoliolate leaves, the prominently acuminate entire leaflets glabrous on both surfaces and glaucous beneath, and by its 5-celled fruits being racemosely arranged on the primary branches. Leaves 16-foliolates. Leaflets chartaceous, to subcoriaceous, palmate, variable in sizes. Fruits 5-angulary, 5-locoulary, glabrous, 3 mm long.

Distribution: Hainan, at altitude 1500 m.

13. **Schefflera hypoleuca** (Kurz) Harms.

Small tree 5-10 m high, with 7-foliated leaves. Leaflets oblong or ovate, unevenly petiolate, generally glaucous beneath, with a terminal paniculate inflorescence formed by umbels. Leaves on petiolate; petiole slender, glabrous, 30 cm long. Leaflets ovate or oblong, apex acute, base rounded, margin entire or serrate or lobed, the upper branches often compound, stellate-tomentose or glabrescent. Flowers in racemosely arranged umbels; umbels many-flowered; Petals 5; ovary 5-celled; calyx stellate tomentose.

Distribution: Yunnan, at altitude 1700 m.

14. **Schefflera hoi** (Dunn) Viguier

Small tree 5-12 m high; with 3-7-foliated leaves, leaflets oblong to lanceolate, with large terminal panicles, flowers racemosely arranged on the lateral branches the lower ones sometimes compound, ferruginous-tomentose; bracts triangular; calyx inconspicuously 5-dentate; Petals 5; stamens 5; filaments same length as petals. Fruits globose, inconspicuously 5-angled.

Distribution: Yunnan, at altitude 1700 m.

15. **Schefflera hypoleucoides** Harms.

Tree 7-15 m high, with 7-foliate leaves. Leaflets oblong-lanceolate to lanceolate, acuminate. Flowers in umbels, singly or racemosely arranged on the branches. Leaves long-petiolate; Petioles glabrous to subglabrous, erect, 30 cm long. Leaves unequally petiolate. Inflorescence a large terminal panicle, tomentose when young; calyx tomentose, margin entire to subentire; Petals 5, triangular-ovate, incurved at apex; ovary 5-celled, disk flat; style 5, connate at base with tips radiating strongly reflexed.

Distribution: Yunnan, at altitude 2000 m.

16. **Schefflera khasiana** (C. B. Clarke) Viguier

A tree with 7-foiolated leaves, leaflets narrow-oblong, acuminate, and with panicled inflorescence. Flowers in umbels, racemosely arranged on the elongated compound lateral branches. Leaves generally 7-foliolate, petiolate; petiole 20 cm long. Leaflets 15-20 cm long, 6-9 cm wide, narrowly oblong; Panicles 20-30 cm long, tomentose or glabrescent. Flowers in umbels; calyx tomentulate 5-dentate; Petals 5, tomentulose without; stamens 5. Fruit globose 4 mm across.

Distribution: Yunnan.

17. **Schefflera kwangsiensis** Merr.

Shrub 2 m tall. Leaves 5-7-foliolate, petiolate. Leaflets oblong-lanceolate, 5-12 cm long, 2-4 cm wide, apex acuminate, base cuneate, margin revolute. Inflorescence terminal corymbose; calyx small, glabrous, or sparsely tomentose; petals 5; stamens 5; ovary 5-locoulary; stigmas 5, sessile.

Distribution: Kwangtung, and Kwangsi.

18. **Schefflera impressa** (Clarke) Harms.

A tree to 20 m tall, with 7-foliate leaves, short-petiolate, lanceolate to oblanceolate leaflets and large terminate; panicles with the flowers in racemosely arranged umbels on the lateral branches. Leaves generally 7-foliated, sometimes 5-foliolated, long-petiolate,

15-30 cm long, leaflets equally petiolate; inflorescence large terminal panicles 30-40 cm long, stellate-tomentose, the lower branches to 20 cm long, the bracts 5 mm long. Flowers in umbels; bracteole 2 mm long, triangular; calyx densely pubescent, 5-dentate; Petals 5, pubescent without, 3 mm long. Fruit globose, 4-6 mm across, 5-angled, 5-celled; style 5, connate into a column; stigma indistinct.

Distribution: Yunnan to Himalaya region, at altitude 3200-3330 m.

19. **Schefflera lutchense** Nakai

Small tree with robusty branchlets, 7-11 foliates and long-petiolate; Petiole 10-15 cm long. Leaflets linear-oblong to oblong-lanceolate, or elliptic, acuminate apex, base acute, margin entire incurved.

Distribution: Taiwan, at altitude 1660 m.

20. **Schefflera macrophylla** (Dunn) Viguier

Tree 5-10 m tall, with large 5-7-foliate leaves, ovate-oblong, short-acuminate leaflets, and large terminal panicles. Flowers in racemosely arranged umbels on the branches, leaves very large, generally 7-foliate, long-petiolate, coriaceous, glabrous above, white tomentose beneath, ovate-oblong, 20-55 cm long, 8-25 cm wide, apex short-acuminate, base round to cordate, margin slightly revolute and entire to obscurely serrate, midrib projecting on both surfaces, lateral nerves 8-12 on each side; petiole 5-17 cm long, glabrous. Inflorescence large panicle, 50 cm long, densely ferruginouse tomentose; flowers in umbels, racemosely arranged on the primary branches, with large bracts at the base, 1.5 cm long; peduncle 2 cm long, with triangular bracteoles at the base. Flowers small; calyx pubescent, 5-dentate petals 5, pubescent without; stamens 5; ovary 5-celled, the disk flat; styles connate into a column, about 1/2 mm long.

Distribution: Yunnan, at altitude 2100 m.

21. **Schefflera metcalfiana** Merr.

Shrub 3-5 m tall, resembling S. *hainanensis* Merr. et Chun in the many and slender petiolate leaflets and the racemosely arranged flowers. It may be readily distinguished from the latter by its shrubby habit, the much smaller size of the leaflets, the shorter petioles and the impressed veins.

Distribution: Kwangsi, Nan-ning.

22. **Schefflera multinervia** Li

Shrub 8 m tall, with 5-foliated leaves. Leaflets oblong-lanceolate, 15-17 cm long, 5-5.5 cm wide, acute apex, cuneate at base, margin integrate, lateral nerves 16-22, oblique. Inflorescence in panicles of 25 cm long; calyx sparsely puberulous or glabrous, 5-dentate; stigma 5; ovary 5-louculary.

Distribution: Yunnan.

23. **Schefflera minutistellata** Merr.

Shrub 1-13 m tall, with 7-17-foliated leaves, long-petiolate, 15-40 cm long; leaflets oblong-lanceolate 10-18 cm long, 2.5-6.5 cm wide, apex acuminate, base rotundate or acute, margin integrate, nerves 8-12. Inflorescence terminal; panicles, 30-40 cm long;

calyx stellate-pubescent, 5-dentate; Petals 5, stamens 5, filaments 3-4 mm long; ovary 5-loculary; styles 2 mm long; stigma capitate.

Distribution: Yunnan, Kweichow, Kwangtung and Kwangsi, at altitude 1600 m.

24. **Schefflera producta** (Dunn) Viguier

Shrub 1.5-3 m tall, with 5-11-foliolate leaves. Leaflets ovate-lanceolate, 8-15 cm long, 3-5 cm wide, lower ones slightly smaller than the medium ones, the apex long-acuminate, base broadly acute to rounded, the margins sparsely serrate, revolute, lateral nerves 10-16 on each side, distinct above, projecting beneath. Flower umbels racemosely arranged; umbels many-flowered; calyx densely tomentose, the margin 5-dentate; ovary 5-celled.

Distribution: Yunnan and Kweichow, at altitude 1700 m.

25. **Schefflera taiwanianum** (Hayata) Nakai

Heptapleurum racemosum Hayata

Shrub with robusty branchlets. Leaflets 5-7-foliolate, oblong to oblanceolate, 12-18 cm long, 4-6 cm wide, acuminate at apex, cuneate at base, entire margin; petiole 2 cm long, glabrous. Flowers in terminal and lateral racemes; often epiphytic.

Distribution: Taiwan, at altitude 1833-2833 m.

26. **Schefflera octophylla** (Lour.) Harms.

Shrub 5 m tall, with 6-8-foliolate leaves. Leaflets oblong, 10-13 cm long, 5 cm wide, acute apex, broadly cuneate at base, entire margin, dark green above, pale green glaucous beneath, subcoriaceous; petioles unequal in length, 1-5 cm long; terminal flowering panicles 30-40 cm long, loosely few-flowered, calyx pubescent; ovary 5-8-celled; Petals 5, fleshy, stamens 5, style column very short but in distinct column, less than 1 mm long; stigma capitate.

Distribution: Yunnan, Kwangsi, Fukien, Kwangtung and Taiwan, at altitude 1080 m.

27. **Schefflera sweliensis** W. W. Sm.

Shrub or small tree 3-10 m tall, with 7-11-foliolate leaves, oblanceolate, long-acuminate leaflets, and large terminal panicles, with the flowers racemosely arranged on the branches. Leaves 7-11, sometimes fewer, petiolate, leaflets narrowly oblanceolate, 15 cm long, 4 cm wide, long-acuminate, at apex, narrowly cuneate at base, entire, nerves 7-9 on both sides. Inflorescence terminal panicles 20-40 cm long, paniculate at base, racemose at apex, white tomentose at first soon becoming glabrescent, bract triangular, to 5 mm long; calyx tomentose to glabrous, 5-dentate; Petals 5, glabrous on both surfaces; ovary 5-celled. Fruit globose 5 mm across, indistinctly 5-angular.

Distribution: Yunnan, at altitude 2000 m.

8. **Schefflera wangii** Li

Small tree 5 m tall, with 7-foliolate leaves. Leaflets oblong-elliptic, 13 cm long, 6 cm wide, acuminate at apex, attenuate at base, margin revolute. It is closely related to *S. chinensis* (Dunn) Li, which differs from other Chinese species of the genus in the fruits being arranged in compact heads. It is distinguished from the later by its 7 leaflets with entire margins, more ascending lateral veins, and tertiary veins conspicuous beneath; the leaflets generally the broadest above the middle. Moreover the heads are smaller and with fewer fruits and arranged in subterminal racemes. In other species, the heads are arranged in large terminal panicles with the branches mostly compound.

Distribution: Yunnan, at altitude 2700 m.

29. **Schefflera wardii** Marquand et Shaw

Shrub 2–3 m tall, with large 3–5–foliolate leaves. Leaflets ovate–oblong, remotely serrate and tomentose beneath, and with large tomentose panicle. Flowers racemosely arranged on the lateral branches. Leaves long-petiolate; petiole 50 cm long, glabrous. Leaflets coriaceous, glabrous above, densely stellate–tomentose beneath, ovate oblong, 20–35 cm long, 10–15 cm wide, apex broadly acuminate, base rounded, margin remotely serrate toward the upper part, the lateral nerves 10–14 on each side. Inflorescence in large panicle, densely white-tomentose. Flowers small, racemosely arranged on the lateral branches; calyx tomentose, 5–dentate; Petals 5, tomentose outside; stamens 5; ovary 5–celled, the disk flat; style connate into a column.

Distribution: Yunnan, at altitude 2500 m.

30. **Schefflera yunnanensis** Li

Scandent shrub, 3–10 m tall, epiphyte. Leaves 5–foliolate, small petiolate. Leaflets coriaceous, glabrous, obovate–oblong, 5.5 cm long, 2.5–3 cm wide, apice acuminate, base cuneate or rounded, margin integrate. Inflorescence corymbose-paniculate. Fruits ovoid, pentagonous–glandulary punctate, 4 mm long, 2.5 mm broad; stigma sessile.

Distribution: Yunnan, at altitude 1900 m.

31. **Schefflera venulosa** (Wight et Arn.) Harms

Shrub sometimes scandent and occasionally epiphytic, with 5–7–foliolate leaves; leaflets elliptic and acute with large terminal panicle. Flowers in umbels, racemosely arranged on lateral branches. Leaves 5–rarely 7–foliolate, petiolate; calyx glabrous, margin entire or subentire; Petals 5, thin glabrous on both surfaces; stamens 5; ovary 5–celled; stigma 5, sessile. Fruit ovoid, 3–4 mm long, 5–angulary, disk conical, 1/4 the length of the fruit.

Distribution: Yunnan and Kwangsi, at altitude 2300 meters.

Family 56. Cornaceae Lk.
(See orig. text pages 872–873)

Genus (1) Cornus L. (See orig. text page 874)

1. **Cornus alsophila** W. W. Sm.

2. **Cornus capitata** Wall. (See orig. text pages 874–875)

> Var. 1. **Cornus capitata** var. **mollis** Rehd.

> Var. 2. **Cornus capitata** var. **angustata** (Chun) Fang

> > Tree 10 m high. Branchlets dark gray, nodded, smooth, lenticellate

glabrous. Leaves opposite, elliptic-oblong, 8 cm long, 3.5 cm wide, acuminate apice, cuneate at base, entire margin, dark shining green above, pale green, glabrous below. Fruit solitary, axillary, red, globose head, 1 cm in diameter; pedicels 6 cm long, red, glabrous.

Distribution: Szechuan and Kiangsi, at altitude 500-800 m.

3. **Cornus chinensis** Wang (See orig. text page 875)

4. **Cornus controversa** Hemsl. (See orig. text pages 876-877)

5. **Cornus ferruginea** Wu

Tree 6 m tall. Leaves opposite, petiolate, oblong or elliptic-oblong, 9 cm long, 3-3.5 cm wide, apice minutely acuminate, base acute, margin entire, incurved, dark green glabrous above, ferruginous brownish hairy beneath especially dense hairy along the midrib and veins below, sub-coriaceous; petiole 15 mm long, deeply ferruginous hairy. Fruit solitary, terminal, black head, 1 cm in diameter; fruiting pedicel 6 cm long, reddish pubescent.

Distribution: Kwangtung and Kwangsi, at altitude 1000 m.

6. **Cornus fordii** Hemsl.

Cornus wilsonianae Wang.

Tree 5-10 m high. Leaves opposite, ovate-elliptic to lanceolate-oblong, 5-12 cm long, 4-5 cm wide, acute apice, ovate to obtuse-cuneate at base, entire margin, dark shining green above light glaucous, glabrous beneath, veins 4 pairs or 3 pairs runing 45 degrees upwardly from the midrib, subcoriaceous; petiole 3-4 cm long, flattened, glabrous. Flowers in terminal panicles. Fruit berry-like, round, 7 mm in diameter, black; pedicels slender, 2 mm long.

Distribution: Kwangtung, Hupeh.

7. **Cornus hemsleyi** Schneid. et Wang (See orgi. text page 877)

8. **Cornus honkongensis** Hemsl.

9. **Cornus hupehensis** Fang

Shrub 8 m high. Leaves obovate-oblong, 8-10 cm long, 4-5 cm wide, short acuminate at apex, broad-cuneate to rounded at base, entire incurved margin, lustrous shining green above, light glaucous and glabrous beneath, sub-coriaceous; petiole 12 mm long, reddish, glabrous. Fruits in terminal and axillary small heads, with persistent bracts; fruiting pedicels 2-6 cm long, pubescent. Flowers white. Fruit (immmature) green.

Distribution: Hupeh.

0. **Cornus kweichowensis** Li

Tree 10 m tall. Leaves opposite, petiolate, chartaceous, ovate to oblong-ovate, 5-8 cm long, 2-4 cm wide, long-acuminate, base cuneate, margin entire; petiole adpressed strigose, 7-12 mm long. Inflorescences in dense corymbose, terminal, 5 cm long; peduncle 2-2.5 cm long. Flowers white, 5 mm in diameter, calyx dense strigose, margin distinct 4-dentate; petals 4 lanceolate, acute, 2.5 mm long, 1 mm wide; stamens 4; filament 2 mm long; ovary 2-loculary.

Distribution: Kweichow.

11. **Cornus kousa** Buerg. (See orig. text page 878)

      Var. 1. Cornus kousa var. **chinensis** Osborn

12. **Cornus macrophylla** Wall. (See orig. text pages 878-879)

13. **Cornus monbeigii** Hemsl.

Shrub 3 m high. Leaves opposite, petiolate, orbicular-cordate, 4-9 cm long, acuminate-acute apice, base cordate to rotundate, nerves white-tomentose and ferrginose-puberulent, 7-9; cymes terminate, minute stipitate. Flowers dense; calyx and petals villosulus; Petals ovate-oblong.

Distribution: Yunnan, at altitude 3200 m.

14. **Cornus oblonga** Wall. (See orig. text pages 879-880)

      Var. 1. Cornus oblonga var. **kiukiangensis** Fang

Shrub 5 m high. Branchlets dark gray, smooth, lenticelled. Leaves opposite, oblanceolate, 7 cm long, 2.5 cm wide, acuminate-acute at apex, cuneate at base, margin entire, lustrous shining green above, pale green glabrous below, thick, coriaceous; petiole 2 cm long, glabrous; young branchlets angular, reddish, glabrous. Flowers white in terminal panicles; peduncles angular, thick, short, purplish red.

Distribution: Kiangsi and Kiukiang, at altitude 1500 m.

      Var. 2. Cornus oblonga f. **pilosula** Li

This form is almost the same with the species except that this form has its leaves with very densely hairy beneath.

Distribution: Yunnan and Szechuan, at altitude 1900-2100 m.

15. **Cornus officinalis** S. et Z.

      Cornus officinale Nakai (See orig. text pages 880-881)

16. **Cornus poliophylla** Schneider et Wangerin (See orig. text page 881)

17. **Cornus rehderiana** Fang

Small tree 6-8 m high; bark greenish, smooth, tight, covered with dense roun projections. Leaves opposite, obovate, 9 cm long, 5 cm wide, short acuminate apice cuneate at base, margin incurved, lustrous dark green above, pale green beneath, sut coriaceous; petiole 1 cm long, glabrous. Flowers in terminal globose heads with petal-like bracts persistent at the base; fruiting pedicel 7 cm long, with 4-angulars in mediately below the heads, the rest portion of the pedicel is round and reddish pubesce all the way.

Distribution: Szechuan and Yunnan, at altitude 1100 m.

18. **Cornus szechuanensis** Fang

Tree 12 m high. Branchlets slender, dark gray, lenticellate. Leaves obovate, 7 long, 4.5 cm wide, short-acuminate apex, cuneate to rounded at base, margin sligh incurved, deep shining green above, light glaucous and glabrous below, subcoriaceou petiole 1-2 cm long, whitish pubescent. Flowers white, solitary, terminal, in globu heads subtended with 4 petal–like bracts, which are obovate, 2.5 cm long, 2 cm wide, acuminate apice, cuneate to rounded at base; flowering pedicels, 8 cm long, whitish pubescent. Fruit an aggregated globular head of 2 cm in diameter, black, on the reddish pedicel.

Distribution: Szechuan, at altitude 1300–2300 m.

19. **Cornus taiwanensis** Kaneh.

Tree 7–13 m high. Branchlets dark purple, smooth, minutely lenticellate. Leaves obovate–oblong, 10 cm long, 6 cm wide, broadest below the middle and tapering upward to a broad acute apex, rounded at base, margin entire; nerves 10 pairs running from the midrib straightly upward, very prominently elevated below and slightly impreessed above, glabrous on both surfaces, subcoriaceous; Petioles round, stout 2–4 cm long, brownish glabrous. Flowers in terminal short panicles, white, small, glabrous.

Distribution: Taiwan, at altitude 833–1000 m.

20. **Cornus ulotricha** Schneider et Wangerin (See orig. text pages 881–883)

21. **Cornus walteri** Wang.

22. **Cornus wilsoniana** Wang

23. **Cornus yunnanensis** Li

Tree 5 m high. Leaves opposite, chartaceous, broad–ovate or ovate–elliptic, 9–11 cm long, 4–5.5 cm wide, long–acuminate at apex, broadly cuneate or sub–rounded at base.

This species is closely related to *Cornus macrophylla* Wall, from which it differs in the fewer lateral nerves and the small short–pedicellate flowers, which are more or less crowded in very small corymbs produced on short axillary branches.

Distribution: Yunnan.

4. – 29. (See orig. text pages 883–884)

Subdivision Ⅱ. Metachlamydeae Engl.

or Sympetalae A. Br.

(See orig. text page 884)

Order XXII Ericales

Family 57. Ericaceae D C.

(See orig. text page 885)

Genus (1) Rhododendron Linn. (See orig. text pages 885–886)

1. **Rhododendron achranthum** Balf. f. et. Sm.

Small shrub 1 m high; branchlets very short, densely scaly; leaf–bud scales early deciduous. Leaves oblong–elliptic 2 cm long, 1 cm broad, densely scaly on both surfaces, scales below much overlapping, brown and green; petioles scaly. Inflorescence terminal, 3–flowered, flower–stalks very short scaly. Flowers magenta–red dull green outside. Calyx well developed, 5 mm long, lobes broadly elliptic, densely scaly except towards the purplish hair–fringed margin. Corolla openly funnel–shaped, 1.5 cm long, scaly outside the lobes, shortly villose within. Stamens 5 or 6, exserted, villose towards the base. Ovary densely scaly, style longer than the stamens, glabrous.

Distribution: Yunnan, altitude 4000–4300 m.

2. **Rhododendron acraium** Balf. f. et. Smith.

Shrub 1–2 m high; branchlets scaly; leaf–bud scales early deciduous. Leaves aromatic oblong–elliptic, mucronate, about 2 cm long, densely covered below with short flaky scales, leaf–stalk 3 mm long, lobes scaly outside, but not or only slightly ciliate. Corolla narrow tubular, 1.3 cm long, not scaly outside, villose in the throat. Stamens 5 included in the tube, minutly pubescent near the base; ovary scaly, style very short, turbinate, glabrous, Capsule 1 cm long, scaly.

Distribution: Northeastern Burma, through Yunnan and Szechuan to Northeastern Asia, altitude 4000–4300. m

3. **Rhododendron** aednogynum Diels

Shrub 3 m tall. branchlets bright green, clad with vestiges of hairs. Leaves leathery, oblong-ovate to oblong-lanceolate, 5–12 cm long, 2–4 cm broad, apex acute or acuminate, base rounded somewhat cordate; upper surface conves, dark green, rugolose, glabrous but with vestige of juvenile hairs in the grooves of midrib, eglandular, nerves 14 on each side, grooved, under surface covered by a thick woolly, tawny, olive indumentum, midrib prominent, other ventaion concealed; petiole 2 cm long, glabrescent, eglandular, inflorescence in umbel, terminal, 12 cm long, rachis tomentose; pedicels 1.5–2 cm long, densely glandular and tomentose, pale reddish; calyx large, cut to the base into 5 yellowish green, unequal oblong or elliptic lobes, clad with clavate-stalked glands ciliate; corolla fleshy, funnel-campanulate, white shaded rose at base or magenta-tint, marked with many crimson spots; lobes 5 emarginate crenulate; stamens 10, unequal, filaments white, pubescent at base; capsule oblong-oval, 1–1.5 cm long, 8 mm broad, deeply grooved surrounded by persistent calyx.

Distribution: N. Yunnan, altitude 3350–4000 m.

4. **Rhododendron** aednophorum Balf. f. et Sm.

Tree 3–4 m high. Leaves oblanceolate, 8 cm. long, 3 cm wide, acute apex, broad cuneate at base, entire revolute margin, dark green smooth above, yellowish wooly with concealed veins beneath., leathery, thick, coriaceous; petiole 3 cm long, angulary glangular stout, pubescent. Flowers pink, terminally clustered. Capsule oblong, 2 cm long, 1 cm broad, set in a long-campanulate lobed calyx, woody, purple, pubescent; pedicels round, erect, stout, 2–4 cm long, glandular, purplish pubescent.

Distribution: Yunnan, altitude 4600–4700 m.

5. **Rhododendron** aednopodum Franch.

Shrub 1–4 m high. Branchlets clad with thin gray tomentose, more or less glandular. Leaves oblong-lanceolate, 20 cm long, 2.5 cm wide, acute or acuminate at apex, wedge-shaped at base, upper surface dark green, smooth, glabrous or vestiges of tomentum, primary veins 12–14 on each side, not conspicuous; petiole 2–3 cm long, clad like the young shoots, cylindric, not grooved. Inflorescence in loose rancemes–corymb of 6–8 flowers, rachis 3.5 cm long, tomentose; pedicels 3–4 cm long, glandular. Corolla, 4 cm long, funnel-campanulate, pale rose, more or less spotted, puberlous within at the base, outside glabrous; lobes 5, rounded; calyx split into 5 unequal ovate parts or pointed membranaceous, glandular on the back and gland ciliate; stamens 10, unequal, 2.5–3.5 cm long, filaments densely hairy over lower quarter; Pistil 4.5 cm long, ovary 5 mm long, densely clad with long-stalked glands which obscure a short non-glandular pubescence, 5-chambered, calyx persistent; style slender, glabrous. Capsule oblong-cylindric, 1.5 cm long, 7 mm broad, glandular, 5–6 chambered., calyx persistent.

Distribution; Eastern Szechuan and Hupeh, altitude 1700–2600 m

6. **Rhododendron** aednostemonum Balf. f. et. Sm.

Tree 5 m tall. Bark smooth, glabrous, whitish gray. Leaves oblanceolate, 8–16 cm long, 2–4 cm wide, acute at apex, cuneate at base, undulate incurved margin, dark green above, pale green, glabrous beneath, coriaceous; petiole 2-3 cm long, glandular cylindric, glabrous. Flowers white, in terminal racemes; corolla 4 cm long 2.5 cm broad, broad-obvate above 1/2 and tapering on the lower part, glabrous.

Distribution: Yunnan, altitude 2300 m

7. **Rhododendron admirabile** Balf. et Sm.

Shrub 3.5 m high. Branchlets whitish, smooth. Leaves broad-lanceolate, 15 cm long, 3 cm wide, acuminate at apex, margin cartilaginea, subcuneate at base; petiole 1.5 cm long. Inflorescence in umbellate-racemose, 10-flowered, corolla tubular campanulate, 4.5 cm; stamens 10 unequal.

Distribution: Szechuan.

8. **Rhododendron adoxum** Balf. et Forrest

Shrub. Leaves oblong-ovate, 11 cm long, 5 cm wide, apex rotundate mucronate, base rotundate unequal, olive-purpuracens above, sordid purpuracens below; petiole 2.5 cm long, glabrescent. Umbels 10-12-flowered, pedicels 2 cm long, glandular, calyx obsolete free, glandular; corolla white, campanulate, 4 cm glabrous, 7-lobed, lobes obovate, emarginate.

Distribution: Yunnan.

9. **Rhododendron adroserum** Balf. et Forrest

Shrub 3.6 m tall. Leaves obovate-oblong 11 cm long, 3 m wide, apex rotundate attenuate-acuminate, margin recurved, base obtuse subcuneate. Inflorescence in racemose-umbels, 10-flowered; calyx 5-lobed, lobes rotundate or ovate; corolla campanulate, 5-lobed, lobes broad-emarginate; stamens 10, unequal, shorter than the corolla.

Distribution: Western Yunnan.

10. **Rhododendron aechmophyllum** Balf. et Forrest

Shrub 1 m tall. Leaves ridged lanceolate, 5.5 cm long, 1.5 cm wide, acuminate mucronate apex, cuneate at base, margin cartilagineous. Flowers pink, in umbels solitary, terminal 4-5-flowered; corolla 5, oval-shaped, 1.2 cm long, 8 mm broad; bracteoles linear, pillose; stamens 10, unequal; filments peberulous. Capsule cylindric, 1.5 cm long, 4 mm broad, lepdote.

Distribution: S.W Szechuan, altitude 3700-4000 m

11. **Rhododendron aganniphum** Balf. et Ward.

Shrub 1 m tall. Leaves oblong or ovate-oblong, 6-9 cm long, 2.5-4 cm wide, apex broadly-acute, mucronulate, base roundate, slightly rugulose under surface yellowish-white and clad with a compact persistent uniform indumentum; petiole 8 mm long, glabrous. Inflorescence umbel, 12-flowered; calyx short fleshy cup with undulate margin or with 5 small teeth; corolla funnel-campanulate, 3.5 cm long, white or white flushed rose, spotted crimson, lobes 5, unequal, crenulate emarginate; stamens 10, sparsely pubescent at base; capsule oblong, straight, 1.4 cm long, 6 mm broad.

Distribution: S.W. Tibet and N.W. Yunnan, altitude 3700-5000 m

12. **Rhododendron agastum** Balf et Sm.

Shrub 3-7 m tall. With thick branches, branchlets more or less glandular. Leaves oblong to oblong-elliptic or oblong-obovate, 6-12.5 cm long, 2-4.5 cm broad, apex broad obtuse to rounded, upper surface olive-green, glandular, lower surface pale olive t fawn, clad with thin film-like indumentum ; petiole 1.5 cm long, slightly grooved , clad with vestiges of short glands and floccose hairs. Inflorescence a raceme umbel, 20-flowered, rachis 2–2.5 cm long, glandular and thinly floccose; calyx lobes 5–7, glandular and gland-fringed; corolla tubular-campanulate, 5 cm long, rose-colored, marked with crimson basal blotch, which may break into lines or spots, lobes 5–7, rounded, emarginate; stamens 10–14 uneuqal, 2.7–3.7 cm long, filamnets pubescent at base.

Distribution: W. Yunnan, altitude 2000–3000 m

13. **Rhododendron agglutinatum** Balf. et Forrest

Shrub 1–2 m high. Leaves leathery, oblong-oval or broadly obovate, 4–7.5 cm long , 2–3.5 cm broad; apex obtuse to sub rounded, base obtuse truncate or sometimes cordate, upper surface glabrous when mature, under surface tawny clad with agglutinate indumentum, the surface not a glossy pellicle, midrib prominent, more or less agglutinate hairs or glabrescent and then yellowish; primary veins 15 on each side; petiole 1.5 cm long often yellowish glabrescent. Inflorescence a compact umbel of about 10–15-flowers; rachis 5 mm long, puberulous; calyx 1 mm long, with 5 obtuse shortly ciliate lobes; corolla funnel-campanulate, white, creamy-white or white tinged rose, lobes 5, emarginate; stamens 10, unequal, 1–2 cm long.

Distribution: S.W. Szechuan, Tibet, and Kansu, altitude 3400–4300 m

14. **Rhododendron aiolopeplum** Balf. et Forrest

Shrub 2–3 m high, branchlets clad with thin grey tomentum. Leaves lanceolate or oblanceolate, 5–10 cm long, 1.5–2.5 cm wide; apex pointed, base obtuse to tapered, upper surface glabrous or rugose, midrib grooved, lower surface covered with indumentum. Inflorescence in short racemes-umbel of 8–10 flowered, rachis 8 mm long, puberulous; calyx very small, 1 mm long, with 5 small rounded lobes; corolla campanulate, 2.5 cm long, white faintly flushed rose, without spot or blotch, lobes 5, emarginate; stamens 10, unequal, 1–2 cm long all shorter than corolla, filaments puberulous at the base.

Distribution: Yunnan, at altitude 4000 m.

15. **Rhododendron alertsenianum** G. Forrest

Shrub 2 m high. Leaves narrow oblong or sub-lanceolate, 6–9.5 cm long, 1.5–2 cm broad, apex obtuse, base obtuse, upper surface glabrescent with vestiges of juvenile tomentose; petiole 1 cm long, glabrescent. Inflorescence an umbel of 5–6 flowers; pedicels 1–18 cm long, rufous floccose, eglandular; calyx fleshy cup-like, 4 mm long, lobes 5, short, rounded; corolla bright crimson-rose, without markings; stamens 10, unequals, filaments glabrous.

Distribution: Yunnan, at altitude 3300 m.

16. **Rhododendron alpicola** Rehd. et Wils.

Shrub 1 m high. Branchlets short and intricate, densely scaly. Leaf scales early deciduous. Leaves elliptic, 8 mm long, densely scaly on both surfaces, scales below overlapping; leaf-stalk scaly. Inflorescence terminal, 1-flowered, flower-bud-scales early deciduous, stalks very short. Flower lavender-purple; calyx cupular, densely scaly on the margin; corolla funnel shaped, not scaly outside; stamens 10, exserted, pubescent towards the base; ovary scaly, shorter than the stamens, pubescent in the lower part.

Distribution: W. Szechuan, at altitude 400–5000 m.

17. **Rhododendron alutaceum** Balf. et Smith

Shrub 4 m tall. Leaves thick leathery, oblong or broadly lanceolate, 8–14 cm long, 2–3.5 cm wide; apex acute or short acuminate, base obtuse or rounded and cordate, lower surface dull buff woolly tomentum, the hairs in the young leaf mixed with glands, midrib raised, the rest of venations concealed; petiole 1–15 cm long. Inflorescence a racemose umbel of about 12 flowers, rachis about 1.8 cm long, sparsely glandular; calyx minute with undulate lobed margin with a few glands; corolla rose spotted, crimson and blotched at base, lobes 5, 1.5 cm long, 2 cm broad.

Distribution: N. W. Yunnan, at altitude 400 m.

18. **Rhododendron ambiguum** Hemsl.

Shrub, closely branched, flowering twigs rather slender and naked except for a few glands. Leaves persistent, scattered, petiolate, lanceolate, acuminate, with a subglobose apical gland, rounded at the base, at first closely glandular scaly on both sides, but soon become naked above, pale beneath between close-set scales, which at first yellow but soon becoming black. Corymbs umbellate, terminal, usually 5–7-flowered.

Distribution: W. Szechuan, at altitude 2300–2800 m.

19. **Rhododendron amesiae** Rehd. et Wils.

Small shrub. Branchlets closely scaly. Leaves ovate-elliptic, bluntly mucronate at the apex, rounded at the base, rahter densely scaly and reticulate above, densely scaly below, leaf-stalks bristly with hairs on the margin. Inflorescence 2–3-flowered, terminal, flower-stalks scaly. Flower purple; calyx very short, densely scaly outside; corolla 5-lobed, tube not scaly outside or only slightly and loosely so; stamens exserted, 10, pubescent in the lower part; ovary densely scaly, 5-celled; style glabrous.

Distribution: Szechuan, at altitude 2300–3100 m.

20. **Rhododendron amundsenianum** Handel-Mazz.

Shrub 30 cm high. Leaves elliptic or obovate-elliptic, 5–12 mm long, 6–9 mm wide, apex rotundate, cuneate at base. Inflorescence in umbels of 3 flowers.

Distribution: Szechuan, at altitude 1300–1400 m.

21. **Rhododendron anhweiense** Wilson

Shrub 1 m tall. Leaves elliptic-oblong, 5 cm long, 2 cm wide, acute apex, cuneate a base, incurved margin, lustrous olive-green above, pale green, pubescent below, coriaceous; petiole 1 cm long, glandular.

Distribution: Anhwei, Hwang-Shan.

22. **Rhododendron anisocalyx** Balf. et Forrest

Shrub 2–3 m tall. Leaves oblong, 10 cm long, 4 cm wide, apex truncate and slightl mucronate, broadly obtuse or narrow truncate at base, entire margin, dark smooth gree glossy above, brownish purple on the underneath, very thick, coriaceous; petiole 1-2 cm long, stout, glabrous, glandular. Flowers yellowish pink, in terminal cymes; calyx 5-lobed, similar color with the corolla; corolla 5 cm long, 4 cm broad, funnel-shaped, shallowly-lobed, glabrous, pedicel 2 cm long, brown, glabrous.

Distribution: North-west Yunnan.

23. **Rhododendron annae** Franch.

Shrub 1-2 m tall. Branchlets glandular, branches below in florescence 4 mm in diameter. Leaves ridged, leathery, narrow elongate-lanceolate, 7-11 cm long, 1.5-3 cm broad, apex acute or acuminate, base obtuse, upper surface bright green, under surface paler; petiole 12 cm long, glabrescent. Inflorescence a racemose umbel of 10 flowers, rachis 2.5 cm long, floccose and glandular; corolla cup-shaped or openly campanulate, creamy-white flushed more or less rose; stamens 10, unequal.

Distribution: Kweichow, Yunnan and Kwangsi, at altitude 1500 m.

24. **Rhododendron anthopogonoides** Maxim.

Shrub densely scaly and slightly pubescent. Leaves broadly elliptic, subcordate at base, obtuse mucronate at apex, 2.5 cm long, 2 cm broad, closely covered with brown overlapping scales below. Inflorescence terminal, capitate, several-flowered; calyx large, lobes broadly-oblong, slightly ciliate; corolla narrow tubular, 1.5 cm long, densely villose inside; stamens 5, included, pubescent.

Distribution: Kansu, Tsing Hai, and Tibet, at altitude 3400 m.

25. **Rhododendron anthosphaerum** Diels

Shrub or small tree 6-10 m high. Branchlets clad with clavate glands and hairs; older branches glabrous. Leaves broadly lanceolate or oblanceolate, 8-14 cm long, 2.5-5 cm wide, apex acute, margin undulate, base obtuse, upper surface glabrous but with vestiges of hairs and glands; petiole 2 cm long, stout, grooved above, clad with vestiges of glands. Inflorescence in umbels, with 12 flowers, calyx cupular, 1 mm long; corolla, tubular-campanulate, 4-5 cm long, rose-magenta with a few markings of dark crimson and a basal black crimson blotch, puberulous inside, lobes 5-7, 2 cm long, 2-2.5 cm broad, rounded, emarginate; stamens 10-14, unequal, 3-4 cm long, filaments more or less puberulous at base.

Distribution: N. W. Yunnan, at altitude 3000-3300 m.

26. **Rhododendron aperanthum** Balf. et Forrest

Shrub 1-2 m tall. Leaves oblong or oblanceolate, 4 cm long, 1.5 cm wide, blunt to rounded at apex, cuneate at base, incurved margin, dark green above, pubescent below Flowers pink.

Distribution: Yunnan, at altitude 4000 m.

27. **Rhododendron apiculatum** Rehd. et Wils.

Shrub 2 m high. Branchlets sparingly scaly. Leaves broadly elliptic, rounded cordate at base, acute triangular-apiculate at the apex, scaly below. Inflorescence terminal, 3-flowered, slightly scaly near the apex. Flower dark purple; calyx shortly lobed, fringed with scales; corolla 5-lobed not scaly outside; stamens 10, slightly pubescent at the lower part; ovary 5-celled, densely scaly.

Distribution: W. Szechuan, at altitude 2900-3100 m.

28. **Rhododendron apodectum** Balf. et Sm.

Shrub 1-3 m tall. Branchlets with thin white indumentum, no gland. Leaves leathery oblong to oblong-elliptic or broadly obovate, 4-7 cm long, 2.5-3.5 cm broad, apex rounded or obtuse, base rounded or obtuse, Inflorescence in terminal umbel of 2-3 flowers; pedicels 1.2 cm long, sparsely tomentose, no gland; calyx 1 cm long, crimson-yellowish, fleshy, lobes 5, unequal, more or less rounded, with undulate fringed hairs on the margins; corolla tubular-campanulate, fleshy, 3-5 cm long, deep rose crimson shaded to orange at the base, lobes 5, rounded, emarginate, 1 cm long, 1.2 cm broad; stamens 10, unequal, filaments pubescent at base. Capsule shortly oblong, truncate, more or less tomentose.

Distribution: W. Yunnan, at altitude 3300-3400 m.

29. **Rhododendron araiophyllum** Balf. et Sm.

Slender branched shrub, 3-5 m tall. Leaves lanceolate, 5-11 cm long, 2-3 cm broad apex acuminate, margin undulate, not roughened, base cuneate, upper surface glaucous, smooth, glabrous except for vestiges of flocks; petiole 1 cm long, glabrous. Inflorescence a racemose umbel of 8 flowers, rachis 1.5 cm long, more or less clad with floccose hairs, pedicels slender 1.5 cm long, calyx cupular, fleshy, 1.5 mm long, glabrous, lobes 5, siminulate or ovate, outside glabrous, margin ciliate; corolla openly campanulate to cup-shaped, 3.5 cm long, white or white-rose outside and with a basal crimson blotch and few or many within, lobes 5, 1.4 cm long, 2 cm broad, rounded, emarginate, subcrenulate; stamens 10, unequal. Capsule narrow oblong-cylindric, straight or very slightly curved, 1-15 cm long, 4 mm broad, brownish, wrinkled, glabrous, 5 - 6 - chambered.

Distribution: W. Yunnan, at altitude 3000-3300 m.

30. **Rhododendron araeliaforme** Balf. et Forrest

Shrub 1-3 m tall. Leaves long-petiolate, 16 cm long, 4 cm wide, oblong - ovate, margin incurved, base broadly rotundate, coriaceous, ridged. Flowers yellow in terminal racemes. Fruit cylindric, 3 cm long, 2.5 cm in diameter, 5-valved, woody, brown, glabrous; pedicel 4 cm long, erect, stout, glabrous.

Distribution: Yunnan and Tibet.

31. **Rhododendron arboreum** W. W. Sm.

Shrub. Leaves lanceolate, 9 cm long, 2 cm wide, acute at apex, narrow cuneate at base, entire margin, dark green glabrous above, pale green below. Inflorescence in terminal racemes. Flowers purple, slightly pubescent outside; corolla blood - red, without spot, bud-scale, rachis, pedicels and calyx wooly or silky-haired.

Of unusual small-leaved form, which is a distinct alpine form. It somewhat resembles *R. peramoeum* Balf. et Foresst.

Distribution: Tibet, at altitude 2330 m.

32. Rhododendron argipeplum Balf. et Cooper

A shrub 3 m high. Flowers very deep pink, no spots.

This species differs from *R. barbatum* Wall. by having a persistent whitish indumentum on the underside of the leaves.

Distribution: Southern Tibet, at altitude 3330 m.

33. Rhododendron argyrophyllum Franch.

A large shrub 2-7 m high, branchlets covered with thin white to grey scarly tomentum, becoming later glabrous; leaves oblong-lanceolate, 6-13 cm long, 1.5-3 cm wide; apex acuminate, commonly reflexed, base tapered to cuneate to subrounded; upper surface smooth, at first light green, later darker at maturity glabrous, veins 14 on each side of the midrib; petiole 1-1.5 cm long, flattish above, deeply grooved, glabrescent. Inflorescence a loose racemose umbel of 6-10 flowers, rachis 1 cm long, rufous tomentose; calyx small 1-2 mm long, with 5 broadly triangular teeth; corolla campanulate, 3-3.5 cm long, narrowed at base, white or white-flusged rose, spotted within deeper pink or rose on the upper part; stamens 12-14, unequal, 1.5-2.5 cm long, shorter than corolla; filaments hairy at the base; capsule narrowly cylindric, 2-3 cm long, 6 mm broad, straight or slightly curved, 9-chambered.

Distribution: Sikang, Yunnan and Szechuan, at altitude 2200-2500 m.

Var. 1. Rhododendron argyrophyllum var. **cupulare** Rehd. et Wils.

This variety differs from the type chiefly in its glabrous branches, smaller leaves inclined to be rounded at the base and in the broader campanulate or cup-shaped corolla. It is similar to *R. hypoglaucum* Hemsl. but differs in its ovary being covered densely with white hairs. Flowers pink.

Distribution: W. Szechuan, at altitude 2300-2800 m.

34. Rhododendron arizelum Balf. et Forrest

Robust shrub or small tree of 6 m high, with thick gnarled branches, branchlets covered with greyish tomentum; Leaves oval or obovate or oblanceolate, 15 cm long, 8 cm wide; apex rounded or notched or retuse, base obtuse or slightly cordate, upper surface dark green, rugulose, under surface clad with thick persistent cinnamon or brown indumentum, primary veins 11-14 on each side of the midrib, more or less concealed by the leaf-indumentum; petiole 2.5-3 cm long, cylindric. Inflorescence a raceme umbel of 15-25-flowers; rhachis 2.5-3.5 cm long, cinnamon tomentose; Pedicel 2.5 cm long, fawn-tomentose, obliquely thickened below calyx; corolla obliquely campanulate; white creamy-yellow tinged rose, with crimson blotches at base, 4.5 cm long, lobes 8; stamens 16; pistil 4 cm long; ovary conoid, truncate, 1 cm long, 7 mm broad, rusty tomentose with fasciate hairs, 12-15-chambered, style glabrous. Capsule oblong cylindric, slightly curved, 3 cm long, 7 mm broad, rusty tomentose or greyish. Flowers bright red.

Distribution: W. Yunnan and S. E. Tibet, at altitude 3330 m.

35. **Rhododendron artosequaneum** Balf. et Forrest

Shrub 1-3 m high; annual branchlets very short laxy scaly. Leaves broadly ovate or almost rounded, deeply cordate at the base, rounded to an obtuse mucro at the apex, 3-4.5 cm long, 2-4 cm wide, not scaly above, rather densely so below, lateral veins scarsely visible; petiole 1-1.5 cm long, slightly scaly. Inflorescence terminal, 3-4-flowered, umbellate, pedicels 12 mm long, very slightly scaly. Flowers rose without marking; calyx very small, undulate, scaly outside; corolla 5-lobed, 3 cm long, quite glabrous outside; stamens 10 as long as the corollas, shortly pubescent on the lower part; anthers very short; ovary 5-celled, densely scaly, style glabrous, stigma deeply lobulate.

Distribution: S. E. Tibet at altitude 3370-4000 m.

36. **Rhododendron asmenistum** Balf. et Forrest

Shrub 1 m high. Leaves oblanceolate to obovate, 7.5 cm long, 2 cm wide, apex obtuse mucronate, margin recurved, base subcuneate; petiole 5 mm long; Inflorescence umbellate, 6-flowered; calyx 1 cm long, 5-parted, cupular; stamens 10, unequal; ovary rufous tomentose. Flowers deep reddish purple.

Distribution: S. E. Tibet.

37. **Rhododendron asperulum** Hutchinson et Ward.

An epiphyte on alder trees, young shoots reddish. Leaves obovate-oblong-lanceolate leathery, loosely glandulary-punctate. Inflorescence, 3-flowered, terminal, pale flesh pink with orange anthers; clayx deeply lobed, oblong, loosely scaly outside; coroll shortly campanulate, 5-lobed, slightly scaly outside; stamens 10, exserted, pubescer in the middle third; ovary ovoid, scaly; capsule 2.5 cm long, opening from the to downwards; seeds minute with long thread-like tails at each end.

Distribution: Southern Tibet, at altitude 2300 m.

38. **Rhododendron asterochnoum** Diels

Small tree with thick flowering shoots. Leaves leathery, oblanceolate, 18-20 c long, 5-6 cm broad; apex obtuse to rounded; base cuneate, undersurface with spars indumentum of stellate hairs; petiole flattened above, 1.5-2.5 cm long. Inflorescenc with many-flowered; flowers set obliquely to pedicel; rhachis 2-2.5 cm long, clothe with hairs like those on the leaf surface; calyx small with triangular teeth; corol funnel-campanulate, white suffused rose, 4.5 cm long, lobes 5, broadly rounded, lon, 2 cm broad, deeply emarginate; stamens 20 unequal, 2-3 cm long, filaments puberulo at the base; pistil 13-14-chambered.

Distribution: Szechuan, at altitude 3330-4000 m.

39. **Rhododendron asterocalyx** Balf. et Forrest

Small shrub 1-2 m high. Leaves leathery, elliptic, shortly oval or obovate, 3.5-5 long, 2-3.5 cm wide, apex rounded with a short mucro, base rounded or truncat petiole 1-2 cm long, grooved above and marked with vestiges of glands. Inflorescence racemose umbel of 5-8 flowers; rhachis 5 mm long, tomentose and glandular; pedicels clad with short stalked sparingly glands, 2 cm long; calyx 6 mm long, slit to near the base into 5 spreading star-like oblong obtuse lobes, which are densely glandular on the back and on the fringes; corolla openly campanulate, pale yellow, 2.5-3 cm long, outside glandular, inside puberulous; lobes 5, 8-10 mm long, 1-1.5 cm broad; stamens 10, 1-1.3 cm long; filaments puberulous; pistil clad with short stalked glands; style glandular to tip and there expanded into a broadish lobulate stigma.

Distribution: N. W. Yunnan.

40. **Rhododendron atentsinense** Handel-Mazz.

Shrub with obovate-oblong leaves, 7-9 cm long, 2.5-3 cm wide, acute apex, cuneate at base. Inflorescence, umbellate, 3-4 flowers, bracts broadly lingulate, Pedicel 9-15 mm long, densely lepidote.

Distribution: Yunnan, at altitude 4000 m.

41. **Rhododendron atrosequameum** Balf. et Forrest.

Shrub 2-3 m high. Flowers blue to purple. Leaves oblong, 4 cm long, 2.5 cm wide, entire margin, dark green glabrous above, brownish thickly covered with indumentum below; veins inconspicuous on both surfaces, thick, coriaceous; petiole 12 mm long, rounded, brown, glandular. Fruit cylindric 1.5 cm long, 1 cm thick, 5-valved splitting from the tip towards the base, whitish tomentose outside; pedicel 2-3 cm long, glandular, brownish tomentose.

Distribution: N. W. Yunnan, at altitude 4000 m.

42. **Rhododendron arovirens** Franch.

Large shrub or small tree, branchlets densely covered with appressed flatened brown hairs. Leaves persistent chartaceous, lanceolate or ovate-lanceolate, 2-7.5 cm long, 1.5-3 cm wide, long-acuminate mucronate apex, densely clothed on both surfaces with appressed shining brown hairs, more densely so along the midrib and veins. Inflorescence, 2-4-flowered, pedicels about 8 mm long, densely clothed with shining brown appressed hairs; calyx small, with deltoid lobes, pubescent like the pedicel; corolla funnel-form with tubes abruptly enlarged at apex, with spreading obtuse lobes, red in scattered dark-red spots at the base of the upper lobes, glabrous; stamens 10, unequal, the longest as long as corolla, short pilose below the middle.

Distribution: Yunnan.

43. **Rhododendron aucubaefolium** Hemsl.

Shrub 3 m tall. Leaves oblong-lanceolate to oblong, 6-9 cm long, acuminate apex, cuneate at base, leathery, coriaceous. Flowers fascicled, lax; calyx small 5-dentate; corolla 1.5-11 cm long; stamens 10, exserted.

Distribution: Hupeh.

44. **Rhododendron augustinii** Hemsl.

Shrub 3 m tall. Leaves oblanceolate, 5 cm long, 2 cm wide, acute apex, cuneate at base, incurved margin, upper surface clad with dark greenish tomentum the lower surface covered with brownish stellate tomentum, thick, leathery; petiole 1 cm long, brownish tomentose, rounded. Flowers light purple in terminal racemes glabrous; pedicels 2 cm long, brownish pubescent, glandular. Pistil and stamens longer than the corolla.

Distribution: W. Hupeh, at altitude 1700-2300 m.

Var. 1. **Rhododendron augustinii** var. **yui** Fang

Shrub 1.5-2 m tall. Leaves dark green above, yellowish below; flowers purple or purplish; calyx and petiole fringed with long hairs.

Distribution: Szechuan, at altitude 2300-2500 m.

45. **Rhododendron aureum** Georgi

Shrub 1 m high, branchlets slightly scaly. Leaves lanceolate, 2.5-7.5 cm long, 1.6-2.6 cm wide, subcrenulate, acute at each end, mucronate, densely impressive scaly below; scales very small. Inflorescence very small, 3-5-flowered, flowering stalk 6 mm long, scaly. Flowers bright yellow; calyx large and leaf, nearly 4 mm long, lobes rounded, scaly on both sides; corolla 5-lobed, broadly tubular, 2.5 cm long, rather densely scaly outside; stamens 10, long exserted, pubescent in lower part; ovary 5-celled, densely scaly; style scaly towards the base, slender, straight.

Distribution: Yunnan, at altitude 3000-3300 m.

46. **Rhododendron auriculatum** Hemsl.

Shrub or small tree 2-4 m tall. Branchlets clad with long-stalked glands. Leaves oblong, oblong-lanceolate or oblong-oblanceolate, 15-30 cm long, 6-10 cm wide, apex broadly obtuse to rounded, base rounded, auricled, margin soft gland-ciliate; upper surface dark green, glabrescent, midrib grooved, primary veins 24 on each side deeply impressed, under surface pale green clad all over with a tomentum of isolated flexuous thread-like hairs, many of which are gland-tipped, midrib pale green, prominent, clad with long soft thread-like glands; petiole stout clad with long-stalked glands, rounded hardly grooved. Inflorescence a large loose umbellate raceme, 7-15-flowered, rachis stout, 3-5 cm long, densely glandular; calyx small, discoid, rim undulate with rounded somewhat membranaceous glandular lobes; corolla funnel shaped, white or rose pink, 6-1 cm long, outside glandular with long-stalked glands; stamens 14, unequal, 4-6 cm long. Capsule oblong, 3.5 cm long, 1 cm broad, purplish, distinctly ribbed, 8-chambered.

Distribution: Western Hupeh, at altitude 1800-2300 m.

47. **Rhododendron bachii** Levl.

Shrub with slender branchlets. Leaves evergreen, not lepidote, glabrous except the midrib; flowers medium sized, solitary, axillary; calyx lobes large and broad, glabrous or fringed with stalked glands or hairs; corolla tube mostly short and spreading, 5-lobed; stamens 5, exserted; ovary 5-celled, bristly; style glabrous or with a few hairs at the base. Capsule very short, surrounded by the persistent calyx.

Distribution: Kweichow, Hupeh, Kwangsi and Hunan, at altitude 650 m.

48. **Rhododendron baileyi** Balf

Shrub 1 m tall, young branchlets densely scaly. Leaves obovate or obovate-oblong narrowed to the base, or rounded or subemarginate at apex, 2.5-4 cm long, 1.5-2.5 cm wide, closely scaly above, densely covered with overlapping cinnamomum scales below. Inflorescence terminal racemose, several-flowered, 5-9 rarely up to 14-flowered; axis densely pubescent; flowers stalks 1.5 cm long, loosely scaly; flower reddish purple with darker spots on the upper 3-lobes of the corolla; calyx deeply 5-lobed, lobes often unequal, densely scaly outside, reddish, sometimes fringed with long weak hairs; corolla tube short, 5-lobed, the tube and lobes scaly outside; stamens 10, variously pubescent according to position; ovary 5-celled, densely scaly; style curved downwards, stout, red, glabrous.

Distribution: S. Tibet, at altitude 3000-3700 m.

49. **Rhododendron rainbridgeanum** Tagg et Forrest

Shrub 1-2 m tall. Leaves oblong-lanceolate or obovate or subelliptic, 6-12 cm long, 2-4.5 cm broad, apex obtuse, beaked, base obtuse to rounded, upper surface minutely rugose, lower surface tawny colored, covered with thin loose felt; petiole 1-1.5 cm long, grooved above, densely clad with longer or sorter setose-glands. Inflorescence umbellate raceme of 6-8-flowers; calyx variable in sizes 4-9 mm long, split to near the base into 5 elongate triangular lobes, setose-glandular on the back and gland fringed; stamens 10, unequal, 2-3 cm long; corolla campanulate, 3.5 cm long, white or creamy yellow, blotched crimson at the base. Capsule cylindric, slightly curved, blackish, 2 cm long, 4 mm broad, more or less rough with withered glands, 5-7-chambered.

Distribution: E. Tibet, at altitude 4000 m.

50. **Rhododendron balfourianum** Diels

Shrub 1-2 m tall. Flowers pale rose, with crimson markings; corolla thick and fleshy, lobes slightly spreading, stamens 12. Leaves silkly shining tomentose, ovate to lanceolate, 7-12 cm long, 2.5-4.5 cm broad, clad beneath with white spongy felt, midrib, petiole and leaf margin at first somewhat glandular.

Distribution: S. W. Szechuan, at altitude 3200-4000 m.

Var. 1. Rhododendron balfourianum var. aganniphoides Diels

Shrub 2-3 m tall. Flowers deep purplish fringed. Leaves dark green above, white felt indumentum beneath, acute apex, cuneate at base finged margin.

Distribution: S. W. Szechuan, at altitude 4300-4450 m.

51. **Rhododendron basilicum** Balf et Sm.

Shrub or tree 3-10 m high, with young shoots of rufous tomentose, later grey. Leaves broad ovate to oblanceolate, 13-22 cm long, 5-12 cm broad, apex rounded, base tapering from the broadest part, obtuse to cuneate, more or less decurrent on petiole, upper surface dark green, glabrous with here and there vestiges of juvenile tomentum, under surface with deep cinnamon to tawn-grey, uniformly clothed with a somewhat spongy indumentum, the upper stratum coffee-color and when worn off revealing a gray skin–like under stratum; petiole 2–3.5 cm long, widened at the base and flat above with marginal wings or ridges; inflorescence a large corymbose–raceme of 25 flowers; rachis 3.5 cm long; calyx small, teeth broadly triangular; corolla broadly campanulate, fleshy, pale yellow or tinged, with a crimson blotch at the base, lobes 8; stamens 16, unequal. capsule straight or slightly curved, 4 cm long, 1 cm broad, densely rufous to-mentose.

Distribution: W. Yunnan, at altitude 3300–3800 m.

52. **Rhododendron batangense** Balf.

Small shrub with small obovate to oblong leaves, apex attenuate, base obtuse, margin recurved, 8 mm long, 2.5 mm wide, petiolate, coriaceous. Flowers solitary, terminal sessile.

Distribution: W. Szechuan.

53. **Rhododendron bathyphyllum** Balf. et Forrest

Shrub 1–2 m tall. Leaves oblong, 4–7 cm long, 1.5–2.5 cm wide, apex obtuse with tips recurved, margin revolute, base obtuse. Inflorescence umbel, 10–15 flowered, calyx 5–lobed, corolla campanulate, white with copious crimson spots on the posterior side, lobes 5, rounded, emarginate; stamens 10, unequal.

Distribution: S. E. Tibet, at altitude 4300 m.

54. **Rhododendron beesianum** Diels

Shrub or small tree 3–7 m tall. Leaves oblong–lanceolate or narrow oblanceolate 15–20 cm long, 4–7 cm broad, apex acuminate, gradually tapering to an obtuse or round-ed base, upper surface smooth and glabrous, under surface clad with a thin smooth non–agglutinate pale cinnamon indumentum; veins not concealed by the indumentum; petiole broad at base, winged or ridged on each side, deeply grooved above, 2–3 cm long, inflorescence in large racemes umbel of 15–25 flowers.

Distribution: Yunnan, at altitude 3500–4300 m.

55. **Rhododendron beimaense** Balf. et Forrest

Shrub 2 m tall. Leaves elliptic–ovate 11 cm long, or ovate 8.5 cm long, 5.5 cm wide, apex rounded, mucronate–apiculate, base rotundate; inflorescence an umbel of 5–6 flowers; corolla 5–lobed, rose–white; ovary glandulose.

Distribution: N. W. Yunnan.

56. **Rhododendron bivelatum** Balf.

Shrub with evergreen leaves. Branchlets densely scaly; leaves obovate oblong-lanceolate, obtuse at apex, gradually narrowed to the base, 3–4 cm long, 1.5–2.5 cm wide, pubescent on the midrib; petiole 1.5 cm long, scaly; corolla 5–lobed not scaly outside; stamens 10, exserted; ovary 5–celled, densely scaly.

Distribution: N. E. Yunnan, at altitude 2700 m.

57. **Rhododendron blandulum** Balf. et Sm.

Shrub 1.5 m tall. Leaves aromatic, petiolate, the Petiole 9.5 cm long; lamina oblong, 7.5 cm long, 3.5 cm wide, apex obtuse, margin revolute, base sub–truncate;

inflorescence an umbel 8-flowered, reddish glandulose; calyx 5-lobed, unequal; corolla campanulate, white or rose, 4 cm long, lobes 5, rotundate.

Distribution: W. Yunnan, at altitude 3200-4000 m.

58. **Rhododendron blepharocalyx** Franch.

Small shrub, densely scaly. Leaves narrow oblong-elliptic, 2 cm long, 12 mm wide, densely scaly on both surfaces; scales overlapping, densely pale yellowish green; leaf-stalk scaly; inflorescence terminal, 3-4-flowered; calyx small scaly outside; corolla narrowly tubular, not scaly outside; ovary scaly.

Distribution: Szechuan, and E. Tibet, at altitude 4300 m.

59. **Rhododendron bodinieri** Franch.

Shrub with branchlets scaly. Leaves oblong-lanceolate to obovate, markedly long-acuminate, rounded to sub-acute at the base, glabrous above, scaly below; inflorescence a terminal raceme; flowers rose spotted with purple; calyx an undulate rim, scaly outside; corolla 5-lobed, not scaly outside; stamens 10, exserted, shortly pubescent on the lower part; ovary 5-celled, scaly.

Distribution: Yunnan, and Kweichow.

60. **Rhododendron bonvalotii** Bur. et Franch.

Shrub branchlets glabrous. Leaves leathery, oblong-lanceolate, or narrowly elliptic, 4-5 cm long, 1.5 cm wide, apex broadly acute, base narrowly obtuse; petiole 8 mm long, round, glabrous; inflorescence umbel, with few-flowers; calyx 5-lobed; corolla 5-lobed, emarginate; stamens 10, unequal.

Distribution: S. W. Szechuan.

61. **Rhododendron brachyandrum** Balf. et Forrest.

Shrub 1 m tall. Leaves 12 cm long, oblong, 11 cm long, 3.5 cm wide; flowers umbellate, pink color; corolla tubular-campanulate, 5 lobed, glabrous.

Distribution: S. E. Tibet.

62. **Rhododendron brachyanthum** Franch.

Shrub branchlets slightly scaly. Leaves oblong to oblong-elliptic, 3-4 cm long, 1.5-2 cm wide, glaucous below and with very few scales; inflorescence terminal umbels with few-flowers; flowers pale yellow-greenish; calyx large leafy, 5-lobed; corolla broadly campanulate, 5-lobed, tube and lobes not scaly outside; stamens 10, sub-equal, exserted, pubescent near their full length; ovary 5 - celled, covered with very small scales.

Distribution: Yunnan, at altitude 3000 m.

63. **Rhododendron bracteatum** Rehd. et Wilson

Shrub 2 m tall. Branchlets twigs not scaly. Leaves ovate-elliptic, obtuse mucronate, rounded at the base, 4-5 cm long, 2 cm broad, laxly scaly above, rather densely so below; inflorescence terminal, 3-4-flowered, umbellate; pedicel 2 cm long, with a few scattered scales; flowers white with spotted red; corolla campanulate, 5-lobed, laxly scaly all over the outside, tube softly pubescent within; stamens 10, pubescent in the lower half; ovary 5-celled, densely scalys; style with few hairs near the base. Capsule 1.5 cm long, laxly scaly.

Distribution: W. Szechuan, at altitude 2300-3300 m.

64. **Rhododendron** brettii Hemsl. et Wils.

Shrub 3 m tall. Branchlets densely clothed with rufous tomentum, which persistent over 2 or more years. Leaves crowded, oblong-lanceolate, short-acuminate, base slightly auricled, upper surface dark green, somewhat wrinkled, often felted lower surface, usually rufous tomentose beneath; petiole 1-2 cm long; flowers 12 or more sub-umbellate, multi-bracteate, pink with dark red blotch, 5-6 cm across; bracts crowded among the leaves and flowers; calyx petaloid, glandular and pilose; corolla widely campanulate, narrowed at base, 5-lobed, tube pubescent; stamens 10, filaments unequal; pitile over-topping stamens, broad, deeply emarginate; ovary 4 mm long, glandular, sparsely pilose. Capsule 1.5-2 cm long, 8 mm broad, furrowed, clothed with shortly stalked glands; calyx-lobes appressed to capsule.

Distribution: Szechuan, at altitude 2750-3000 m.

65. **Rhododendron breviperulatum** Hayata

Much branched shrub; young shoots slender, clothed with appressed flattened shining brown hairs. Floral winter-buds scales several, ovate, strigose along the middle, otherwise glabrous; leaves chartaceous, persistnet, scattered and partly crowded, ovate elliptic to oblong-ovate, 2.5 cm long, 2 cm wide, obtuse and mucronulate, broad cuneate to rounded at base, clothed with scattered brownish shining hairs, changing to grey, reticulate beneath; inflorescence 3-several-flowered; calyx minute, with 5-ovate ciliate lobes; corolla 5-lobed, funnel-form, about 2 cm long; stamens 5, shorter than corolla; anthers oblong, apiculate at base.

Distribution: Taiwan.

66. **Rhododendron brevistylum** Franch.

Shrub 3 m high. Branchlets purplish scaly. Leaves elliptic lanceolate, acute and mucronate, narrowed to the base, 10 cm long, 5 cm broad, very laxy and scaly and reticulated above, laxy scaly beneath; inflorescence terminal, 5-flowered; flowers-bud scales early deciduous; flowers-stalk 1.5 cm long, scaly; flowers pale to deep rose with deep crimson markings; calyx saucer-shape, undulate lobed, scaly outside; corolla widely funnel-shape, 4 cm long, loosely scaly outside; stamens 10, slightly exserted densely pubescent in the lower half.

Distribution: Yunnan, at altitude 4000-4300 m.

67. **Rhododendron brunneifolium** Balf. et Forrest

Shrub 1 m tall. Leaves oblong-ovate, 7 cm long, 3 cm wide, apex rotundate, minutely apiculate, margin plane, base obtuse, olive green above, pale green pubescent beneath, petiole 1 cm long; flowers in umbel of 3-4-flowered; pedicels 3 cm long; corolla tubular campanulate, rose colored.

Distribution: E. Tibet, at altitude 4300 m.

68. Rhododendron bullatum Franch.

Loosely branched shrub 3 m tall; branchlets densely and softly woolly. Leaves ovate-elliptic, abruptly acuminate, rounded at the base, 5–10 cm long, 1.5–2.5 cm wide, bullate above, loosely, woolly, tomentose below and densely punctate, with distinct lateral veins; leaf-stalks 1.5 cm long, densely wooly; inflorescence terminal, 2–3-flowered, densely woolly tomentose; flowers white very fragrant; calyx deep lobed, lobes very broad, densely fringed with hairs, scaly outside; corolla 6 cm long, scaly outside, 5-lobed; stamens 10, pubescent in the lower part; ovary 5–6-celled, densely woolly.

Distribution: Yunnan, at altitude 3700–3800 m.

69. Rhododendron bureavii Franch.

Small tree or shrub 2 m tall. Branchlets thickly clad with reddish rusty indumentum of hairs mixed with glands; leaves leathery, ovate or boradly elliptic, 6–12 cm long, 2.5–5 cm wide, apex broadly acuminate, base obtuse or rounded, upper surface slightly rugose, glabrous at maturity, veins 12, under surface clad with thick, broght, rusty-red woolly indumentum of hiars, mixed with small glands; inflorescence short racemose umbel of 10–15-flowers, rachis rusty glandular; calyx 1 cm long, rusty glandular, cut to near the base into 5 lobes, margin fringed with glandular hairs; corolla, tubular-campanulate, 4 mm long, rose or reddish with crimson markings, crenulate, emarginate; stamens 10, unequal; filaments densely pubescent at base. Capsule ovoid, 1.5 cm long, 1 cm broad, blackish with vestiges of hairs and glands.

Distribution: Yunnan, at altitude 3300–4000 m.

70. Rhododendron bureavioides Balf.

Shrub 2–3 m tall. Leaves oblong-oval, 10–14 cm long, 4–5 cm wide, apex obtuse or acuminate, base rounded or cordulate, upper surface smooth, somewhat glossy and glabrous with vestiges of juvenile hairs, lower surface clad with thick rusty red indumentum; petiole thick, rusty woolly, 1 cm long; flowers a racemose umbel, 15-flowered, bracts and bracteoles more or less persistent during the flowering period; pedicel 1.5 cm long, woolly and glandular; corolla 4.5 cm long, campanulate, rose with deep blotch at the base.

Distribution: Szechuan.

71. Rhododendron burriflorum Balf. et Forrest.

Shrub 4.5 m tall. Leaves oval or oblong-ovate, 16 cm long, 5.5 cm wide, obtuse mucronate apex, margin undulate, base rotundate, upper surface olive-green, lower surface tomentose; petiole 2 cm long, glandular.

Distribution: Yunnan.

72. Rhododendron caeruleum Levl.

Shrub 2 m tall. This differs from the others in having scales on the outside of the calyx; leaves punctate and bracts punctate, ciliate; stamens and tyle exserted.

Distribution: Yunnan, at altitude 2800 m.

73. Rhododendron callimorphum Balf. et Sm.

Shrub 3 m tall. Leaves broadly elliptic or broadly ovate, 3–7 cm long, 2–4.5cm wide, apex rounded, base cordulate or subtruncate, upper surface dark green, glossy, under surface glaucous, semipapillate, minutely punctate with gland vestiges; petiole 1.5 cm long, glandular; inflorescence terminal umbel, 5-8-flowered; corolla open-campanulate, 3.5-4.5 cm long, soft rose colored; stamens 10, unequal.

Distribution: W. Yunnan, at altitude 3300 m.

74. Rhododendron calophytum Franch.

Large tree of 13-17 m high, about 60 cm in width old bark cinnamon-red, paling with age. Branches stout and loose greyish dawny when young. Leaves clustered mostly towards the end of branches, blades oblanceolate to oblong from a gradually tapering base, abruptly acute, 18-30 cm by 4-7 cm, coriaceous, dull green above, paler below, puberulous and woolly downy along the midrib when young, at length glabrous except some vestiges of down on the very prominent midrib, with 20-25 pairs of lateral veins; petiole short, stout, 1.5-2.5 cm long, inflorescence large globose, of up to 30 fragrant flowers, up to 25 cm across, bracts broad-elliptic to oblong or spatulate, often long-apiculate, brownish with a silvery appressed tomentum within and without, up to 5 cm long; bract-eoles filiform up to 3 cm long, silvery tomentose; peduncle stout, conical, up to 2.5 cm long; pedicels up to 8.5 cm long, glabrous, often scarlet on the exterior side; calyx very small, disc-shaped, obscurely lobed; corolla broadly campanulate, 4-5 cm by 6-7 cm across the limb, white flushed with rose, particularly without, to rose, with a dark-purple-red blotch; lobes 5, short and broad, emarginate, and more or less wavy, 1.3-2 cm by 2.2-3.5 cm; stamens unequal, up to 20 or more; filaments more or less pilose in the lower third, or near the base only 1.5-3 cm long; anthers dark brown, 3-3.5 mm long; ovary oblong, rounded, glabrous, 7 mm long; style stout, up to 3 cm long, terminating in the exserted large discoid green stigma, up to 1 cm in diameter. Capsule sub-cylindrical, slightly curved, up to 3-4 cm long, by 1.5 cm wide, blackish brown, smooth.

A very beautiful and decorative *Rhododendron* was discovered by Pere G. David in Mupin, West Szechuan, with cinnamon-brown bark. Generally a tree or an evergreen bush, up to 15 m high and up to 1.5 m in circumference.

Distribution: West Szechuan, at altitude 2800-3150 m at 29°-20' to 32°-30' N. Lat.

75. Rhododendron caloxanthum Balf.

Shrub 1.5-2.5 m tall. Leaves oblong, 5 cm long, 3 cm wide, acute apiculate apex, rounded or truncate at base, margin entire, thick, coriaceous; petiole 1 cm long, round glabrous. Flowers yellow.

Distribution: Yunnan, at altitude 4150 m.

76. Rhododendron calvescens Balf.

Shrub 1-2 m tall. Leaves oblong, 6-10 cm long, 2.5-3.5 cm wide, apex obtuse, base truncate or cordate, occasionally rounded, lower surface clad with rufous vestiges indumentum; midrib with short glands; petiole 1 cm long, glabrous, with traces of hairs and glands.

Distribution: S. E. Tibet.

77. Rhododendron campanulatum D. Don

Shrub of 2-3 m high. Leaves oblong, 9 cm long, 4.5 cm wide, blunt apex, truncate at base, incurved margin, dark green above, brownish felted beneath, thick, cariaceous; petiole 2 cm long, stout, brown, glandular; flowers white in terminal racemes, corolla 4 cm long, glabrous.

Distribution: S. Tibet.

78. Rhododendron campylocarpum Hook.

Shrub or small tree 6-7 m tall. Leaves oblong, 5 cm long, 3 cm wide, rounded mucronate at apex, truncate or rounded at base, revolute margin, dark green, glabrous above, pale green, glaucous beneath, pubescent below, thick coriaceous; petiole 2.5 cm long, glabrous and glandular; flowers pale yellow, with crimson nectaries at base of the corolla lobes; calyx greenish red; pedicels red, on top of its with a few hairs.

Distribution: E. Tibet, at altitude 3170-3330 m.

79. Rhododendron campyllogynum Franch.

Shrub 15-30 m high; leaves very small elliptic-ovate, 1.5 cm long, 1 cm wide, rounded with mucronate apex, cuneate at base, incurved margin, dark green smooth above, pubescent brownish glaucous beneath; flower solitary, terminal on a long pedicel, bluish, campanulate, 5-lobed; calyx 5-lobed to the base, large foliaged.

Distribution: On the moorland of S. E. Tibet at altitude of 4300 m.

80. Rhododendron cantabile Balf.

Shrub 1 m tall. Leaves oblong or ovate-elliptic, rounded at base, densely scaly on both surfaces, scales slightly imbricate, rusty or yellow; inflorescence terminal, globose, 10-flowered; flowers dark-violet; calyx glabrous outside fringed with hairs; corolla open-funnel-shape, not lepidote outside; stamens 10, long-exserted; ovary scaly, style laxy scaly in the lower half, slightly exceeding the stamens, red.

Distribution: Yunnan, at altitude 4700 m.

81. Rhododendron capitatum Maxim.

Shrub 1 m tall. Branchlets densely scaly. Leaves elliptic, 2 cm long, densely scaly on both surfaces; inflorescence terminal, 5-flowered; corolla narrow funnel-shaped, not scaly outside; stamens 10, exserted, villose in lower part, ovary scaly. Capsule ovoid, scaly.

Distribution: Kansu, and Tibet, at altitude 3350 m.

82. Rhododendron cardiobasis Sleumer

Shrub 3 m tall. Leaves elliptic or suborbicular-ovate, 8-12 cm long, 5-9 cm wide, veins 7-8 pairs; inflorescence terminal in corymb, lax, 6-7-flowered; calyx 5-lobed, deltoid; corolla campanulate, 7-lobed; stamens 14, unequal.

Distribution: Kwangtung, Kwangsi and Kweichow.

83. Rhododendron cardioeides Balf. et Forrest

Shrub 2 m tall. Leaves elliptic, 5.5 cm long, 3.5 cm wide, apex obtuse, margin plane, cartilagineous, base cordate; flowers in umbels, 4-flowered; calyx cupuliform; corolla campanulate, 3 cm long, 1.5 cm broad, lobes rotundate, emarginate.

Distribution: N. W. Yunan, at altitude 3150 m.

84. **Rhododendron** catacosmum Balf.

Shrub 2-3 m tall. Leaves obovate, 6-11 cm long, 3.5 cm broad, apex rounded, base obtuse, upper surface rugulose glabrous or with vestiges of indumentum on grooved midrib; petiole 1-1.5 cm long; calyx a large petaloid cup, as much as 2 cm long, irregularly lobed, lobes 5, unequal, corolla broadly campanulate, crimson rose, 4-4.5 cm long, fleshy at base, with 5 pounched nectaries, lobes 5 rounded, emarginate, 1.3 cm long, 2 cm broad; stamens 10-12, unequal; capsule straight oblong, 2 cm long, 1 cm broad, fulvous tomentose.

Distribution: S. E. Tibet, at altitude 4300-4600 m.

85. **Rhododendron** catapastum Balf. et Forrest.

Shrub 2.5 m tall. Leaves chartaceous, 10.5 cm long, 4.5 cm wide, acuminate apex, obtuse at base, margin plane; veins 8-10, inconspicuous; flowers in umbels, 4-5-flowered, solitary, 2-3-fascicled; calyx tubular; corolla, tubular-campanulate; disc puberulous; capsule 1.2 cm long, 4 mm in diameter, 5-valved.

Distribution: Yunnan.

86. **Rhododendron** cavaleriei Levl.

Shrub 2-3 m high. Leaves oblanceolate, gradually acute at both ends. Inflorescence subumbellate, 3-flowered; flowers white to rose; calyx obsolete glabrous; corolla narrowly funnel-shaped, glabrous outside; stamens 10 exserted, glabrous.

Distribution: Kweichow, and Kwangsi, at altitude 1900 m.

87. **Rhododendron** cephalanthoides Balf. et Sm.

Shrub 1 m high. Leaves oblong-elliptic, 2 cm long, 1.5 cm broad, inflorescence terminal capitate; few-flowered; flowers white with yellow tube; calyx well-developed, lobes scaly; corolla narrowly tubular, not scaly outside, villose within; stamens 5, included, glabrous; ovary and capsule all scaly.

Distribution: Yunnan, and Tibet, at altitude 4300 m.

88. **Rhododendron** cephalanthum Franch.

Shrub with branchlets densely tomentose and bristly when young, clothed by the persistent leaf-bud-scales; leaves oblong-elliptic, mucronate, thick, leathery, recurved margin, densely covered with several layers of flaky scales below; inflorescence densely capitate, terminal, several-flowered; flowers white; calyx large deeply lobed 5, lobes scaly outside, densely fringed with long hairs; corolla narrowly tubular, 5-lobed, villose within the throat. Capsule scaly.

Distribution: Szechuan, and Tibet, at altitude 4500 m.

89. **Rhododendron** cerasinum Tagg.

Shrub 3-4 m tall. Leaves oblong to oblong-elliptic, 6-5 cm long, 2.3 cm wide, apex, obtuse, base obtuse to semi-rounded, under surface sub-glaucous; petiole 1 cm long, grooved above rounded below, glandular; inflorescence umbellate, with 6-7 pendulous flowers, pedicel 2 cm long, densely glandular; calyx somewhat fleshy, densely glandular, fringed with ovoid sessile glands; corolla campanulate, creamy white, 3-3.5 cm long, with cherry-red band around the summit.

Distribution: E. Tibet.

90. **Rhododendron** ceraceum Balf. et Sm.

Shrub with broadly lanceolate leaves and slightly puberulous mature fruit; flowers red.

Distribution: Yunnan, altitude 2900 m.

91. **Rhododendron** cerinum Balf. et Forrest

Shrub with purplish branchlets. Leaves oblong-ovate, 5.5 cm long, 2.7 cm wide, obtuse mucronate apex, sub-cunneate at base; flowers terminal in umbels, 6-flowered.

Distribution: Yunnan, at altitude 3500 m.

92. **Rhododendron** cerochitum Balf. et Forrest

Shrub 5 m tall. Leaves lanceolate to oblong-lanceolate or oblong, 7-12 cm long, 2.5-4.5 cm wide, apex abruptly acuminate, base obtuse or broadly cuneate, upper surface mat glaucous, midrib grooved, under surface light glaucous; inflorescence terminal racemose umbel, about 7-flowered; calyx with 5-pointed teeth, imbricate on the margin; corolla funnel shaped, 5 cm long, with 5 basal pouched nectaries; stamens 10, unequal, 3-4 cm long.

Distribution: W. Yunnan, at altitude 3300-3450 m.

93. **Rhododendron** chaetomallum Balf. et Forrest

Shrub 1-1.5 m tall. Leaves leathery, obovate or oblong-obovate, 9 cm long, 4 cm broad, apex rounded, or broadly obtuse, base obtuse, upper surface dark olive green, with vestiges of juvenile indumentum, under surface clad with a tawny persistent woolly indumentum; petiole 5 mm long, clad with indumentum; inflorescence in terminal umbel of 4-6 flowers, rachis pilose; calyx red, fleshy, 3 mm-1 cm long, cup-shaped, glabrous. Capsule straight, 1.5-2 cm long, 7 mm in diameter, densely woolly, brownish.

Distribution: S. E. Tibet, and Yunnan, at altitude 3700-4300 m.

94. **Rhododendron** chalarocladum Balf. et Forrest

Shrub with laxy racemose characters. Leaves oblong, or elongate-ovate, 8 cm long, 4 cm wide; flowers in umbels of 3-4 flowered, rose pale pink.

Distribution: E. Tibet.

95. **Rhododendron** chamaetorum Balf. et Ward.

Shrub 1 m tall. Branchlets rusty dark gray; flowers pink; in terminal racemes some flowers white, fragrant.

Distribution: Yunnan, at altitude 4000 m.

96. **Rhododendron** championae Hook.

Shrub 2 m high. Leaves lanceolate, much confined to the apex of branchlets; flowers white, with orange spots on the upper lip. Characterized by the glandular bristle on the branchlets, petioles and peduncles as well as by the bristly hairs on both surfaces of the leaves.

Distribution: Kwangtung, Chekiang, Hongkong, and Fukien, at altitude 800 m.

97. **Rhododendron charianthum** Hutchinson

Shrub branchlets sparingly scaly – glandular. Leaves oblanceolate, or elliptic-oblanceolate, bluntly mucronate, cuneate at base, 3–5 cm long, 1.5–2 cm wide, scaly on both surfaces; inflorescence 9–10 flowers, a terminal corymb, with a short axis; flowers rosy, with dense spots on the upper of the corolla within; corolla gaping, not scaly outside, 5–lobed; ovary, 5–celled, not scaly outside. Capsule very short, 1 cm long, minutely scaly.

Distribution: Yunnan, Szechuan, and Tibet.

98. **Rhododendron charitostreptum** Balf. et Ward.

Shrub 1 m tall. Flower small, yellow, in terminal corymb; leaves oblong 6 cm long, 3 cm wide, blunt apex, cuneate at base, thick, coriaceous.

Distribution: Tibet.

99. **Rhododendron charopoeum** Balf. et Farrer

Shrub 15 cm high. Leaves crowded, obovate oblanceolate, rounded apex, glaucous-papillous below; inflorescence terminal, 1–flowered, rose-purplish, nodding, calyx with 1 or 2 lobes developed; corolla tubular-campanulate, 5–lobed, glabrous outside.

Distribution: North-eastern Burma to Yunnan, at altitude 3700–4300 m.

100. **Rhododendron chartophyllum** Franch.

Shrub 1–3 m. Leaves deciduous; flowers from pure white to blue-lavender, with a few deep markings.

Distribution: Yunnan, at altitude 3000 m.

101. **Rhododendron chasmanthum** Diels

Shrub 1–2 m tall. Flowers in terminal sub-umbels, 3–4–flowered, pale lavender rose with pale olive markings; calyx rather unequal, deeply 5–lobed; corolla 5–lobed, ovary 5–celled, densely scaly.

Distribution: N. W. Yunnan and S. E. Tibet, at altitude 3330 m.

102. **Rhododendron chasmanthoides** Balf. et Forrest

Shrub 8 m tall. Leaves oblong-ovate, 10 cm long, 4 cm wide, obtuse at apex, rotundate or broad-obtuse at base, flowers in umbels, 4–6 flowered, bracteoles linear.

Distribution: Yunnan, at altitude 2700–3300 m.

103. **Rhododendron cheilanthum** Balf. et Forrest

Shrub 1 m tall. Leaves oblong-oval, oval or oboval, 2.2 cm long, 1 cm broad.

Distribution: Yunnan, at altitude 3700 m.

104. **Rhododendron chienianum** Fang

Tree 10 m high. Leaves coriaceous, lanceolate or oblanceolate, 5–9 cm long, 1.5–2 cm wide, acuminate at apex, cuneate or obtuse at base, margin revolute; petiole 8–12 mm long; flowers in racemose-corymbs, bracts minutely pilose; calyx 5–lobed acute; corolla campanulate, purplish, 3 mm long, lobes 5, rotundate; stamens 5, unequal; flowers 8–15 in racemose umbel; ovary cylindrical ovoid; capsule cylindric, furrowed, curved, 2–2.5 cm long, glandular.

Distribution: Szechuan, at altitude 2000–2300 m.

105. Rhododendron chlanidotum Balf. et Forrest

Shrub, leaves oblong or oblanceolate 10 cm long, 3 cm wide, obtuse at both end, margin plane; flowers in umbels, 5–flowered; calyx lobes 5; corolla golden yellow.

Distribution: Tibet, at altitude 4500 m.

106. Rhododendron chloranthum Balf. et Forrest

Shrub 1 m tall. Leaves deciduous, obovate, rounded at apex, 2.5 cm long, 2 cm wide, scaly beneath; inflorescence terminal, 4–flowered; flowers yellow with tinged green at base; calyx triangular–lobed, slightly scaly on the margin; stamens 10, exserted, villose in the lower half; ovary loosely scaly, style curved, thick, glabrous.

Distribution: N. W. Yunnan, at altitude 3300 m.

107. Rhododendron chryseum Balf. et Ward.

Shrub 1 m high, branchlets densely scaly. Leaves aromatic, ovate–elliptic, about 3 cm long, 1.5 cm wide, densely scaly on both surfaces; inflorescence terminal, 4–5 flowered; flowered bright yellow; calyx well developed, lobe scaly outside; stamens 5, long–exserted, villose towards the base; ovary scaly.

Distribution: Yunnan, at altitude 4000–4300 m.

108. Rhododendron chrysocalyx Levl. et Vaniot

Much branched twiggy shrub, the branchlets tortuous, clothed with appressed flattened red–brown strigose hairs. Leaves persistent, chartaceous, dimorphic, narrow lanceolate to oblanceolate, 1.5–4 cm long, 0.5–1 cm long, acute or obtuse, mucronate, base narrow cuneate, margin revolute, crenate serrate, ciliate, upper surface shining dark green, reticulate, lower surface with veins elevated, both surfaces with scattered flattened strigose hairs; flowers terminal, fascicled, 10–12 or more, fascicles with 2–3 flowers; calyx and ovary with dense red–brown strigose hairs; calyx annular, obscurely toothed, ciliate; corolla rotate–funnel–form, tube narrow cylindric; fruit oblong–ovate 1 cm long; stamens 5, long–exserted, about twice the lenght of the corolla.

Distribution: Kwangsi, and Kweichow, at altitude 700 m.

109. Rhododendron chrysodoron Tagg. et Hutch.

Shrub with few leaves forming a rosette below the inflorescence, elliptic, somewhat rounded to a blunt mucronate apex; flowers terminal cluster of 5 bright canary–yellow unspotted flowers; calyx saucer–like.

Distribution: Yunnan.

110. Rhododendron chunii Fang

Small shrub 2 m high. Branchlets clad with red–brown strigose hairs; leaves coriaceous, crowded at the end of branchlets, ovate to obovate, 10–18 mm long, 9–10 mm wide, acute or short acuminate at apex, broadly cuneate at base, revolute and slightly crenulate margin; petiole 2-3 mm long, strigose; flowers appear before leaves, 3-4 in terminal clustered umbels, lilac-purple.

Distribution: Kwangtung.

111. Rhododendron ciliatum Hook. f.

A stuggling shrub 1-2 m high, growing on rocks; corolla white, upper petal tinged bluish pink, more so at base of corolla, filaments white, anthers pale brown, style pale pink, stigma palest brown.

Distribution: S. E. Tibet.

112. Rhododendron ciliato-pedicellatum Hayata

Shrub, leaves obovate-oblong, 10 cm long, 4 cm wide, acuminate apex, obtuse-acute at base, recurved margin; petiole 2 cm long.

Distribution: Fukien.

113. Rhododendron ciliicalyx Franch.

Shrub 1-3 m high. Branchlets covered with scales; leaves elliptic, obovate-elliptic or oblong-lanceolate; inflorescence in umbels, 3-flowered; flowers white or rose; calyx 5-lobed near the base; corolla, 5-lobed, funnel-shaped; stamens 10-11; ovary 6-celled, densely scaly; capsule 6-valved, oblique at base.

Distribution: Yunnan, at altitude 6400 m.

114. Rhododendron ciliipes Hutch.

Shrub, leaves oblong-lanceolate, acute apex, rounded to sub-acute at base, bristly hairy margin, 5-7 cm long, 1-2.5 cm wide, inflorescence 1-flowered; flowers white with green or yellowish blotch inside the base, fragrant; stamens 10 shorter than corolla, pubescent on lower half; ovary scaly.

Distribution: Yunnan, at altitude 3330 m.

115. Rhododendron cinnabarinum Hook.

Shrub 2-4 m high. Flowers bright pinkish mauve, anthers and stigma yellow brown, style deep pink.

Distribution: S. Tibet, at altitude 4300 m.

116. Rhododendron circinnatum Cowan et Ward.

Shrub or small tree 8 m high, with gnarled and twisted branches, covered with thick greyish-buff indumentum; leaves elliptic-lanceolate, to narrowly oblong, 10-14 cm long, 3-4 cm wide, toward the apex tapering or somewhat rounded, obliquely cordate at base, densely covered with densely woolly tomentum of hairs; flowers in many-flowered umbels, rhachis 1 cm long, pedicel robust 2 cm long, calyx mere a rim densely glandular, corolla tubular-campanulate, 2.5-3 cm long, lobes 5, rounded, emarginate; stamens 10, unequal.

Distribution: S. E. Tibet, at altitude 4300-4700 m.

117. Rhododendron citriniflorum Balf. et Forrest

Shrub 1 m tall. Leaves obovate, or oblong-obovate, 3.5-5 cm long, 1.5-2 cm broad, apex obtuse, base obtuse, under surface clad with dense indumentum; inflorescence a terminal umbel of 4-6-flowered; calyx tubular, 3 mm long; corolla campanulate, lemon-yellow, 4 cm long.

Distribution: W. Yunnan, and S. Tibet, at altitude 4300 m.

118. **Rhododendron clementinae** G. Forrest

Shrub 1-3 m tall. Leaves oval to oblong-oval, 6-14 cm long, 3.5-7 cm wide, apex rounded to obtuse, deflexed, base rounded or cordulate, lower surface covered with thick whitish felt indumentum; petiole 2 cm long; inflorescence a racemose umbel with 15 flowers; calyx lobes triangular; corolla campanulate, creamy white, flushed with rose or bright rose deeper crimson markings; stamens 12 - 14, unequal; capsule cylindric, 2 cm long, 1 cm broad, grooved, deep purple-black.

Distribution: N. W. Yunnan, and W. Szechuan, at altitude 3700 m.

119. **Rhododendron clivicolum** Balf. et Sm.

Shrub 1.5 m tall. Leaves oblong or elliptic-oblong, aromatic, 2.5 cm long, 1.5 cm wide, reticulate above, densely scaly below; flowers white with yellow tube; calyx with twisted hairs fringed; corolla 2 cm long, villose within; stamens 5, included, pubescent towards the base; ovary scaly.

Distribution: Yunnan, at altitude 3300-4000 m.

120. **Rhododendron cloiophorum** Balf. et Forrest

Shrub about 1 m tall. Leaves obovate, 3.5 cm long, 1-1.8 cm wide, flowers in terminal umbel; calyx 1 cm long; corolla 3.7 cm long, rose with a darker margin, emarginate or crenulate; stamens 10, unequal.

Distribution: W. Yunnan, at altitude 3700 m.

121. **Rhododendron coccinopeplum** Balf. et Forrest

Shrub 1 m tall. Leaves 9 cm long, 2 cm wide.

Distribution: W. Szechuan, at altitude 4000 m.

122. **Rhododendron cochium** Balf. et Forrest

Shrub 1 m tall. Leaves oblong, 7 cm long, 3.5 cm wide, with brownish felt indumentum below, thick, coriaceous, mucronate and rounded apex, broad-cuneate at base, entire margin, thick; flowers dark red.

Distribution: N. W. Yunnan, at altitude 4450 m.

123. **Rhododendron codonanthum** Balf. et Forrest

Shrub about 1 m tall. Leaves oblanceolate, 3.5 cm long, 1-2 cm wide; flowers in umbel, 6-flowered, bright yellow with bright markings; stamens 10.

Distribution: N. W. Yunnan, at altitude 4000-4300 m.

124. **Rhododendron colletum** Balf. et Forrest

Shrub 2-3 m tall. Leaves narrowly oblanceolate, 9-14 cm long, 3-4.5 cm wide, apex acuminate, cuneate base, with non-agglutinate indumentum below; calyx 5-lobed; corolla openly campanulate, 5-lobed, flushed rose, with crimson markings, emarginate, undulate; stamens 10, unequal; capsule oblique to pedicel.

Distribution: N. Yunnan, at altitude 3300-3700 m.

125. Rhododendron coeloneurum Diels

Small tree 8 m tall. Leaves oblong-elliptic, 6-12 cm long 2-4 cm broad, apex obtuse or acute, usually apiculate, base cuneate or broadly cuneate; flowers 6-9-flowered, umbellate; corolla funnel shaped, 4-4.5 cm long; stamens 10, unequal, lobes 5, broadly rounded; flower purplish.

Distribution: Szechuan, at altitude 2100 m.

126. Rhododendron comisteum Balf. et Forrest

Shrub 1 m tall. Leaves lanceolate or oblanceolate, 2.5-5 cm long, 1-2 cm wide, obtuse apex, margin recurved, base cuneate; inflorescence terminal umbel, 6-8 flowered; corolla rose with crimson spots posterior, fleshy at base.

Distribution: S. E. Tibet, at altitude 3300-3700 m.

127. Rhododendron commodum Balf. et Forrest

Shrub 1 m tall. Leaves obovate-elliptic; flowers yellow, small; stamens 10 densely hairy to the base; capsule with calyx lobes persistent.

Distribution: Yunnan, at altitude 3300-4000 m.

128. Rhododendron complexum Balf. et Sm.

Low shrub below 1 m high; inflorescence 3-flowered, flower deep rose-purple; stamens 5, included.

Distribution: Yunnan, at altitude 3700-4000 m.

129. Rhododendron concatenans Hutch.

Shrub, flowers yellow, calyx green, filaments white, anthers brown, style pale yellow, stigma green, leaves obovate 5 cm long, 3 cm broad, brownish thick felt beneath.

Distribution: S. E. Tibet, at altitude 3330 m.

130. Rhododendron concinnum Hemsl.

Shrub, branchlets twiggy, densely scaly; Leaves oblong-lanceolate, acute at both ends; inflorescence 3-flowered, purplish, spotted; corolla, 5 lobed, densely scaly outside; ovary 5-celled.

Distribution: Szechuan, at altitude 4150 m.

131. Rhododendron coombense Hemsl.

Dwarf shrub densely branching. Leaves oblong-lanceolate; flowers purple.

Distribution: Szechuan, at altitude 2000-2500 m.

132. Rhododendron cariaceum Franch.

Shrub or small tree 3-9 m tall. Leaves narrow lanceolate, 10-18 cm long, 3-6 cm broad obtuse apex, cuneate or rounded at base; corolla white or white-rose flushed; inflorescence a laxy corymb-racemose, 15-20-flowered; stamens 10-14, unequal, filaments puberulous; capsule more or less curved.

Distribution: Yunnan, and S. E. Tibet, at altitude 3300-3700 m.

133. Rhododendron coryamum Tagg. et Forrest

Shrub 3-7 m tall. Leaves narrowly elliptic or oblong-lanceolate, 7-17 cm long, 1.8-

4 cm broad; inflorescence a laxy racemose umbel of 20–30-flowered; corolla funnel-campanulate, creamy-white, with brownish crimson spots within; stamen 10–12; capsule oblong, blackish, ribbed, 6-chambered.

Distribution: S. E. Tibet, at altitude 4000–4700 m.

134. **Rhododendron corphyeum** Balf. et Forrest

Shrub or tree of 5–7 m high. Leaves oblong-obovate to oblanceolate, 17–44 cm long, 6–12 cm broad, broadest near rounded or subtruncate or retuse apex, gradually tapered to the cuneate base and then decurrent on the very short broad petiole; Primary veins 14–16, under surface white or greyish clothed with thin skin-like or crusted indumentum of aggrutinate hairs; inflorescence a racemose umbel of 20 or more flowers; corolla obliquely campanulate, creamy-white with crimson blotch at base prolonged upwards as spotted streams; lobes 8; stamens 16, shorter than corolla; capsule slightly curved, 3–4 cm long, 1 cm in diameter, sligntly ribbed, rusty – brown to greyish tomentose; Fruit-stalk 5 cm long.

Distribution: N. W. Yunnan, at altitude 4,000 m.

135. **Rhododendron cowaniatum** Fang

Shrub 3–5 m tall. Leaves lanceolate, 10 cm long, 2 cm broad, acute apex, acute at base. Flowers purplish.

Distribution: Szechuan.

136. **Rhododendron cosmetum** Balf. et Forrest.

Shrub 0.5 m high. Leaves oblong-elliptic or oblanceolate. Inflorescence terminal, 2–3-flowered. Flowers purple; calyx bright crimson, lobes ciliate; corolla openly funnel-shaped, thinly pubescent outside; stamens 10, exserted.

Distribution: Yunnan, at altitude 3700–40000 m.

137. **Rhododendron costulatum** Franch.

Shrub with uni-flowers, purplish color.

Distribution: Szechuan.

138. **Rhododendron crassum** Franch.

Shrub or tree 7 m high. Leaves lanceolate or obovate-lanceolate. Flowers white, stamens 15–21; ovary 10-celled.

Distribution: Yunnan, 3000–3300 m.

139. **Rhododendron crinigerum** Franch. var. **euadenium** Tagg. et Forrest

Shrub 3–4 m tall. Leaves lanceolate or oblanceolate, 7–18 cm long, 2–4 cm broad, acuminate apex, cuneate at base; petiole 1.5 cm long, with setose glands. Inflorescence a racemose umbel of 12 flowers; calyx cup-like split almost to the base into 5 lobes; corolla campanulate, 3–4 cm long, white; stamens 10, unequal. Capsule slightly curved, densely glandular.

Distribution: Yunnan, and E. Tibet, at altitude 3300–4300 m.

140. **Rhododendron croceum** Balf. et Sm.

Shrub or tree 5–7 m high. Leaves oblong, 5.5–12 cm long, 2–6 cm broad apex obtuse, base truncate or cordate, margin more or less glandular at base. Inflorescence racemose umbel of 7–8 flowers. Leaves lower surface with vestiges of a thin juvenile indumentum; petiole 2–2.5 cm long; calyx 1 cm long, 5–lobed; corolla cup-shaped, bright yellow.

Distribution: W. Yunnan, at altitude 3700–4300 m.

141. **Rhododendron crentum** Levl.

Small tree, branchlets clad with indumentum and glands in mixture. Leaves broadly oval–lanceolate, 5–7.5 cm long, 2–3 cm broad, apex acute, margin recurved, base obtuse, under surface clad with rusty indumentum; petiole 2 cm long rusty and expanded at base. Flowers in umbel, about 10, white or white flushed with rose; stamens 10, unequal, densely pubescent.

Distribution: E. N. Yunnan.

142. **Rhododendron cucullatum** Handel–Mazz.

Shrub 1–3 m high. Leaves narrow obovate to oblanceolate, 4–8 cm long, 2–3 cm wide, apex blunt, slightly hooded, base narrowed to the petiole. Inflorescence a small compact umbel of many flowers; calyx short glandular; corolla white with crimson spotted; stamens 10, 1–1.5 cm long.

Distribution: Szechuan, and Yunnan, at altitude 3900–4250 m.

143. **Rhododendron cyanocarpum** (Franch.) Sm.

Shrub 1–7 m high. Leaves broadly elliptic to orbicular, 5–11 cm long, 4–7 cm broad, rounded at both ends. Inflorescence a loose umbel of 8–10 flowers; corolla widely campanulate 5–6 cm long, white; stamens 10 unequal.

Distribution: W. Yunnan, at altitude 3300–4300 m.

144. **Rhododendron damascenum** Balf. et Forrest

Shrub below 1 m high. Leaves obovate 1.7 cm long, apex rotundate, base attenuate, margin revolute; calyx white, 5–parted.

Distribution: Yunnan, at altitude 5000–5500 m.

145. **Rhododendron dasycladum** Balf. et Sm.

Shrub 3 m high. Leaves oblong sometimes oblong–elliptic, 5–8 cm long, 2.8–3.8 cm broad. Inflorescence umbel, of 5–8 flowers; corolla, 5–lobed, rose color.

Distribution: N. W. Yunnan, at altitude 4000 m.

146. **Rhododendron dasypetalum** Balf. et Forrest

Shrub 1 m high. Leaves oblong–elliptic. Inflorescence terminal 12–flowered; corolla pale blue color, softly pubescent outside the tube; stamens 10 shortly exserted, pubescent towards the base.

Distribution: N. W. Yunnan, at altitude 3300 m.

147. **Rhododendron davidii** Franch.

Shrub 3–5 m high. Leaves lanceolate or oblong–lanceolate, 10–17 cm long, 3–4 cm broad, apex acute to acuminate, more or less beaked, base cuneate. Inflorescence an elongate raceme of 8–12 flowered; calyx disc–like, with short broadly rounded lobes; corolla openly campanulate, 5 cm long, rose red color or lilac–colored; stamens 14–16.

Distribution: W. Szechuan, at altitude 3300 m.

148. Rhododendron davidsonianum Rehd. et Wils.

Shrub with leggy branches. Leaves narrowly lanceolate or oblanceolate, acute and mucronate apex, subacute at base. Flowers pink with red spots; calyx undulate scaly outside; corolla 5-lobed not scaly-outside; stamens 10.

Distribution: W. Szechuan, at altitude 2000-3300 m.

149. Rhododendron decorum Franch.

Straggling shrub 2-7 m high. Leaves oblong or oblong-ovate, 5-15 cm long, 3-7 cm broad; apex blunt to rounded, base cuneate to obtuse, rarely subrounded, never cordate, under surface pale glaucous green. Inflorescence a racemose corymb of 8-10 flowers; calyx small 6-7-lobed; corolla, white rose.

Distribution: W. Szechuan, Sikang, at altitude 2000-3000 m.

150. Rhododendron dekatanum Cowan

Shrub 1.5 m high. Leaves broadly oblong or oblong-ovate, 3-6 cm long, 2-3.5 cm wide. Flowers in umbel of 3 flowers.

Distribution: S. Tibet, at altitude 3200 m.

151. Rhododendron delavayi Franch.'

Shrub varying in size from 1-12 m high. Young shoots white floccose. Leaves oblong-lanceolate to oblong-oblanceolate, 7-15 cm long, 2-3 cm broad, apex obtuse to acute, base tapered, punctate with small glands and hair flocks, under surface clad with whitish tomentum. Inflorescence a small round compact umbel of 10-20 flowers; pedicel 1 cm long, densely tomentose; calyx with 5 triangular teeth, tomentose more or less glandular; corolla campanulate 4-5 cm long, ovary 8 mm long, conoid, blunt, densely tomentose.

Distribution: W. Yunnan, at altitude 2700-3300 m.

152. Rhododendron dendritrichum Balf. et Forrest

Shrub 3-5 m high. Branchlets clad with dense ash-grey indumentum. Leaves oblanceolate, 10-16 cm long, 3-4.5 cm wide, apex obtuse, somewhat beaked, base tapered. Inflorescence a short raceme-umbel; calyx with 5 minute teeth; corolla 3.5 cm long, white.

Distribution: N. W. Yunnan, at altitude 4000-4700 m.

153. Rhododendron dendrocharis Franch.

Shrub usually epiphytic. Flowers white. Leaves fringed with long hairs; stamens 10, exserted, usually pubescent.

Distribution: E. Tibet and Szechuan, at altitude 2700-3000 m.

154. Rhododendron depile Balf. et Forrest

Shrub 2 m high. Leaves 7 cm long, including the petiole. Blade 5.5 cm long, 3 cm wide, apex obtuse, base broad-obtuse, margin cartiliagineous recurved.

Distribution: W. Yunnan, at altitude 4000 m.

155. Rhododendron denudatum Levl.

Shrub 4 m tall. Leaves lanceolate to oblong–elliptic, 10–15 cm long, 3–5.5 cm wide, acuminate, base cuneate, under surface clad with woolly tomentum; corolla with deep crimson blotch at the base; stamens 10–13.

Distribution: Yunnan, at altitude 3000 m.

156. **Rhododendron desquamatum** Balf. et Forrest

Shrub with densely scaly branchlets. Leaves broadly oblong–elliptic, triangular acuminate and mucronate, 8 cm long, 4 cm wide.

Distribution: W. Yunnan, at altitude 3300 m.

157. **Rhododendron diacritum** Balf. et Sm.

Shrub below 1 m high. Branchlets densely scaly. Leaves elliptic, 1 cm long, densely scaly on both surfaces. Inflorescence terminal, 1–flowered. Flower deep rose–purple, with white throat; stamens 10, exserted; capsule 8 mm long, scaly.

Distribution: Yunnan, at altitude 4300–4700 m.

158. **Rhododendron diaprepes** Balf. et Sm.

Shrub 3–8 m high. Leaves oblong–elliptic to oblong–lanceolate or oblong–oblanceolate 10–30 cm long, 5–10 cm broad, apex abruptly obtuse, base rounded to caudate; petiole 2.5–4 cm long, calyx 5–lobed; corolla funnel–campanulate, as much as 10 cm long, 13 cm across, white flushed with rose; stamens 18–20, 4–7 cm long, filaments hairy at base; capsule large oblong–cylindric, 6.5 cm long, 1.5–2 cm broad, distinctly ribbed, 10–12–chambered.

Distribution; West Yunnan to upper Burma, at altitude 3300–3700 m.

159. **Rhododendron diachroanthum** Diels

Shrub 2 m high. Leaves oblong to obovate–oblanceolate, narrowed to cuneate base, 4–10 cm long, 2–4 cm broad, apex broadly obtuse, upper surface rugulose, under surface clothed with thin greyish white indumentum. Inflorescence an open umbel with 4–8 flowers; corolla campanulate, 4 cm long, 5–lobed with 5 nectary pouches at base, orange flushed with salmon–rose; stamens 10, clustered, around the style, 2–3 cm long, filaments pinkish.

Distribution: W. Yunnan, at altitude 3700–4000 m.

160. **Rhododendron dictyotum** Balf.

Shrub 3–4 m high. Leaves oblong–elliptic, oblong–lanceolate or oblanceolate, 5–12 cm long, 2.5–5 cm broad, apex obtuse, base rounded, under surface clad with felt indumentum; petiole 1.6–2 cm long. Inflorescence loose raceme truss of 8–15 flowers. Flowers white, with rose margins.

Distribution: S. E. Tibet, at altitude 3700–4300 m.

161. **Rhododendron dichropeplum** Balf. et Forrest

Shrub 4 m tall. Leaves coriaceous, oblong, ovate–oblong, 12 cm long, 4 cm wide, obtuse at base, broad mucronate apex.

Distribution: Yunnan, at altitude 3700 m.

162. **Rhododendron didymum** Balf. et Forrest

Shrub very low. Leaves in whorls, obovate, 2–5 cm long, 1–2 cm broad. Flowers in short umbel, with 5 black–crimson lobes, 1 cm long, entire or emarginate.

Distribution: S. E. Tibet, at altitude 4700–5000 m.

163. **Rhododendron dignabile** Cowan

Shrub 3–7 m high. Flowers tinged pink, lemon–yellow, magenta at base. Leaves oblong, 10 cm long, 3.6 cm wide, acute apex, truncate at base, lower surface with brownish indumentum; corolla with apple red white patches, dark crimson blotched at base.

Distribution: S. E. Tibet, at altitude 3700 m.

164. **Rhododendron discolor** Franch.

A robusty shrub in cultivation of 1–2 m high. Leaves oblong – elliptic to oblong-lanceolate, 10–20 cm long, 2.5–7 cm wide. Inflorescence a loose truss of 10 flowers; calyx small but distinctly lobed, lobes triangular; corolla funnel-campanulate, 5–8 cm long, pale pink, becoming white later; stamens 14–16.

Distribution: Szechuan, and Hupeh, at altitude 1300–2700 m.

165. **Rhododendron dolerum** Balf. et Forrest

Shrub 1 m high. Leaves elongate–ovate, 6.5 cm long, 3 cm wide, with purplish glands. Flowers in umbels of 4–5 flowers.

Distribution: W. Szechuan, at altitude 4300 m.

166. **Rhododendron doshangense** Tagg.

A tangled shrub 1 m high. Leaves oval or obovate, Flowers in a racemose umbel; stamens 10, unequal.

Distribution: S. E. Tibet, at altitude 4000–4700 m.

167. **Rhododendron drumonium** Balf. et Ward.

Shrub tufted. Leaves small, elliptic; calyx large 3 mm long; corolla 1.5 cm long, villose within the tube; stamens 10, exserted.

Distribution: Yunnan, at altitude 3300–4000 m.

168. **Rhododendron dryophyllum** Balf. et Forrest

Shrub 3 m high. Leaves oblong-elliptic or oblong-lanceolate, 9–14 cm long, 2.5–3.5 cm broad. Upper surface with yellow–buff indumentum. Inflorescence a racemose–umbel of about 15 flowers; corolla 5 cm long, white.

Distribution: N. W. Yunnan at altitude 3700–4300 m.

169. **Rhododendron dumicola** Tagg. et Forrest

Shrub 1 m tall. Leaves oblong-elliptic, 7 cm long, 3 cm broad. Flowers umbellate 5–7-flowered, white flushed with rose and with faint blotch at the base; corolla campanulate, 5-lobed, rounded, 1–1.5 cm long, 1.5 cm wide.

Distribution: N. W. Yunnan, at altitude 4300 m.

170. **Rhododendron dumosulum** Balf. et Forrest

Shrub 1m high. Branch nodular, annual growth short. Leaves oblong-elliptic to lanceolate, 4–8 cm long, 1–2 cm broad; calyx 1 mm long; corolla obliquely funnel-shaped, 2 cm long, 3 cm across, white flushed with rose.

Distribution: N. W. Yunnan at altitude 4300 m.

171. Rhododendron duseimatum Balf. et Forrest

Shrub 1.5 cm tall. Leaves ovate-oblong, 11 cm long, 3 cm wide, apex apiculate, base broadly obtuse. Inflorescence in umbels of 10-flowered.

Distribution: S. E. Tibet, at altitude 4000 m.

172. Rhododendron eclecteum Balf. et Forrest

Shrub 1 m high. Flowers yellow; calyx cupular-campanulate, 1 cm long, 5-lobed; corolla tubular-campanulate, spotted with basal blotches; stamens shorter than corolla; capsule cylindric, 2 cm long, 7 mm in diameter.

Distribution: Yunnan, at altitude 4300 m.

173. Rhododendron emaculatum Balf. et Forrest

Shrub 2 m tall. Leaves oblong-oblanceolate, 6-12 cm long, 2-3.5 cm wide, apex acuminate, base wedge-shaped, or blunt, under surface clad with grey thin indumentum. Inflorescence umbellate of 10-flowered; corolla deep magenta-rose without marking.

Distribution: S. E. Tibet, at altitude 4700 m.

174. Rhododendron emarginatum Hemsl.

Shrub below 1 m tall. Leaves in whorls of 3-4 obovate, emarginate at the apex, narrow to the base, 4 cm long, 2 cm wide, **punctuate-lepidote** on the lower surface, 1-flowered with a few bracts at base. Flower-stalk 2 cm long, with glands or scaly-glandular; calyx rim-like, scaly outside; stamens 10, exserted; ovary ovoid, short scaly.

Distribution: Yunnan, at altitude 2000 m.

175. Rhododendron epapillatum Balf. et Cooper

Shrub 3-4 m high. Corolla pale pink, spotted with dark-red basal patches.

Distribution: S. E. Tibet, at altitude 3200 m.

176. Rhododendron erastum Balf. et Forrest.

Shrub of a few cm long, creeping, with narrow oblong-lanceolate leaves. Flowers in umbels of 3-4 flowered, clear begonia-pink color; stamens 10.

Distribution: N. W. Yunnan, at altitude 4700 m.

177. Rhododendron eriandrum Levl.

Shrub, 1-2 m tall. Leaves elliptic, obtuse at both ends, slightly mucronate at apex, laxy scaly below. Flowers terminal, 3-4 flowered, deep rose-lavender color with olive-brown marking.

Distribution: Yunnan, at altitude 3000-3300 m.

178. Rhododendron erileucum Balf. et Forrest

Shrub 2.7 m high. Leaves oval, 7 cm long, 3 cm wide, short acuminate apex, obtuse at base, lower surface covered with waxy-white papillae. Flowers white, 3-4, butterfly shaped, with 5 lobes of spreading lim.

Distribution: Yunnan, at altitude 3000-3300 m.

179. Rhododendron eriogynum Balf. et Sm.

Shrub or small tree 3 m high. Leaves lanceolate or oblong-elliptic, 12-20 cm long

5-7.5 cm wide, apex obtuse, base cuneate to rounded, under surface covered with whitish tomentum of stellate hairs and becoming light brown and falling away. Inflorescence racemose umbel of 12-16-flowered; corolla tubular-campanulate, 4-5 cm long, fleshy, reddish, within lobes with dark tinged areas; stamens 10, 2.5-3.5 cm long; capsule oblong ovoid, blunt, 2 cm long, 8 mm broad, slightly curved, blackish, beaked, brown tomentose, 6-chambered.

Distribution: Yunnan, at altitude 3000 m.

180. Rhododendron eritimum Balf. et Sm.

Shrub 6 m tall. Leaves oblong, 10 cm long, 3 cm wide. Flowers purplish red in terminal cluster; calyx and corolla with dense whitish hairs.

Distribution: Yunnan, at altitude 3000 m.

181. Rhododendron edgarianum Rehd. et Wils.

Shrub 1 m high. Leaves elliptic, densely scaly on both surfaces, scales below overlapping, dark reddish brown. Inflorescence terminal 1-flowered, rose-purple; calyx fairy large, 2 mm long, loosely scaly up to the middle outside; corolla funnel-shaped, not scaly outside; stamens 10.

Distribution: W. Szechuan, at altitude 3600-4600 m.

182. Rhododendron edgeworthii Hook.

Shrub 2-3 m tall.

Distribution: S. Tibet, at altitude 2700 m.

183. Rhododendron elegantulum Tagg. et Forrest

Shrub 1-16 m tall. Leaves oblong-elliptic, 5-9 cm long, 1.5-3 cm wide. Flowers in umbels 10-20 flowered; corolla 3 cm long, ridged at base of the tube; stamens 10, unequal; capsule ovoid, 1.5 cm long, densely glandular.

Distribution: Szechuan, at altitude 4000-4700 m.

184. Rhododendron ellipticum Maxim.

Shrub, leaves elliptic, 6-9 cm long, 2.2-4.5 cm broad; stamens 5, glandular. Leaves acuminate apex, cuneate at base undulate incurved margin, lustrous dark green above pale glabrous below; petiole 2-3 cm long, brownish pubescent, glandular. Flowers in terminal racemes.

Distribution: Taiwan, and Liukiu Islands.

185. Rhododendron eritimum Balf. et Sm.

Shrub 4 m tall. Leaves oblong to oblanceolate, or narrow lanceolate, 8 cm long, 2.5 cm wide. Flowers terminal, deep-red-purple.

Distribution: Yunnan, S. Tibet, at altitude 4000 m.

186. Rhododendron erosum Cowan

Shrub 3-7 m tall. Leaves oblong 6 cm long, 2.5 cm wide, brownish felt indumentum under surface, blunt apex, truncate at base. Flowers terminal raceme.

Distribution: S. Tibet, at altitude 3400 m.

187. Rhododendron erubescens Hutch.

Shrub with rigid straight branches. Leaves oblong-elliptic, 7-14 cm long, 3-4 cm broad. Flowers in terminal umbel, 8 - flowered. Flowers white puberulous within; stamens 12-14.

Distribution: S. Szechuan, at altitude 3380 m.

188. Rhododendron erythrocalyx Balf. et Forrest

Shrub 2-3 m tall. Leaves oval oblong-oval to ovate, 7-10 cm long, 3.5-5 cm wide. Flowers terminal umbel of 4-6 flowers; calyx reddish; corolla creamy white; stamens 10 unequal.

Distribution: N. W. Yunnan, at altitude 4300 m.

189. Rhododendron estulosum Balf. et Forrest

Shrub 1-2 m tall. Leaves oblong or oval-oblong, 5-9 cm long, 2.5-4 cm wide. Flowers a laxy umbel, 8-10 flowered; stamens 10, unequal.

Distribution: Yunnan, at altitude 4300-3700 m.

190. Rhododendron esquirolii Levl.

Shrub; leaves oblong-lanceolate, acute - acuminate. Inflorescence axillary, 1-2-flowered; flowers rose-violet; stamens 10, shorter than corolla; ovary and style glabrous.

Distribution: Kweichow.

191. Rhododendron euanthum Balf. et Sm.

Shrub 3-6 m tall. Leaves oblong-elliptic, 7.5 cm long, 3.7 cm wide. Flowers rose-lavender color.

Distribution: Yunnan, at altitude 3350-4000 m.

192. Rhododendron euchaites Balf. et Forrest

Shrub 1.5 cm tall. Leaves oblong or oblong-ovate.

Distribution: Yunnan, at altitude 3000 m.

193. Rhododendron eudoxum Balf. et Forrest

Shrub 2 m tall. Leaves oblong-oval or obovate, 3-7 cm long, 2.5 cm wide. Flowers terminal umbel of 5-6 flowers; calyx subfoliaceous, 7 mm long; corolla tubular-campanulate, deep clear crimson-rose color.

Distribution: W. Yunnan, at altitude 3700-4300 m.

194. Rhododendron euonymifolium Levl.

Shrub small, branchlets glandular. Leaves narrowly cuneate-oblanceolate, mucronate, scarsely emarginate, 4 cm long, 1.5 cm wide; stamens 10, pubescent.

Distribution: Kweichow, and Kwangsi.

195. Rhododendron eurysiphon Tagg et Forrest

Shrub 1-2 m tall. Leaves oblong-lanceolate, 3-5.5 cm long, 1.2-2.5 cm wide Flowers creamy-white. Capsule oblong, 1.5 cm long, 0.5 cm broad.

Distribution: S. E. Tibet, at altitude 3700 m.

196. Rhododendron epipastum Balf. et Forrest

Shrub, leaves oblong-ovate, 7-8 cm long, 2.5 cm wide.

Distribution: Tibet, at altitude 4000 m.

197. Rhododendron exaspermatum Hutch.

Shrub, leaves broadly oblong, 10 cm long, 4.5 cm wide, blunt and mucronate apex, truncate at base, incurved margin, purplish hairy underneath, thick. Flowers terminal raceme, pruplish; corolla 4 cm long, 3 cm broad.

Distribution: S. E. Tibet, at altitude 3150 m.

198. Rhododendron excellens Hemsl.

Shrub 3 m tall. Leaves oblong-elliptic, rounded at both ends, mucronate, 20 cm long, 4-6.5 cm wide, lateral veins 18-20. Flowers white 8 cm in diameter; calyx tubular, 5-lobed; corolla tubular, densely scaly; stamen 15.

Distribution: Yunnan.

199. Rhododendron faberii Hemsl.

Shrub with thick branches. Leaves oblong-oval up to 14 cm long, 4.5 cm broad, apex acute, base rounded, scarcely auriculate, upper surface rugulose, under surface buff-brown, clad with woolly indumentum. Flowers an umbel of 10-flowered; calyx large, 1 cm long split almost to the base into 5 large lobes; lobes ovate, rounded, 1.5 cm long, 2 cm broad; corolla 4 cm long, lobes 5, rounded, slightly emarginate.

Distribution: Szechuan, Mt. Omei.

200. Rhododendron faberioides Balf.

Shrub with somewhat thick tomentose branches. Leaves oblong-oval, 10 cm long, apex, shortly beaked, base somewhat rounded, under surface with dense woolly tomentum. Flowers in umbel, 10-flowered; calyx 1 cm long, split into 5 large lobes, glandular on the back, fringed with glands; corolla 5 lobed, shortly rounded, emarginate; stamens 10, shorter than style.

Distribution: W. Szechuan, at altitude 2700-3000 m.

201. Rhododendron facetum Balf. et Ward.

Shrub 5-7 m tall. Leaves oblong-elliptic to oblong-lanceolate, 12-20 cm long, 4-7 cm wide, apex obtuse, base cuneate to semirounded. Flowers in racemose-umbel of 8-10 flowers; calyx 5 mm long, with 5 unequal triangular lobes; capsule short oblong, blunt, 1.5 cm long, 7 mm broad.

Distribution: Szechuan at altitude 3000 m.

202. Rhododendron faithae Chun

Shrub 4-8 m tall. Leaves elliptic-oblong, 20-25 cm long, 7-9 cm wide, obtuse or rounded at base, acute apex, revolute margin; petiole 2.5-4 cm long; coriaceous. Flowers in terminal racemose-umbel, rachis 4 cm long; corolla white lobes 7, unequal.

Distribution: Kwangtung.

203. Rhododendron fargesii Franch.

Shrub 1-6 m tall. Leaves elliptic to oblong-elliptic, 5-8 cm long, 3.6-4.5 cm wide, apex rounded, base abruptly rounded, truncate to cordate under surface pale glaucous; petiole, 1.5-2.5 cm long, often purplish. Flowers racemose-umbel of 6-10-flowers;

stamens 14.

Distribution: Szechuan, and Hupeh, at altitude 2300-3300 m.

204. **Rhododendron farinosum** Levl.

Shrub 1-2 m high. Branchlets clad with thin tomentum. Leaves oblong-elliptic to obovate, 5-8 cm long, 2-3 cm broad, apex obtuse to rounded, base obtuse to semi-rounded; under surface covered with white woolly tomentum; petiole clad with white tomentum, 1 cm long. Flowers an umbel of 6 flowers; calyx short 5-toothed; corolla 5 unequally lobed, white.

Distribution: Yunnan, at altitude 3000-3300 m.

205. **Rhododendron feddei** Levl.

Shrub, leaves membranaceous, lanceolate, concolored; capsule angustate linear.

Distribution: Kweichow.

206. **Rhododendron farrerae** Tate et Sweet

Shrub with short rigid shining brown branchlets, shoots clothed with villose hairs. Leaves usually 3 at the end of the branchlets, ovate 2.5 cm long, 1.5 cm wide; caly 5-toothed pubescent; corolla, rotate-funnel-form, with narrow tube and spreading un-dulate lobes; stamens 8-10; ovary densely clothed with villose hairs.

Distribution: Kwangtung, and Hongkong.

207. **Rhododendron fastigiatum** Franch.

Shrub 0.5 m tall. Leaves elliptic-lanceolate. Flowers purple, 4-5-flowered.

Distribution: Yunnan, and Szechuan, at altitude 3100 m.

208. **Rhododendron fictolacteum** Balf.

Shrub or tree of 5-12 m high. Branchlets tomentose. Leaves oblong-ovate to ob-lanceolate, 15-30 cm long, 6-12 cm broad; apex obtuse to rounded, base tapered cuneate to rounded or subcordate, upper surface light rugulose, dark green, ultimatl glabrous, under surface clothed with buff to rusty-brown tomentum; petiole 2.5-4 c long, cylindric, not grooved. Inflorescence a corymb of 12-15 flowers, rachis 1.5- cm long; pedicel 3 cm long, pink tinted with white tomentum; calyx 1-2 mm long, thickened rim, with 7-8 short undulate teeth; corolla obliquely campanulate, 3-4 c long, 6.5 cm across, white, creamy white, tinted rose with basal blotch and radiati spots, lobes 7-8, undulate and emarginate; stamens 14-16, 1.5-3.5 cm long, filamen puberulous at base; ovary 1 cm long, densely tomentose, with fasciate hairs, 7- chambered; stigma discoid, pinkish; capsule 3 cm long, 7 mm broad, distinctly ribbe

Distribution: Yunnan, and Tibet, at altitude 3300-4700 m.

209. **Rhododendron fissotectum** Balf. et Forrest

Shrub 2 m tall. Leaves ovate to oblong-ovate, 6 cm long, 3 cm wide, mucro-apicula apex, base cordate or rounded, margin revolute. Flowers in compact umbel, 6-flowere calyx inconspicuous; corolla rose color, 5-lobed.

Distribution: N. W. Yunnan.

210. **Rhododendron fittianum** Balf.

Small aromatic shrub; leaves elliptic–oblong, 3 cm long, 0.5 cm wide.

Distribution: W Yunnan.

211. **Rhododendron flavidum** Franch.

Dwarf shrub. Leaves ovate–oblong, 5–10 cm long, apiculate apex, base rounded.

Distribution: Szechuan, at altitude 3600–4000 m.

212. **Rhododendron flavorufum** Balf. et Forrest

Shrub 1–1.5 cm long, with short stout eglandular branches. Leaves ovate, elliptic or oblong–oval, 4.5–12.5 cm long, 2.5–6 cm wide, apex and base rounded. Flowers in short racemose–umbel of 8–10 flowers; corolla white, 3 cm long, 5–lobed, emarginate; stamens 10, unequal; capsule slightly oblique to pedicel; oblong–ovoid, 1.7 cm long, 5 mm in diameter.

Distribution: S. E. Tibet and Yunnan, at altitude 4000–4700 m.

213. **Rhododendron floccigerum** Franch.

Shrub 1–2 m tall. Leaves narrowly oblong, oblong–elliptic, to semi–lanceolate 5–12 cm long, 1–2 cm wide, apex short acuminate, base wedge–shaped. Flowers in an umbel, 4–7–flowered; calyx saucer–shape, 1–3 mm long; corolla tubular–campanulate, 3.5 cm long, lobes 5, with nectars at base; capsule slightly curved 3 cm long.

Distribution: Yunnan, at altitude 3230 m.

214. **Rhododendron floribunda** Franch.

Shrub or small pyramidal tree, 3–5 m tall. Leaves lanceolate convex above, 7–15 cm long, 3–5 cm broad, apex apiculate, base broadly cuneate, upper surface bullet with scattered stellate hairs first, later glabrous. Inflorescence a racemose umbel of 8–12 flowers; pedicel 1 cm long, white tomentose; calyx cup tomentose, lobes 5, narrow triangular; corolla 5, widely campanulate, 4 cm long, capsule cylindric, 3 cm long 1 cm broad, 8–10–celled.

Distribution: Szechuan, at altitude 1300–2700 m.

215. **Rhododendron fukienense** Franch.

Shrub, leaves lanceolate or oblong–lanceolate, 5–9 cm long, 1.5–2.5 cm wide.

Distribution: Fukien, and Chekiang, at altitude 300–1000 m.

216. **Rhododendron fordii** Hemsl.

Shrub 3 m tall. Leaves obovate–lanceolate 5–7 cm long, rounded apex, with felt tomentum under neath. Flowers in corymb of 4–6–flowered; calyx teeth triangular.

Distribution: Kwangtung.

217. **Rhododendron forrestii** Balf.

A prostrating shrub of 0.5 meter long, climbing over moist boulders and rooting freely from the stems. Leaves broadly ovate or orbicular, from 1 cm or less long to as much as 3 cm long, 0.5–2 cm wide. Flowers solitary, terminal with base persistent of bracts on pedicel; calyx short with 5 lobes, glandular and gland–fringed; corolla tubular–campanulate, 3 cm long, with 5 fleshy pouched nectaries at the base; stamens 10, almost equal, the longest very slightly shorter than the style; capsule oblong, truncate, 1 cm long, 4 mm broad, 5-ribbed, glandular.

Distribution: S. E. Tibet, at altitude 3600 m.

218. Rhododendron fortunei Lindl.

Shrub 3-4 m high. Leaves oblong to oblong-elliptic, 7-17 cm long, 3.5-8 cm wide, apex sub-rounded, sub-obtuse or abrupt-acute, base rounded to truncate or cordulate, under surface pale glaucous green; petiole 2-3 cm long; stamens 14; capsule oblong, ovoid, 2-3 cm long, 1-1.5 cm broad, slightly furrowed, roughened by withered glands.

Distribution: Chekiang, at altitude 1000 m.

Var. 1. Rhododendron fortunei var. houlstonii (Hemsl.) Wils. et Rehd.

Shrub with gray and smooth mark. Leaves oblong, 9 cm long, 3 cm wide, acute apex, broadly cuneate at base, incurved margin, under surface brownish glaucous, glabrous, thick, coriaceous; petiole 3-4 cm long, glandular, brown. Flowers 5 cm long, 6 cm broad, with rim-like calyx.

Distribution: Hupeh.

219. Rhododendron foveolatum Rehd. et Wils.

Shrub with white-tomentose branchlets. Leaves oblong-oblanceolate, apex acute, base attenuate, margin reflexed, 9-10 cm long, 2-3 cm wide, under surface densely tomentose, cinero-foveolate-lanugilose, 10-12 nerves; corolla tubular-campanulate, 5-lobed.

Distribution: Yunnan.

220. Rhododendron fragariflorum Ward.

Shrublets forming carpets not over 0.5 m thick. Leaves elliptic-ovate, aromatic.

Distribution: Southern Tibet, at altitude 5000 m.

221. Rhododendron fuchsiifolium Levl.

Shrub, leaves elliptic-ovate, acute or acuminate, rather densely strigose above, strigose below, flattened hairs on the midrib, otherwise glabrous. Closely related to *R. microphytum* Franch. but differs in the corolla having outside 5 rows of stipitate glands extending from the base to about the middle of the lobes, while the *R. microphyton* the corolla is perfect glabrous outside. In *R. microphton*, there are scattered red-brown hairs on the whole underside, rarely it is near glabrous.

Distribution: Kweichow.

222. Rhododendron fulvastrum Balf. et Forrest

Shrub below 1 m high. Leaves oblong-oval, 3-6.5 cm long, 1-1.7 cm broad. Inflorescence umellate, 4-flowered. Flowers lemon-yellow, without markings, 3-3.5 cm long, lobes 5, rounded, emarginate.

Distribution: S. E. Tibet, at altitude 4700 m.

223. Rhododendron fulvoides Balf et Forrest

Shrub 3-7 m high, clad with scarfy brown indumentum, older shoots nearly bare Leaves oblanceolate or elongated-obovate, apex acute or shortly acuminate, base obtus-

or wedge-shaped, under surface clad with a coarse glanular buff to tawny indumentum. Flowers in a racemose umbel of 20 flowers; calyx saucer shaped, with 5 obscure lobes; corolla campanulate, 5-lobed, emarginate, white, white flushed rose with a crimson basal blotch and a few spots or lines, spreading from it; stamens 10, unequal.

Distribution: N. W. Yunnan, at altitude 4000-4600 m.

224. **Rhododendron** **fulvum** Balf et Sm.

Shrub 1-2 m high. Branches thick fulvous or greyish tomentose about 7 mm in diameter, below the florescences. Leaves obovate to broad oblanceolate, 12-17 cm long, 4-6 cm broad, base rounded, under surface clad with a soft suede-like indumentum. Inflorescence an umbel, a loose rounded truss of about 20 flowers.

Distribution: W. Yunnan, and Tibet, at altitude 2700-3300 m.

225. **Rhododendron** **galactinum** Balf

Shrub 8 m high. Leaves oblong-ovate to lanceolate or oblanceolate, 12-21 cm long, 5-8 cm broad; apex acuminate or obtuse, base broad cuneate or rounded, under surface buff-grey or pale cinnamon, clothed with a velvety indumentum; petiole 3.5 cm long, slightly grooved above near lamina base. Flowers a racemose umbel of about 15 flowers, rachis 1 cm long; calyx short, with 7 triangular teeth of about 1 mm long; corolla bell-shaped, about 3 cm long, pale rose with deep crimson blotches within at base; stamens 14.

Distribution: Szechuan, at altitude 2800-3300 m.

226. **Rhododendron** **genestierianum** Forrest

Shrub up to 4 m tall. Branchlets purplish with long internodes. Leaves clustered oblanceolate, acutely acuminate, long-narrowed to the base, 10-15 cm long, 2.5-4 cm broad, very glaucous below, glabrous above, scales below very few and minute. Inflorescence terminal, racemose, about 12-flowered. Flowers plum-purple, covered with glaucous bloom; calyx small, shortly lobed glabrous; corolla tubular, 5-lobed; stamens 10, glabrous, shortly exserted; ovary 5-celled, glandular, style curved; capsule 1 cm long, loosely scaly.

Distribution: Yunnan, at altitude 4130 m.

27. **Rhododendron** **giganteum** G. Forrest

Shrub or a large tree up to 27 m high, with straight bole, young branches clad with a thin greyish felt-like indumentum. Leaves elliptic or oblanceolate, 12-27 cm long, 4-12 cm broad, apex broadly acute, base narrowed, slightly auricled; upper surface bright mat green, glabrous or with vestiges of indumentum, midrib and primary veins deeply grooved; under surface clothed with a buff or light-cinnamon indumentum, midrib prominently raised, primary veins raised, 21-24 on each side; petiole 2.5-4 cm long. Inflorescence a corymbose-raceme of 20-25 flowers, rachis 4-5 cm long; calyx 2-3 mm long, with 8 small triangular teeth, tomentose; corolla funnel-campanulate 6-6.5 cm long, fleshy, deep rose-crimson at the base, with 8 nectar pouches, lobes 8; stamens 16, unequal, 2.6-4.2 cm long, filaments glabrous; pistil 5 cm long, ovary oblong, 9-12 mm long, clad with dense fawn–pink tomentum, 16–chambered, style stout, glabrous, expanded below the broad discoid stigma; capsule woody, oblong, slightly curved and ridged, 4 cm long, 1.5 cm broad, with deep rusty–brown tomentum, glabrescent.

Distribution: S. W. Yunnan, at altitude 3000 m.

228. **Rhododendron giraudissii** Levl.

Shrub 2 m high. Leaves ovate 9–15 cm long, 3–5 cm broad, riged, coriaceous, base truncate or subcordate, glabrous; petiole 15–20 mm long.

Distribution: Yunnan, at altitude 2700 m.

229. **Rhododendron glanduliferum** Franch.

Shrub. Leaves oblong–lanceolate to oblanceolate, 15 cm long, 3.5–4 cm broad apex, shortly acuminate, margin revolute, base cuneate, under surface pale, glabrous; petiole 2 cm long, rounded, Inflorescence loose umbel of 5–6 flowers, densely glandular with stalked glands; calyx small, with indistict lobes, densely clad with glands; corolla white, 5–6 cm long, densely clad with glands; stamens 14–16 unequal.

Distribution: Yunnan.

230. **Rhododendron glaphyllum** Balf et Forrest

Shrub 0.5 m high. Leaves oval, subsessile, apex rounded or obtuse, apiculate mucronate, base rotundate, margin plane.

Distribution: E. Tibet.

231. **Rhododendron glauco-aureum** Balf. et Forrest

Shrub 20 m high. Leaves oval, persistent, 1.5 cm long, 7 mm wide.

Distribution: W. Yunnan.

232. **Rhododendron glauco-peplum** Balf. et Forrest

Shrub 2–3 m high. Branchlets with vestiges of glands. Leaves ovate or oblong–oval 5–8 cm long, 2–3 cm broad, apex broadly acute, mucronate, base slightly cordate, unde surface greyish white clad with agglutinate indumentum. Flowers in racemose–umbel c about 10 flowers, bright rose, with conspicuous crimson markings.

Distribution: Yunnan, at altitude 3700 m.

233. **Rhododendron glauco–phyllum** Rehd.

Shrub, prostrate, 0.5 m high. Corolla pink, spotted inside, filaments pink, caly pale green.

Distribution: S. E. Tibet, at altitude 3300 m.

234. **Rhododendron glischrum** Balf. et Smith

Shrub or a small tree, 8 m high. Branchlets covered with densely bristly seto: glands. Leaves oblanceolate, 10–25 cm long, 2.5–6 cm broad, apex acuminate, marg fringed with glandular setae, base narrowed or broadly–cuneate or narrowly rounde or cordulate, upper surface marked with more or less vestiges of glandular setae a floccose hairs, under surface clad with long curved dense setae; petiole 2 cm lon covered with bristly setae; calyx split almost to the base into 5 lobes, unequal, oblon obtuse, densely setose glandular; corolla, deep rose 4 cm long, with a crimson blotch base. Capsule oblong, straight or slightly curved, 1.5–2 cm long, 4–5 mm broad, 7–8-chambered, setose glandular, encase at the base in the persistent calyx.

Distribution: N. W. Yunnan, at altitude 4300–4600 m.

35. Rhododendron globigerum Balf. et Forrest

Shrub 1 m high. Leaves oblong-oval to oboval, 3–8 cm long, 1.5–3 cm wide; apex obtuse, base cuneate, under surface clad with woolly fulvous bristrate indumentum; petiole 1 cm long, grey to fawn-tomentose. Inflorescence a compact umbel, densely woolly eglandular; calyx small, undulate tomentose rim; corolla white with crimson markings; stamens 10, unequal.

Distribution: S. W. Szechuan, at altitude 3700–4000 m.

36. Rhododendron grande Wight

Tree 8–10 m high. Leaves oblong, 7 cm long, 3 cm broad, acute apex, slightly cordate at base, margin plane, thick dark green glabrous above, whitish felt below, coriaceous; petiole 2 cm long, thick, brownish glandular, rounded. Flowers in terminal raceme, corolla pink, spotted chiefly on the upper half and deep magenta patch at the base of corolla.

Distribution: S. Tibet.

37. Rhododendron gymnanthum Diels

Shrub 1–2 m high. Leaves persistent, petiolate, chartaceous, oblanceolate, apex acute, base angustate, 10–12 cm long, 2.5–3 cm broad. Flowers rose, with crimson markings, base purple.

Distribution: S. E. Tibet, and Yunnan, at altitude 4300 m.

38. Rhododendron gymnocarpum Balf. et Sm.

Shrub 1 m high. Leaves oblong-elliptic to oblong-oblanceolate, 4–7 cm long, 1.5–2.5 cm broad; apex obtuse, base cuneate to semi-rounded, upper surface slightly rugulose, under surface clad with fawn semi-woolly indumentum of branched hairs, forming a pad over an under layer of many small epidermal glands; petiole 5 mm long, sparsely clad with whitish indumentum or glabrous. Inflorescence a loose umbel, 3–4 flowers; stamens 10; pistil 3 cm long.

Distribution: S. E. Tibet, at altitude 4700 m.

39. Rhododendron gymnogynum Balf. et Forrest

Tree 13 m high. Leaves 9.5 cm long, oblong or oblong-ovate, apex broad-acute, rostrate-mucronate margin, recurved, base obtuse; veins 24 pinnate, obscure sulcate. Inflorescence racemose umbellate of 10 flowers; calyx with 7 deltoide lobes; corolla oblique-campanulate, 3 cm long, 7-lobed, lobes rotundate, emarginate; stamens 14, 2.7 cm long.

Distribution: W. Yunnan and Tibet, at altitude 3700 m.

40. Rhododendron gymnomiscum Balf. et Ward.

Shrub, branchlets setulose. Leaves oblong-elliptic, 2.5 cm long, densely rusty scaly below. Inflorescence terminal, few-flowered, capitate. Flower yellow; calyx well developed 1 cm long, scaly; corolla narrow, tubular, not scaly outside, villose within; stamens 5, included, glabrous; ovary scaly, turbinate.

Distribution: Tibet and Yunnan, at altitude 4700 m.

241. **Rhododendron habrotrichum** Balf. et Sm.

Shrub 3-4 m tall. Leaves elliptic-oblong, 10-18 cm long, 4-8 cm broad, apex abruptly acuminate, margin fringed with long setae, base cordate or rounded, upper surface dark green, under surface pale green punctutate with vestiges of small hairs. Inflorescence a compact many-flowered umbel; rachis short, glandular-setose; corolla 5 cm long, white or pale rose without marking or faintly blotched, lobes 5, unequal; stamens 10, unequal. Capsule 2 cm long 5 mm broad, blackish or glandular-setulose, 6-7-chamber-edencase at the base in the more or less persistent calyx.

Distribution: W. Yunnan, at altitude 3330 m.

242. **Rhododendron haemaleum** Balf. et Forrest

Shrub 1 m tall; Leaves oblanceolate or oblong or obovate, 4-8 cm long, 1.5-2.5 cm broad apex, obtuse or rounded, base tapered and forming a slight wing to the petiole, under surface clad with compact fawn smooth indumentum. Inflorescence a terminal umbel of 3-5 flowers; corolla fleshy, tubular-camapnulate, black crimson 3-4 cm long, tube gibbous at base.

Distribution: S. E. Tibet and Yunnan, at altitude 4000 m.

243. **Rhododendron haematocheilum** Craib

Shrub. Leaves oblong, 7.6 cm long, 3.2 cm broad; coriaceous, apex rotundate or obtuse, apiculate, base rotundate or rotundate-subcordate, petiole stout, channelled above.

Distribution: Yunnan, and Szechuan.

244. **Rhododendron haematodes** Franch.

A dawrf shrub 1 m high. Young shoots woolly tomentose. Leaves oblong to obovate, 4.5-8 cm long, 2-3 cm broad apex, obtuse to rounded, shortly mucronate base cuneate to rounded, upper surface slightly rugulose, under surface densely rufous woolly tomentose; petiole 1 cm long, densely woolly tomentose. Inflorescence an umbel of 6-8 flowers; pedicel 2 cm long, woolly to bristly; corolla 5-lobed, with 5 pouches at base inside crimson colored; stamens 10-12, unequal, 1.5-2.7 cm long.

Distribution: Yunnan, and Tibet, at altitude 3700-4000 m.

245. **Rhododendron hainanense** Merr.

Shrub with many erect twiggy branches. Shoots clad with many flattened appresse grey-brown hairs. Leaves linear-lanceolate, 2-4 cm long, 4-8 mm broad. Flower broad, red, deeply 5 lobed, 1-3 flowered; ovary densely setose-pilose.

Distribution: Eastern China, and Hainan.

246. **Rhododendron hanceanum** Hemsl.

Shrub 1 m high. Leaves ovate-lanceolate to obovate, acutely-acuminate, rounded o obtuse at base, 3.5-7.5 cm long, 2-4 cm broad, finely scaly below. Flowers small, pa yellow; corolla, 5-lobed, not scaly outside.

Distribution: W. Szechuan, at altitude 2300–3000 m.

247. Rhododendron hancockii Hemsl.

Shrub, leaves oblong-elliptic, lanceolate, acute apex, cuneate at base; calyx in small segments, free, unequal, deltoides; corolla white, lobes obovate-elliptic; ovary 6-(5-) chambered.

Distribution: Yunnan, and Kwangsi, at altitude 830 m.

248. Rhododendron hedyosmum Balf

Shrub 30 cm tall. Leaves elongate-oblong, 2 cm long, 7 mm wide, apex mucronate, base obtuse or subcuneate, margin revolute; stamens 5; ovary 5-celled.

Distribution: Szechuan.

249. Rhododendron hedythamnum Balf et Forrest

Shrub 1–2 m tall. Shoot clad with vestiges of glands. Leaves elliptic to rounded, 3.5–5.5 cm long, 3–4 cm broad, midrib grooved with vestiges of gland and hairs. Inflorescence umbellate with 6 flowers; corolla pale rose without spots; stamens 10, 1.3–2.3 cm long; filaments puberulous.

Distribution: Yunnan, at altitude 3700 m.

250. Rhododendron heliolepis Franch.

Shrub or trees up to 10m high. Leaves evergreen, densely scaly below. Inflorescence several-flowered. Flowers violet, mauve or red, often spotted; calyx very small, scaly; corolla more or less funnel-shaped, scaly outside; stamens 10, exserted, glabrescent or rarely glabrous; ovary scaly; style glabrous or pubescent in the lower part; capsule medium-sized.

Distribution: Northern Burma to Kansu, Yunnan and Tibet, at altitude 4000 m.

251. Rhododendron helvolum Balf. et Forrest

Shrub 1–2 m tall. Leaves oblong, 5 cm long, 2 cm broad, blunt and mucronate apex, cuneate at base, under surface covered with brownish felt indumentum, somewhat rugulose on the upper surface; petiole 2 cm long, flattened and winged. Flowers pink, in terminal racemes.

Distribution: Szechuan, and Yunnan, at altitude 4300 m.

52. Rhododendron helyolum Balf. et Forrest

Shrub 2.5 m tall. Leaves oblong, 10.5 cm long, 3.6 cm wide, apex attenuate acute, margin plane, base broad-obtuse. Flowers with flushed rose marking, deepest round the margin of crimson color.

Distribution: Yunnan, at altitude 3700 m.

53. Rhododendron hemidartum Balf.

Shrub 1 m tall. Branchlets clothed with shaggy gland-tipped hairs. Leaves oblong to obovate, 10 cm long, 3.5 cm broad, apex rounded or broadly obtuse, base slightly auricled, upper surface with glaucous bloom, under surface clad with a tawny indumentum. Inflorescence a compact umbel of 10-flowered; calyx 5-lobed, unequal; corolla deep rich crimson without marking, lobes 5, broadly rounded, emarginate, 1 cm long, 1.7 cm broad. Capsule short woody, truncate, cylindric, deeply grooved, 1.3 cm long, 7 mm broad.

Distribution: S. E. Tibet, at altitude 3700–4600 m.

254. **Rhododendron hemitrichotum** Balf. et Forrest

Shrub about 1 m tall. Leaves oblanceolate, acute, 2.5 cm long, 1 cm wide, pubescent above, glaucous below, densley scaly. Inflorescence densely crowded near the apex of the shoots, axillary, 1–2-flowered. Flowers pale rose, deeper on the margin; calyx shortly tubular, not lobed, densely scaly outside; stamens 8, shortly exserted; pubescent towards the base.

Distribution: Szechuan, at altitude 4000 m.

255. **Rhododendron hemsleyanum** Wilson

Shrub 6 m high. Leaves oblong to oblong-ovate, 15–20 cm long, 8–10 cm broad, apex rounded, base deeply auricled-cordate; petiole 5 cm long, glabrous. Inflorescence a racemose-corymb, or 10 or more flowers, 7 cm long; calyx undulate rim, densely clad with long-stalked glands; stamens 10, included; pistil 4.5 cm long, ovary conical, densely glandular, 7 mm long; style glandular throughout with stalked glands.

Distribution: Szechuan, Mt. Omei.

256. **Rhododendron henryi** Hance

Shrub 1 m or more tall. Leaves clustered at the ends of shoots, lustrous green on both surfaces, elliptic-ovate, acutely acuminate, cuminate at the base, 5–10 cm long 2.5–4 cm wide. Inflorescence axillary, 3–4-flowered, flowering stalks densely bristly pilose. Flowers pink; calyx obsoletely undulate lobed; corolla narrowly funnel shaped, 4 cm long, glabrous; stamens 10, exserted.

Distribution: Kwangtung, Kwangsi, Szechuan, Chekiang, Fukien, at altitude 660 2000 m.

257. **Rhododendron heptamerum** Balf

Shrub 2–3 m tall. Leaves oblanceolate, 7 cm long, 2 cm wide, acute apex, cuneate base, incurved margin pubescent on both surfaces. Flowers purple or reddish purple

Distribution: Yunnan, and Tibet, at altitude 4160 m.

258. **Rhododendron hesperium** Balf. et Forrest

Shrub 1–2 m tall. Leaves oblanceolate or oblong-oblanceolate, acute at both end 3–6 cm long, 1–2 cm wide, shining above, laxy scaly below. Inflorescence paired at apex of the shoots, each bud 2–3-flowered, or rarely up to 6-flowered; corolla de rose or rose-lavender, deepest at the base; calyx mere a rim, scaly outside; cord 3 cm long, 5-lobed, but not scaly outside, lobes very slightly so; stamens 10, exserte

Distribution: Yunnan, at altitude 3000–3300 m.

259. **Rhododendron hexamerum** Handel-Mazz.

Shrub, leaves broad-ovate, membranaceous, spatulate, 2 cm long, 4 mm wide, ac apex, cuneate at base; corolla 6-lobed, orbicular, emarginate, rufous-villose; stan

12, 2.5 cm long, filaments glabrous.

Distribution: Szechuan, at altitude 2200–2700 m.

260. **Rhododendron himertum** Balf. et Forrest

Small shrub, branchlets covered with sparesely grey floccose hairs. Leaves narrow obovate or ovate, 3–5 cm long, 1–2 cm broad. Inflorescence umbellate, 4 – flowers; calyx 4 mm long woolly tomentose; corolla 3 cm long, yellow, lobes 5, rounded, emarginate; stamens 10, shorter than corolla and pistil.

Distribution: Yunnan, and Tibet, at altitude 4000–4200 m.

261. **Rhododendron hippophaeoides** Balf et Sm.

Shrub about 1 m tall. Leaves scattered, spreading, narrowly oblong – lanceolate, obtusely mucronate, gradually narrowed to the base. Inflorescence terminal, 6–8-flowered, usually compact. Flowers pale lilac to rose, not spotted; stalks scaly; calyx 5-lobed; corolla with a short wide tube, hairy inside, spreading near the right angles, not scaly, not notched; stamens 10, exserted.

Distribution: Yunnan, and Szechuan, at altitude 3180 m.

262. **Rhododendron hirsuticostatum** Handel–Mazz.

Shrub with straight leggy branches and semi–deciduous leaves. Leaves narrow oblong, gradually narrowed to an obtuse apex, obtuse at the base, 4–5 cm long, 1.5–2 cm broad, softly pubescent on the lower half of the midrib below. Inflorescence terminal and axillary, 2–flowered. Flowers white rose not spotted; ovary 5 – celled, densely scaly.

Distribution: Szechuan, at altitude 2200–2500 m.

263. **Rhododendron hirtipes** Tagg.

Shrub or a gnarled tree of 6–8 m high. Shoots and petioles with bristly setose glands; bud scales not very persistent. Leaves oblong-oval, oval or broadly–elliptic, apex well-rounded, base rounded to cordulate, margin first ciliate, finely asperous, with the bases of the fallen cilia. Inflorescence a somewhat laxy umbel of 3–5 flowers; calyx split to the base into 5, unequal lobes, fringed with glands; corolla 4 cm long, whitish to rose-pink, spotted with carmine dots, 5 lobes ovate, emarginate.

Distribution: S. E. Tibet, at altitude 4100 m.

264. **Rhododendron hogsonii** Hook. f.

Shrub or tree 10–13 m high, with few branches. Leaves oblong spatulate, about 40 cm long, 14 cm wide at the middle, blunt apex, tapering down to an obtuse base, margin entire, dark lustrous green above, yellowish brown felt–like indumentum below; midrib and primary veins prominent below and impressed above, thick, leathery; petiole thick, 4 cm long, grooved above, glabrous, brown and glandular below. Flowers pale blush deeper pink where lobes join; bright magonta patch at base of upper half of the corolla, filaments and ovary white; style tinged rose; stigma lemon green; anthers brown.

Distribution: S. Tibet, at altitude 4000 m.

65. **Rhododendron honkongense** Hutchinson

Shrub, leaves more or less oblanceolate or obovate-oblanceolate, narrowed to the base, broadest about or above the middle. Flowers white with violet specks; calyx lobes small, rounded, and densely fringed with shortly stalked glands. Capsule warted, scarcely 2.5 cm long, the persistent calyx-lobes becoming reflexed.

Distribution: Hongkong and Kwangtung, at altitude 800 m.

266. **Rhododendron hormophorum** Balf. et Forrest

Shrub 1-2 m tall. Flowers lavender, pinkish purple. Leaves oblong-elliptic, 5 cm long, 1.5 cm wide, acute apex, cuneate at base, entire margin; petiole 1 cm long, glandular, brownish pubescent.

Distribution: S. Szechuan, at altitude 3240 m.

267. **Rhododendron horeum** Balf. et Forrest

Shrub 0.5 m tall, with leaves crowded in rosettes, young shoots clad with whitish tomentum. Leaves obovate, 3-5 cm long, 1-2 cm broad, apex rounded, base wedge-shaped from the widest part, but in short leaves more obtuse, under surface clad with thick indumentum with a soft woolly surface, midrib prominent wide at base, tapering to apex. Inflorescence umbel of 4 flowers; corolla 5-lobed deep crimson, with 5 pouches at base; stamens 10.

Distribution: S. Tibet, at altitude 4130 m.

268. **Rhododendron horaeum** Balf. et Forrest

Shrub 0.5 m tall. Leaves oblong, 5 cm long, 2 cm wide, acute at apex, and mucronate, base cuneate, bluish glaucous beneath. Flowers carlet red.

Distribution: Tibet, at altitude 4000 m.

269. **Rhododendron houlstonii** Hemsl. et Wils.

Shrub 2-4 m tall. Leaves oblong-oblanceolate, oblong-elliptic 7-15 cm long, 2.5 cm wide, apex rounded or obtuse, abruptly cuspidate, base obtuse rounded to cuneate Inflorescence umbellate 6-10-flowered; calyx small, oblique, shortly toothed glandular stamens 14, unequal. Capsule bluish purple, cylindric, 2.5 cm long, 7 mm broad.

Distribution: Hupeh, and Eastern Szechuan, at altitude 1500-2300 m.

270. **Rhododendron huianum** Fang

Shrub 5 m tall. Leaves oblong-lanceolate, 10-14 cm long, 2.5-3.5 cm broad, ape abruptly acuminate, base cuneate or broadly cuneate, veins 18-20; corolla lilac colored, 7-lobed, ovate slightly emarginate; stamens 12-14.

Distribution: Szechuan, at altitude 1200-3000 m.

271. **Rhododendron humicola** Fang

Shrub 15 cm tall. Leaves rounded or oval, 2.5 cm long, 2 cm broad, blunt ape obtuse at base, incurved margin, under surface brownish tomentose, bristly hairy young stems, petioles and midribs. Flowers in terminal racemes, purple; calyx red.

Distribution: Yunnan, at altitude 4130-4500 m.

272. **Rhododendron hunnewellianum** Rehd. et Wils.

Shrub 2-5 m high. Leaves narrowly oblong-lanceolate, rarely narrow-lanceola

7-15 cm long, 1.5-2.5 cm broad, apex acuminate, base tapered, wedgeshaped, under surface clad with white indumentum; petiole 1-1.5 cm long, thinly floccose glandular. Inflorescence racemose umble, of 7-flowered, calyx clad with white hairs and small glands. Capsule cylindric, 2-2.5 cm long.

Distribution: W. Szechuan, at altitude 2000-3300 m.

273. **Rhododendron hylothreptum** Balf. et Sm.

Shrub 2 m tall. Flowers pinkish purple, white at base, corolla lobes spotted. Leaves oblong, 9 cm long, 3.5 cm broad, blunt and mucronate apex, obtuse at base, entire margin, coriaceous, petiole 2 cm long, glandular.

Distribution: Yunnan, at altitude 3700-4000 m.

274. **Rhododendron hyperythrum** Hayata

Shrub. Leaves oblong to elliptic-oblong, or elliptic-lanceolate, 7-12 cm long, 2-3.5 cm broad, apex subacute or shortly acuminate, base obtuse; petiole 1.5-2.5 cm long, calyx saucer-shaped, with 5 small teeth; corolla funnel-campanulate, purple spotted; stamens 10, unequal.

Distribution: Taiwan, central region of the Island.

275. **Rhododendron hypoglaucum** Hemsl.

Small tree or shrub up to 6 m tall. Leaves oblong-elliptic, oblong-lanceolate, or oblanceolate, 6-11 cm long, 2-4 cm broad, apex triangular-acuminate, deflexed with a stiff mucron, base narrowed obtuse to semi-rounded, under surface clad with white tomentose; petiole 1-1.5 cm long, rounded; stamens 10-12, unequal.

Distribution: Hupeh, at altitude 1600-2700 m.

276. **Rhododendron hypolepidotum** Balf. et Forrest

Shrub, aromatic, 1.5 m tall. Leaves crowded at the tops of branches, petiotate, the petiole 3 mm long, oblong, base obtuse, perminent scaly on the back; scales rather numerous, scattered; corolla campanulate, yellow, 5-lobed.

Distribution: N. W. Yunnan, at altitude 4300 m.

277. **Rhododendron hypophaeum** Balf. et Forrest

Shrub 1-2 m tall. Branchlets with scattered scales. Leaves oblanceolate to oblong, acutely acuminate, subacute at the base, 4-6 cm long, 1.5-2.5 cm wide, Flowers white rose; calyx a mere rim; corolla 5-lobed not scaly outside; ovary 5-celled, densely scaly.

Distribution: S. W. Szechuan, at altitude 3700 m.

278. **Rhododendron idoneum** Balf. et Sm.

Small shrub, branchlets covered with small black scales. Leaves broadly elliptic, 2.5 cm long, 1 cm broad, densely scaly on both surfaces. Inflorescence 1-2-flowered, terminal. Flowers mauve or light purplish-blue; stamens 10, long-exserted, villose towards the base; ovary scaly, style much longer than the stamens. Capsule 3 mm long, sparingly scaly.

Distribution: Yunnan, at altitude 5000-5300 m.

279. Rhododendron igneum Cowan

Shrub 3–4 m tall. Leaves elliptic or broadly elliptic or subobovate, 3–7.5 cm long, 2–3.5 cm wide, apex acute, obtuse sub-rotundate base, margin plane. Inflorescence 2–3-flowered, sub-terminal.

Distribution: Tibet, at altitude 2800 m.

280. Rhododendron imberbe Hutchinson

Shrub, branchlets scaly. Leaves oblong, shortly acuminate, obtuse to truncate at base, incurved margin, under surface glaucous, coriaceous; petiole 2 cm long, glandular. Flowers in terminal racemes.

Distribution: S. W. China.

281. Rhododendron impeditum Balf. et Sm.

Shrub cushion-like, about 0.5 m high. Leaves broadly elliptic, densely scaly on both surfaces. Scales below overlapping, very pale yellow-green. Flowers deep purple-blue, white inside the throat; stamens 10, exserted, villose towards the base; ovary scaly, longer than the stamens.

Distribution: Yunnan, at altitude 4300–4700 m.

282. Rhododendron indicum Sweet

Shrub 2 m high; usually low or prostrate, clothed with chestnut-brown hairs. Leaves crowded, persistent, subcoriaceous, narrow lanceolate or lanceolate to oblanceolate, 2–4 cm long, 4–12 mm wide, acute at apex and base, crenate serrulate and ciliolate margin, with scattered red-brown hairs on both surfaces. Inflorescence 1–2-flowered, covered with strigose brown hairs; corolla bright red to scarlet, sometimes rose-red.

Distribution: Hongkong, and Japan.

283. Rhododendron inopinum Balf.

Low shrub. Leaves oval-oblong, 4–12 cm long, 2–4 cm broad, acute to acuminate apex, base rounded or obtuse. Inflorescence a racemose umbel of 10 flowers; stamens 10, unequal.

Distribution: Szechuan.

284. Rhododendron iodes Balf. et Forrest

Shrub 2–3 m high. Leaves lanceolate, rarely oblanceolate, 6–11 cm long, 2.5 cm broad, apex acute, margin slightly recurved, base tapered. Inflorescence a racemose umbel of 10–12 flowers; calyx with 5 short lobes; corolla white with crimson spots but without basal blotch, lobes 5, 1.2 cm long. Capsule cylindric, straight, 1.5 cm long, 5 mm broad, 6–8-chambered.

Distribution: S. E. Tibet, at altitude 4000 m.

285. Rhododendron insculptum Hutchinson

An epiphyte. Leaves whorled, broadly obovate-spathulate.

Distribution: S. E. Tibet, at altitude 2000–2300 m.

286. Rhododendron insigne Hemsl.

Shrub 2–4 m high. Leaves oblong-lanceolate or oblong-oblanceolate, 7–13 cm long,

2-4.5 cm wide. Inflorescence a short laxy corymb of 8 or more flowers; corolla deep pink with crimson spots inside; stamens 10-14.

Distribution: Szechuan, at altitude 2300-2600 m.

287. **Rhododendron intortum** Balf. et Forrest

Shrub 3 m tall. Leaves oblong-oval, 8.5 cm long, 4 cm wide, apex acuminate, margin plane. Inflorescence in racemose umbel; corolla white.

Distribution: N. W. Yunnan, at altitude 4300-4460 m.

288. **Rhododendron intricatum** Franch.

Shrub 1 m high. Leaves elliptic densely covered with scales. Flowers bluish pink or blue; calyx short scaly outside; corolla narrow tubular; stamens 10, not exserted, slightly pubescent towards the base.

Distribution: W. Szechuan 4000-4500 m.

289. **Rhododendron invictum** Balf. et Farrer

Shrub 2 m high. Leaves elliptic or oblong - elliptic, obtuse at apex, rounded or broadly obtuse at the base, 2.5-4 cm long, 2.5 cm wide, Inflorescence terminal, 2 or more flowered. Flowers purple, stamens 10, exserted, pubescent towards the base; style hairy at the base. Capsule 1.3 cm long, scaly.

Distribution: Kansu, at altitude 2700-3000 m.

290. **Rhododendron irroratum** Franch.

Small tree 8 m high. Branchlets tomentose. Leaves lanceolate or oblanceolate narrowly elliptic, 5-12 cm long, 1.5-3 cm broad, narrowed to both ends, apex acute, margin more or less undulate; petiole 1.5-2 cm long, distinctly grooved above. Inflorescence laxy racemose umbel of about 15 flowers; rhachis rufous glandular; pedicel densely glandular with short clavate glands; calyx small, densely glandular, 5-lobed, rounded or broadly triangular; corolla tubular-campanulate, 3-5 cm long, white or creamy yellow, deep rose color; stamens 10, unequal. Capsule oblong cylindric, 2.5-3 cm long, 8 mm broad, purplish-brown, grooved, warted by the withered glands, 8-10-chambered.

Distribution: Mid-West Yunnan, at altitude 2400-2800 m.

291. **Rhododendron juncundum** Balf. et Sm.

Shrub or tree, 2-7 m high. Leaves elliptic or elliptic-oblong, 5-7 cm long, 2.5-3.5 cm broad; apex broadly obtuse, apiculate, base rounded to cordulate, under surface glaucous with waxy papillae punctuate with minute vestiges of glands and hairs, but to the eye glabrous at maturity; petiole 1.5 cm long clad with long-stalked setose glands. Inflorescence an umbel of 5-7 flowers; calyx densely glandular, lobes unequal, oblong-obtuse or rounded, 2-5 mm long; corolla pale rose or almost white, 3.5 cm long, emarginate, 1.2 cm long.

Distribution: Mid-west Yunnan, at altitude 3300-4000 m.

292. **Rhododendron kanehirae** Wils.

Shrub 3 m tall. Branchlets clothed with chestnut-brown hairs. Leaves persistent, dimorphic, spring leaves linear-lanceolate to oblong-lanceolate, 2-5 cm long, 2-4 mm wide, acute and mucronate apex, attenuate at base, obscurely crenate serrulate margin, dark green above, pale beneath, clothed on both sides with shining brown strigose hairs. Summer leaves with linear-lanceolate to narrow obovate, 2-5 cm long, 2-3 mm wide, acute or rounded at apex, otherwise like the spring leaves; petiole 2 mm long, densely clothed with setose hairs. Inflorescence 1-2-flowered, densely clothed with chestnut-brown hairs; corolla narrow funnel-form, 3 cm long, 2.5 cm broad, carmine-red to scarlets color; stamens 10, unequal, shorter than corolla, filaments pubescent below the middle. Capsule cylindric-oblong, 1 cm long, setose.

Distribution: Taiwan.

293. Rhododendron kawakamii Hayata

Shrub 1-2 m tall, usually epiphytic, branchlets usually glandular. Leaves obovate, slightly apiculate, about 5 cm long, 2.5-3 cm wide, finely punctuate glandular below. Inflorescence umbelllate of 3-4 flowers; stamens 10, unequal, villose at the base. Capsule 12 mm long, minutely scaly.

Distribution: Taiwan, at altitude 2300 m.

294. Rhododendron keleticum Balf. et Forrest

Shrub semi-prostrate. Leaves obovate-elliptic, very mucronate, weakly ciliate, densely scaly below. Inflorescence terminal, 1-2 flowered. Flowers deeply crimson with dark marking; stamens 10, exserted, pubescent towards the base; ovary scaly; style pubescent. Capsule short, enclosed by the persistent calyx.

Distribution: S. E. Tibet, at altitude 4500 m.

295. Rhododendron keysii Nutt.

Shrub 1-3 m tall. Leaves oblanceolate, 8-10 cm long, 3.5 cm wide, acuminate apex, obtuse at base, incurved margin; corolla salmon pink, lobes yellowish.

Distribution: S. E. Tibet, at altitude 3000 m.

296. Rhododendron kongboense Kingdon Ward et Ruthschild

Small shrub, leaves aromatic, oblong-lanceolate, obtuse on both ends, 2-2.5 cm long, 0.7-1 cm wide, shining and lepidote with small black scales above, completely covered with felt of brown overlapping scales below. Flowers terminal, rose color; stamens 5, filaments glabrous.

Distribution: Tibet, at altitude 3300 m.

297. Rhododendron kwangtungense Merr. et Chun

Shrub 2.5 m tall.

In general aspect it allies to R. mariae Hance, but differs in its white flowers and in its capitate glandular indumentum, the capitate hairs being mixed with the longer spreading bristle-like hairs on the branchlets, petioles, pedicels, and younger leaves.

Distribution: Kwangtung, at altitude 450 m.

298. Rhododendron lacteum Franch.

Small tree of 5-10 m tall. Branchlets more or less modular with conspicuous scars on the fallen leaves. Leaves oblong-elliptic, broadest slightly above the middle, 10-17 cm long, 6–8 cm broad, apex rounded with short acuminate tip, margin somewhat undulate, base cordate or cordulate, upper surface slightly rugulose, at maturity glabrous or with vestiges of hairs, under surface clad of white indumentum. Inflorescence in large racemose umbel, 15–20 cm across, of 20–30 flowers; rachis 3 cm long, floccose-pubescent; calyx small, with 5 minute teeth; corolla wide-campanulate with rounded base, 4.5 cm long, creamy white to a clear canary-yellow, unspotted, lobes 5, emarginate; stamens 10, unequal, 1.5–2.5 cm long, filaments puberulous at the base; pistile 3 cm long; ovary 7 mm long; stigma small, lobulate. Capsule curved, 3 cm long, 5 mm broad, clad with remains of the ovary indumentum, 10-chambered.

Distribution: Yunnan, at altitude 4000 m.

299. Rhododendron lampropeplum Balf. et Forrest

Shrub about 1 m tall. Leaves oblong or oblong-oval, 3.5–5 cm long, 1–2.5 cm broad, under surface clad with thick brown woolly indumentum. Inflorescence small compact many-flowered umbel. Flowers white, flushed with rose, crimson spotted.

Distribution: S. W. Szechun, at altitude 4000–4700 m.

300. Rhododendron lanatum Hook. f.

Shrub 1–3 m tall; corolla pale yellow, spotted on adaxial side, filaments and style white, stigma green, pedicel green with brown hairs. Leaves upper surface with pale green indumentum, lower surface clad with brown indumentum densely. Leaves oblong, 10 cm long, 4–6 cm wide, minutely acuminate apex, truncate at base, margin plane; petiole thick, rounded clad with dense brownish felt-like indumentum, 2 cm long.

Distribution: S. E. Tibet, at altitude 3700–4300 m.

Var. 1. Rhododendron lanatum var. luciferum Cowan

Flowers lemon yellow; corolla creamy with bright red spotting.

The narrower oblong leaf with pointed apex separates this variety from its type species. The indumentum of the dried leaves is skinned off rooled up and sold by the Tibetans as wicks for their butter lamp. The varietal name luciferum means "bringing Light".

Distribution: S. Tibet, at altitude 4800 m.

301. Rhododendron lasiopodum Hutchinson

Shrub 5 m high. Leaves broadly elliptic, rounded at both ends or shortly triangular acuminate at the apex. Inflorescence 2-flowered, tomentose at base. Flowers white, yellow inside the base, fragrant; corolla funnel-shaped laxy scaly all over; stamens 10, softly villose lower half. Capsule 2.5 cm long, straight, densely scaly.

Distribution: W. Yunnan, at altitude 2700–3000 m.

302. Rhododendron lasiostylum Hayata

Upright much branched shrub, 1 m tall. Branchlets clad with brownish hairs. Leaves deciduous, dimorphic. Spring leaves lanceolate to ovate - lanceolate, rounded and mucronate apex, cuneate at base. Inflorescence 2–4-flowered; stalks densely covered with brown hairs; corolla funnelform, pink, with spreading lobes; stamens 10, unequal, as long as the corolla lobes, papillose below the middle. Capsule cylindric-ovoid, 1 cm long, densely strigose.

Distribution: Taiwan, at altitude 2300 m.

303. **Rhododendron laxiflorum** Balf. et Forrest

Shrub 4-7 m tall. Leaves oblanceolate to oblong-elliptic, 8-13.5 cm long, 2-4 cm broad, apex broadly acute to obtuse, margin roughened; base cuneate, upper surface with vestiges of hairs and glands, lower surface minutely punctate of red. Inflorescence a loose racemose umbel, 12 flowers; rachis sparsely glandular. Capsule oblong-cylindric, blunt, 2-2.5 cm long, 8-10 mm broad, straight or slightly curved, 8-10 chambered.

Distribution: Yunnan, at altitude 2700 m.

304. **Rhododendron leclerei** Leu.

Shrub, branchlets scaly. Leaves lanceolate, acute 5-7 cm long, 2-2.5 cm wide, reticulate above, densely covered with scales below. Flowers blue; stamens 10, slightly exserted, glabrous; ovary densely scaly.

Distribution: Yunnan, at altitude 3330 m.

305. **Rhododendron ledoides** Balf. et Sm.

Shrub about 1 m high. Leaves linear-lanceolate, acutely mucronate apex, under surface densely clad with flaky scales. Inflorescence dense capitate, terminal, subglobose. Flowers pale rose; corolla narrow tubular, not scaly outside, villose within; stamens 5, included, filaments glabrous. Capsule scaly, clad with persistent corolla.

Distributiion: Yunnan, at altitude 4000-4700 m.

306. **Rhododendron leilungense** Balf. et Forrest

Shrub about 1 m tall. Leaves broadly ovate-elliptic, rounded to small mucro at apex, rounded to subacute base. Inflorescence terminal and axillary. Flowers pale rose; calyx saucer-shapedd, scarcely lobed; corolla 5-lobed, tube not scaly outside, lobes minutely scaly; stamens 10, pubescent in the lower part.

Distribution: Yunnan, at altitude 3000 m.

307. **Rhododendron leiopodum** Hayata

Shrub 1-2 m tall. Leaves clustered at the ends of the shoots, fascicled lateral, 1-flowered, varying from pink to white.

Distribution: Taiwan, at altitude from 160-2666 m.

308. **Rhododendron lepidanthum** Balf. et Sm.

Shrub tortuously branched up to 2 m high. Leaves aromatic, broadly elliptic impressed reticulate above, covered below with loose flaky scales. Inflorescence terminal, capitate, 8-flowered, flower stalks 8 mm long, densely scaly; stamens 5, included, slightly hairy towards the base.

Distribution: Yunnan, and Tibet, at altitude 3700-4300 m.

309. **Rhododendron leptothrium** Balf. et Forrest

Shrub or tree 8 m tall. Leaves oblanceolate, 6 cm long, 2 cm wide, acute on both ends. Flowers purpish red, in terminal racemes.

Distribution: Yunnan, and Szechuan, at altitude 4200 m.

310. **Rhododendron leucandrum** Levl.

Shrub, leaves ovate, coriaceous, margin revolute undulate, petiolate, brownish punctate. Flowers rose; stamens 10, white villose at base, stigma bilobed.

Distribution: Kweichow.

311. **Rhododendron leucaspis** Tagg

Shrub; calyx with 2 sepals red and 3 sepals green, corolla white, salver-shaped, sometimes with a pinkish tinge; filaments creamy, anther dark brown; ovary green; stigma brownish.

Distribution: S. E. Tibet.

312. **Rhododendron leucopetalum** Balf. et Forrest

Small shrub 1 m tall. Leaves obovate 5.5 cm long, 3 cm broad. Flowers in terminal umbel, of 4-6 flowers; corolla openly campanulate, pure white, 3.7 cm long, tube glabrous, somewhat fleshy, 5-gibbous at base.

Distribution: N. W. Yunnan, at altitude 4000-4300 m.

313. **Rhododendron levinei** Merr.

Shrub 3-4 m tall, with ridged moderate stout branches, dotted with glistening chestnut brown lepidote glands and strigose hairs. Leaves clustered elliptic to elliptic-obovate, 4.5-8 cm long, 2.5-4 cm wide, rounded or truncate, emarginate, base rounded or slightly abruptly narrowed, margin slightly recurved, ciliate, upper surface with few scattered setose hairs, lower surface glaucescent, densely dotted with glistening chestnut brown lepidote glands. Fruit ellipsoid, 2.5 cm long, 1.5 cm broad.

Distribution: Kwangtung.

314. **Rhododendron levistratum** Balf. et Forrest

Shrub 2-3 m tall. Leaves lanceolate, oblong - lanceolate, 5-9 cm long, 2-3.5 cm broad apex acute, base obtuse. Inflorescence a racemose umbel of 15-flowered; corolla white, flushed with rose, without basal blotch, but copiously spotted crimson, lobes 5, crenulate.

Distribution: N. W. Yunnan, at altitude 4000-4300 m.

315. **Rhododendron liliiflorum** Levl.

Shrub 2 m tall. Leaves oblonceolate, shortly narrowed at the base, 6-14 cm long, 2-4 cm wide, leathery, finely scaly below, lateral nerves 10, pairs. Flowers white, fragrant; calyx lobed to nearly the base on one side only sparingly scaly outside; corolla funnel-shaped, lobes slightly fringed with short hairs; stamens 10, rather short; ovary 5-celled, scaly.

Distribution: Yunnan, and Kweichow, at altitude 1800 m.

316. **Rhododendron lindleyi** T. Moore

Shrub 2-3 m tall. Leaves oblong, 10 cm long, 4 cm wide, mucronate blunt apex, truncate at base, thick coriaceous. Flowers fragrant, pure white with golden patch inside at base, lobes sometimes with a faint pink tinge; calyx green, spotted and striate rose, filaments 10, creamy, anthers brown, style green at base, reddish at upper end. Inflorescence 3-4 flowered.

Distribution: S. Tibet, at altitude 2800 m.

317. Rhododendron liratum Balf. et Forrest

Shrub 0.5 m tall. Leaves oblong-ovate, 5 cm long, 2 cm broad. Flowers in umbel of 1-2-flowered.

Distribution: W. Yunnan, at altitude 3700 m.

318. Rhododendron litangense Balf.

Shrub 0.5 m tall. Leaves oblong-elliptic 2.5 cm long, loosely scaly on both surface. Inflorescence terminal, 1-2-flowered. Flowers dull purple; corolla not scaly outside; stamens 10, exserted.

Distribution: S. W. Szechuan, at altitude 4000-4300 m.

319. Rhododendron litiense Balf. et Forrest

Shrub 1-3 m high. Leaves oblong or oblong-oval, 4-7.5 cm long, 2-3 cm broad. Inflorescence a racemose umbel of 5-6-flowers; corolla yellow, without blotch at base, 2-3 cm long, glabrous outside, lobes 5, emarginate, undulate.

Distribution: Yunnan, at altitude 3000-3300 m.

320. Rhododendron lochimum Balf.

Shrub with leggy branches. Leaves oblanceolate, acuminate apex, acute at base. Inflorescence terminal and axillary on the upper leaf-axils, 3-4-flowered; corolla 5-lobed, glabrous outside; stamens 10, exserted; ovary 5-celled, densely scaly.

Distribution: West Szechuan.

321. Rhododendron longesquamatum Schneider

Shrub 3-3 m tall, sometomes much larger. Leaves oblong oblong-obovate, or oblong-oblanceolate, 6-12 cm long, 2-4 cm broad, apex obtuse to acute, base obtuse to sub-rounded or somewhat auricled, margin first ciliate, somewhat asperuos finally. Inflorescence racemose umbel of 12 flowers, lower surface of leaves, somewhat punctate with minute glands; corolla openly campanulate, 4 cm long, pink to rose, blotched deep crimson at the base; stamens 10, unequal.

Distribution: W. Szechuan, at altitude 3300-4000 m.

322. Rhododendron longiperulatum Hayata

Shrub clothed with appressed chestnut-brown hairs. Leaves scattered, chartaceous, sub-persistent, ovate to ovate-lanceolate, 1.5-2 cm long, 3-4 mm wide. Flowers red, 5-lobed. Capsule ovoid-oblong nearly 1 cm long, strigose.

Distribution: Taiwan.

323. Rhododendron longipes Rehd. et Wilson

Shrub 1-2.5 m tall. Leaves oblanceolate, acuminate apex, cuneate at base, 8-13 cm long, 2-3.5 cm wide. Flowers in umbellate raceme of 10-15 flowers; corolla rose color; stamens 12.

Distribution: W. Szechuan at altitude 2000–2500 m.

324. Rhododendron longistylium Rehd.

Shrub 2 m tall. Leaves narrowly oblanceolate, narrowed from the above to the middle to the base, 2.5–5 cm long, 1–1.5 cm broad, laxy scaly below.

Distribution: W. Szechuan, at altitude 1000–2300 m.

325. Rhododendron lophophorum Balf. et Forrest

Shrub 2–3 m tall. Leaves oblong-elliptic or obovate, 5–10.5 cm long, 2.5–3.5 cm broad, apex obtuse, base narrowly obtuse, upper surface with vestiges of glands and floccose hairs, under surface buff dull tawny, clad with punctate persistent glandular-punctulate indumentum of agglutinate hairs; corolla white flushed rose.

Distribution: Yunnan, at altitude 4300 m.

326. Rhododendron lophogynum Balf. et Forrest

Shrub 1 m tall. Leaves oblanceolate. Inflorescence terminal, 3-flowered.

Distribution: Yunnan, at altitude 3300–3700 m.

327. Rhododendron lopsangianum Cowan

Shrub 1–2 m tall. Leaves oblong-elliptic 7 cm long, 4 cm wide, obtuse on both ends, margin recurved.

Distribution: S. Tibet, at altitude 3700 m.

328. Rhododendron ioptotogynum Balf. et Forrest

Shrub with very small oblong clustered leaves.

Distribution: Yunnan.

329. Rhododendron mackenzianum Balf. et Forrest

Shrub or tree 6–7 m tall. Leaves elliptic-lanceolate, 10 cm long, 3 cm wide, acute apex, cuneate at base, incurved margin, coriaceous; petiole 2–3 cm long, rounded, brown glabrous. Flowers red, in terminal raceme, some flowers white, flushed with rose at base.

Distribution: Yunnan, at altitude 200–2100 m.

330. Rhododendron maculiferum Franch.

Shrub 2–10 m tall. Leaves oblong-oval, elliptic or obovate, 6–11 cm long, 2.5–4.5 cm broad, apex obtuse, base rounded. Flowers white.

Distribution: Szechuan, Hupeh and Kweichow, at altitude 2830 m.

331, Rhododendron maddenii Hook. f.

Shrub 1–4 m tall. Flowers with up to 10 flowers in a truss, very fragrant; corolla distinctly pink, especially towards the base of the tube outside, golden green at base inside, filaments from 20–27, white or palest green, anthers pale brown; style pale green; large stigma greenish brown; calyx green; pedicels reddish. Glands on under surface of the leaves, golden brown.

Distribution: S. E. Tibet, at altitude 2700 m.

32. Rhododendron magnificum Ward

Shrub or small tree 5 m tall; calyx green; corolla white or pale mauve, with purplish base; filaments white, anthers dark brown, greenish; style white; stigma brown; pedicel greenish red; indumentum silvery.

Distribution: S. E. Tibet, at altitude 2800 m.

333. **Rhododendron magorianum** Balf.

Shrub, leaves obovate, 7–10 cm long, 3–4 cm broad, apex rounded, base obtuse, racemose umbel of 11 flowers; corolla white, suffused-rose; stamens 12–14.

Distribution: Szechuan, at altitude 2300 m.

334. **Rhododendron makinoi** Tagg

Shrub 4 m tall. Leaves obovate, 7–13 cm long, 3.5–7 cm broad; apex rounded, base obtuse, under surface with dense woolly tomentum; corollas tubular-campanulate, 4 cm long, somewhat oblique; stamens 10, unequal. Leaves with markedly rugose on the upper surface and by the rich colored and densely woolly indumentum below.

Distribution: Yunnan, at altitude 3300–3700 m.

335. **Rhododendron mandarinorum** Diels

Shrub. Leaves oblong-lanceolate, base rotundate, apex mucronate.

Distribution: Szechuan, at altitude 2100–2200 m.

336. **Rhododendron mannophorum** Balf.

Shrub 0.5 m tall. Leaves oblong or oblong-lanceolate, 6 cm long, 1.7 cm wide.

Distribution: S. E. Tibet.

337. **Rhododendron manopeplum** Balf. et Forrest

Shrub 1 m high. Leaves oblong-oval to ovate, 5–9 cm long, 3–4.5 cm wide. Flowers creamy-white, flushed with rose, faintly spotted, lobes 5, rounded, emarginate, 1.5–2.2 cm long; stamens 10, unequal.

Distribution: S. E. Tibet.

338. **Rhododendron ludlowii** Cowan

Shrub 30 cm high.

Distribution: S. E. Tibet, at altitude 4500 m.

339. **Rhododendron lukiangense** Franch.

Shrub, leaves oblong-lanceolate, narrowed to both ends, apex acute or acuminate, margin not asperous, eglandular. Inflorescence raceme-umbel; corolla red to magenta rose, with a small base-blotch and spotted. Capsule narrow cylindric, 1.5–2.5 cm long distinctly ribbed, 6-chambered.

Distribution: N. W. Yunnan, at altitude 3300 m.

340. **Rhododendron lutescens** Franch.

Shrub 1–2 m tall. Leaves varying in size and shape, but always with auminate apex Inflorescence lateral, 1-flowered, occasionaly 2 or more flowers develop in each fascicle; ovary 5-celled covered with silvery overlapping scales. Capsule 12 cm long oblique at base, densely scaly.

Distribution: W. Szechuan, and Yunnan, at altitude 3000 m.

341. **Rhododendron lyi** Lévl.

Shrub. 2 m tall. Leaves oblanceolate, scaly and bristly with long hairs, short narrowed at base, 3-7 cm long, 1.5-3.5 cm wide. Flowers white, with yellowish blotch within the back of the tube, scented; calyx, 5-lobed, densely scaly outside and fringed with a few long hairs; stamens 10, pubescent.

Distribution: Kweichow, at altitude 2800 m.

342. **Rhododendron mariae** Hance

Shrub 1-3 m high. Leaves persistent, coriaceous, dimorphic, clustered at ends of branches; spring leaves oblanceolate-elliptic, 2-4 cm long, 1.5-3.5 cm wide, acute mucronate, cuneate at base. Inflorescence 7-12-flowered, clothed with appressed shining rufous-brown hairs; corolla lilac colored, fragrant; stamens 5, exserted.

Distribution: Kwangtung, and Kwangsi, at altitude 1000 m.

343. **Rhododendron mariesii** Hemsl. et Wilson

Shrub 1-3 m high. Leaves deciduous, chartaceous, 2-3 at the ends of branchlets, broadly ovate or elliptic, 3-7.5 cm long, 2-4 cm wide, acute, mucronate, cuneate at base, at first with yellowish silky hairs, at maturity glabrous; petiole 1-2 cm long, purplish. Inflorescence 1-2 or occasionally up to 5-flowered; calyx 5 lobed; corolla with spreading lobes, rose-purple, spotted with red-purple on the upper lobes, glabrous.

Distribution: Kiangsu, Fukien, Taiwan, Kiangsi, Hupeh, to S. E. Szechuan, at altitude 300-1300 m.

344. **Rhododendron martinianum** Balf. et Forrest

Shrub 1-2 m high. Leaves leathery, rigid, elliptic or elliptic-oblong, 2.5 cm long, long, 1-2.5 cm wide, apex rounded, margin recurved, somewhat undulate, upper surface clad with stalked glands and hair flocks, under surface pale glaucous. Capsule curved to sickle-shaped, 2.5 cm long, 6 mm broad, 5-6-chambered.

Distribution: Yunnan, and Tibet, at altitude 3300-4000 m.

345. **Rhododendron maximowiczianum** Levl.

Shrub .

Distribution: Yunnan.

346. **Rhododendron meddianum** G. Forrest

Shrub 2 m tall. Leaves oval or oblong-oval, 10 cm long, 4.5 cm broad.

Distribution: Yunnan, at altitude 3300-4000 m.

347. **Rhododendron megacalyx** Balf. et Ward

Small tree 2-4 m high. Leaves elliptic to oblong, from rounded to obscurely wedge-shaped base, obtuse to rounded tip. 3.7 cm long, 1.5 cm wide. Flowers large, 10cm long, white.

Distribution: N. Burma to S. Tibet, at altitude 3700 m.

348. **Rhododendron megaphyllum** Balf. et Forrest

Shrub 9 m tall. Leaves petiolate 20 cm long, lamina obovate sometimes elliptic always broader above the middle, often fiddle-shaped, narrower or broader as much as

18 cm long, 12 cm broad, apex often recurved rounded sometimes subtruncate, slightly emarginate, margin broadly cartilaginous entire not recurved or slightly so, base wedge-shaped or obtuse or rounded sometimes showing an abrupt narrowing towards the base prolonged as a narrow wing along the petiole, under surface cinnamon-brown, the midrib black-purple, whole surface clad with indumentum. Inflorescence a racemose-umbel with brown tomentum; flowers 20 in truss; calyx with 8 small teeth; corolla yellow with crimson base or rose base, campanulate obliquely, 8-lobed, lobes imbricate short and broad, 8 mm long, 1.4 cm broad, emarginate; stamens 16, unequal, shorter than corolla about, 2.5 cm long, shortest 1.8 cm long, filaments slightly widened at base; ovary ovoid, truncate, about 8 cm long, grooved, 10-11-locular, eglandular, enwrapped in a pinkish soft woolly tomentum of compact arranged fasciate hairs. The stalks of the hairs long, many-celled, the branches thick-walled, unicellular pointed; style glabrous much dilated below the lobulate discoid stigma. Capsule cylindric slightly falcate, 2 cm long, 1 cm in diameter, more or less clad with bright brown fasciate hairs, dehiscing by valves of 1 or more carpels. Seeds flat dark-brown, oblong as much as 3 mm long, 1 mm across with a lateral wing aril, a large chalzal membranous crest, the funicular end only slightly produced, often pointed.

Distribution: Yunnan, at altitude 4500 m.

349. **Rhododendron megeratum** Balf. et Forrest

Shrub 1 m tall. Branchlets reddish to greenish brown when young. Leaves crowded, oblong elliptic, shortly subacute at both ends, mucronulate at tip, margin slightly recurved, 3 cm long, 1.5 cm wide.

Distribution: Yunnan and Tibet, at altitude 4000-4200 m.

350. **Rhododendron mekongense** Franch.

Shrub 1 m high. Leaves deciduous, oblanceolate, 3-4 cm long, 2.5 cm wide. Flowers 3-4, terminal, pale yellow, tinged with green; stamens 10, exserted.

Distribution: E. Tibet, and Yunnan, at altitude 3700 m.

351. **Rhododendron melianthum** Balf. et Ward

Shrub 2.5 m tall. Leaves oblong to obovate, 3 cm long, 1.5 cm wide, cuneate at base, rounded apex, with water-glands, slightly glaucous beneath.

Distribution: Tibet, and Yunnan, at altitude 1500 m.

352. **Rhododendron mengtszense** Balf. et Sm.

Shrub or tree about 6 m high. Branchlets setose glandular. Leaves narrowly oblanceolate, 11-16.5 cm long, 2.5-3.5 cm wide, apex acute, margin undulate and roughened base cuneate to obtuse, upper surface to eye glabrous but punctate with bases of fallen glands and hairs, under surface paler. Inflorescence a raceme umbel of 8 flowers. Flowers purple-red, blotched with deep crimson in the 5 nectar pouches at base stamens 10, unequal.

Distribution: S. E. Yunnan, at altitude 2700 m.

53. **Rhododendron mesopolium** Balf. et Forrest

Shrub 0.5 m tall. Leaves oblong, 6.5 cm long, 2 cm wide, margin recurved. Flowers yellowish-red.

Distribution: S. E. Tibet.

354. **Rhododendron metrium** Balf. et Forrest

Shrub 1.5 m tall. Leaves oval, 8 cm long. Inflorescence an umbel, 5-flowered; flowers white, campanulate, 3.5 cm long.

Distribution: S. E. Tibet, at altitude 4000 m.

355. **Rhododendron micranthum** Turczaninow

Shrub 1-2.5 m tall. Branchlets lepidote and pubescent. Leaves persistent and scattered, oblanceolate to lanceolate, 1.5-4 cm long, 0.5-1.5 cm wide, acute or obtuse apex and gland-tipped, narrowed at base to the petiole, finely reticulate, with scattered lepidote glands above, densely covered with rusty brown lepidote scales below. Flowers white, ascending, spreading, numerous, in terminal racemose clusters; corolla rotate-campanulate, 5-lobed; ovary ovoid, lepidote. Fruit oblong, lepidote, shining dark-brown. Seed fusiform, winged at the end, yellow-brown.

Distribution: Hopei, Shansi, Honan, Hupeh, Kansu, Szechuan, and Yunnan, at altitude 1200 m.

356. **Rhododendron micromeres** Tagg

Shrub 1-2 m tall, epiphytic. Leaves oblong or elliptic, 3-7 cm long, 1.5-3 cm wide. Flowers 3-7, pale yellow.

Distribution: Tibet, at altitude 3000-3300 m.

357. **Rhododendron microgynum** Balf. et Forrest

Shrub 1 m tall. Leaves lanceolate or oblanceolate, 4-7 cm long, 1.5-2 cm wide, narrow, sharp pointed apex, cuneate at base, under surface with felt indumentum. Flowers terminal umbel, 5-6-flowered, dull soft rose, without basal blotch, but spotted.

Distribution: S. E. Tibet, at altitude 4000 m.

358. **Rhododendron microphyton** Franch.

Shrub 2-3 m tall. Flowers pink or purple.

Distribution: Yunnan, at altitude 2000 m.

359. **Rhododendron mimetes** Tagg et Forrest

Shrub 1-2 m tall. Leaves elliptic to oblong-oval, 6-10, 2.5-4 cm wide, apex blunt or short acuminate, base blunt or rounded, under surface clad with loosely felty indumentum. Inflorescence a laxy racemose umbel, 10-flowered.

Distribution: S. W. Szechuan, at altitude 2700-4000 m.

360. **Rhododendron miniatum** Cowan

Shrub 2-5 m tall. Flowers deeply fleshy rose, filaments white, anthers dark brown, stigma deep rose; calyx irregular, deep rose.

Distribution: S. E. Tibet, at altitude 3170 m.

361. **Rhododendron minutiflorum** H.

Shrub 2-3 m tall. Leaves broadly obovate to oblong, cuneate at base, acuminate apex, revolute and crenulate at margin. Flowers terminal, 3-flowered, umbel, bracts minute, triangular.

Distribution: Kwangsi.

362. **Rhododendron mishmiense** Hutch.

Shrub with branchlets covered densely with reddish brown hairs. Leaves oblong, 7 cm long, 3.5 cm wide, acute-acuminate apex, obtuse at base, under surface densely covered with felty white indumentum and midrib covered with dense reddish brown hairs. Flowers white, terminal.

Distribution: S. E. Tibet, at altitude 3330 m.

363. **Rhododendron missionarum** Lévl.

Shrub. Leaves obovate-lanceolate, narrowed to the base, apex triangular mucronate, 5-6.5 cm long, 2-3.5 cm wide, glaucous and scaly below. Flowers violet or white; calyx 5-lobed; corolla 5-lobed, 5 cm long; ovary 5-celled.

Distribution: N. E. Yunnan, at altitude 3000 m.

364. **Rhododendron molle** D. Don

Shrub about 1 m tall. Leaves deciduous, oblong to oblanceolate, 6-15 cm long, 2.5-5 cm wide, obtuse mucronulate apex, cuneate at base ciliate, often revolute margin, softly pubescent above, thickly clothed with whitish pubescent below. Corolla golden yellow with blotch, and dots; stamens 5. Capsule cylindric oblong, finely pubescent and sparringly setose.

Distribution: Chekiang, Kiangsu, Hupeh, Anhwei, Hunan and Szechuan, at altitude 700-800 m.

365. **Rhododendron mollicomum** Bàlf. et Sm.

Shrub, leaves narrow-lanceolate. Flowers crimson color; corolla narrowly tubular, calyx not lobed, scaly and pubescent outside; stamens 8, exserted. Fruit 1 cm long, scaly, pubescent.

Distribution: Yunnan, at altitude 3300-3700 m.

366. **Rhododendron monanthum** Balf. et Sm.

Shrub about 1 m tall. Leaves elliptic to obovate, 2.5-4 cm long, 1-2 cm wide. Flowers solitary, bright yellow, stalks curved, 1 cm long, densely scaly.

Distribution: Yunnan, at altitude 3300-3700 m.

367. **Rhododendron monbeigii** Rehd. et Wils.

Shrub, leaves oblanceolate. Flowers 10-12, racemose umbellate, villose.

Distribution: W. Yunnan

368. **Rhododendron morii** Hayata

Shrub, leaves oblong, acute on both ends with short acuminate apex, entire margin, pale brownish and glabrous beneath, 7 cm long, 2.5 cm wide, thick. Flowers solitary, terminal.

Distribution: Taiwan, at altitude 3000-3300 m.

369. **Rhododendron moupinense** Franch.

Shrub sometimes epiphyte. Leaves elliptic to ovate-elliptic, rounded on both ends, densely scaly below. Flowers terminal, 1-2-flowered; calyx 5-lobed; corolla funnel-shaped, glabrous outside; stamens 10, scarcely exserted.

Distribution: E. Tibet; and Szechuan, at altitude 2000-2800 m.

370. **Rhododendron mucronatum** G. Don

Shrub 2 m high. Leaves dimorphic, spring leaves deciduous, membranous, lanceolate to ovate-lanceolate, on both surfaces clad with rufous hairs. Flowers 1-3-flowered, covered with flattened hairs, pure white, fragrant. Capsule conic-ovoid, on persistent calyx-lobes.

Distribution: Szechuan at altitude 1200 m. and cultivated in Kiangsu.

371. **Rhododendron mucronulatum** Turczaninow

Shrub sparingly scaly. Leaves deciduous, elliptic-lanceolate or lanceolate, acute and mucronate narrowed to the base, 2.5-8 cm long, 3 cm wide, scaly on both surfaces. Inflorescence terminal, clustered at the ends of the shoots, 1-flowered. Flowers bright mauve pink; calyx short, densely scaly outside, corolla funnel-shaped, softly pubescent outside. Capsule 1.5 cm long, curved scaly.

Distribution: Hopei, and Shantung Lau Shan, at altitude 340 m.

372. **Rhododendron muliense** Balf. et Forrest

Shrub. Leaves oblong-elliptic. Flowers 5-6; calyx 1 cm long; corolla scaly outside, 2 cm long, stamens 10, exserted; ovary scaly, style pubescent towards the base. Capsule 3 mm long, scaly.

Distribution: Sikang and Szechuan, at altitude 3000-3700 m.

373. **Rhododendron myiageum** Balf. et Forrest

Shrub about 1.5 m tall. Leaves orbicular, 2-6.5 cm long, 1.5-4 cm broad, mucronulate apex, base cordulate sometimes truncate, under surface glaucous pappilate, more or less glandular towards the base. Flowers in umbel of 4-5 flower; corolla white with spots and faint basal blotch, 5-lobed, rounded.

Distribution: W. Yunnan, at altitude 3300 m.

374. **Rhododendron naamkwanense** Merr.

(Azalea tsutsutsi)

Shrub 1 m tall. Leaves oblong-obovate, 1-2.5 cm long, 5-10 mm wide, petiole 2 mm long. Flowers 2 or 3, terminal.

Distribution: Kwangtung.

375. **Rhododendron nakaharai** Hayata

Shrub clothed with flattened appressed shining brown hairs. Leaves scattered, oblanceolate, elliptic or elliptic-obovate, obtuse or acutish mucronate, narrowed at base, recurved slightly ciliate at margin; corolla funnel-shaped, with obovate rounded lobes, tube villose at base within; stamens 10, half as long as corolla.

Distribution: Taiwan.

376. **Rhododendron nakotiltum** Balf. et Forrest

Shrub 3.5 m tall. Leaves oblong or oblong-ovate, 6.5-11 cm long, 2.5-3.5 cm wide, apex broadly acuminate, base broadly obtuse, under surface clad with thin grey felty indumentum. Flowers in compact terminal umbel; calyx 5-lobed, glabrous on the back, and with few marginal hairs; corolla openly campanulate oblique, 3.5 cm long, pale rose with posterior basal blotch.

Distribution: N. W. Yunnan, at altitude 3700-4000 m.

377. Rhododendron nankotaisanense Hayata

Shrub, leaves oblong-lanceolate to ovate, 5.5-9 cm long, 2.5 cm broad. Inflorescence an umbellate corymb; calyx saucer-shaped, with 5 minute triangular acute or obtuse teeth; corolla 5-lobed, unequal, rounded, emarginate.

Distribution: Taiwan, Nankotaisan, at altitude 3300 m.

378. Rhododendron nanothamnum Balf. et Forrest

Shrub 1 m high. Leaves oblong-ovate. Flowers white, in umbellate head of 6-8 flowers; corolla campanulate, 3 cm long; ovary glandular.

Distribution: S. E. Tibet.

379. Rhododendron nebrites Balf. et Forrest

Shrub 1 m tall. Leaves oblong-obovate, 6 cm long.

Distribution: S. E. Tibet.

280. Rhododendron nematocalyx Balf. et Sm.

Shrub 4 m tall. Leaves oblong or lanceolate-oblong, 10.5 cm long, 3 cm wide. Capsule long, 3 cm long, persistent, 3 mm in diameter. Inflorescence an umbels, of 2-3 flowers, axillary, 3-5-fascicled.

Distribution: W. Yunnan, at altitude 2300 m.

381. Rhododendron nakotiltum Balf. et Forrest

Shrub with oblong leaves, acute apex, broadly cuneate at base, entire margin, glaucous beneath. Flowers in terminal racemose umbel.

Distribution: Yunnan.

382. Rhododendron neriiflorum Franch.

Shrub 3-3 m tall. Leaves oblong to oval, blunt or rounded at both ends. Flowers in umbel of 5-12 flowers, bright crimson color. Capsule cylindric 2 cm long, 4 mm broad, grooved, curved, floccose glabrescent.

Distribution: Mid-west Yunnan, at altitude 3000-4000 m.

383. Rhododendron nigropunctatum Bur. et Franch.

Shrub 30-40 cm high, with a neat rounded crown with black scales. Leaves elliptic or obovate, apex rounded, base sub-cuneate; corymb terminal, 1-2-flowered; corolla pale purple, sub-sessile.

Distribution: West China, at altitude 3300-3700 m.

384. Rhododendron ningyuenense Handel-Mazz.

Shrub or tree 5 m tall. Leaves oblong-lanceolate, 5-9.5 cm long, 1.2-3 cm wide both ends narrowed, more acute apex, base cuneate. Inflorescence short racemose umbel, 3–6 flowers; corolla whitish, unspotted; stamens 10.

Distribution: Szechuan, at altitude 2700–3300 m.

85. **Rhododendron niphargum** Balf. et Ward

Shrub 5–8 m high. Leaves broadly oblanceolate or oblong-oblanceolate or obovate, 10–20 cm long, 4–6.5 cm wide, base tapered, apex obtuse, under surface clad with thin white felty indumentum. Inflorescence in racemose umbel of 10–15 flowers; calyx with 5 triangular lobes; corolla campanulate, rose flushed with rose or pale rose deep crimson blotch on the posterior side; stamens 10, unequal. Capsule 4–5 cm long, 4 mm broad, thin, cylindric, distinctly ribbed, more or less sickle-like, blackish.

Distribution; Tibet, Szechuan, and Yunnan, at altitude 3300–4300 m.

86. **Rhododendron nitidulum** Rehd. et Wils.

Shrub 1 m tall. Leaves broadly elliptic, 1.5 cm long, 6 mm wide. Flower violet purple; corolla widely funnel-shaped, 1.5 cm long, not scaly outside; stamen 8–10, exserted.

Distribution: Szechuan, at altitude 3300–4000 m.

87. **Rhododendron nivale** Hook. f.

Shrub below 1 m high. Leaves very small, oblong, 1 cm long, 6 mm wide, greenish glandular beneath; corolla purple, filaments purple, anthers scarlet, stigma dark red, ovary bright green.

Distribution: S. E. Tibet, at altitude 3300 m.

88. **Rhododendron niveum** Hook.

Shrub 2–3 m high. Leaves oblong, 12 cm long, 3 cm wide, acute at apex, obtuse at base, entire, coriaceous, brownish indumentum beneath; petiole 1.5 cm long, glandular. Flowers white.

Distribution: S. E. Tibet, at altitude 4000 m.

89. **Rhododendron obscurum** Franch.

Shrub 2.5 m tall. Leaves oblong or oblong-oval, 8.5 cm long, 2.5 cm wide. Flowers solitary, umbellate, 5-flowered, terminal, 2–3-fascicled; corolla purple-red.

Distribution: Yunnan, at altitude 2000–2230 m.

90. **Rhododendron ochraceum** Rehd. et Wilson

Shrub, 3 m tall. Leaves narrowly oblanceolate, 5–8 cm long, 1–3 cm wide. Inflorescence short umbel, 8–12-flowered, calyx small, cubular, lobes 5, triangular acute pilose; corolla crimson rose, unspotted, lobes 5, subrounded.

Distribution: W. Szechuan, at altitude 2700–3330 m.

91. **Rhododendron ochroanthum** Balf. et Sm.

Shrub 30–60 cm tall. Leaves oblanceolate, 2 cm long, 1 m wide. Flower deep purplish.

Distribution: N. W. Yunnan, at altitude 4300 m.

92. **Rhododendron odoriferum** Hutch.

Shrub, leaves elliptic to oblanceolate, obtuse rounded at both ends, 10 cm long, 5.5

cm wide. Inflorescence 6-7-flowered. Flowers white flushed with rose outside, tu
inside tinged with green, fragrant; ovary 10-11-celled.

Distribution: Tibet, at altitude 2700 m.

393. **Rhododendron oldhamii** Maxim.

Much branched shrub 1-3 m tall. Branchlets densely clothed with rufous hair
Leaves persistent, partly deciduous, lanceolate-oblong, to elliptic-ovate, rounded
subacute at base, acute with gland-tipped at apex, mostly 3-8 cm long, 1.2-4 cm wid
upper surface loose covered with rufous shaggy hairs; leaf-stalk shaggy, up to 8 ╮
long. Flowers in terminal umbels; calyx segments rounded, up to 6 mm long; coro
3-5 cm wide, 4 cm long, red or some of the lobes tinged with rose, very minutely pa
pilose in the tube; stamens 10, unequal; ovary shaggy, style 4-4.5 cm long. Capsₓ
broad-ovate, 8 mm long, 6 mm broad, shaggy, glandular.

Distribution: Taiwan, at altitude 2700 m.

394. **Rhododendron oleifolium** Franch.

Shrub evergreen with leggy branches. Leaves narrow-lanceolate, acute at both enc
Inflorescence axillary, 1-2-flowered. Flowers pink to almost white; calyx 5-lobed; cc
olla 5-lobed, 2.5 cm long, pubescent, scaly all over the outside; stamens 10, pubescₑ
in the lower part, slightly exserted. Capsule densely glandular, scaly; ovary 5-cellₑ

Distribution: Yunnan and Tibet, at altitude 2700-3300 m.

395. **Rhododendron ombrochares** Balf. et Ward

Shrub 3-5 m tall; corolla crimson color, filaments white. Leaves oblong, 12
long, 3-4 cm wide, short acuminate apex, truncate at base, entire margin, thick, brow
ish glaucous beneath; Petiole 1.5 cm long, brown, grooved above, glandular.

Distribution: S. E. Tibet, at altitude 2700 m.

396. **Rhododendron openshawianum** Rehd. et Wilson

Shrub or small tree 5-12 m high. Leaves oblong-oblanceolate 10-15 cm long, 2-₃
cm wide, acuminate apex, cuneate at base. Inflorescence umbellate raceme of 8-1
flowered. Rachis sparsely villose. Capsule oblong-ovate, 2.5-3 cm long, 1-1.2 cm
diameter, glabrous, multilocular. Seeds oblong, 3-3.5 cm long,

Distribution: W. Szechuan, at altitude 2300-2800 m.

397. **Rhododendron orbiculare** Decaisne

Shrub 3 m high. Leaves broadly-ovate to orbicular, 4-10 cm long, 4-8 cm wic
Flowers in loose corymb of 7-10 flowers; pedicels 4-6 cm long, clad with few glanc
chiefly at the base; calyx with a swollen basal part and narrow undulate rim, fring
with glands; corolla campanulate rose, 3.5-4 cm long, imbricate, rounded, retus
stamens 14, unequal. Capsule cylindric, curved 1.5-2 cm long, dehiscing almost to
base into 7-8 narrow curved valves.

Distribution: W. Szechuan, at altitude 2700-3300 m.

398. **Rhododendron oreinum** Balf.

Shrub, Leaves oblong-ovate 8 mm long, 3.5 mm wide, apex obtuse, margin recurvₑ base obtuse; corolla rose color, 1 cm long, tube campanulate.

Distribution: W. Szechuan.

99. Rhododendron oreodoxa Franch.

Shrub, young shoots clad with a thin white to greyish tomentum. Leaves narrowly elliptic or oblanceolate –elliptic, 5–10 cm long, 2–3.5 cm broad, apex obtuse to rounded, base obtuse to rounded, under surface pale glaucous, epidermis papillate. Inflorescence racemose umbel, 10–12 flowered; rachis glandular tomentose; corolla pale rose with or without spots; stamens 14. Capsule oblong–cylindric, 2 cm long, 7 mm broad, distinctly ribbed, 6–7–chambered.

Distribution: Szechuan, and Kansu, at altitude 2400–3300 m.

00. Rhododendron oreotrephes W. W. Smith

Shrub 2 m tall. Branchlets not scaly. Leaves ovate–elliptic, obtusely mucronate 4–5 cm long, 2–2.5 cm wide, laxy scaly above, densely so below. Inflorescence terminal, 3–4–flowered, umbellate. Flowers white, spotted inside; stamens 10, pubescent in the lower half; ovary 5–celled, densely scaly.

Distribution: Szechuan, Yunnan and Tibet, at altitude 2300–3300 m.

01. Rhododendron orestrum Balf. et Forrest

Shrub 2 m high. Leaves elliptic or suborbicular, 5.5cm long, 4.5 cm wide.

Distribution: Tibet.

02. Rhododendron orthocladum Balf. et Forrest

Shrub about 1 m tall. Leaves oblanceolate, 2.5 cm long, densely scaly on both surfaces. Inflorescence terminal, 1–3–flowered. Flowers mauve; stamens 10, exserted.

Distribution: N. Yunnan, at altitude 3700–4000 m.

03. Rhododendron oulotrichum Balf. et Forrest

Shrub about 1 m high. Leaves obovate–elliptic, deciduous, 2.5 cm long, 2 cm broad. Inflorescence terminal, 3–flowered. Flowers yellow.

Distribution: W. Yunnan, at altitude 3300 m.

04. Rhododendron ovatum (Lindl.) Planch.

Shrub 4 m tall; bark pale and glabrous; branchlets with scattered glands and hairs. Leaves evergreen, broadly ovate, rounded at base, acute and long mucronate at tip, 2.5–5 cm long, 2–2.5 cm wide, glabrous except along the midrib hairy, no scales. Inflorescence 1–flowered, axillary. Flowers white or white with pink spotted with short stalked glands; calyx lobes large, rounded obovate, glabrous except the base, glandular outside; corolla 5–lobed, glabrous, pubescent inside the throat; stamens 5, filaments pubescent; ovary bristly, 5–celled. Capsule 3 mm long, broadly ovoid, shortly bristly, surrounded by the enlarged persistent clayx.

Distribution: Kwangtung, Kwangsi, Fukien, Hunan, Chekiang, Hupeh, Kiangsi, Kiangsu and Anhwei, at altitude 530 m.

5. Rhododendron oxyphyllum Franch.

Shrub 5 m high. Leaves oblong–lanceolate, acutely acuminate at apex, shortly cuneate

at base. Inflorescence axillary, several-flowered. Flowers white with yellow insi
the corolla; stamens 10, pubescent in the lower half; ovary and style glabrous. Caps
4 cm long, beaked by the long persistent style.

Distribution: S. Yunnan, and Kwangsi, at altitude 1700-1900 m.

406. Rhododendron pachypodum Balf. et Sm.

Shrub about 2 m high. Leaves oblanceolate or elliptic-lanceolate, long-acuminat
narrowed to the base, 10 cm long, 3.5 cm broad, densely scaly and glaucous beneat
Flowers yellow; calyx oblique; corolla scaly all over the outside. Capsule densely c
vered with golden scales, 6-ribbed.

Distribution: Yunnan, at altitude 3000-3300 m.

407. Rhododendron pachytrichum Franchet

Shrub 2-6 m high; branchlets covered with brownish shaggy branched hairs, wh
spread to the base of the stalks. Leaves narrow-oblong to oblanceolate, or obova
6-13 cm long, 2-4 cm wide, obtuse to acuminate at apex, distinctly cuspitate, mar
reflexed, ciliate with short branched hairs, cuneate to rounded or cordulate at bas
Inflorescence a raceme umbel, 7-10-flowered; corolla white to pale rose, with a de
purple basal blotch; stamens 10, unequal.

Distribution: W. Szechuan and Sikang, at altitude 2300-3700 m.

408. Rhododendron pagophilum Balf. et Ward

Shrub 2.5 m high. Leaves oblong-elliptic or obovate, 5.5 cm long, 3 cm wide, ac
to rotundate at apex, obtuse at base, margin plane. Flowers 3-4, rose, pink.

Distribution: Tibet and Yunnan, at altitude 4300 m.

409. Rhododendron paludosum Hutch. et Ward

Shrub, branchlets covered with blakish scales. Leaves elliptic, obtuse or round
at apex, upper surface densely covered with deeply impressed scales. Flowers bri
violet colored; calyx large for the flower, lobes ovate-oblong, loosely scaly outsi
not ciliate; stamen 8, far-exserted; ovary 5-celled, scaly.

Distribution: Tibet and Yunnan, at altitude 4000 m.

410. Rhododendron panteumorphum Balf. et Sm.

Shrub 1.2 m tall. Leaves oblong-elliptic, 9 cm long, 5 cm wide. Flowers yellow
racemose umbel of 8-flowered.

Distribution: Yunnan, at altitude 3700-4000 m.

411. Rhododendron pendulum Hook.

Shrubs struggling along the ground.

Distribution: S. E. Tibet, at altitude 3500 m.

412. Rhododendron pennivenium Balf. et Forrest

Shrub 3-7 m tall. Leaves oblong-elliptic to broadly-lanceolate, 8-15 cm long, 2.
cm broad, acute at apex, obtuse to cuneate at base, upper surface smooth, glabrous
with vestiges of tomentum; corolla deep crimson color.

Distribution: Yunnan, at altitude 3700 m.

413. Rhododendron parmoenum Balf. et Forrest

Shrub 2–4 m high. Leaves very narrow lanceolate, 7–15 cm long, 1–2 cm wide, tapered acuminate at apex, tapered and cuneate at base, under surface white or gray covered with compact persistent indumentum. Inflorescence a racemose umbel of 15–20–flowered, rachis rufous densely tomentose. Flowers flesh–cherry or deep rose–crimson color. Capsule 2 cm long, 10–12–chambered.

Distribution: W. Yunnan, at altitude 3000–3300 m.

414. Rhododendron peregrinum Tagg

Shrub or small tree; leaves oblong–elliptic or broadly–elliptic, 10–18 cm long, 5–8 cm broad, obtuse or shortly acuminate at apex, rounded to subcordate at base, under surface with bristly indumentum. Flowers 12–15, white, bright red, with lines and spots; stamens 14.

Distribution: S. W. Szechuan.

415. Rhododendron persicinum Handel–Mazz.

Shrub 5 m tall. Flowers peach–bloom color or rose.

Distribution: Yunnan, at altitude 3050–3400 m.

416. Rhododendron perulatum Balf. et Forrest

Shrub about 1 m high. Leaves lanceolate or oblanceolate, 3–7 cm long, 1–2 cm broad, under surface clad with felty indumentum. Flowers deep rose, 5–7–flowered racemose umbel.

Distribution: S. E. Tibet, at altitude 3700–4300 m.

417. Rhododendron petrocharis Diels

Shrub, leaves ovate–elliptic, mucronate, 2.5 cm long, 6 mm broad. Flowers white; stamens 10, inlcuded, ovary scaly.

Distribution: Szechuan, at altitude 1800 m.

418. Rhododendron phaeochrysum Balf. et Sm.

Shrub 4–5 m high. Leaves oblong or obovate–oblong, 12 cm long, 5 cm wide, obtuse on both ends, margin plane. Under surface with dense brownish grey felty indumentum; petiole 2 cm long, glandular, grooved above. Flowers white in terminal racemes, glabrous.

Distribution: Yúnnan, and Szechuan, at altitude 3850–4700 m.

419. Rhododendron phaeochlorum Balf. et Forrest

Shrub 1 m tall. Leaves oblong–ovate or ovate, 6.5 cm long, base obtuse or cordulate, apex obtuse, margin recurved. Flowers 5–7, white.

Distribution: S. E. Tibet.

420. Rhododendron pholidotum Balf. et Sm.

Shrub 3 m tall. Leaves ovate–elliptic, acute, rounded at base, 5–6.5 cm long, 2.5–3 cm wide. Inflorescence terminal, 5–flowered. Flowers rose to rose–purple, spotted; stamens 10; ovary scaly; style short pubescent towards the base.

Distribution: N. Yunnan, at altitude 3300–4000 m.

421. **Rhododendron** **pilicalyx** Hutch.

Shrub 1 m tall. Leaves obovate or obovate – elliptic. Inflorescence 3-flowered. Flowers white with a little pink, corolla 6 cm long, 5-lobed, scaly all over the outside.

Distribution: Yunnan, at altitude 2700 m.

422. **Rhododendron** **pingianum** Fang

Small tree 4-7 m high. Leaves coriaceous, oblong lanceolate, or oblanceolate, 10-15 cm long, 2.8-3.5 cm wide, apex obtuse to rounded, mucronate, base obtuse to subrotundate, rarely cuneate, lower surface clad with thick, white indumentum. Flowers 12-18 on a racemose umbel; corolla purple; stamens 10, anthers yellow.

Distribution: Szechuan, at altitude 2750 m.

423. **Rhododendron** **pittosporaefolium** Hemsl.

Shrub 2-8 m high. Leaves lanceolate to oblong, rarely broadest above the middle. Flowers fragrant, 3-8 flowered, in axillary fascicles, several and crowded together at the ends of the last season's growth. Fruit spindle-shaped, 2.5-4 cm long, 0.4 cm broad, furrowed.

Distribution: Szechuan, Hupeh, Hunan, Kwangsi, and Anhwei, at altitude 1300-2000 m.

424. **Rhododendron** **planetum** Balf.

Shrub, leaves oblong or elongate-oblong, 10-20 cm long, 3-6 cm broad, apex obtuse or sub-acute, base cuneate, under surface springled with vestiges of indumentum; petiole 2 cm long, flattish above. Flowers in terminal umbel of 10 flowers, pink, without blotch, or spots; stamens 12-14, unequal.

Distribution: Szechuan, at altitude 1170-1330 m.

425. **Rhododendron** **platyphyllum** Balf. et Sm.

Shrub; leaves broadly elliptic, emarginate, 5 cm long, 2.5 cm broad. Flowers terminal, capitate, several-flowered. Flowers white; stamens 5, included.

Distribution: Yunnan, at altitude 3700-4000 m.

426. **Rhododendron** **platypodum** Diels

Shrub or tree 2.7 m high. Leaves broadly-elliptic to rounded, 8-11 cm 5-7 cm broad, apex rounded, base obtuse. Flowers pinkish-red; stamens 14.

Distribution: Szechuan, at altitude 2000-2300 m.

427. **Rhododendron** **pilovittatum** Balf. et Sm.

A robusty shrub 3 m tall. Leaves 8 cm long, 4 cm wide, oblong, acutish crenomucronate, margin plane, base obtuse. Inflorescence racemose umbellate, reddis glandulate, small stipitate; bracts ovate obtuse, cuneate, 2.5 cm long, 1.5 cm broad interior densely glandulose; corolla tubular-campanulate, 5-lobed emarginate, 1.5 c long; stamens 10, unequal.

Distribution: Yunnan, at altitude 3000 m.

428. **Rhododendron** **pocophorum** Balf.

Shrub 1-4 m tall. Leaves oblong to oblong-obovate, 10-15 cm long, 4-6 cm wide apex rounded with conspicuous mucro, base gradullay tapered obtuse, upper surface often glaucous with a waxy bloom, at maturity glabrous, under surface with fulvous brown indumentum; petiole 1-1.5 cm long, grooved, clad with setulose glands and branched hairs. Inflorescence a compact umbel of 15-20 flowers; rachis 5 mm long, fulvous-tomentose, pedicels 1 cm long, densely glandular and sparingly pilose; calyx about 1 cm long, split into irregular unequal lobes, fringed with stalked glands; capsule broadly oblong, densely glandular, 1 cm long, 8 mm wide.

Distribution: S. E. Tibet, at altitude 4000-4800 m.

429. Rhododendron plebeium Balf. et Sm.

Shrub 3.5 m tall. Branchlets red-purple, lepidote. Leaves oblong or elliptic-oblong, 8.5 cm long, 4 cm wide, apex acuminate mucro, base rotundate, margin plane, lepidote white spotted on both surfaces and on the corolla base; calyx cupular, lepidote, puberulent. Capsule oblong, sub-cylindric, cinero-olivaceous, white lepidote, 1.1 cm long, 5 mm in diameter, 5-valved, 5-dehiscent. Seeds red-brown, fusiform, 1.25 mm long.

Distribution: W. Yunnan, at altitude 3300 m.

430. Rhododendron pleistanthum Balf.

Shrub 3-4 m tall. Leaves small, oblanceolate, 5 cm long, 1.5 cm wide, acute-acuminate at both ends, not scaly on the upper surface. Flowers violet.

General characters like that of *R. davidianum*, but the scales on the lower surface of the leaves much fewer and laxer, 3-4 times their own diameter apart; flower stalks and calyx outside not at all scaly; some of the stamens glabrous, the other slightly pubescent.

Distribution: Yunnan, at altitude 2700 m.

431. Rhododendron poecilodermum Balf. et Forrest

Shrub 1-2 m high. Branchlets robusty with short annual growth and congested foliage. Leaves thick, narrow-lanceolate or oblanceolate, 5-12 cm long, 1-2.3 cm wide, apex acute; base narrowed to the wide petiole; upper surface mat, slightly rugulose, glabrescent with vestiges of rufous hairs, lower surface clad with soft, thick, rufous bistrate indumentum, mid-rib raised and widened at base, primary veins concealed; petiole 0.5-1 cm long, 5 mm broad, rufous-tomentose. Inflorescence a compact many-flowered umbel; rachis 7 mm long, somewhat hairy; calyx with 5 semi-rounded calyx-lobes, pubescent; corolla funnel-shaped, white, creamy-white, with crimson spots, lobes 5, rounded, emarginate.

Distribution: S. E. Tibet, and Yunnan, at altitude 4000-4300 m.

432. Rhododendron pogonostylum Balf. et Sm.

Shrub or small tree 5 m tall. Branchlets with vestiges of a thin indumentum and hairs and short stalked glands. Leaves oblong-lanceolate or oblong-ovate, 7-12 cm long, 3-4.5 cm broad; apex acute, margin roughened, base obtuse or somewhat rounded, upper surface glabrous except for glands and hair vestiges in the deeply grooved midrib and primary veins about 16 on each side grooved; under surface pale, minutely punctate; petiole 1.5-2 cm long, grooved, glabrescent. Inflorescence a short racemose umbel, 8-flowered; calyx 5 lobed, glandular and floccose; corolla tubular, about 4 cm long, tubular-campanulate, pink, inside puberulent and spotted dark red on the back, outside more or less glandular; stamens 10, 2-3 cm long, filaments densely pubescent at base. Capsule slightly curved, 4 cm long, 1 cm broad, blackish, 8-chambered.

Distribution: S. E. Yunnan, at altitude 2300-2800 m.

433. **Rhododendron polifolium** Franch.

Shrub, leaves small, oblong-oblanceolate, nearly 1.5 cm long, 1 cm wide, densely scaly on both surfaces, scales below much overlapping, uniform yellowish-brown; leaf-stalks densely scaly. Inflorescence 1-flowered, axillary. Flowers mauve colored; stamens 10, exserted; ovary scaly, longer than the stamens.

Distribution: Sikang, and Szechuan, at altitude 3060 m.

434. **Rhododendron poliopeplum** Balf. et Forrest

Shrub 0.5 m high. Leaves oblong-obovate, 6.5 cm long, 2.5 cm wide. Apex rotundate, base cuneate, margin recurved. Inflorescence in umbel of 7 flowers; corolla, 5 lobed; stamens 10, unequal.

Distribution: S. E. Tibet.

435. **Rhododendron polycladum** Franch.

Shrub 1 m tall. Leaves elliptic, 2.5 cm long, 12 mm broad, loose scaly above, densely so below. Inflorescence terminal, 1-2-flowered. Flowers purple; stamens 10, long-exserted, pubescent towards the base.

Distribution: Szechuan, at altitude 3500 m in grasslands.

436. **Rhododendron polylepis** Franch.

Shrub 4 m high, branchlets densely covered with flaky scales. Leaves oblanceolate or oblong-oblanceolate, acute at both ends, 5-10 cm long, 2-3.5 cm wide, glabrous and dull above, very densely covered with black brown scales below. Inflorescence terminal, 3-5-flowered. Flowers dark purple; calyx shallowly lobed, very densely scaly outside; corolla very densely covered with scales over all the outside; stamens 10, long-exserted, ovary 5-celled, densely covered with reddish-brown scales.

Distribution: W. Szechuan, and W. Yunnan, at altitude 2300-3000 m.

437. **Rhododendron pupulare** Cowan

Shrub 1-5 m high. Leaves elliptic or elliptic-oblong, 3.5-8 cm long, 1.5-3.5 cm broad, apex obtuse, mucro long-terminate, margin revolute, base rotundate. Flower 3-5, pilose, deep crimson color, deep magenta patches at base of each petal; filament and style white, with upper 1/3 red, anthers and stigma black brown.

Distribution: S. E. Tibet, at altitude 3700 m.

438. **Rhododendron porphyrophyllum** Balf. et Forrest

A creeping shrub about 1 m high. Leaves oblanceolate or lanceolate or lanceolate-oval, 2.5 cm long, 7-15 cm wide. Flowers solitary, calyx fleshy; corolla campanulate deep rose, 4 cm long, with 4 nectar-pouches at base.

Distribution: Yunnan and Tibet, at altitude 4000-4300 m.

439. **Rhododendron porrosquameum** Balf. et Forrest

Aromatic shrub 5 m high. Leaves 10 cm long, 3 cm wide, apex acuminate, base obtuse, margin plane. Flowers in umbels of 4-6 flowers; calyx cupular, 5 cm long, unequal, 5-lobed, white lepidote; corolla campanulate, 5-lobed, lepidote, 3 cm long, stamens 10, unequal.

Distribution: Yunnan.

440. **Rhododendron potanini** Batalin

Tree of 5 m high. Leaves oblong or sub-ovate, 7-9 cm long, 2.5-4 cm wide, apex obtuse and mucronate, base rounded; margin scarcely revolute; upper surface glabrous, mat, finely reticulate, under surface paler, smooth, midrib in the lower half densely covered with dilated branching hairs, lateral veins 15-16, prominent; petiole slender, 2-2.5 cm long, like midrib densely clad below. Inflorescence sub-umbellate, short racemose, 7-8-flowered; calyx irregularly 5-toothed, teeth short, scarcely 1 mm long, triangular, more or less hairy; corolla broadly and openly campanulate, 3 cm long, unspotted, glabrous, lobes 5, broader than long, rounded margin, not revolute; stamens 10, included, reaching only to the base of lobes, filaments gradually and slightly dilated at the base and sparcely hairy in the lower half.

Distribution: North China, Eastern Kansu.

441. **Rhododendron pothinum** Balf. et Forrest

Shrub 1 m tall. Leaves oblong-oval or oboval, 7 cm long, 2.5 cm broad, apex obtuse or rounded, with short projecting red tuberculate mucro, margin cartilagineous plane or slightly recurved or sometimes roughened, occasionally with bristles towards the base, base obtuse. Flowers in terminal, 4-5 flowered umbel. Bracts and bracteoles falling as the flowers open; calyx bright red conspicuous, with a darker crimson cup, with somewhat unequal slightly fleshy lobes; corolla deep crimson, without spots slightly dark blotched at the base posteriorly, 5-gibbous ridges inside; stamens 10, slightly unequal. Capsule slightly over 1 cm long, cylindric, bristly or warted by scars of bristles, 5-valved dehiscing to the base from the apex.

Distribution: S. E. Tibet, and Yunnan, at altitude 4300-4700 m.

442. **Rhododendron praeclarum** Balf. et Forrest

Small decumbent shrub. Branchlets densely lepidote. Leaves elliptic or oblong-elliptic, mucronate. Inflorescence terminal; capitate, 8-flowered. Flowers yellow; stamens 5, included, glabrous.

Distribution: Kansu.

443. **Rhododendron praestans** Balf. et Sm.

Shrub 7-10 m high. Leaves sub-sessile, oblong-oblanceolate, oblong-obovate, 18-38 cm long, 7-14 cm broad, with the broadest part near the apex, gradually tapered to the base; apex rounded, at times emarginate, base cuneate and decurrent as marginal wings on the petiole; upper surface dark green, under surface grey white to fawn, clothed with a thin skin-like or slightly scarf indumentum; veins 13–16; petiole short, flattish above. Inflorescence a racemose umbel of 15-flowered; pedicels 3 cm long, tomentose, obliquely expanded below calyx; calyx minute with 8 short teeth, tomentose; corolla obliquely campanulate, 3.5–4.5 cm long, magenta-rose or flushed that color with crimson blotch at base; stamens 16, 2–2.5 cm long; filaments glabrous; pistil 4 cm long; ovary oblong, conic 1 cm long, buff or pinkish tomentose, 8–11-chambered.

Distribution: Yunnan and Tibet, at altitude 3700–4300 m.

444. Rhododendron praevernum Hutch.

Shrub. Leaves elliptic-oblanceolate, 10–18 cm long, 2.5–6 cm broad; apex acute base narrowed to cuneate. Inflorescence terminal umbel of 10 flowers; corolla white rose with a large dark wine-red blotch at the base and smaller spots above, lobes 5 deeply emarginate, 2 cm long, 3 cm broad. Capsule woody, oblique at base, 4 cm long 10–12-chambered.

Distribution: Hupeh, and Szechuan, at altitude 4300 m.

445. Rhododendron prasinocalyx Balf. et Forrest

Shrub 4.5 m high. Leaves oblong, 11 cm long, 4 cm wide, apex mucronate, base truncate or obtuse or subcordulate. Flowers in umbels of 6 flowers, pinkish.

Distribution: N. W. Yunnan.

446. Rhododendron prattii Franch.

Shrub; leaves broadly ovate to elongate-elliptic, 8–14 cm long, 5–8 cm broad, apex shortly acute or acuminate, base blunt rounded or subcordate, under surface clad with brown indumentum. Flowers in racemose umbel of 10–20 flowers, fawn tomentose; corolla pink, white spotted; stamens 10.

Distribution: Szechuan, at altitude 4300 m.

447. Rhododendron preptum Balf. et Forrest

Shrub, leaves oblong, 12 cm long, 4 cm wide, blunt acuminate, obtuse at base dark green lustrous above, glaucous with blue felty indumentum below, incurved margin, coriaceous. Flowers in terminal racemose umbel, rich pink. Capsule 3 cm long, 5-valved slightly curved, purplish brown, glabrous, pedicels 3–4 cm long, rounded, purplish.

Distribution: Yunnan, at altitude 3800 m.

448. Rhododendron probum Balf. et Forrest

Shrub 2.5 m tall. Leaves ovate or obovate, 8 cm long, rugulose glandulose, apex rotundate mucronulate apiculate, base rotundate or truncate. Umbel 8 flowered; calyx cupular, dense glandular; corolla white, rose-marginate.

Distribution: W. Yunnan, at altitude 4000 m.

449. Rhododendron prunum Tagg et Forrest

Shrub, procumbens. Leaves oblong-elliptic or oblong-lanceolate, 3–6.5 cm long, 1 2 cm wide, blunt at apex, margin thick, recurved and slightly hooded at apex; wedge shaped at base, upper surface slightly rugose, under surface dull gray to fawn, clad with dense bistrate indumentum, the upper layer forming a loose felty surface over a thin white under layer. Inflorescence a racemose umbel of 8–12 flowers, surrounded by the persistent bud–scales and bracts; corolla obliquely campanulate, 3.5 cm long, creamy yellow with copious deep marking crimson, lobes 5, rounded, crenulate; stamens 10, unequal. Capsule ovoid, blackish, grooved.

Distribution: Yunnan, at altitude 3000–4700 m.

450. Rhododendron prostratum Sm.

Very small shrub. Leaves broadly oblong–elliptic, mucronate, 2–2.5 cm long, 1–1.5 cm broad. Inflorescence 1–3–flowered, densely bristly and sparingly scaly. Flowers pink violet, slightly spotted with red; corolla widely funnel-shape nearly glabrous outside; stamens 10, exserted long-pilose near the base. Capsule 8 mm long, scaly.

Distribution: Yunnan, at altitude 5000–5500 m.

451. Rhododendron proteoides Balf. et Sm.

A much branched shrub of 1 m tall. Leaves oblong, 2–4 cm long, 0.5–1 cm broad, apex blunt, margin revolute, base attenuate. Inflorescence a compact umbel of 8 flowers. Flowers pale yellow with crimson markings, lobes 5, unequal. Capsule more or less woolly tomentose, truncate, about 1 cm long, 5 mm broad.

Distribution: Yunnan, at altitude 4000–4700 m.

452. Rhododendron protistum Balf. et Forrest

Shrub 9 m high. Leaves lanceolate to oblanceolate, 20–45 cm long, 7–21 cm broad; apex obtuse, broadest part about the middle, from there tapered to the cuneate base, very slightly decurrent on petiole; upper surface dark green, rugose, glabrous, midrib grooved, primary veins 24–26; under surface green, veiled by a thin open cobweb tomentum which does not conceal the epidermis except at the margins of lamina, where it forms a grey white indumentum, midrib prominent; petiole 3–5 cm long. Inflorescence a racemose umbel of 20–30 flowers; rachis 6 cm long, cobweb-tomentose; calyx short with 8 minute teeth; corolla creamy-white with lobes, flushed rose; stamens 16, unequal, 3.5–4.5 cm long; ovary conoid, 8 mm long, fawn-pink tomentose, 16-chambered; stigma large, discoid. Capsule 3.5–4.5 cm long, 1–1.5 cm in diameter, rusty-grey tomentose.

Distribution: N. W. Yunnan, at altitude 3300–3700 m.

453. Rhododendron pruniflorum Hutch. et Ward

Shrub 1 m tall. Leaves oblong, 5–7 cm long, 2–4 cm broad, blunt and mucronate at apex, cuneate at base, bluish glaucous and glandular with very prominent primary veins beneath. Flower reddish purple, glaucous, filaments reddish purple, style red, stigma green.

Distribution: S. E. Tibet, at altitude 2700 m.

454. Rhododendron przewalskii Maxim.

Shrub about 2 m tall. Leaves oblong 7–10 cm long, 2.5–5.5 cm broad, acute-acuminate apex, broad cuneate at base, lustrous green above, pale cinnamon below, glabrous;

Flowers in terminal umbels, white, spotted purplish.

Distribution: Szechuan, and Kansu, at altitude 3700-4000 m.

455. Rhododendron pseudochrysanthum Hayata

Shrub 1-3 m high. Leaves ovate to elliptic, or oblong-lanceolate, thick, rigid, 4-7 cm long, 2-3 cm broad; acute at apex, sharply pointed cuspidate at apex, margin somewhat recurved; rounded at base, upper surface dark green, glossy at first grayish-floccose and glandular with stalked glands, later glabrescent, mibrib deeply grooved, lateral veins 15 pairs, slightly impressed; glabrescent at maturity under surface, pale green, somewhat glossy, midrib raised, more or less retaining floccose hairs and glands of the young leaf, lateral veins not raised; petiole 1-1.5 cm long, gray floccose and glandular with stalked glands, slightly grooved above. Inflorescence in umbel of 9 or more flowers; calyx 5-lobed, unequal, triangular, gland-fringed; corolla campanulate, 3-4 cm long, 4.5 cm across, pink with deeper rose lines outside along the petal ridges, spotted crimson within on the posterior side, lobes 5, 1.5-2 cm long, 2.5 cm broad; stamens 10, 1.5-2.5 cm long, filaments white, puberulose at base; anthers straw-colored; Pistil 3.5 cm long, ovary conoid, 5 mm long, densely glandular; style white, glandular a third of its length; stigma loculate crimson. Capsule oblong, woody, 1 cm long, furrowed, glandular, 5-chambered.

Distribution: Taiwan, at altitude 3000-4300 m.

456. Rhododendron pseudociliicalyx Hutch.

Shrub densely scaly, bristy. Leaves elliptic or elliptic-lanceolate, equally narrowed to both ends, obtusely mucronate apex, 6-9 cm long, 2.5-3.5 cm wide, laxy reticulate above, glaucous green below, covered with densely very unequal-sized and pale orange-yellow scales, the scales less than their own diameter apart, with laxy papillae between leaf-stalk densely scaly, fringed with weak hairs. Inflorescence with 3-4-flowered; calyx saucer-shaped, undulately lobed; corolla lobes 5, scaly on the margin and outside; ovary 5-celled.

Distribution: Probably Yunnan.

457. Rhododendron pseudoyanthinum Balf.

This is a distinct species which has been confused with *R. concinnum* Hemsl. Leaves considerably larger than that species and a more showy garden plant. The flowers are decidedly larger and darker than in *R. concinnum.*

Distribution: W. Szechuan, at altitude 2500-4000 m.

458. Rhododendron pubescens Balf. et Forrest

Shrub 1 m tall. branchlets long-pilose and shortly pubescent. Leaves narrowly lanceolate, to linear-oblong, acute, densely villose on both surfaces, also scaly below scales laxy; leaf-stalks villose, leaf-blade 2-3 cm long, 4-7 mm broad, with revolute margin, attenuate or blunt base. Flowers in 2-3-flowered umbels, white pinkish.

Distribution: Szechuan, at altitude 2200 m.

459. Rhododendron pubigerum Balf. et Forrest

Shrub 1 m tall. Leaves 7 cm long, 3 cm wide, apex rotundate mucronate, base rotundate or sub-cordulate, margin plane; corolla campanulate, 5-lobed; ovary truncate, 4 mm long.

Distribution: S. E. Tibet.

460. **Rhododendron pubitubum** G. Forrest

Shrub 30 cm high. Leaves very small, elliptic, 1 cm long, 3 mm broad, acute apex, cuneate base, incurved margin, white glandular above, brownish tomentose and glandular below. Flowers white, terminal, racemose.

Distribution: Yunnan.

461. **Rhododendron pudorosum** Cowan.

Shrub or tree of 12 m tall, rather straggling. Flowers very bright pink, with deep magenta basal patch; ovary and of basal half of filaments pale pink, anthers pale brown; style rose; stigma lemon yellow; corolla mauve pink. Leaves oblanceolate or oblong, 8–22 cm long, 3–7 cm wide, apex obtuse or rotundate mucronulate, margin revolute, base rotundate free cordulate or broadly cuneate. Inflorescence an umbel, 16–24-flowered; rachis 3 cm long; bracts obovate membranceous, obovate-spathulate, 3.5 cm long, 1 cm wide cinero-pilose, apex acuminate; bracteole linear, 1 cm long, pilose; calyx cupular; stamens 16 unequal; corolla campanulate rosé; ovary oblong-ovoid, 5 mm long, 4 mm wide, sulcate white-tomentose, eglandulose.

Distribution: S. Tibet, at altitude 4130 m.

462. **Rhododendron pumilum** Hook.

Small shrub 20 cm high. Leaves small, oblong, 2 cm long, 1 cm wide. Flowers solitary, terminal; flower-stalks 6 cm long, purple, white glandular; calyx red, corolla pinkish red; filaments pink, anther brown; style red; stigma pinkish.

Distribution: S. E. Tibet, at altitude 4000 m.

463. **Rhododendron puralbum** Balf. et Sm.

Shrub 4–5 m high. Leaves oblong-oval to oblong-ovate, 5–12 cm long, 3–5 cm broad, apex gradually narrowed to an obtuse, or subacute point; base broadly rounded or truncate, at times cordulate, under surface bright glaucous green; petiole 2–3 cm long. Inflorescence a loose terminal umbel of about 8 flowers; pedicel 3–4.5 cm long, with glands near the calyx cup; corolla an open cup or saucer-shaped, pure white, 4 cm long, lobes 5, large, rounded, emarginate, 1.5 cm long, 3 cm broad.

Distribution: Yunnan, and Tibet, at altitude 3700–4300 m.

464. **Rhododendron purdomii** Rehd. et Wisl.

A robust shrub with thick branches, young shoots puberulous. Leaves oblanceolate to oblong-elliptic 6–8 cm long, 2.5–3.5 cm wide, apex acute or obtuse; base cuneate; margin revolute, Inflorescence a racemose umbel of 10 or more flowers; rachis 1 cm long, rufous-tomentose; pedicel 1–15 cm long, clad with a whitish-grey hairy tomentum; calyx cupular; lobes 5, broadly-triangular, sparsely pubescent; stamens 10, shorter than corolla.

Distribution: Shensi.

465. Rhododendron pycnocladum Balf. et Sm.

Shrub 1 m tall. Leaves elliptic or oblong-elliptic, 1 cm long, 6 mm wide, apex rotundate mucronate, margin revolute, base cuneate; calyx 5-lobed; corolla lepidote, 1 cm long, white villose. Flowers purplish blue.

Distribution: Yunnan, at altitude 3300-3700 m.

466. Rhododendron pyrrhoanthum Balf.

A prostrate shrub, leaves oblong-oval, 5-8 cm long, 2.5-4 cm wide, apex obtuse; margin recurved, base obtuse to semi-rounded, under surface pale yellow green, the prominent midrib and veins sparsely sprinkled with short glands and small floccose hairs; petiole 1 cm long, glandular; corolla campanulate, blood-red, unspotted, 3.5 cm long, tube fleshy with 5 pouches at base, lobes 5 rounded, emarginate, 8 mm long, 2 cm wide.

Distribution: Yunnan.

467. Rhododendron racemosum Franch.

Shrub with rather leggy branches; branchlets covered with small glands. Leaves oblong-elliptic, mucronate, 2.5-5 cm long, 1-1.5 cm wide, glaucous below, densely scaly. Inflorescence axillary, few-flowered, sometimes forming a raceme along the branchlets. Flowers pink to white; corolla funnel-shaped, 5-lobed, slightly scaly outside; stamens 10; ovary 5-celled, densely scaly.

Distribution: Yunnan, Szechuan, and Tibet, at altitude 2800-3300 m.

468. Rhododendron radendum Fang

Small shrub 1 m tall. Leaves ovate-lanceolate, apex acute or obtuse, margin revolute, base obtuse or broad obtuse, 1-18 cm long, 3-6 mm wide. Flowers rose white, 8-10 flowered, in terminal racemose umbel; stamens 5, included.

Distribution: Sikang, at altitude 3040 m.

469. Rhododendron radicans Balf. et Forrest

Shrub 1 m tall. Leaves narrowly oblanceolate, very mucronate, 1.5 cm long, 3 mm wide. Inflorescence terminal, 1-flowered. Flowers purple; stamens 10, shortly exserted.

Distribution: S. E. Tibet, at altitude 4700-4800 m.

470. Rhododendron radinum Balf. et Sm.

Shrub 1 m high, with very short twigy branches, covered with scales and short bristles. Leaves narrowly oblanceolate, mucronate, 2 cm long, 3 mm wide, Flowers white flushed with rose, terminal; corolla covered with flaky scales outside, villose inside the throat; stamens 5, included.

Distribution: Yunnan, and Szechuan, at altitude 3700-4000 m.

471. Rhododendron ramosissimum Franch.

Shrub 1 m tall. Leaves broadly-elliptic, 1 cm long, densely scaly on both surfaces. Inflorescence terminal, 1-flowered. Flowers dark-purple; stamens 10, exserted, pubescent towards the base. Capsule 3 mm long, densely scaly, topped by the persistent style.

Distribution: W. Szechuan and Yunnan, at altitude 3700-3800 m. on moorelands.

472. Rhododendron ramsdenianum Cowan

Tree 12-14 m high. Branchlets with vestiges of hair flocks, later glabrous. Leaves broadly-lanceolate to oblong-lanceolate, 8-10 cm long, 2-4 cm broad, apex acute; margin cartilaginous, base widely cuneate, scarcely rounded, under surface covered with traces of hairs flocks. Inflorescence a short raceme of 12-15 flowers; corolla tubular-campanulate, 3.5-4 cm long, fleshy, scarlet crimson, unspotted, with 5 nectar pouches at the base; ovary narrow, 5-chambered, conoid, 8 mm long, glabrous or sparsely clad with floccose hairs; style glabrous.

Distribution: S. E. Tibet, at altitude 2700 m.

473. Rhododendron rarosquameum Balf.

Shrub 1 m tall. Leaves elliptic-oblong, 5.5 cm long, 2 cm wide, apex rounded or obtuse, attenuate and acute or acuminate, mucronate, base cuneate or obtuse or rounded, margin cartilaginous. Flowers in umbel, solitary, terminal, 4-5-flowered. Flowers violet.

Distribution: Yunnan, at altitude 2890 m.

474. Rhododendron rasile Balf. et Sm.

Shrub 2.5 m tall. Leaves oblong, 17 cm long, 7 cm wide, apex obtuse, margin cartilaginous, base oblique. Flowers in umbel of 7-flowered; corolla tubular, 7-lobed, lobes rotundate, emarginate, white rose; stamens 16, unequal.

Distribution: Yunnan, at altitude 2000-2330 m.

475. Rhododendron recurvum Balf. et Forrest

Shrub 2-3 m tall. Leaves narrowly-lanceolate, to oblanceolate, 4-9 cm long, 1-2 cm wide, apex acute or short acuminate, margin strongly recurved, base gradually tapered to the broad petiole, under surface clad with thick rufous, woolly-orange indumentum. Inflorescence a racemose umbel of about 20 flowers, rachis tomentose with long woolly hairs; calyx very small, little over 1 mm long, more or less glandular and pubescent; corolla funnelshaped, 2.8 cm long, white flushed with rose and a few posterior spots of crimson, lobes 5, 1 cm long, 1.4 cm broad, emarginate crenulate; stamens 10, unequal.

Distribution: N. W. Yunnan, at altitude 3300-4100 m.

476. Rhododendron redowskianum Maxim.

Shrub of only 10 cm high. Leaves spathulate-oblanceolate, 5-15 mm long, 3-6 mm broad; apex subtriangular, base attenuate cuneate, subdecurrent, margin ciliate with gland-tipped hairs. Flowers solitary; corolla rotate, split to the base on the lower side; stamens 10, little longer than the corolla-tube.

Distribution: Manchuria.

77. Rhododendron reginaldii Balf.

Shrub or small tree 4 m tall. Leaves oblong, glabrous; corolla 7-lobed; stamens

14. Flowers pale pink.

Distribution: Southern Kansu.

478. Rhododendron repens Balf. et Forrest

Creeping shrub of 10 cm above the ground, of slow growth, forming a gnaled woody stem. Leaves ovate–oblong or elliptic varying in sizes. Flowers solitary, rarely 2, stamens 10. Capsule 2 cm long, 5 mm broad, almost straight.

Distribution: Yunnan, and Tibet, at altitude 4000–4300 m.

479. Rhododendron rhaibocarpum Balf. et Sm.

Shrub 1–2 m high. Leaves elliptic to oval, 3–7 cm long, 1.5–3.5 cm wide, apex obtuse, apiculate, base sub–truncate, hardly cordate, upper surface mat green glabrous or with traces of juvenile hair flocks, veins 9–12, under surface pale green, thinly veiled with minute hairs. Flowers in umbel of 8 flowers; corolla funnel–shaped, occasionally flushed with rose of small blotch of crimson at the base; stamens 10, unequal. Capsule narrow, sickle–shaped, purplish–black.

Distribution: W. Yunnan, and Tibet, at altitude 3700–4000 m.

480. Rhododendron rhantum Balf. et Sm.

Shrub 8 m tall. Leaves oblong, 8 cm long, 3.5 cm wide, apex obtuse or sub–rounded, mucronate, margin cartilaginous, base obtuse or sub–rounded. Inflorescence umbellate of 7–flowered; calyx 7–lobed, deltoid, red–glandular; corolla 7–lobed, rose to red; stamens 14, unequal.

Distribution: Yunnan, at altitude 3700–4000 m.

481. Rhododendron reparicum Ward

Very small shrub. Leaves elliptic or oblong–elliptic, rounded at both ends, with a small reflexed mucro at the apex, 2 cm long, 1.5 cm broad. Flowers 2–4 flowered, terminal, bright purple with darker spots on the upper lobes; calyx red; lobes elliptic–ovate, finely ciliate; corolla 2.5 cm long, softly pubescent outside; stamens 10, long–exserted; ovary densely scaly, style red, longer than the stamens. Capsule 1 cm long, densely scaly.

Distribution: S. Tibet, at altitude 3300–3700 m.

482. Rhododendron ririei Hemsl.

Shrub 6 m high. Leaves oblong–elliptic lanceolate or oblong–lanceolate, 7–15 cm long, 2.7–5 cm wide; apex obtuse or shortly acuminate, somewhat cuspidate, base cuneate or narrowly rounded, under surface silvery white and clad with skin–like indumentum. Inflorescence a corymbose raceme of about 10 flowers; pedicels clad with white cobweb tomentum, 1 cm long; corolla purplish with 5 black–purple nectar pouches at the base of the tube, lobes 5 or 7, rounded, emarginate or crenulate, 2 cm long, 2–2.5 cm broad; stamens 10, unequal. Capsule oblong–cylindric, 3 cm long, 1 cm broad, with withered tomentum, 10–chambered.

Distribution: Szechuan Mt. Omei.

483. Rhododendron rivulare Handel–Mazz.

Shrub 1 m tall. Leaves ovate-lanceolate, 5-9 cm long, 2-3.5 cm broad, acuminate and long-mucronate apex, rounded at base, ciliate, under surface yellowish and hirsute; calyx with narrow triangular long-ciliate lobes; stamens 5, filaments sparsely pubescent at base.

Distribution: Kweichow, Kwangsi and Szechuan, at altitude 750-900 m.

484. Rhododendron rockii Wilson

Small tree or shrub, 4-6 m tall. Bark pale grey, young shoots whitish floccose. Leaves oblong-lanceolate to oblong-oblanceolate, 6-12 cm long usually 8-10, 1-2 cm broad, usually 1.5-2 cm broad, apex shortly acuminate, base attenuate or cuneate, primary veins 12-15 pairs, under surface clad with a grey to tawny floccose tomentum, covering a white crustaceous under stratum; petiole 1.8 cm long. Inflorescence a racemose umbel of 6-12 flowers; calyx ring-like, with 5 triangular teeth, more or less floccose or glabrescent, corolla 3-4 cm long, 4-5 cm broad, pale rose or pinkish-purple, spotted, puberulous within at the base, lobes 5, rounded or at times truncate, emarginate; stamens 10, unequal.

Distribution: S. Kansu, at altitude 2000-2700 m.

485. Rhododendron roseatum Hutch.

Shrub. 3 m tall. Leaves ovate, acute-triangular-acuminate, broadly rounded at the base, 7.5-10 cm long, 3-4.5 cm broad, glaucous very densely scaly below, scales unequally in sizes, reddish. Flower umbellate, 4-flowered, white flushed with rose outside; calyx obscurely 5-lobed, densely ciliate with weak hairs; corolla widely funnel-shaped, densely scaly all over the outside, lobes 5 fringed with scales; stamens 10, exserted; ovary 6-celled, densely scaly.

Distribution: W. Yunnan, at altitude 3000 m.

486. Rhododendron russotinctum Balf. et Forrest

Shrub 2-3 m tall. Leaves narrowly oblong, 5-9.5 cm long, 1.5-2.5 cm wide, narrowed to an apiculate tip, base obtuse to shortly rounded, margin slightly recurved, upper surface with trace of hairs and glands, under surface clad with rusty - red indumentum, the surface loosely felty, and more or less detersile. Flowers in racemose umbel of 8 flowers; rachis rufous and floccose, 8 mm long; calyx cupular glandular, 5-lobed; corolla 3-4 cm long, white flushed rose with crimson spots, lobes rounded, emarginate; stamens 10, unequal, shorter than corolla and pistil.

Distribution: N. W. Yunnan, at altitude 4300 m.

487. Rhododendron roxianum G. Forrest

Shrub 3 m tall. Leaves 7-10 cm long, 1-1.5 cm wide, linear-oblanceolate or lanceolate, apex acute, base angustate, margin revolute, under surface ferruginous-tomentose. Flowers in umbellate compositae of 10 flowers; corolla white rose tinged.

Distribution: Yunnan, at altitude 4000-4700 m.

488. Rhododendron rubiginosum Franch.

Shrub or tree up to 3 m high. Branchlets scaly, purplish. Leaves elliptic-lanceolate, acutely acuminate, 6 cm long, 2.5 cm broad, very densely covered below with rusty-colored much over-lapping scales. Inflorescence terminal, 4-8 flowered. Flowers mauve, spotted with brown; calyx with undulate lobes, scaly outside; stamens 10, slightly exserted; ovary densely scaly.

Distribution: Yunnan, at altitude 2500-3700 m.

489. Rhododendron rubropilosum Hayata

Shrub 3 m tall. Leaves oblong-lanceolate to elliptic-lanceolate, 2-4 cm long, 1-1.5 cm wide, acute, glandular-mucronate apex, cuneate at base; lower surface covered with pale grey hairs along the midrib and veins; corolla funnel-form, with spreading lobes, pink, spotted with rose; stamens 7-10, unequal shorter than corolla. Capsule conic-ovoid, 1 cm long, densely clothed with shaggy hairs of brown colored.

Distribution: Taiwan, slopes of Arisan.

490. Rhododendron rubrohirtum Handel-Mazz.

Shrub 1-3 m tall. Branchlets, petioles, leaves all clad with dense red hirtum. Leaves elliptic-oblong, 4 cm long, 2 cm wide, acute-acuminate apex, obtuse at base, upper surface covered with white hairs and lower surface with dense red hairs. Flowers terminal, violet to rose colored.

Distribution: Yunnan.

491. Rhododendron rubropunctatum Hayata

Shrub, leaves lanceolate, 5-10 cm long, 1-2 cm wide, long-acuminate apex, cuneate at base, margin plane. Flowers in terminal racemes; corolla rotating - campanulate; style longer than the corolla; pedicels long, slender, glabrous.

Distribution: Taiwan.

492. Rhododendron rude Tagg et Forrest

Shrub 2-3 m tall; shoots and petiole bristly with long setose glands. Leaves broadly oblanceolate to oblong-obovate, 10-19 cm long, 4.5-7.5 cm broad; apex abruptly acuminate and cuspidate, margin ciliate, base rounded or cordulate, setose glands, the gland-tip often falling away on mature leaves; petiole 1.5-2 cm long, bristly with gland-tipped setose. Capsule oblong, 1.5 cm long, 5 mm broad, almost included in the persistent calyx.

Distribution: N. W. Yunnan, at altitude 4000 m.

493. Rhododendron rufescens Franch.

Shrub below 1 m tall. Leaves oblong to oblong-elliptic, obtusely mucronate at the apex, rounded or subacute at the base, 2 cm long, 1 cm wide, densely covered with reddish purple scales below. Inflorescence terminal, several-flowered. Flowers white to pale blue; calyx deeply lobed, densely ciliate; corolla narrowly tubular, not scaly outside; stamens 5, glabrous.

Distribution: Szechuan, at altitude 3700-4300 m.

494. Rhododendron rufo-hirtum Handel-Mazz.

Shrub with hirtus and long rufous hairs. Leaves ovate-lanceolate, crowded at the ends of the branchlets, 2.5–6 cm long, rarely 9 cm long, 2–2.5 cm wide, acuminate apex, cuneate at base. Flowers of few–flowered inflorescence; pedicels almost wanting, clothed with yellow strigose hairs.

Distribution: Yunnan.

495. **Rhododendron rufosquamosum** Hutch.

Shrub 1 m tall. Leaves oblanceolate, obtusely triangular–acuminate apex, gradually narrowed to an acute base, densely scaly below. Flowers white, pink in buds; calyx small, plate–like, scarcely lobed, densely scaly outside and closely fringed with long weak hairs; corolla lobes 5, tube softly pubescent outside the base; stamens 10; ovary 6–celled, scaly.

Distribution: S. W. Yunnan, at altitude 1600 m.

496. **Rhododendron rufum** Batalin.

Shrub or small tree. Leaves elliptic, oblong or oblong–ovate, 7–11 cm long, 3–4.5 cm broad; apex obtuse; base obtuse or sub–rounded, under surface clad with dense rusty–brown to loosely woolly–tawny indumentum. Flowers white or pinkish–purple, spotted crimson, puberulous within at base; stamens 10, unequal. Capsule oblong, woody, 2–2.5 cm long, 7 mm broad, clad with brownish deciduous tomentum, 5–6–chambered.

Distribution: Szechuan, and Kansu, at altitude 3700–3800 m.

497. **Rhododendron rupicolum** W. W. Sm.

Shrub or below 1 m tall. Leaves broadly elliptic, 1.5 cm long, 1 cm wide, densely scaly on both surfaces. Inflorescence terminal 3–6–flowered. Flowers deep plum–crimson; corolla funnel–shaped, 2.5 cm long, scaly outside the lobes, shortly villose within; ovary deeply scaly above and pubescent near the base; style longer than the stamens.

Distribution: Yunnan, at altitude 4300 m.

498. **Rhododendron russatum** Balf. et Forrest

Shrub 1 m tall. Leaves oblong–lanceolate, sub–acute, about 2.5 cm long, 1.5 cm broad, densely scaly on both surfaces. Flowers deep purple–blue with white throat; stamens 10, exserted, villose towards the base; ovary densely scaly.

Distribution: N. W. Yunnan, at altitude 4000 m.

99. **Rhododendron russotinctum** Balf. et Forrest

Shrub 1–2.5 m tall. Leaves narrowly oblong, 9.5 cm long, 2.5 cm broad, narrowed to the shortly apiculate tip, margin cartilaginous recurved, base obtuse or slightly rounded, lower surface covered with dense bristrate indumentum; petiole 1.5 cm long, grooved above, stout wrinkled red often dark–red, glandular, more or less floccose; calyx and corolla all 5–lobed; stamens 10, shorter than corolla; ovary truncate, conoid, grooved, 5 mm long, densely glandular.

Distribution: Yunnan, and Tibet, at altitude 4300 m.

00. **Rhododendron saluenense** Franch.

Shrub 70 cm tall. Leaves oblong-elliptic, mucronate apex, 2.5 cm long, 1.5 cm broad, scaly on both surfaces. Inflorescence terminal, 2-3 flowered. Flowers deep purple-crimson, with darker markings; stamens 10, exserted; ovary scaly.

Distribution: N. W. Yunnan, and Tibet, at altitude 4000-4300 m.

501. **Rhododendron sanguineum** Franch.

Shrub 1 m tall. Branchlets clad with thin white indumentum, eglandular. Leaves obovate, oval or narrowly-oblong, 4-6 cm long, 2-2.5 cm broad; apex rounded or obtuse, base obtuse and slightly prolonged on the petiole. Inflorescence a terminal umbel of 3-4 flowers; calyx 2-3.5 mm long, lobes red, ovate or rounded, floccosely woolley at base, corolla tubular-campanulate, bright crimson, 3.5 cm long, with 5 fleshy pouches at base; stamens 10, sub-equal. Capsule oblong-cylindric truncate 1.6-2.5 cm long.

Distribution: W. Yunnan, and Tibet, at altitude 4300-4700 m.

502. **Rhododendron sargentianum** Rehd. et Wilson

Small shrub about 60 cm high. Leaves elliptic, mucronate, 12 mm long, 4 mm wide, reticulate above, clothed below with loose flaky scales. Flowers lemon yellow; corolla rather wide-tubular, densely scaly outside, villose within; stamens 5, included, glabrous. Capsule 3 mm long, scaly.

Distribution: W. Szechuan, at altitude 3000-3700 m.

503. **Rhododendron sasakii** Wilson

Loosely branched shrub of 2 m tall. Leaves crowded, oblanceolate, 1.5-3 cm long, 3.5 mm wide, acutish to obtuse or rounded, mucronate, cuneate at base, rarely rounded, on both surfaces clad with appressed pilose hairs. Inflorescence 2-several-flowered; pedicels clothed with red-brown hairs; corolla deeply red, deeply 5-lobed; stamens 5, as long as the corolla.

Distribution: Taiwan, at Nanto.

504. **Rhododendron scabrifolium** Franch.

Small tree 3 m high. Leaves broadly oblanceolate, very acute, 4-5 cm long, 2-2.5 cm wide, scabrid and rather bullet above, softly tomentose and reticulate below. Flowers axillary, in the upper leaves of 2-3 flowers, pink or white; corolla narrowly tubular slightly scaly on the back of the lobes; stamens 10, exserted, slightly pubescent towards the base. Capsule slightly pubescent and glandular.

Distribution: Yunnan, at altitude 1700-2300 m.

Var. 1. **Rhododendron scabrifolium** var. **pauciflora** Franch.

This variety differs from the typical form of the species in the flowers being terminal and smaller; pistils much longer than the corolla tubes.

Distribution: Yunnan.

505. **Rhododendron schistocalyx** Balf. et Forrest

Shrub 4-5 m tall. Leaves oblong-lanceolate, 10-20 cm long, 2-7 cm broad, apex obtuse or semi-rounded, shortly mucronulate, base cuneate or obtuse or rounded, under surface clad with vestiges of juvenile tomentum of stellate hairs. Inflorescence a racemose umbel of 10 flowers. Flowers bright rose to crimson, ridged at base with 5 nectar pouches, lobes 5, broadly rounded.

Distribution: W. Yunnan, at altitude 3300-3700 m.

06. Rhododendron schizopeplum Balf. et Forrest

Shrub 1-4 m high. Leaves elliptic, oblong-elliptic or oblong, 8 cm long, 3.5 cm broad; apex obtuse; base cordulate or rounded; petiole 1 cm long, with vestiges of juvenile floccose hairs; corolla rose to deep crimson spots, lobes 5. 8 mm long, 2 cm broad; stamens 10, unequal.

Distribution: N. W. Yunnan, at altitude 4000-4700 m.

07. Rhododendron scintillans Balf. et Sm.

Shrub. Leaves oblanceolate, 2.5 cm long, 1 cm broad, densely scaly on both surfaces. Inflorescence terminal, lavender blue color, 3-flowered; stamens 10, exserted; ovary scaly; style longer than the stamens.

Distribution: Yunnan, at altitude 3700 m.

508. Rhododendron sclerocladum Balf. et Forrest

Shrub barely 1 m high. Leaves oblong-ovate or obovate, 1.4 cm long, 6 mm broad, rounded or broad obtuse mucronate at apex, margin obscure crenulate, membranceous, cuneate or obtuse, at base lower surface rufescent and blotched or somewhat punctulate lepidote with contiguous imbricate stalked bilocular peltate scales; corolla purple-rose; calyx cupular, 5-lobed, greenish, yellowish or pink.

Distribution: Yunnan, at altitude 3700 m.

509. Rhododendron scopulorum Hutch.

Shrub 4-6 m tall. Leaves obovate-oblanceolate, rounded to a small blunt mucronate at apex, subacute at base, 7-8 cm long, 2.5-3 cm wide, laxy and lepidote below; corolla white, 6 cm long, yellowish green within at the base, funnel-shaped, loosely covered with scales and finely pubescent; stamens 10, exserted; ovary 6-celled.

Distribution: Tibet, at altitude 2000 m.

510. Rhododendron scottianum Hutch.

Shrub 4 m high. Leaves obovate or more rarely elliptic-obovate, narrowed to a broadish base, mucronate at apex, 5-10 cm long, 1.5-4 cm wide. Flowers umbellate, 2-4-flowered, white, occasionally flushed with rose outside, a yellow blotch inside the base, fragrant; stamens 10-11, pilose in lower fourth; ovary 5-7-celled, densely scaly, style scaly in the lower 2/3.

Distribution: Yunnan, at altitude 2000-2700 m.

511. Rhododendron scyphocalyx Balf. et Forrest

Shrub 1.5 m high. Leaves obovate, 9.5 cm long, 4 cm wide, apex rotundate, mucronate, base auriculate. Inflorescence umbellate or 4-flowers.

Distribution: W. Yunnan, at altitude 3700 m.

512. Rhododendron searsiae Rehd. et Wils.

Shrub 3 m high. Flowers light violet with purple spots on the lower lobe. Leave oblanceolate, acutely acuminate, mucronate apex, acute at base, 5-8 cm long, 1.5-3 c broad. Flowers mauve; corolla 5-lobed; stamens 10, shortly pubescent in the lowe part; ovary 5-celled, densely scaly. Capsule finely scaly.

Distribution: Szechuan, at altitude 2300-2800 m.

513. Rhododendron selense Franch.

Shrub 1-2 cm high. Leaves oblong, oblong-oval or obovate, 2-5 cm long, 1.5-3 c broad, apex obtuse or somewhat rounded, base broadly obtuse to rounded but neer cor dulate, under surface pale green and clad with vestiges of glands. Flowers in umbel 4-5-flowered, white flushed rose or rose-colored; stamens 10, unequal. Capsule nar row, cylindric, curved, 1.5 cm long, 4 mm broad.

Distribution: W. Yunnan, at altitude 3300-4000 m.

514. Rhododendron semilunatum Balf. et Forrest

Shrub 1 m high. Leaves oblong-oblanceolate, mucronate, 2 cm long, 1 cm wide Inflorescence terminal, 3-flowered. Flowers deep yellow; corolla widely – tubular slightly scaly outside the lobes; stamens 10, exserted.

Distribution: S. E. Tibet, at altitude 3700-4000 m.

515. Rhododendron semnum Balf. et Forrest

Shrub 6 m tall. Leaves oblanceolate, 45 cm long, 13 cm wide, apex rotundate, bas 2 cm wide. Inflorescence umbellate of 20 flowers; rachis 2 cm long, rufous-tomentose corolla obliquely – campanulate, 8 – lobed, 5 cm llong; ovary oblong – ovoid, truncat curved, 12-lobulared; stamens 16, unequal. Capsule oblong, 3.5 cm long.

Distribution: Yunnan.

516. Rhododendron seniavinii Maxim.

Shrub 2 m high. Leaves dimorphic, crowded at the ends of the branchlets; sprin leaves ovate to oblong-lanceolate, 2-6 cm long, 1-2.5 cm wide, acuminate or acut mucronate, broad-cuneate at base; summer leaves much smaller, ovate to oval. Inflore scence 3-10-flowered; corolla white; stamens 5, longer than the corolla. Capsul truncate narrow-ovoid, densely strigose.

Distribution: Kweichow, Fukien and Hunan, at altitude 1350-1400 m.

517. Rhododendron serotimum Hutch.

Shrub 3 m tall. Leaves oblong-elliptic, 9-16 cm long, 4-7 cm broad, apex rounded base slightly and unequally cordate, under surface glaucous green. Inflorescence a racemose umbel of 7-8-flowered; rachis 2-3 cm long, minutely glandular; coroll white, 6 cm long, slightly flushed rose outside, blotched and tinged with red within and at the back of the tube more or less spotted; stamens 14-16, unequal, 3-4 cm long.

Distribution: Yunnan, at altitude 2700 m.

518. Rhododendron serpens Balf. et Forrest

Shrub of creeping habit. Leaves oval to oblong-obovate 1-5 cm long, 1-2.5 cm broad obtuse on both ends. Flowers in terminal umbel, red.

Distribution: Yunnan, at altitude 4600 m.

519. Rhododendron scheltonae Hemsl.

Shrub 1-2 m high; bark grey and rough. Leaves elliptic-ovate, 6-8 cm long, 3-4 cm wide, apiculate, base obliquely or rounded. Flowers white; calyx annular, oblique, 7-toothed, glandular; corolla 7-lobed, widely-campanulate, spreading.

Distribution: Szechuan, at altitude 2750 m.

520. Rhododendron sheriffii Cowan

Shrub 2-4 m or tree of 5-7 m high. Leaves oblong-elliptic or oblong-oval, 4.5-6 cm long, 2.5-4 cm wide; apex rotundate or obtuse, mucronate, margin cartilaginous recurved, base rotundate. Flowers rich deep carmine color, with deep magenta patches at the base of each petal; calyx carmine, filaments basal half deep rose.

Distribution: Tibet, at altitude 4130 m.

521. Rhododendron shweliense Balf. et Forrest

Shrub 1 m high, with aromatic foliage. Leaves few, elliptic-lanceolate, slightly mucronate. Flowers greenish yellow; calyx large, leafy, 5-lobed to the base; corolla 5-lobed; stamens 10, hairy in lower part.

Distribution: Yunnan, at altitude 3300-3700 m.

522. Rhododendron sidereum Balf.

Shrub or tree up to 10 m high. Branchlets clothed with a grey thin agglutinate indumentum, later glabrescent. Leaves oblong - elliptic, oblong - oblanceolate, 9-23cm long, 3-5 cm broad, apex acute or obtuse, base gradually tapered from the broadest part, cuneate or sometimes rounded, margin slightly recurved; under surface slightly silvery-grey to fawn clothed with a smooth parchment-like indumentum. Inflorescence a corymb of 15-20-flowered; rachis 5-6 cm long, greyish floccose; calyx oblique, very short; corolla ventricose-campanulate, creamy- white to clear yellow with crimson blotch at base, 3-4 cm long, lobes 8, stamens 16, unequal; pistil 12 - chambered. Capsule slightly curved, 2.5 cm long, 1 cm in diameter, slightly ridged, clothed with a more or less persistent grey to fawn tomentum.

Distribution: North Burma to W. Yunnan, at altitude 3000-3700 m.

523. Rhododendron siderophyllum Franch.

Shrub 1-3 m high. Leaves oblanceolate or elliptic-oblanceolate, subacute or sub-acuminate, acute at the base, 5-9 cm long, 2-3.5 cm broad. Inflorescence terminal and axillary in a dense cluster at the apex of the shoots, each about 4-flowered. Flowers whitish to violet; calyx cupular, undulate margin, very densely scaly outside; corolla 5-lobed; stamens 10, ovary 5-celled.

Distribution: Yunnan, at altitude 2600 m.

524. Rhododendron sigillatum Balf. et Forrest

Shrub 2-4 m high. Leaves oblong-elliptic, oval, or oblong-ovate. Inflorescence a racemose umbel of 10 flowers; corolla white with crimson markings on the posterior side; stamens 10, unequal; pistil 2.5 cm long, 5-chambered.

Distribution: N. W. Yunnan, and Szechuan, at altitude 4000 m.

525. Rhododendron silvaticum Cowan

Shrub 7-8 m tall. Leaves oblong or oblong-lanceolate, 10-25 cm long, 3.5-7.5 cm broad; obtuse or rotundate mucronate at apex, cuneate or rotundate at base; petiole cm long, robusty, sparsely tomentose; under surface of leaves whitish grey on young leaves and light cinnamon-brown on older ones, with a thin more or less compact persistent indumentum of two layers of branched hairs. Inflorescence a compact truss of 18-flowered; calyx a mere rim, lobes minute; corolla campanulate, dark magenta to reddish-purple, with 5 nectar pouches at base, lobes 5, rounded or notched, about 1. cm long and broad; stamens 10.

Distribution: S. E. Tibet, at altitude 3000-3700 m.

526. Rhododendron simiarum Hance

Shrub 2-3 m high. Leaves clustered at branch tips, oblanceolate to obovate, 4-9 cm long, 2-3 cm broad; apex obtuse or rounded, base cuneate narrowed to the petiole under surface clad with a greyish to fawn or buff crustaceous indumentum. Inflorescence a racemose corymb of 4-6 flowers; calyx discoid with 5 small triangular acute glandular and gland-fringed teeth; corolla funnel-campanulate, 4 cm long, pink, within pale with few rose pink dots, spreading, emarginate, pistile 5 - chambered; stamens 10-12 Capsule ovoid, woody, 1 cm long, often rufous pubescent.

Distribution: Kwangtung, Hainan, Kwangsi and Chekiang, at altitude 1700 m.

527. Rhododendron simsii Planchon

Small tree 5 m high, or shrub of 2-3 m tall. Leaves dimorphic; spring leaves elliptic or ovate to oblong-elliptic, 2-5 cm long, 1-2 cm wide, acute or sometimes acuminate a apex, base cuneate or broadly cuneate, sparingly rugose and dull green above, paler and more densely strigose beneath, at least on the midrib and veins. Inflorescence 2-3-flowered; calyx with ovate to lanceolate lobes, strigose and ciliate; corolla broad-funnel-form, 4-5 cm across, rose-red to bright or dark red, spotted; stamens usually 10, rarely 8 or 9, about as long as the corolla. Capsule 1 cm long, ovoid, setose with persistent calyx at the base.

Distribution: Wide-spread in warmer part of China, also in Taiwan, a variety occurring in the Kawanabe Island, at altitude sea-leved to 2000 m.

528. Rhododendron sino-falconeri Balf.

Shrub or small tree 6-7 m high. Flowering shoots covered with a pale yellowish tomentum, later glabrescent. Leaves oblong-elliptic or elliptic, 20 cm long, 12 cm broad, slightly the broadest part above the middle; obtuse to rounded at apex, obtusely rounded at base pale cinnamon clothed with a soft spongy indumentum beneath, with a fine woolly above; petiole 3.5-4.5 cm long, slightly winged. Inflorescence umbellate on a short rachis; pedicels 4 cm long, pale cinnamon - tomentose; calyx cup - shaped, densely tomentose; corolla pale yellow, 5 cm long, lobes 8, rounded, emarginate; stamens 16, unequal, shorter than corolla; ovary 16-17-chambered, densely tomentose with fasciate hairs.

Distribution: Yunnan, at altitude 3000 m.

529. Rhododendron sino-grande Balf. et Sm.

Shrub 7 m tall. Leaves oblong or oblong-elliptic, 40 cm long, 19 cm wide; rotundate with mucronate at apex, margin cartilaginous plane, obtuse or cordulate at base, covered with slivery gray or fawn skin-like indumentum beneath; petiole 3.5 cm long, 1-1.5 cm broad. Inflorescence a racemose truss of about 20 flowers; calyx clothed with same tomentum and fringed with 8-10 very short broad teeth; corolla ventricose-campanulate, 5-6 cm long, dull creamy-white, with crimson blotches at base, lobes 8-10; stamens 18-20, unequal, filaments puberulous at base; pistil 5 cm long; ovary conoid, 1 cm long, densely pink-fawn tomentose, 17-20-chambered. Capsule large, woody, set obliquely on the enlarged calyx-rim, 7 cm long, 1.7 cm in diameter, clothed with rusty to gray tommentum.

Distribution: Yunnan, Burma and Tibet, at altitude 3300-4300 m.

530. Rhododendron sino-lepidotum Balf.

Shrub 45 cm high. Leaves aromatic, oblong or elliptic-oblong, 2 cm long, 1 cm wide, obtuse or acutish mucronate at apex, margin revolute, obtuse at base. Flowers 1-3, deep rose, white lepidote; ovary white lepidote; 2 mm long. Capsule oblong, 4 mm long, 3 mm in diameter.

Distribution: Yunnan, at altitude 3700 m.

531. Rhododendron sino-nuttallii Balf. et Forrest

Shrub 2.5 m tall. Leaves oblong, 22 cm long, 10 cm broad, blunt mucronate apex, broadly cuneate at base, incurved margin, lustrous dark green above, very prominently reticulated and midrib and veins highly elevated, brownish glaucous beneath; petiole thick, flattened, brownish glandular, 3-4 cm long. Flowers terminal in 2 or 3, white; pedicel stout, 3-4 cm long, brownish glandular.

Distribution: Yunnan and Tibet, at altitude 2170 m.

532. Rhododendron souliei Franch.

Shrub 2 m tall. Leaves broadly ovate or orbicular, 4 cm long, 3.5 cm broad, abruptly mucronate apex, cordate at base; corolla 5-lobed, purplish, 25-35 mm long, lobes rotundate, emarginate; stamens 10, included.

Distribution: Szechuan and Sikang, at altitude 3700-4000 m.

533. Rhododendron spanotrichum Balf. et Sm.

Small tree 7 m high. Leaves oblanceolate, 7-12 cm long, 2-4 cm broad; apex beaked, shortly acuminate; margin rough, undulate; base obtuse or cuneate, under surface glabrous, punctate with the bases of fallen glands or hairs; petiole 1 cm long, glabrescent, punctate like the leaves. Inflorescence a racemose umbel of 10 flowers; corolla crimson with a darker blotch at the base, lobes 5, unequal, elliptic to rounded, emarginate, crenulate; stamens 10, unequal.

Distribution: S. E. Yunnan, at altitude 2500 m.

534. **Rhododendron** **sperabile** Balf. et Farrer var. *weihsiense* Tagg. et Forrest

Shrub of 1 meter tall. Flowers with rich vivid crimson and black marking at base; narrow tapered leaves less lanceolate, at times elongate–elliptic, evenly tapered to a narrow base; Leaves covered by indumentum less dense than that of the typical form and of a lighter color, white to pale fawn; the upper surface less bullate.

Distribution: Yunnan, at altitude 4300 m.

535. **Rhododendron** **sperabiloides** Tagg et Forrest

Shrub 1 m high. Leaves oblong–elliptic to oblanceolate, 3–7 cm long, 2–3 cm broad; apex obtuse, mucronate, under surface clad with an interrupted scarly tomentum; petiole 1 cm long, clad with tomentum. Flowers in umbel of 6–flowered; corolla deep to light crimson, lobes 5, broadly rounded, emarginate; stamens 10, unequal. Capsule narrow cylindric, 1.3 cm long, 3 mm broad, more or less curved, grooved, brownish–floccose.

Distribution: S. E. Tibet, at altitude 4000–4800 m.

536. **Rhododendron** **sphaeranthum** Balf. et Sm.

Shrub, branchlets covered with scales and short hairs. Leaves narrow–lanceolate, mucronate, 2.5 cm long, 1 cm broad, reticulate above. Inflorescence terminal, capitate, several–flowered. Flowers pink; corolla narrow–tubular; stamens 5, included, pubescent towards the base; ovary scaly; style short, turbinate.

Distribution: Yunnan, at altitude 4000–4700 m.

537. **Rhododendron** **sphaeroblastum** Balf. et Forrest

Shrub 2 m high. Leaves oval or oblong–oval, apex obtuse or subrotundate, base rotundate, margin plane. Inflorescence racemose umbel of 12–flowered; corolla white, rose flushed, 5–lobed; stamens 10, unequal. Capsule 9–locular, 2 cm long, 6 mm in diameter.

Distribution: S. W. Szechuan, at altitude 4460–4600 m.

538. **Rhododendron** **spiciferum** Franch.

Shrub, branchlets bristly pubescent. Leaves narrowly oblanceolate, acute, 2.5 cm long, bristly with slender hairs above and on the margin, softly pubescent below; also scaly. Inflorescence axillary towards the apex of the shoots, numerous and forming a pseudo–spike, bud–scales markedly glandular, and shortly villose. Flowers pink; calyx well developed lobes densely ciliated, scaly outside; corolla narrow–tubular, loosely scaly on the back of the lobes; stamens 10, exserted. Capsule scaly and shortly pubescent.

Distribution: Yunnan, at altitude 2000–2300 m.

539. **Rhododendron** **spilanthum** Hutch.

Shrub 1 m high. Leaves very small, lanceolate 1.5 cm long, 2 mm broad whitish glandular on both surfaces. Flowers blue–purplish.

Distribution: Szechuan, at altitude 3800 m.

540. **Rhododendron** **spilotum** Balf. et Forrest

Shrub below 1 m high. Leaves oblong, 15 cm long, 5 cm broad, dark green above, brownish felty tomentose below, blunt mucronate apex, truncate at base; petiole 2 cm long, stout, flattened above, densely whitish glandular or bristly hairy. Flowers terminal, capitate.

Distribution: Tibet at altitude 3300–3700 m.

541. Rhododendron spinuliferum Franch.

Shrub 1–2.5 m tall. Leaves lanceolate or oblong-lanceolate, apex acuminate, base acute, 2.5–4.5 cm long, 1 cm wide. Inflorescence terminal, 4–flowered; corolla red, tubular; stamens 10, exserted; ovary 2 cm long, woolly and sparingly glandular; style as long as the longer stamens, sparingly puberulous below.

Distribution: Yunnan, at altitude 800 m.

542. Rhododendron squamata Lindl.

Shrub blooming before the leaves. Flowers large solitary, rose colored, spotted with crimson on one side.

Distribution: Hongkong.

543. Rhododendron squarrosum Balf.

Shrub, leaves oblong, 8 cm long, 3 cm wide, apex acute, base acute, margin–undulate. Flowers terminal, white.

Distribution: Tibet.

544. Rhododendron stamineum Franch.

Shrub 2–3 m high. Branchlets glabrous. Leaves oblanceolate, gradually acute at both ends, 8 cm long, 2.5 cm broad, very obscurely nerved. Inflorescence sub–umbellate, 3–flowered, white to rose; corolla narrowly funnel – shaped, 2.5–3 cm long, glabrous; stamens 10, exserted, glabrous; ovary glabrous; style glabrous. Capsule 5 cm long, slightly puberulous.

Distribution: Szechuan, Kweichow, Yunnan, Hupeh, Anhwei, Hunan and Kwangsi, at altitude 400–1700 m.

545. Rhododendron stenaulum Balf. et Sm.

Shrub 6–9 m high. Branchlets pale grey, glabrous. Leaves oblong–lanceolate, acutely and rather long–acuminate, very shortly narrowed at the base, 7.5–12.5cm long, 2.5–4 cm broad, glabrous, with numerous lateral nerves reticulate, not impressed on the upper surface; leaf-stalks 1.5 cm long. Inflorescence axillary, 1–flowered; bud-scales persistent and softly puberulous outside; flowers stalk 2 cm long, glabrous; calyx obsolete, undulately lobed, glabrous; corolla narrowly funnel-shaped, 5 cm long, glabrous; stamens 10, nearly glabrous, rather short; ovary long, glabrous; style much longer than the stamens, glabrous.

Distribution: W. Yunnan, at altitude 3000 m.

546. Rhododendron stenoplastum Balf. et Forrest

Shrub 3 m high; completely covered by lepidote indumentum. Leaves sub–coriaceous, petiolate, lanceolate, or oblanceolate, acuminate apex, 10 cm long, 2.5 cm broad, base unequally cuneate, punctulate lepidote below; petiole 1.5 cm long. Inflorescence terminal, 6-flowered; calyx small, 1.5 cm long, corolla campanulate, rose and maculate 5-lobed, 3 cm long; tube puberulous, lobe rotundate; stamens 10, unequal, included, filaments puberulous; ovary lepidote.

Distribution: Yunnan.

547. Rhododendron stereophyllum Balf. et Sm.

Shrub 2 m high; branchlets covered with small resinous glands. Leaves obovate, rounded to a mucronate apex, 4-5 cm long, 1.5-3 cm broad, equally and rather densely scaly on both surfaces; scales below small and uniform; petiole 1 cm long, scaly. Inflorescence terminal and axillary, 3-4-flowered; calyx short and rim-like, densely scaly outside; stamens 10, hairy in lower part; ovary scaly; style glabrous.

Distribution: Yunnan, at altitude 3300 m.

548. Rhododendron stewartianum Diels

Shrub 1-2 m high. Leaves leathery, obovate to elliptic, 5-12 cm long, 3-6.5 cm broad; apex rounded to obtuse; base blunt to rounded, upper surface bright green, more or less glaucous; lateral veins 12 pairs, under surface minutely papillate beneath, a thin smooth evanescent creamy yellow fairnose indumentum; petiole 1 cm long, slightly grooved. Inflorescence terminal umbel of 3-7-flowered; calyx cup-shaped, variable in size, about 1 cm long, greenish yellow, or rarely tinged crimson; lobes 5, unequal, glabrous or rarely glandular-fringed; corolla tubular-campanulate, 4.5 cm long, very variable in color, from pure white or clear soft yellow through white flushed rose to deep rose margined deep crimson, with or without markings, base with 5 gibbous nectaries, lobes 5, emarginate, 1.5 cm long, 2.5 cm broad; stamens 10, unequal, 2.5-3.5 cm long, filaments densely puberulous at base. Capsule oblong, blunt, 1.5-2.5 cm long, 6-10 mm broad blackish, encased by the more or less persistent calyx at base.

Distribution: Yunnan and Tibet, at altitude 3300-4700 m.

549. Rhododendron stictophyllum Balf.

A dwarf small-leaved shrub with very many thin short curved branches. Leaves narrowly elliptic, about 3 mm long, densely scaly on both surfaces, the scales overlaping below, mostly rusty-red; petiole scaly. Inflorescence 1-flowered, terminal; flowering stalk minute, scaly. Flowers mauve to rose; corolla openly funnel-shaped, 1 cm long, not scaly outside, or only slightly so; stamens 10, exserted, glabrous; ovary densely scaly, style as long as the stamens, glabrous.

Distribution: W. Szechuan and Yunnan, at altitude 5000 m.

550. Rhododendron strigillosum Franch.

Shrub 6.5 m high. Branchlets more or less thickly beset with long stiff bristles, for the most part tipped with glands. Leaves oblanceolate, 8-16 cm long, 2.5-4.5 cm broad; apex acuminate, cuspidate, base tapered narrowly rounded or cordulate; margin recurved, at first ciliate; upper surface convex bright green, at first clad with soft filiform hairs, finely glabrous, midrib deeply grooved, primary veins 17-20, slightly impressed; under surface somewhat glossy, clad all over with isolated crisped hairs, midrib very prominent, clad with a loose tawny tomentum; petiole 1-1.5 cm long, clad with long bristles, many of them gland-tipped, mixed with shorter floccose-branched hairs. Inflorescence a racemose umbel, 8-12-flowered; rachis 7 mm long, glandular; calyx very small, a thickened angular rim, with 5 small setose glandular teeth; corolla tubular-campanulate, fleshy deep red without spotting, in some forms paler, 4-6 cm long, tube 3-4.5 cm long, lobes 5 oval to rounded, basal nectar pouches marked black crimson within, lobes spreading, emarginate, 1.5-2.5 cm long, 2-3 cm broad; stamens 10, unequal, 2.5-4 cm long, filaments slender, glabrous; pistil 4-5 cm long; ovary ovoid 5 mm long, densely clad with setose glands of reddish colored; style reddish; stigma small.

Distribution: Yunnan and Szechuan, at altitude 2300-3000 m.

551. **Rhododendron** suberosum Balf. et Forrest

Shrub 2 m high. Leaves lanceolate, 6.5 cm long, 2 cm broad, acuminate mucronate apex, margin recurved, base cuneate. Inflorescence in axillary umbel; corolla rose, convex, 5-lobed.

Distribution: Yunnan, at altitude 2000 m.

552. **Rhododendron** sulfureum Franch.

Shrub about 1 m high. Leaves broadly-elliptic, rounded to a blunt mucro at the apex, 2.5-5 cm long, 5-10 mm broad, pale and densely scaly below. Inflorescence terminal of 4-5 flowers each. Flowers bright yellow; calyx large deeply 5-lobed, lobes fringed with few hairs; corolla broadly tubular, 5-lobed, scaly outside; stamens 10, densely bearded from well above the base to the middle; ovary 5-celled; densely scaly; style stout, short, and curved. Capsule 7 mm long, thick and reticulate and scaly.

Distribution: Yunnan at altitude 3000-3300 m.

553. **Rhododendron** superanubium Hutch.

Shrub about 1 m tall. Branchlets laxy scaly. Leaves oblanceolate to obovate-oblanceolate, rarely elliptic, 3-8 cm long, 1.5-3 cm broad, densely scaly above. Inflorescence up to 3-flowered but often 1-flowered; flowering stalk densely scaly. Flowers dull white, with rose exterior, fragrant; calyx cupular slightly lobed, scaly outside, usually fringed with long hairs; corolla widely funnel-shaped; tube 3 cm long densely scaly outside and softly pubescent towards the base; lobes 5, scaly outside; stamens 10, densely scaly in the lower half; ovary 6-celled, densely scaly, style scaly in lower half. Capsule 2.5 cm long, straight, rather scaly, tipped by the persistent base of style.

Distribution: Yunnan, at altitude 3300-4000 m.

554. **Rhododendron** surasianum Balf. et Craib

A spreading shrub of 4 m high. Branchlets short laxy, leafy towards the apex, Leaves elliptic-obovate or oblong-obovate, rounded to a shortly cuneate base, acutely acuminate at the apex, 6-10 cm long, 2.3-4 cm broad, densely lepidote below, lateral veins 6–7 pairs. Flowers bud–scales slightly keeled and densely lepidote towards the apex, apiculate and fringed with soft white hairs. Inflorescence umbellate, 2–3–flowered; corolla pale pink, 7.5 cm long, tube about 4 cm long, fairy narrow at the base rather densely lepidote outside and finely pubescent towards the base; lobes 5, broadly oblong, 3 cm long, lepidote outside except towards the margin; stamens 10, unequal, exserted; ovary 5–celled.

Distribution: E. Yunnan, at altitude 3500 m.

555. **Rhododendron** szechuanense Franch.

Shrub 1–3 m high. Leaves oblong–oblanceolate or narrowly oblong–oval, 9–25 cm long, 3–7 cm broad; apex broadly obtuse or semi–rounded, narrowed from the broadest part to a cuneate obtusely rounded base, lateral veins 17–22 pairs; under surface pale green, along the midrib covered with loose woolly tomentum. Inflorescence a dense ccrymbose raceme of 8–10 flowers; calyx small, disc–like, undulately 5–lobed, glabrous or sparsely floccose; corolla widely–campanulate, 5–7.5 cm long, rose pink, spotted deeper rose within, not blotched at base, deeply puberulous within, lobes 5, rarely 6, unequal, 2–2.5 cm long, 3–4 cm broad, deeply notched; stamens 13–15, unequal, 3–4 cm long, filaments white, distinctly hairy at base, anthers nearly black; ovary conoid, 7 mm long, 12–chambered; style capitate, reddish. Capsule woody, oblong, distinctly ribbed.

Distribution: Szechuan, Hupeh, and Kwangsi, at altitude 1700–2700 m.

556. **Rhododendron** sycnanthum Balf. et Sm.

Shrub 1–3 m high. Leaves small obovate, shortly mucronate, 2.5–3.5 cm long, 1.2–2 cm broad, laxy scaly below. Inflorescence terminal, 2–3–flowered. Flowers deep rose lavender, with olivi–brown markings; calyx mere a rim with a few small scales only on the margin; corolla scarcely 2.5 cm long, not scaly outside; stamens 10, scarcely as long as the corolla; ovary 5–celled, scaly.

Distribution: N. W. Yunnan, at altitude 3000–3300 m.

557. **Rhododendron** sycollum Balf. et Forrest

Shrub 3–4 m high. Leaves lanceolate or oblong–lanceolate, 6–9 cm long, 2–3.3 cm broad; apex, obtuse to acuminate, beaked, base obtuse, under surface pale buff to cinnamon clad with a thin somewhat crustaceous agglutinate indumentum. Inflorescence terminal umbel of 15 flowers; calyx a small fleshy rim, with slightly pointed lobes, floccose; corolla campanulate, washed rose, deepest on margins with small crimson spotted within on the posterior side, lobes 5.1 cm long, 2.3 cm broad, undulate and crenulate; stamens 10, unequal.

Distribution: N. W. Yunnan, at altitude 3700–4300 m.

558. **Rhododendron** taggianum Hutch.

Shrub 2–2.5 cm tall. Leaves oblong, 14 cm long, 5 cm broad, blunt and mucronate apex, obtuse at base, incurved margin, coriaceous, prominently reticulated on both surfaces, glandular and hairy along the midribs on both surfaces; petiole brownish glandular, flattened above, 4-5 cm long, stout. Inflorescence in terminal umbel. Flowers white.

Distribution: N. W. Yunnan, at altitude 3700 m.

559. **Rhododendron** tanakai Hayata

Shrub 2-5 m tall. Leaves glabrous, clustered at the ends of branchlets, lanceolate-oblong, 5-12 cm long, usually 8-10 cm long, 1.5-3 cm usually 2.5-3.5 cm broad, acute or short acuminate at apex, base narrowed cuneate, margin slightly recurved. Flowers fascicled, fascicles lateral about the end of shoots, 1-flowered; corolla funnel-form campanulate, about 5 cm long and broad, deeply 5-lobed, lobes spreading, spathulate, obovate, emarginate; stamens 10, shorter than corolla. Fruit dark brown, cylindric, 2-3.5 cm long, furrowed, often crowned with remains of style.

Distribution: Taiwan, at altitude 1660-2600 m.

560. **Rhododendron** tanastylum Balf. et Ward

Shrub or tree 3-6 m high. Leaves broadly lanceolate or oblanceolate, narrowed to both ends from the near middle, 7.5-12 cm long, 2.5-4.3 cm broad; apex shortly acuminate or obtuse, margin undulate; base obtuse or sub-cuneate. Flowers in racemose umbel of 8 flowered; calyx cupular fleshy, lobes 5; corolla tubular campanulate 4-5 cm long, fleshy with 5 nectar pouches at base, deep crimson with many or few deeper crimson tinted spots, lobes 5, emarginate. Capsule oblong, blunt 1.5 cm long, 5 mm broad, blackish, glabrous, 8-chambered.

Distribution: East Burma to W. Yunnan, at altitude 300-3700 m.

561. **Rhododendron** taliense Franch.

Shrub 1-3 m high, shoots woolly tomentose. Leaves oblong-ovate to broadly lanceolate, 5-10 cm long, 2-3.5 cm broad; apex broadly acute to shortly acuminate, sharply pointed by inrolling of margin over tip of midrib, base blunt or rounded to sub-cordate, upper surface dark green, rugulose, glabrescent with vestiges of a juvenile tomentum, under surface clad with a tawny felty-like indumentum with a soft non-agglutinate, non-pellicled surface. Inflorescence a compact umbel of 10-15 flowers; calyx 2-3 mm long, with 5 small ovate to triangular lobes; corolla funnel-campanulate, 3.5 cm long, creamy yellow or creamy, fleshed rose with deep crimson markings, lobes 5, rounded, crenulate; stamens 10, unequal.

Distribution: W. Yunnan, at altitude 3300-4000 m.

562. **Rhododendron** tapetiforme Balf. et Ward

Small shrublets forming a carpet; branchlets scaly. Leaves broadly elliptic, densely scaly on both surfaces. Inflorescence terminal, 2-3-flowered. Flowers pink; calyx very short fringed with short hairs; corolla openly funnel-shaped, 1.5 cm long, not scaly outside; stamens 10, exserted; ovary scaly, style glabous, as long as the stamens.

Distribution: Tibet, Yunnan, at altitude 5000 m, an alpine species found only at high altitude.

563. Rhododendron taronense Hutch.

An epiphytic shrub 3-5 m high, growing on trees in the jungles. Leaves narrowly elliptic to elliptic-lanceolate, acute at both ends, abruptly mucronate, 10-14 cm long, 4-5.5 cm broad, not scaly above, laxy scaly below, lateral veins 10 pairs. Inflorescence umbellate, 5-flowered, densely scaly. Flowers white with large yellow blotch near the base, fragrant, fleshy; calyx rim-like, scaly outside; corolla 5 cm long; tube laxy scaly outside, lobes 5; stamens 10, nearly as long as the corolla, pubescent in lower half; ovary 6-celled, densely scaly. Capsule oblique at the base, 6-celled, the valves closely warted-scaly, not keeled.

Distribution: Tibet.

564. Rhododendron tatsinense Franch.

Shrub with small twiggy laxy scaly branchlets. Leaves oblong-lanceolate, acute, 2.5 cm long, 1 cm broad, laxy and scaly above. Inflorescence terminal, 3-4-flowered, umbellate; calyx mere a rim, sub-entire, glabrous; corolla, 5-lobed; stamens 10, exserted, pubescent in the lower part; ovary densely scaly.

Distribution: Szechuan, and Yunnan, at altitude 3200 m.

565. Rhododendron telopeoides

Shrub 2-3 m high. Leaves oblong, 6 cm long, 3 cm wide, blunt mucronate apex obtuse at base, glabrous on both surfaces. Flowers yellow, in terminal raceme.

Distribution: N. W. Yunnan, at altitude 4300 m.

566. Rhododendron telmateium Balf. et Sm.

Shrub 1 m tall. Branchlets densely scaly. Leaves oblanceolate, 3 mm long, 2 mm broad, densely scaly on both surfaces. Inflorescence terminal, 1-flowered. Flowers deep rosy-purple with white corolla throat. corolla openly funnel-shaped; stamens usually 10, exserted, pubescent; ovary scaly, style glabrous, longer than the stamens.

Distribution: Sikang and Yunnan, at altitude 3300-4000 m.

567. Rhododendron telopeum Balf. et Forrest

Shrub 1 m high. Leaves shortly elliptic or semi-orbicular, 2.5-5 cm long, 1.7-3 cm broad; apex rounded, mucronate, base rounded to cordulate, under surface glaucous papillate and punctate with minute dots the base of withered hairs or glands; petiole 1 cm long, with vestiges of glands. Inflorescence a laxy umbel of 4-flowers; calyx small, few mm long, glandular, lobes short, and gland-fringed; corolla bright yellow, with faint basal crimson blotch, lobes 5, broad, emarginate; stamens 10, unequal. Capsule 1.5-2 cm long, slightly curve.

Distribution: S. E. Tibet, at altitude 4000 m.

568. Rhododendron temenium Balf. et Forrest

Shrub 1 m tall. Leaves in terminal rosettes of 5-7 leaves, persistent for two years their position on older branches marked by nodulose swellings formed by the clustered nodes of the foliage-leave at the shoot apex. Leaves petiolate, 6.5 cm long, clustered in a pseudo-whorl at the ends of each years' growth, oblong or oblong-oval, sometime oblong–oval, 6 cm long, 2 cm broad, rounded at the apex, mucronate, margin cartilaginous, floccosely ciliate and slightly notched, base obtuse or slightly rounded, under surface paler tawny with very prominent red–tinted midrib.

Distribution: S. E. Tibet and Yunnan, at altitude 4300 m.

9. Rhododendron tephropeplum Balf. et Farrer

Shrub 1.3 m high. Leaves few, scattered, oblong–lanceolate to obovate – elliptic, rounded and very prominently mucronate at the apex, abruptly narrowed to the base 3–5 cm long, 1–2 cm broad. The upper most leaves narrowly winged. Inflorescence in terminal umbel, 4–5–flowered. Flowers magenta rose, with crimson tube, not spotted, broadly tubular, with 5 spreading recurved, emarginate lobes; calyx large 5–parted; ovary 5–celled, densely lepidote.

Distribution: S. E. Tibet, Yunnan and North Burma, at altitude 4300 m.

0. Rhododendron thayerianum Rehd. et Wils.

Shrub 3–4 m tall. Leaves crowded, closely clustered around the flower truss, leathery, narrow–oblanceolate, 7–13 cm long, 1.5–3 cm wide, apex acute to acuminate, slightly recurved; base cuneate; margin recurved; under surface clad with (except the midrib) a smooth curstaceous, skin–like pale–brown indumentum; petiole stout, curved. Inflorescence a compact racemose corymb of 10–20 flowers; rachis elongate, thin, 3–4 cm long, glandular with short–stalked glands; calyx 2–4 mm long, with distinct 5 lobes, densely glandular. Capsule oblong–cylindric, about 2 cm long, 4–6 mm broad, greenish grey, encrusted with blackish shrivelled glands, 6–8–chambered.

Distribution: W. Szechuan, at altitude 3000 m.

1. Rhododendron theiochrum Balf. et Sm.

Shrub 1 m high. Leaves broadly–obovate, broadly and obtusely mucronate at the apex, broadly wedge–shaped at the base, 1.5–6.5 cm long, 2–3 cm broad, closely scaly below. Inflorescence in terminal umbel of few – flowered. Flowers bright sulphur–yellow; calyx deeply, 5–lobed, densely scaly outside but not hairy; corolla broadly campanulate; stamens 10, densely bearded between the middle and the base; ovary 5–celled, densely scaly.

Distribution: Yunnan, at altitude 3300–3700 m.

2. Rhododendron theiophyllum Balf. et Forrest

Shrub 4 m high. Leaves oblong–ovate, 12 cm long, 4 cm wide, rostrate–acute, obtuse or sub–rounded, unequal at base. Inflorescence in umbellate racemes of 10–flowered; corolla obliquely maculate, 3–5 cm long, 5–lobed; stamens 10, unequal. Capsule oblique, glabrous.

Distribution: N. W. Szechuan.

3. Rhododendron thomsonii Hook.

Shrub 2–4 m high. Flowers rose–pink, with magenta patches at base; calyx very large, irregular, same color, fleshy, filaments and style white, anthers brown, stigma rose; ovary glandular.

Distribution: Tibet, at altitude 3700 m.

Var. 1. **Rhododendron** thomsonii var. **pallidum** Cowan

Shrub 2-3 m high. Leaves obovate, 8 cm long, 5 cm broad, bl apex, truncate or cordulate at base. Flowers magenta rose-pi patches at base; calyx green to rose at margin; filaments and st white.

Distribution: Tibet, at altitude 3700 m.

574. **Rhododendron** thymifolium Maxim.

Shrub. Leaves narrowly oblanceolate, 4 mm long, densely scaly on both surface Inflorescence terminal, 1-flowered. Flowers mauve; calyx short, scaly outside; cor funnel-shaped, not scaly outside; stamens 10, exserted, pubescent towards the ba ovary densely scaly, style shorter than the stamens.

Distribution: Kansu and Tibet, at altitude 4000 m.

575. **Rhododendron** thyodocum Balf. et Cooper

Shrub 1 m high. Leaves distinctly petiolate, oblong or elliptic-oblong, 3.5 cm lo 2.5 cm broad; apex rounded, mucronate, margin somewhat cartilaginous slightly curved; obtuse at base; under surface clad with smooth compact indumentum. Flowe lemon-yellow.

Distribution: E. Tibet, at altitude 3700 m.

576. **Rhododendron** timeteum Balf. et Forrest

Shrub 2 m high. Leaves oval, or elliptic or oblong-oval, 6 cm long, 3 cm wide, a rounded or obtuse, base rounded or broadly obtuse, margin cartilaginous, smooth. florescence umbellate, solitary, terminal, 4-flowered; corolla lavender or purpli rose with deep crimson markings, 5-lobed; ovary 6 mm long, leptidote. Capsule 5-val dehiscent.

Distribution: W. Szechuan and Sikang, at altitude 3700 m.

577. **Rhododendron** torquatum Balf. et Forrest

Shrub 1 m high. Leaves oblanceolate, 4 cm long, 2 cm broad, rounded and mucron apex, broadly cuneate at base, bluish glaucous and glandular beneath. Flowers termi purplish red.

Distribution: S. E. Tibet, at altitude 4300 m.

578. **Rhododendron** traillianum G. Forrest et Sm.

Shrub or tree 7-10 m high. Leaves oblong, 12 cm long, 5 cm wide, short acute a mucronate apex, broadly obtuse at base, slightly recurved margin, thick, cariaceo dark green above, brownish, smooth, felty, tomentose below. Flowers with campanula 5-lobed, corolla, white with red spots, stamens unequal, anthers yellowish-white; p tile longer than stamens.

Distribution: Yunnan, and Sikang, at altitude 3700 m.

579. **Rhododendron** trichocladium Franch.

Shrub 1 m high. Branchlets clothed with long weak hairs; leaf-bud-scales early ciduous. Leaves deciduous, oblong, rounded at each end, mucronate at the apex about 4 cm long, 2 cm broad, pubescent and finely reticulate above, minutely scaly below, usually fringed with hairs. Inflorescence terminal, 3-5-flowered; petiole 2 mm long, pilose. Flowers greenish yellow, spotted with dark green; calyx well developed, lobes oblanceolate, densely fringed with long hairs, scaly on the back; corolla widely funnel-shaped, about 2.5 cm long, scaly outside; stamens 10, shortly exserted, pubescent in the lower part; ovary scaly; style abruptly bent, glabrous. Capsule 1 cm long, scaly.

Distribution: Yunnan and Tibet, at altitude 4000-4300 m.

580. **Rhododendron** **trichoforum** Balf.

Loosely branched shrub forming a few longer erect virgate branches. Foliage-bud oblong-ovoid, pointed; outer most scale-leaves crustaceous, rounded or broadly triangular keeled and mucronate, more or less ciliate. Young leaves conduplicate-convolute, ciliate, both surfaces scaly, the upper also puberulous and bearing bristles with the midrib slightly depressed and puberulous. The under surface densely hairy on midrib. Leaves petiolate, 9.5 cm long, 3.5 cm wide, narrowed to an acute tip, with a prominent red hydathodal mucro, margin cartilaginous slightly recurved; base cordulate or sub-truncate. Upper surface opaque dark green, when young usually red, the red tint often remaining on the leaves in their second year, slightly shagreened distantly black spotted with remains of juvenile scales, also most minute puberulous. Under surface paler scaly with yellowish peltate scales about 1 mm apart each with a broad umbo and narrow fringe. Flowers in terminal usually 4-flowered umbel; bracteoles filiform with spathulate apex, about 1.5 cm long, shorter than pedicel, hairy on the back and scaly on the underside of broader tip; calyx samll cup-shaped or saucer-shaped; corolla of butterfly-form, with funnel-shaped laterally compressed tube, pinkish passing into white at base of posterior petal; limb rich violet, with a white area on posterior petal and many green spots, 4 cm long, 5-lobed; lobes ovate or oblong-ovate, 2 cm long; stamens 10, unequal, the longest equalling corolla, some 4 cm long, the shortest 2 cm long; ovary 4 mm long, conoid, truncate, densely scaly hair-crested; style pink hairy at base.

Distribution: Szechuan and Yunnan,

81. **Rhododendron** **trichophlebium** Balf. et Forrest

Small shrub. Leaves sub-sessile, oblong-oval, 1.5-3 cm long, 0.5-1 cm broad; apex acute, margin recurved; base obtuse; under surface clothed with white floccose hairs. Inflorescence an umbel of 4-flowered; calyx 5-lobed, ciliate, rounded, more or less glandular; corolla campanulate, fleshy, crimson, lobes 5 rounded, emarginate.

Distribution: S. E. Tibet.

2. **Rhododendron** **trichostomum** Franch.

Bush 1-2 m tall. Leaves ovate or ovate-oblong, 8-10mm long. Inflorescence capitate 10-15 flowered; corolla white or rose.

Distribution: Szechuan and Yunnan, at altitude 3300-4300 m.

583. Rhododendron triflorum Hook. f.

Shrub 1-2 m high; Leaves oblong, 6 cm long, 3 cm broad, acute apex, rounded or obtuse at base, brownish glandular beneath. Flowers lemon-yellow, spotted green yellow; filamnets and style rose-yellow.

Distribution: Tibet, at altitude 3300 m.

584. Rhododendron triplonaevium Balf. et Forrest

Shrub 2-3 m high. Leaves lanceolate or oblong-lanceolate, 7-15 cm long, 2-3.5 cm broad, apex shortly acuminate or obtuse, margin slightly recurved, base tapered and narrowly rounded. Inflorescence racemose umbel of 12-flowered; corolla campanulate, 3 cm long, white or white flushed rose, marked with a triradiate crimson blotch at base, lobes 5, rounded, crenulate, emarginate. Capsule slightly curved, 2 cm long, 6 mm broad.

Distribution: N. W. Yunnan, at altitude 3700-4000 m.

585. Rhododendron tsaii Fang

Shrub 30 cm high. Leaves elliptic or oblong-elliptic or oblong-oblanceolate, 6-12 mm long, 3-5 mm wide; apex acute, margin revolute, base cuneate or obtuse; petiole 1 mm long, lepidote. Flowers purplish white, terminal, 5-7 flowered on a rachis; corolla, lobes 5, funnel-shaped, 5 mm long; stamens 5, 3-4 mm long; anthers purple; ovary elliptic, densely scaly.

Distribution: Yunnan, at altitude 2900 m.

586. Rhododendron tsangpoense Hutch. et Ward

Shrub 40 cm high, forming dense tangled shrub. Leaves obovate, rounded at the apex very conspicuously mucronate, narrowed at the base, 2.5-4 cm long, 1.5-2 cm wide glabrous above, laxy scaly below. Inflorescence terminal 3-4-flowered. Flowers pin or deep cerise; calyx large, deeply 5-lobed; stamens 10, densely hairy near the top ovary 5-celled, scaly.

Distribution: Tibet, at altitude 4000-4300 m.

587. Rhododendron tsariense Cowan

Shrub 1-3 m tall. Leaves elliptic-oblong or elliptic-obovate, 2.2-6.2 cm long, 1 cm wide; apex obtuse or rotundate abruptly acuminate, margin revolute, base rotunda or sub-cordulate. Flowers in racemose umbellate, 3-4-flowered; corolla rose to ros white. Capsule cylindric, cinnamon-tomentose, dehiscent, 5-valved, 2 cm long, 5 m broad.

Distribution: S. Tibet, at altitude 4700 m.

588. Rhododendron tsoi Merr.

Shrub 1 m high. Leaves elliptic, 5-12 mm long, 5-8 mm wide; apex rotundate or o tuse, apiculate; base acute, coriaceous; petiole 1-3 mm long, densely castaneo-setos Flowers pink, in terminal umbellating fascicled; corolla tube 3-4 mm long, exteri glabrous, internal puberulous; stamens 5. Capsule oblong-ovoid, 2 mm long.

Distribution: Kwangtung.

89. **Rhododendron tutcherae** Hemsl. et Wilson

Tree 13 m high. Branchlets bristly, with long stiff hairs. Leaves narrowly oblan-ceolate, gradually acuminate, narrowed to the base, 7.5–10 cm long, 2–2.5 cm broad, shortly setulose on the lower surface, especially on the midrib, with numerous lateral veins; ketiole very bristly, 1.5 cm long. Inflorescence axillary and terminal, 1–flow-ered; pedicels 2 cm long, glabrous or slightly pilose. Flowers violet; calyx obsolete, slightly dentate, glabrous; corolla narrowly-funnel-shaped, 5–lobed, 4 cm long, glab-rous outside; stamens 10, exserted, pubescent towards the base; ovary tomentose; style glabrous, as long as the stamens.

Distribution: S. Yunnan, at altitude 2000 m.

90. **Rhododendron umbelliferum** Levl.

Shrub, with inflorescence of an umbel of 9 flowered. Flowers rose color; stamens 10, unequal, exserted; stigma capitate, emarginate.

Distribution: Kweichow.

91. **Rhododendron uniflorum** Hutch. et Ward

Dwarf shrub with subprocumbent branches, young branchlets slightly scaly. Leaves in clusters, oblong–obovate, rounded to a mucronate apex, 1.5–2 cm long, 1–1.5 cm broad, glaucous below. Inflorescence terminal, 1–flowered. Flowers purple; calyx with rounded lobes, scaly outside; corolla funnel-shaped, 2.5 cm long, shortly lobed, softly pubescent, with a few scattered scales outside; stamens 10, included, just above the base shortly pubescent; ovary scaly; style slightly longer than stamens.

Distribution: S. Tibet, at altitude 3700–4000 m.

92. **Rhododendron uvarifolium** Diels

Shrub 7–8 m high. Leaves narrowly oblanceolate, 12–23 cm long, 3–6 cm broad, apex obtuse or acute, somewhat beaked, base tapered; veins 14–16; under surface clad with thin white felty tomentum. Inflorescence a racemose umbel of 6–8–flowers, rachis 1 cm long, more or less rufous floccose; pedicel 2 cm long, slightly floccose; calyx minute, 1 mm long, rim undulate with minute or somewhat rounded or pointed lobes, glabrous or sparsely floccose; ccrolla funnel–campanulate, pink with crimson spots and a deep crimson blotch at the base; lobes 5, 1 cm long, emarginate; stamens 10, unequal; pistil 3.5 cm long, ovary 8 mm long, thin, slightly puberulous, or glabrous, 8–chambered; style glabrous.

Distribution: N. W. Yunnan, at altitude 2300–3800 m.

93. **Rhododendron valentinianum** Forrest

Small shrub 1 m high. with rosettes of 4–5 small leaves at the end of the shoots. Young twigs densely setose. Leaves elliptic or oblong–elliptic, 4 cm long, 2 cm wide, setose ciliate on the margin, setose above, densely scaly below, with more or less con-tiguous scales; leaf-stalks 1 cm long, setose and scaly. Inflorescence 2–3– flowered umbel, terminal. Flowers bright yellow; calyx leafy, 1 cm long, lobes 5, oblong, scaly outside, densely woolly–setulose on the margin; corolla 4 cm long, 5–lobed, pubescent,

with long hairs on both sides, lobes fringed with scales; stamens 10, shorter than co
rolla; ovary densely lepidote; style scaly at base. Capsule enclosed by the calyx.

Distribution: Yunnan, at altitude 3700 m.

594. Rhododendron vaccinioides Hook.

A common epiphyte in the forest, of few cm long or high. Leaves small, 12 mm long
2 mm broad, rounded, emarginate apex, cuneate at base, whitish-brown glandular to
mentose beneath.

Distribution: S. E. Tibet.

595. Rhododendron venator Tagg

A slim shrub with more or less ascending branches reaching 2-3 m high. Leaves 6
14 cm long, 2.4 cm broad, oblong-lanceolate to oblong-oblanceolate, acute with a re
curved tip mucro, base cordulate, under surface pale glaucous green. Flowers dee
crimson, with 5 black crimson nectar pouches at the base. Capsule 1.5 cm long, slightl
curved, 5-valved.

Distribution: S. E. Tibet, at altitude 2700 m.

596. Rhododendron vellereum Hutch.

Small tree 2-5 m tall. Leaves oblong-elliptic to oblong-lanceolate, 6-11 cm long, 2
4.5 cm broad, apex acute or obtuse, base rounded or rarely cordulate; upper surfac
smooth to minutely rugulose, under surface silvery-white to fawn, clad with a thickis
spongy indumentum, the surface forming a kid-glove-like pellicle which tends to split
midrib raised, more or less clothed with indumentum, rest of venation concealed. In
florescence short umbel-raceme of 15-20-flowered, rachis 1 cm long; calyx 5-lobe
forming a rim fringed with short floccose hairs; corolla, white flushed rose with purpl
or carmine spots, lobes 5, 1 cm long. Capsule narrow-cylindric, grooved, 5-6-cham
bered.

Distribution: S. E. Tibet, at altitude 3300-3700 m.

597. Rhododendron vernicosum Franch.

A spreading shrub of 2-8 m high. Leaves oblong-oval to oblong-elliptic, 6-12 cm
long, 3-5 cm broad; apex broadly obtuse or rounded; base broadly obtusely sub-rounded
upper surface smooth, glabrous, mat, but wax-covered and becoming glossy when rubbe
or heated, midrib grooved, veins 14-16; under surface pale glaucous. Inflorescence a
racemose umbel of 10-flowered; calyx fleshy, an oblique expansion of pedicel; lobes 7,
broadly rounded to triangular, densely glandular and fringed with glands; corolla widel
funnel-shaped, 4 cm long, white to bright rose, with or without crimson markings;
stamens 14, unequal, 2-3 cm long, filaments glabrous; pistil 4 cm long, ovary conoid,
5 mm long, slightly grooved, 6-7-chambered, densely clad with shortly stalked glands;
style glandular throughout with dark-red glands; stigma lobulate.

Distribution: W. Szechuan, Yunnan and Sikang, at altitude 3000-3700 m.

598. Rhododendron verruculosum Rehd. et Wilson

Shrub 1 m high. Branchlets short, densely scaly; leaf-bud-scales early deciduous. Leaves broadly–elliptic, 12 mm long, 8 mm wide, scaly on both surfaces, the scales above thick and fleshy, those below thin and from half to their own diameter apart. Inflorescence terminal, 1–flowered; flower–bud–scale subpersistent; petioles 3 mm long, scaly. Flowers purple; calyx well developed, lobes as broad as long, scaly outside, fringed with short hairs; corolla openly funnel–shaped, about 12 mm long, scaly only outside the lobes; stamens 7–8, exserted, villose in the lower part; ovary scaly; style longer than the stamens, glabrous.

Distribution: W. Szechuan, at altitude 330 m.

599. Rhododendron vesiculiferum Tagg

Small gnarled shrub or medium–sized tree; shoots and petioles densely bristly with gland–tipped setae. Leaves oblanceolate to oblong–oblanceolate, 8–16 cm long, 2–4.5 cm broad; apex abruptly acuminate; base rounded to cordulate; margin ciliate; upper surface markedly rugulose almost bullate, at first sparsely floccose and sparsely glandular–setose, finally glabrous, midrib deeply grooved; lateral veins 20–24 pairs, deeply impressed; under surface paler and clad with isolated crisped setose hairs, midrib very prominent and bristly towards the petiole. Inflorescence an umbel of 10–15 flowered; rachis 1 cm long, floccose; calyx 1 cm long, purplish, split to near the base into 5 oblong, oval to lanceolate lobes, 7–8 mm long, 2–4 mm broad, ciliate with long–stalked glands; corolla campanulate, 3–3.5 cm long, purplish–rose, with a blotch of deep crimson or purple at the base; lobes 5 broadly rounded, 1.3 cm long, 1.8 cm broad, distinctly emarginate; stamens 10, unequal, filaments widened at base and there puberulous; pistil 3 cm long; ovary ovoid, 5 mm long, truncate, clad with long setose ascending glands and with shorter visicular floccose hairs; style setose – glandular and visicular–floccose for about 1/3 its length.

Distribution: S. E. Tibet, at altitude 3000–3700 m.

600. Rhododendron vestitum Tagg et Forrest

Shrub 1–2 m high; with twisted branches of short annual growth. Leaves oval to elliptic or at times obovate, 3.5–5 cm long, 1.5–3 cm broad, very broadly obtuse or rounded, at apex, apiculate, broad obtuse or somewhat rounded at base, minutely rugulose upper surface, veins 9–12; under surface clad with a tawny to brown detersile loose indumentum of branched hairs giving a patched–scurfy surface; midrib raised, glandular; reticulations more or less hidden; petiole 5–7 mm long, glandular–setose, the glands extending to the base of the leaf–margin. Inflorescence an umbel of 6–flowered; pedicel 1.5 cm long, clad with long–setose glands and shorter–stalked glands; calyx small, fleshy; lobes rounded or traingular, gland–fringed; corolla funnel–campanulate, white flushed rose, deep rose in bud, with a few crimson markings and a basal crimson blotch; lobes 5, 1 cm long, 1.3 cm broad; stamens 10, unequal. Capsule cylindric, slightly, curved, 1–1.5 cm long, 4 mm broad, slightly grooved, rough with vestiges of glands.

Distribution: S. E. Tibet, at altitude 4700 m.

601. Rhododendron viali Delavay et Franch.

Shrub 2 m high. Leaves coriaceous, obovate sub-acute, and obtuse at base, 3-4 cm long, petiole 12-18 mm long; pedicel 4-5 mm long, densely setulose; calyx membranaceous; lobes 5-7 mm long, obovate, glandular - ciliate; corolla intense red, long-tubular; lobes 5, rotundate; stamens 5, included; ovary dense papillose.

Distribution: Yunnan, at altitude 1130 m.

602. **Rhododendron** vicarium Balf.

Much branched shrub with twiggy erect branches. Leaves oblong-oval, oval or oblong-ovate, 9 mm long, 3 mm broad, obtuse or rounded at apex and there mucronate, the margin slightly recurved, broadly obtuse at base; under surface tawny rust-colored clothed with contiguous peltate scales but often with a narrow naked interval between forming a bistrate indumentum, some scales rust-colored of an upper stratum with a broad umbo full of secretion and an equally broad scintillating fringe, others equally mixed, of a lower stratum uncolored, Flowers 1-2 at the apex of the shoots, nearly sessile; bracts few, more or less persistent during the flowering; outer ones crustaceous rounded hooded keeled mucrolanulate, rust-lepidote outside, margin thinner ciliate; innermost membranaceous pale brown oblong or obovate-oblong, about 6.5 mm long, 3.5 mm broad, lepidote and puberulous outside woolly ciliate; corolla blue-violet; ovary narrow cylindric, 2 mm long, slightly sulcate, densely imbricately yellowish lepidote; style red-purple. Capsule reddened covered by the vestiges of peltate scales, narrow-oblong, about 4 mm long, 1.75 mm in diameter, dehiscing by 5 valves from apex to base.

Distribution: W. Szechuan.

603. **Rhododendron** vicinum Balf. et Forrest

A fragrant shrub of 8 m high. Leaves rigid, oblong-oval, 7 cm long, 3 cm wide, attenuate acute, acuminate-mucronate at apex, margin recurved, obtuse rotundate at base. Inflorescence long-racemose; bracts and braceoles deciduous; corolla oblique-campanulate, white, rose-flushed, base sparingly puberulous; ovary 4 mm long, sub-cylindic, curved.

Distribution: N. W. Yunnan.

604. **Rhododendron** villosum Hemsl. et Wislon

Shrub about 2-7 m tall; branchlets densely long-haired and dotted with scales. Leaves oblong-oblanceolate, rounded or slightly cordate at base, acutely triangular-acuminate, mucronate, 5-10 cm long, 2-3.5 cm broad, laxy scaly below; petioles densely setose Inflorescence terminal, umbellate, 3-flowered, pedicels 1.5 cm long, densely setose with bristly hairs. Flowers light purple or rose; calyx 5-lobed; corolla 5-lobed with scattered scales all over the outside and more or less bristly in the lower part; stamens 10, long-exserted, villose in the lower part; ovary 5-celled, covered with long bristles and small scales; style smooth. Capsule 2 cm long, curved, laxly covered with small scales, persistent calyx-lobes ciliate.

Distribution: Szechuan, at altitude 2300-4650 m.

605. **Rhododendron** violaceum Rehd. et Wils.

Shrub 1 m tall. Leaves narrowly oblong–elliptic, 1 cm long, densely scaly on both surfaces, the scales below overlapping, petioles scaly. Inflorescence terminal, 1–3–flowered, flowers sub-sessile, violet–purple; corolla openly funnel–shaped, nearly 12 mm long, not scaly outside; stamens 10, exserted, villose towards the base; ovary scaly.

Distribution: W. Szechuan, at altitude 4000–4500 m.

506. Rhododendron virgatum Hook. f.

Shrub 1–2 m high. Leaves oblong, 3 cm long, 1.5 cm broad, blunt mucronate at apex, obtuse at base, reddish glandular beneath; corolla rich pink, deeper at the base; filaments white; anther red–brown; style pink; stigma dull red; ovary green bud–scales, pale reddish brown; scales on leaves dark golden–brown.

Distribution: S. E. Tibet, and Yunnan, at altitude 3000 m.

507. Rhododendron wallichii Hook. f.

Shrub occurred in Bhutan and southern Tibet in coniferous forest, at altitude of 3700 m; described by Hooker in "Rhododendrons of the Sikkim Himalaya" in 1849 (t. 5)

508. Rhododendron wardii W. W. Sm.

Shrub 5–7 m high. Leaves oblong–elliptic or semi–orbicular, 6–10 cm long, 2–5 cm broad; apex rounded or broadly obtuse, apiculate; base rounded, truncate, or cordulate; veins 10–15; under surface pale glaucous green, with few vestiges of a juvenile indumentum. Inflorescence a racemose umbel of 7–14–flowered; rachis 1–15 cm long, tomentose and glandular; calyx cup–shaped, fleshy, 6–12 mm long, lobes 5, unequal, yellowish–fringed on the margin with glands; corolla cup–shaped slightly fleshy, 3.5–4 cm long, bright yellow; lobes 5, 2 cm long; stamens 10, 1–2 cm long, filaments glabrous. Capsule 1.5–2.5 cm long, curved, encased in the more or less persistent calyx.

Distribution: W. Yunnan and Tibet, at altitude 4000–4700 m.

509. Rhododendron wasonii Hemsl. et Wils.

Shrub about 1 m high. Leaves oval or ovate or broadly lanceolate, 5–10 cm long, 2.5–4.5 cm broad; apex acute to shortly acuminate, often cuspidate; base rounded to obtuse or cordulate; under surface clad with a uniform somewhat scarfy felty, on young leaves white, but later changing into bright–brown or rusty–red. Inflorescence a laxy corymb of about 10 flowers; rachis 1 cm long, floccose; calyx with 5 sharp–pointed triangular teeth, the whole white to fawn tomentose; corolla 3–4 cm long, pinkish rose or creamy–white and spotted within; stamens 10, unequal.

Distribution: W. Szechuan, at altitude 3000–3700 m.

510. Rhododendron websterianum Rehd. et Wils.

Shrub 1 m high. Leaves narrowly elliptic, about 1 cm long, densely scaly on both surfaces, the scales below densely packed, and yellowish–grey; leaf–stalks scaly. Inflorescence terminal, usually 1–flowered. Flowers rose–purple; calyx rose–purple shortly ciliated; corolla openly funnel–shaped, not scaly outside; stamens 10, exserted, villose towards the base; ovary scaly. Capsule scaly, 3 mm long, surrounded by per—

sistent calyx.

Distribution: W. Szechuan, at altitude 4100-4900 m.

611. Rhododendron weldianum Rehd. et Wils.

Shrub 2-5 m high. Leaves oblong-elliptic, 6-11 cm long, 3-4 cm broad; apex acut or shortly acuminate, base tapered or rarely rounded; under surface clad with dens woolly tomentum, which at first whitish, later a rusty-brown. Inflorescence an umbel late raceme of 6-12 flowers; calyx obsolete; corolla funnel-campanulate; lobes broadl ovate, 9-10 mm long; stamens 2 cm long. Capsule 2-2.5 cm long, woolly.

Distribution: W. Szechuan, at altitude 3000-3300 m.

612. Rhododendron westlandii Hemsl.

Shrub or small tree, 7 m high, completely glabrous. Leaves broadly oblanceolate acutely acuminate, shortly cuneate at base, 6-12 cm long, 2.5-4 cm broad, glabrous Inflorescence axillary, several-flowered. Flowers sweet scented, lilac; calyx obso lete, undulate lobed; corolla narrowly funnel-shaped, glabrous; stamens 10, pubesce between the middle and the base; ovary long, glabrous; style glabrous.

Distribution: Hongkong, Lanto Island, Kwangtung, Hainan, Hupeh, and Kiangs at altitude 800 m.

613. Rhododendron williamsianum Rehd. et Wilson

Shrub 1-2 m high. Branchlets horizentally forming a flattish bush. Leaves broad elliptic to rounded, ovate or cordate, 1.5-4 cm long, 1.3-3.3 cm broad; apex round or blunt; base cordate, rarely truncate; under surface glaucous, papillate, punctulat with small glands and hairs. Inflorescence a racemose umbel of 3-5-flowered; cal minute, glandular, with 5 short rounded lobes; corolla campanulate, 3-4 cm long, pa rose without spots, lobes 5, rounded or suborbicular, shallowly emarginate; stame 10, unequal; ovary oblong-conoid, green, glandular, 4-5 mm long; style curved, cl with glands throughout, glands on lower half stalked, those towards the stigma more less sessile. Capsule oblong-cylindric, 5-6-chambered, the small calyx persistent the base.

Distribution: Szechuan, at altitude 2700-3300 m.

614. Rhododendron wilsonae Hemsl. et Wilson

Shrub 2 m high. Leaves whorled, narrowly elliptic, sub-acutely acuminate, 6-10 long, 2.5-3.5 cm broad; veins 12 pairs. Inflorescence terminal and axillary, 1-flower calyx obsolete, triangular lobed, glabrous; corolla widely funnel-shaped, 3 cm lo 5-lobed, glabrous; stamens 10, exserted. Capsule 2.5 cm long, smooth.

Distribution: W. Hupeh, at altitude 1700-2000 m.

615. Rhododendron wilsonii Hemsl. et Wilson

Shrub 1-5 m high. Leaves oblong-obovate to oblanceolate, 5-12 cm long, 2-4 broad; apex obtuse; base cuneate or more or less rounded; upper surface gloss under surface felted, woolly tomentose at first and later glabrous. Inflorescence racemose umbel of 10 flowers; rachis pubescent; calyx 2-3 mm long, with 5 triangu teeth, densely tomentose; corolla flesh-pink with red spots or with a blotch, 3-3.5 cm long; lobes 5, emarginate; stamens 10, unequal. Capsule cylindric, slightly curved, clad with a brownish tomentum or glabrescent.

Distribution: W. Szechuan at altitude, 2300-3000 m.

16. Rhododendron wongii Hemsl. et Wils.

Shrub 1-2 m high. Leaves oblong-elliptic, very obtuse at both ends but mucronate at apex, 2.5 cm long, 12 mm broad, scaly below. Inflorescence terminal, 3-flowered, flower stalks 1 cm long, laxy scaly. Flowers creamy colored; calyx distinct, 5-lobed, lobes scaly outside, sometimes with 2 or 3 weak hairs on the margin; corolla less than 2.5 cm long, 5-lobed, not scaly outside; stamens 10, long-exserted, villose in the lower part; ovary 5-celled, densely scaly; style glabrous.

Distribution: Szechuan, at altitude 3700 m.

17. Rhododendron wuense Balf.

Shrub 6 m high. Leaves oblong-oval or oval, 8.5 cm long, 4 cm broad, apex shortly rostrate, margin recurved, base rounded or cordulate; upper surface mat, minute rugulose, under surface clad with rusty indumentum. Inflorescence a short racemose umbel of few-flowered; calyx 1.5 cm long, split into 5 unequal lobes, lobes fringed with short glands on the margins; corolla campanulate, 3.5 cm long, lobes 5, 1 cm long, 2 cm broad, emarginate.

Distribution: Western China.

18. Rhododendron xanthinum Balf. et Sm.

Shrub 1 m high. Flowers precocious, canary-yellow. Leaves oblong, 2.5 cm long, 1 cm broad, mucronate apex, obtuse at base, brownish hairy below.

Distribution: Yunnan, at altitude 3300 m.

19. Rhododendron xanthostephanum Merr.

Shrub 1-2 m high. Leaves oblanceolate, 6 cm long, 2.2 cm broad, acutely mucronate apex, obtuse at base, incurved margin, under surface reddish-brown felted. Flowers yellow.

Distribution: S. E. Tibet and Yunnan, at altitude 4500 m.

20. Rhododendron youngae Fang

Shrub 4 m tall. Leaves oblong-elliptic, 5-12 cm long, 2-4 cm broad, apex acute, usually deflexed with a stiff mucro; base obtuse or nearly rounded; upper surface bright green; veins 10-12 pairs, under surface clad with brownish indumentum. Flowers 6-8 in terminal umbel; corolla purple spotted rose; campanulate funnel-form; stamens 10, unequal; anthers oblong, yellow; ovary ovoid, 5 mm long, densely brown tomentose and glandular.

Distribution: Szechuan, at altitude 2000 m.

21. Rhododendron yungningense Balf.

Shrub 20 cm high. Leaves oblanceolate, 1 cm long, densely scaly on both sides. Inflorescence terminal, 1-2-flowered. Flowers deep purple; calyx with broad ovate

lobes, fringed with very short hairs; corolla openly funnel-shaped; stamens 10, ex
serted, villose towards the base; ovary scaly; style glabrous, longer than the stamens

Distribution: S. W. Szechuan, at altitude 3300-4300 m.

622. Rhododendron yunnanense Franch.

Evergreen shrub with leggy branches and leaves often dropping or reflexed; youn
branchlets with scattered blackish glands. Leaves oblanceolate or obovate-oblanceolate
rounded or triangular mucronate at apex, acute at base, 3-5 cm long, 1.5-2.5 cm broad
Inflorescence terminal or lateral, 3-5-flowered, very shortly racemose. Flowers pink
ish or nearly white, spotted with red, corolla 5-lobed, 4 cm long, slightly irregular
not scaly outside; stamens 10, long-exserted, shortly pubescent in the lower part
ovary 5-celled, densely scaly. Capsule laxy scaly glandular.

Distribution: Yunnan, at altitude 3000 m.

623. Rhododendron zaleucum Balf.

Shrub or tree up to 12 m high. Leaves lanceolate or oblong - lanceolate, acutel
acuminate, rounded to sub-acute at base, 3-8 cm long, 1.5-4 cm broad, very glaucou
below. Inflorescence terminal, 3-4-flowered. Flowers white or rose, fragrant; caly
small, lobed, densely scaly outside; corolla 5-lobed, 4 cm long, tubes and lobes wi
numerous fleshy scales outside; stamens 10, little longer than corolla-tube, short
pubescent towards the base; ovary 5-celled, scaly. Capsule 13 mm long, closely gland
ular, scaly.

Distribution: W. Yunnan, and Burma, at altitude 3000-3700 m.

Order XXIII Ebenales

Family 58. Ebenaceae Juss.

(See orig. text page 886)

Genus (1) Diospyros Linn. (See orig. text page 886)

Key to the species

A. Branchlets usually glabrous, very rarely slightly pubescent.

  B. Inflorescence branched, distinctly pubescent --(34) *D. tucheri*

  BB. Inflorescence rarely branched, if so glabrous.

    C. Fruit glabrous at least when mature.

      D. Fruit about 3 cm in diameter ---------(15) *D. longibracteata*

      DD. Fruit 1–2 cm in diameter or less rarely more.

        E. Persistent calyx in fruit shallow 4–lobed, the lobes triangular.

          F. Petiole 15 mm or more longer leaves ovate, pale glaucescent beneath ------------------------- *D. glaucifolia*

          FF. Petiole 5–10 mm long.

            G. Leaves 11–15 cm long. -- (31) *D. susarticulata*

            GG. Leaves less than 10 cm long.

              H. Leaves reddish chestnut-brown when dry; veins not prominent, not reticulate --(21) *D. morrissiana*

              HH. Leaves reddish when dry; veins prominent beneath; reticulate ---------- (27) *D. rubra*

        EE. Persistent calyx in fruit deeply 4–lobed, the lobes obtuse to ovate.

          F. Calyx lobes in flower cruciform, 3–5 mm long; leaves 2.5–5 cm wide. --------------------- (16) *D. lotus*

          FF. Calyx lobes in flower broadly ovate, 1 mm long; leaves less than 2.5 cm wide. ----------------(22) *D. nitida*

    CC. Fruit pubescent, rarely glabrous.

      D. Fruit 1.5–2 cm long; leaves not over 8 cm long; clayx lobes lanceolate, 1.8–2.5 cm long--------------------------- *D. rhombifolia*

      DD. Fruit 3–4 cm long; leaves over 10 cm long; clayx lobes broadly ovate to rounded.

        E. Fruit oblong-ovate to subcylindrical, about 4 cm long; leaves somewhat coriaceous ----------------(17) *D. maclurei*

        EE. Fruit globose, 3 cm in diameter; leaves very coriaceous ---(11) *D. hainanensis*

AA. Branchlets usually distinctly pubescent, rarely sub-glabrous.

    B. Inflorescence composed of an elongated panicle; branches corymb-like compact, pubescent --------------------------------- (7) *D. ehretioides*

  BB. Inflorescence not paniculate, flowers solitary, or rarely in loose racemes. (as in *D. diversilimba*).

    C. Leaves prominently pubescent on midrib beneath.

      D. Leaves ovate or lanceolate to ovate-lanceolate.

        E. Fruit sessile, strigose, about 1 cm in diameter -------------------- *D. strigosa*

       EE. Fruit not sessile, sparsely pubescent, about 3 cm in diameter. ------ (30) *D. sunyiensis*

     DD. Leaves elliptic to oblong-lanceolate.

        E. Sepals uniformly pubescent; leaf margin ciliate ------------- *D. chunii*

       EE. Sepals pubescent only at base, leaf-margin not ciliate ------------ (8) *D. eriantha*

  CC. Leaves not distinctly pubescent on midrib beneath.

      D. Leaves ovate, glabrous or pubescent, often as broad as long, 4-10 cm wide, 10-14 cm long; fruit large, variable in size, edible ----------- (14) *D. kaki*

     DD. Leaves otherwise, rarely if ever as broad as long, and if so less than 2.5 cm wide.

        E. Fruit very small, 0.5 cm long; leaves less than 3 cm long; calyx lobes subulate to narrowly lanceolate -- (37) *D. vaccinioides*

       EE. Fruit 1.5-3 cm long; leaves various.

         F. Peduncles of fruit 4-6 cm long; leaves oblong-lanceolate ----------- *D. sinensis*

        FF. Peduncles of fruit less than 2 cm long.

          G. Base of calyx lobes when in fruit broad about 10 mm; leaves distinct pale beneath ---- (32) *D. tsangii*

         GG. Base of calyx lobes when in fruit usually less than 6 mm; leaves of the same color on both sides.

           H. Leaves polymorphic; gland conspicuous on lower surface of leaves ----------(5) *D. diversilimba*

          HH. Leaves not polymorphic, elliptical to ovate; glands inconspicuous.

            I. Branches spiny; fruit pubescent ----------------------- *D. foochowensis*

           II. Branches not spiny; fruit glabrous ------------------- *D. chowii*

1. **Diospyros armata** Hemsl. (See orig. text page 887)

2. **Diospyros chunii** Metcalf et Chen.

Small tree 4 m high. Branches terete. Branchlets brown, pubescent; Leaves alternate, elliptical to ovate or lanceolate, olive green on both sides, 7-10.5 cm long, 2-3 cm wide, sparsely pubescent on both sides, mid-nerve or principal veins tomentose below, base obtuse, apex acute or obtuse, margin entire, ciliated nerves 4 to 5 on each side; petiole 5-6 mm long, pubescent; fruit conic-ovate, pedicellate, pubescent, about 1 cm in diameter, 2.5 cm long; peduncle 3-4 mm long; calyx 4-lobed, densely pubescent, broadly-ovate, overlapping.

Distribution: Hainan, at altitude 1550 m.

3. **Diospyros corallina** Chun et Chen

Tree 8 m high. Leaves alternate, minutely petiolate, subcoriaceous, elliptic-oblong, 15-20 cm long, 5-8 cm wide, acute apex, broadly acute or cuneate at base, margin entire; petiole 5-8 mm long. Fruit solitary, sessile, axillary, depressed globose, 2.5 cm broad, 2 cm high, red, 8-loculary; seeds elliptic-oblong 10-12 mm long, 7-8 mm wide.

This species is characterized by large few-nerved leaves, sessile oblate, red fruits, 5-lobed calyx.

Distribution: Hainan.

4. **Diospyros esquirolii** Levl.

Tree 12-14 meters high. Leaves elliptic-oblong, acute on both ends, entire margin; petiole slender about 1 cm long.

It relates to *Diospyros dumetorim* W. W. Sm.

Distribution: Kweichow.

5. **Diospyros diversilimba** Merr. et Chun

Shrub 2-3 m high. Leaves oblong, membranaceous, 3-7 cm long, 1.5-3 cm wide, glabrous and olive-colored on both surfaces, obtuse-acuminate apice, base rotundate or obtuse or minutely cordate; petiole pubescent or glabrous, 4-5 mm long; flowers axillary; soliatry, pedicellate; sepals 4 oblong. Fruit globose, 6-loculary; style 3. To cook the fruits with water getting reddish black used for dye.

Distribution: Hainan.

6. **Diospyros dumetorum** W. W. Sm.

Shrub about 10 meters high. Leaves lanceolate or oblanceolate, 2-3.5 cm long, 1-1.3 cm wide, acute apex, rotundate or broadly cuneate at base, densely fulvo-pillose beneath; calyx campanulate, 3 mm long, densely pilose; corolla olive-colored, 5-6 cm long, glabrous outside and whitish pilose inside, stamens 16. Tree of 10 cm high. Flowers olive-green, fragrant.

Distribution: Yunnan, Sikong, at altitude 2800 m.

7. **Diospyros ehretioides** Wallich

Tree, branches ferruginous, branchlets and racemes reddish brown tomentose;

Leaves elliptic glabrous, sometimes slightly pubescent, ferruginous beneath, 15-16 cm long, 5-6 cm wide, acute at apex, round at base, margin entire, nerves 10-11 on both side, curved toward margin; petiole 1 cm long; flowers subsessile, reflexed; peduncle trichotomous, calyx of male flowers 4-parted, pubescent, lobes obtuse; corolla campanulate, calyx ciliate; fruit a drupe, globose, deppressed, when young pubescent.

Distribution: Hainan.

8. **Diospyros eriantha** Champ. (See orig. text page 887)

9. **Diospyros foochowensis** Metcalf et Chen

Small shrub 1-2 m high. Branches erect, spiny. Branchlets pubescent; leaves elliptic to broadly ovate or orbicular oblong, pale green on both surfaces, 2.5-3.5 cm long, 1.7 cm wide glabrous above, sparsely pubescent below, base round to obtuse, apex obtuse, sometimes obtuse-acuminate, margin entire; nerves 4-5 on each side, inconspicuous, running from prominent midrib to near the margin; petiole 2 mm long; fruit globose pubescent 1.5-5 cm in diameter; peduncle pubescent, 1.5 cm long; calyx 4-lobed, broadly-ovate acute, slightly pubescent above, more so beneath.

Distribution: Fukien, Foochow.

10. **Diospyros forrestii** Anth.

Shrub 6 m high. Leaves alternate, oblong-lanceolate, 10-15 cm long, 2.5-4 cm wide, coriaceous, glabrous, small acuminate apex, cuneate at base; petiole 1 cm long; Flowers pale waxy yellow, fragrant; corolla tubular-campanulate, 6-lobed, tube 8 mm long, lobes ovate 6 mm long, 2.5 mm wide; stamens 24, inserted at the base of the corollas, Fruit globose 1.5 cm in diameter, axillary, solitary, 5-loculary.

Distribution: Yunnan, at altitude 2800 m.

11. **Diospyros hainanensis** Merr. (See orig. text page 888)

12. **Diospyros howii** Merr. et Chun

Tree 6-8 m high. Leaves coriaceous, elliptic to oblong-elliptic, black olive-green, glabrous above, below a little paler, both sides glabrous, 2-4.5 cm long 12 cm wide, base acute, apex obtusely acuminate, male flowers solitary, axillary, 4-parted, or inflorescence rarely 2-flowered, pedicels slender, up to 7 mm long, sparsely pubescent; calyx lobes 4, round, shorter, subreniform; corolla tube cylindrical, 8 mm long, 4-lobed; calyx persistent, not thickened; seeds few, 1 cm long, 6 mm wide.

Distribution: Hainan, at altitude 1300 m.

13. **Diospyros inflata** Merr. et Chun

Tree 8-15 m high. Bark black, young fruits densely brownish pubescent.

This species is remarkable for its inflated, enlarged, ovoid, and almost closed accrescent pistillate calyx with completely encloses the fruit. The apical orifice is small and the lobes are usually spreading. The fruit and the inside of the inflated calyx are densely covered with stiff, shining, pale brown or pinkish-brown, almost stinging hairs. This structure reminds one of the indumentum on the fruit of the Philippine *Diospyros discolor* Willd.

Distribution: Hainan.

14. **Diospyros kaki** Linn. (See orig. text page 888)

Var. 1. **Diospyros kaki** var. **sylvestris** Makino (See orig. text pages 888-890)

15. **Diospyros longibracteata** Lecomte

Tree, leaves alternate; petiole 10-12 mm long; leaves coriaceous dark green, glabrous, lanceolate to oblong-lanceolate, 13 cm long, 4-5.5 cm wide, attenuate at both ends and with the apex short and obtuse. Fruit subspherical, little depressed at apex, 3 cm in diameter, glabrous at maturity, with a few brown hairs at oblique apex; calyx with 4-separate-lobes; seeds 14-15 mm in length, shining and brown.

Distribution: Hainan, at altitude 310 m.

16. **Diospyros lotus** Linn. (See orig. text page 890)

Var. 1. **Diospyros lotus** var. **glabra** (DC.) Makino

A form almost similar in characters with the type except the parts being glabrous.

Distribution: Yunnan, Kwangsi and Anhwei, at altitude 1800 m.

17. **Diospyros maclurei** Merr. (See orig. text page 890)

18. **Diospyros metcalfii** Chun et Chen

Tree 15 m high. Leaves alternate, membranaceous, petiolate, elliptic or obovate, 10-13 cm long, 4-6 cm wide, apex abruptly acute, base cuneate to subobtuse. Fruit solitary, pedunculate, subglobose, 5-6 cm in diam.

Distribution: Hainan.

19. **Diospyros mollifolia** Rehder et Wilson (See orig. text pages 890-891)

20. **Diospyros maritima** Blume

Tree 5-6 m high. Bark dark gray. Branchlets slender reddish brown, glabrous. Leaves elliptic oblong, 12 cm long, 5 cm wide, acute apex, obtuse cuneate at base, margin entire, incurved, thick, coriaceous, lustrous dark green above, light green glaucous, glabrous beneath; petiole 1 cm long, flattened; fruit flat-rounded, 2.5 cm in diameter, with 4-parted persistent calyx, solitary, subsessile.

Distribution: Kwangsi and Yunnan, at altitude 800-1100 m.

21. **Diospyros morrisiana** Hance (See orig. text page 892)

22. **Diospyros nitida** Merr.

Small tree to 10 m high; branchlets grayish striate, more or less pubescent, the branchlets slender, black, usually rather densely pubescent; Leaves alternate, lanceolate, acuminate very when dry, leaves 5-8 cm long, 1.5-3 cm wide, submembranaceous, glabrous, very shining above, rather dull and slightly pubescent beneath, especially on the midrib, the apex rather slender, the acumen blunt, the base acute; nerves obscure; petiole 4-5 mm long, pubescent. Inflorescence cymose; faciculate, the fascicles 4 to 8 flowered; calyx 4-lobed, lobes broadly ovate, 1 mm long, the margins ciliate; corolla 4 mm long, urceolate, the lobes ovate, acute, 2 mm long; stamens 16, unequal, inserted to the receptacle or at the base of the corolla, glabrous or minutely puberulous; the anthers dehiscing by longitudinal slits; ovary glabrous; fruit somewhat fleshy, globose, black, shining, and more or less wrinkled when dry, 10–12 mm in diameter, 4–celled, each cell with one seed; 6 mm long, brown, reticulate; the fruiting calyx about 1 cm in diameter, the lobes spreading, elliptical–ovate, rounded.

Distribution: Hainan.

23. **Diospyros oleifera** Cheng

Tree 14 m high. Leaves chartaceous, deciduous, oblong or oblong – obovate, or obovate, rarely elliptic, apex acuminate, base rotundate, oblique–rotundate or broadly cuneate, margin incurved, 7.5–16.5 cm long, 3.5–8.5 cm wide, cineroflavo–villose; lateral veins 7–9, adpressed above, elevated below; petiole 8–10 mm long. Fruit solitary, pedunculate, 8–10 mm long, depressed ovoid, 4–loculeous 4–parted.

The fruit of this is edible when mature. When young it yields valuable varnish oil used in making umbrella.

Distribution: Chekiang, Kiangsi, Anhwei and is commonly cultivated in the warm parts of central Chekiang.

24. **Diospyros oldhamii** Maxim.

Small tree with whitish gray bark. Branchlets slender, smooth. Leaves elliptic–ovate, acute apex, cuneate at base, incurved margin, subcoriaceous, dark green above pale glaucous beneath; petiole slender, 1–2 cm long, glabrous; lateral veins, 8–10 pairs prominently elevated beneath and inconspicuous above.

Distribution: Taiwan.

25. **Diospyros potingensis** Merr. et Chun

Tree 5–7 m high. Leaves firm, chartaceous, oblong or oblong–elliptic, 7–14 cm long 2.5–5 cm wide, obtuse–acuminate apex, broadly–cuneate at base, olive–green on both surfaces, long–adpressed hirsute below; lateral nerves 9–11 pairs, distinctly elevated petiole 5–8 mm long, glabrous or sparsely hirsute. Fruit solitary, axillary, ovoid, 2.5 3 cm long, densely minutely hirsute, 4–loculary, each cell with one seed; yellow when ripe, tomentose.

Distribution: Kwangtung and Hainan, at altitude 520 m.

26. **Diospyros roi** Lecomte

Small shrub in densely forest ravine, about 8 m high. Leaves oblong, alternate, 1 cm long, 5 cm wide, acute apex, broad–cuneate at base, entire incurved margin, thick coriaceous, lustrous green above, light olive–green below; lateral veins inconspicuou on both surfaces, midrib prominently elevated below and depressed above, glabrous o both surfaces; petiole 1 cm long, grooved, glabrous, brown. Fruit solitary, axillary sub–sessile, with persistent calyx, 2–3 cm in diameter, globose, yellow.

Distribution: Hainan.

27. **Diospyros rubra** H. Lecomte

Small tree, 7 m high. Leaves alternate, glabrous, subcoriaceous, elliptic, some what rounded, apex obtuse, base acuminate, 10 cm long, 3–5 cm wide, brilliantly gree above, dull below, nerves 6–8 on each side, curved, united near the margin; veins loosely reticulated; petiole glabrous, 10 – 12 mm long; fruit subsessile, globular, reddish–orange, apiculate, provided with some hairs around the summit, about 1.5 cm in diam.; calyx with fruit triangularly lobed, more or less sharp toward the base, 3.5 mm long, puberulent.

Distribution: Hainan, at altitude 550 m.

28. **Diospyros sasakii** Hayata

Small tree or shrub. Branchlets very slender, dark gray. Leaves elliptic–oblong somewhat spindle–shaped, acuminate at apex and base, irregularly minutely serrate margin, membranaceous; petiole slender 1–2 cm long, glabrous.

Distribution: Taiwan.

29. **Diospyros siderophyllus** Li

Small tree, 5 m high. Leaves subcoriaceous, oblong, 8–14 cm long, 2–4 cm wide, small obtuse–acuminate, acute at base, deep–olive–green above, minutely adpressed hirsute below; petiole 1 cm long, hirsute. Fruit axillary, solitary, sessile, 2 cm in diam. densely brownish hirsute, 5 or 6–loculary; sepals 4, coriaceous, triangular, 8 mm long, 6 mm wide, hirsute.

This species resmbles *D. roi* Lecomte, differing in the leaves being narrower, olivaceous when dry, and with more numerous lateral veins. It differs further in the fruit, with its persistent calyx, densely brownish–appressed–hirsute, and the seeds are fewer in number.

Distribution: Kwangsi.

30. **Diospyros sunyiensis** Chun et Chen

Shrub 4 m tall. Branches terete when young fulvous–tomentose, an length glabrous, dull colored, densely lenticellate; leaves persistent, alternate, petiolate, subcoriaceous, oblong, 11–19 cm long, 4–6 cm wide, base rounded or cordalulate, apex abruptly acuminate with an obtuse acumen, margin recurved, upper surface deep green, glabrous except the midrib, lower surface paler, fulvous–pilose on the whole surface, densely so along the midrib; lateral veins 7–9, like the midrib impressed above and elevated beneath, ultimate veinlets lax, transverse nerves obosolete on the upper surface, slightly elevated beneath; petiole stout, grooved above, fulvous–tomentose, 5–10 mm long; flowers solitary, pedunculate; fruit globose 3 cm in diam.; peduncle 2 cm long, straight, fulvous–tomentose.

Distribution: Kwangtung.

31. **Diospyros susarticulata** Lecomte

Tree; branchlets glabrous; leaves alternate, coriaceous, glabrous, elliptic–oblong, decurrent at the base, 7–16 cm long, 3.5–7 cm wide; nerves 10–11 pairs, curved and running together near the margin; reticulations evident on both surfaces; petiole glabrous, 7.5– mm long; flower and fruit subsessile, globular, the fruit 2 cm in diameter; persistent calyx 4 triangular lobes, 4–5 mm in length.

Distribution: Kwangtung, and Hainan.

32. **Diospyros tsangii** Merr.

Small tree or shrub 3 m high; branchlets terete, glabrous, sprinkled with lenticels; Leaves membranaceous, oblong to oblong-elliptic, 4-8 cm long, 1.5-3 cm wide, pale olive green above and ferruginous pubescent on mid-nerves, paler beneath; sparsely ciliate, glabrous, apex acuminate, base acute; primary nerves 3-4, distinct beneath; petiole 3-6 mm long, ferruginous-pubescent; fruit depressed globose, 8-celled, densely pale black, pubescent.

Distribution: Kwangtung and Fukien.

33. **Diospyros utilis** Hemsl.

Large tree up to 20 m high and 1 m in diameter. Leaves alternate, large, oblong, 25-30 cm long, 8-10 cm wide, short acuminate apex, broad-cuneate at base, entire, slightly incurved margin, lustrous dark green, glabrous above, pale green glabrous below except whitish hairy along the midrib beneath, thick, coriaceous; veins inconspicuous on both surfaces; petiole thick, short, 6 mm long, whitish hairy. Fruit globose, 3-5 cm in diam., 4-8-seeded; seed flat-triangular, 3 cm long, 3 mm in the thicker side and 1 mm in thinner side.

Indivivual plants of this species grow into large trees which furnish valuable wood, used for making furnitures. The fruit when ripe is edible, locally called "Mao-Shih," (毛柿 hairy persimon).

Distribution: Taiwan.

34. **Diospyros tucheri** Dunn (See orig. text page 892)

35. **Diospyros yentangensis** Hu

Small tree 7 m high. Branchlets grayish brown, lenticellate; leaves oblong, 7 cm long, 3 cm wide, acute apex, broad-cuneate at base, incurved margin, lustrous dark green above, pale green glabrous except along the midrib whitish hairy beneath, coriaceous; petiole 1.5 cm long, glabrous, brown.

Young fruits yields a kind of oil for varnishing purpose.

Distribution: Chekiang, Yentang and Kiangsi, at altitude 450 m.

36. **Diospyros yunnanensis** Rehd. et Wilson (See orig. text pages 892-893)

37. - 40. (See orig. text pages 893-894)

Var. 1. Diospyros vaccinioides Lindl. var. **oblonga** Merr. et Chun

Small shrub, 3 m high. Bark blackish gray. Branchlets very slender, smooth, glabrous. Leaves small, oblong, 2.5 cm long, 1 cm wide acute-emarginate at apex, narrow-cuneate at base, entire incurved margin, lustrous dark green above, pale, brownish green, glabrous beneath; veins inconspicuous on both surfaces; petiole 1 mm long, alternate, coriaceous.

Distribution: Kwangtung, Hongkong and Hainan, at altitude 430 m.

Family 59. Symplocaceae Miers (Sweetleaf family)

Deciduous or evergreen trees or shrubs; winter-buds usually several, super-posed, small, with several outer scales; Leaves alternate, simple, estipulate; flowers perfect or sometimes unisexual, regular, in axillary spicate clusters, or in racemes or panicles; calyx with 5, rarely 4, imbricate lobes; corolla 5 ro 10 rarely 4-lobed, sometimes divided nearly to the base, lobes imbricate; stamens 15 or more, rarely 4-10, often in several series, distinct or united in fascicles, usually adnate to the corolla; ovary inferior or half inferior, 2-5-celled, with usually 2 ovules in each cell; style 1, with 1-5 stigmas; Fruit a drupe with 1-5-seeded stone. Containing one genus.

Genus (1) Symplocos Jacq.

Characeters see that of family. (Greek symplocos, connected, in reference to the often united stamans) About 290 species widely distributed in tropics and subtropics.

1. **Symplocos adinandrifolia** Hayata

   Bobua adinandrifolia (Hayata) Kan. et Sasaki.

   Large tree; branchlets gray, slender. Leaves oblanceolate, 12 cm long, 3.5-4 cm wide, acuminate at apex, acute at base, incurved margin, lustrous dark green above, pale green, glabrous below, subcoriaceous, lateral nerves 5 pairs, not very conspicuous on both surfaces; petiole 1 cm long, glabrous, grooved.

   Distribution: Taiwan.

2. **Symplocos aenea** Handel-Mazz.

   Shrub or small tree, 10 m high. Leaves linear-oblong or oblanceolate, 10-15 cm long, the apex small caudate-acuminate, base cuneate or subrotundate-cuneate, margin remotely mucronate-serrulate, coriaceous; lateral nerves 11-16 pairs; petiole 15-20 mm long; flowers glomerous, axillary, 10-15-florous, sessile, white, 8-10 mm in diameter. Bracts ovate, margin glandular-serrate, glabrous; bracteoles broad-obovate, rotundate, lobes pubescent-ciliate; calyx lobes rotundate, obovate, 1 mm long, tube glabrous, unequal in length, corolla lobes 4-5 mm long; stamens 50, indistinctly pentadelphous; fruit cylindrical, 7-8 mm long, 3 mm across, stipitate.

   Distribution: Szechuan, Nan-Chuan Hsien, at altitude 1500-1800 m.

3. **Symplocos angustifolia** Guill.

   Shrub; leaves narrow-lanceolate, 9 cm long, 1 cm wide, crowded on the upper part of the branchlets, acuminate at both ends, minutely serrate margin, light green above, paler below, subcoriaceous; petiole 5 mm long, flattened; fruit globose, green, 4 mm in diameter; calyx lobes persistent; fruits in stout axillary racemes, sessile.

   Distribution: Hainan.

4. **Symplocos argyi** Levl.

   Symplocos szechuanensis Brand

   Shrub; leaves broad-lanceolate, petiolate, glabrous membranaceous, acuminate apex, remotely denticulate margin; flowers axillary, fascicled, globose, compact; petals small, ovate.

Distribution: Kiangsu, Kiangsi, Chekiang, and Hunan.

5. **Symplocos atriolivacea** Merr. et Chun

Shrub 3-3.5 m tall. Leaves chartaceous, or submembranaceous, small petiolate, atro-olivaceous or subconcolored oblong-ovate, 12-16 cm long, 3.5-5.5 cm wide, acuminate apex, broadly acute at base, margin indistinctly serrulate; petiole 5 mm long, glabrous. Inflorescence axillary, fascicled, subsessile; bracts broad-ovate; clayx tube 1 mm long, pubescent, lobes 5, ovate; stamens 20, filaments 2-3 mm long; ovary 3-loculary, calyx persistent.

Distribution: Hainan, at altitude 2100 m.

6. **Symplocos austro-sinensis** Handel-Mazz.

Tree, leaves lanceolate, or elliptic, 4-10 cm long, 3-5 cm wide, caudate-acuminate apex, cuneate at base, minutely denticulate margin, chartaceous, olivaceous above; laterally nerves 6-8 pairs, obliquely running toward the margin; petiole 10-15 mm long, glabrous. Flowers 10-florae, sessile, bracts and bracteoles persitent; stamens 30, distinctly pentadelphous. Fruit cylindrical, 8 mm long striate.

Distribution: Kwangsi

7. **Symplocos acutangula** Brand

Shrub 3 m high. Leaves alternate, elliptic-oblong, 8 cm long, 3 cm wide, acute apex, cuneate at base, minutely serrate margin, dark green above, light green glabrous beneath, subcoriaceous; petiole 1 cm long, glabrous. Fruit drupaceous, clustered in axils of leaves.

Distribution: Kwangtung, Chekiang, Fukien, and Kiangsu, at altitude 1100 m.

8. **Symplocos adnophylla** Wall.

Symplocos stewardii Sleumer

Tree 3-12 m high. Leaves lanceolate-oblong, 7-8 cm long, 2 cm wide, attenuate acute apex, cuneate at base, minutely serrate margin, dark green above, reddish brown glabrous beneath, subcoriaceous; petiole 1 cm long, glabrous. Flowers whitish yellow, in axillary racemes. Fruit globose, 1 cm long, 4 cm in diameter, solitary, axillary; pedicels 2 cm long, slender, glabrous. Fruit black.

Distribution: Kwangtung, Hainan, and Kwangsi.

9. **Symplocos adenopus** Hance

Small shrub, 3 m tall, Leaves oblong, 10 cm long, 5 cm wide, attenuate-acuminate apex, broad cuneate at base shallowly serrate at margin, lustrous dark green above, pale green and brownish tomentose to reddish hairy along the midrib and veins beneath, veins 5-6 pairs very prominently elevated below and depressed above, coriaceous; petiole 1 cm long, reddish pubescent. Fruit in pairs, axillary, sessile, cylindrical, 1 cm long, 2 mm in diameter, brown, apiculate.

Distribution: Hainan, Yunnan, Kwangtung, Kwangsi and Kweichow, at altitude

1200 m.

10. **Symplocos** alata Brand

Small tree 2-8 m high. Branchlets ferruginous-hirsute. Leaves ovate, 5-6 cm long, 2-3 cm wide, cuspidate base subrotundate, margin minutely serrulate. Racemes simple, flowers pedicellate; bracts 3 pairs. Fruit brownish black, cylindrical, 8-9 mm long, sulcate.

Distribution: Szechuan, Nan Chuan, Yunnan, and Kwangsi, at altitude 1700 m.

11. **Symplocos anomala** Brand

Shrub 3 m high. Leaves subcoriaceous, lanceolate to oblong-lanceolate, 6 cm long, 2.5 cm wide, long-acute apex, cuneate at base, margin entire, dark shining green above, paler glabrous beneath; petiole 8 mm long, flattened. Flowers white, in clustered racemes, axillary, 5-florae, hirsute, sub-umbellate; calyx tube puberulous; lobes rotundate, imbricate, ciliate, corolla 5, 3 mm long; stamens 30; ovary sericeous-puberulous, 3-loculary. Fruit dark-brown, ovoid, 3 mm long, 3-celled, minutely pilose.

Distribution: Szechuan, Kwangsi, Hupeh, Yunnan, Kwangtung, Chekiang, Anhwei, Hunan, Hainan and Kweichow, at altitude 600-1100 m.

Var. 1. **Symplocos anomala** var **nitida** Li

Shrub, 5 m high. Leaves elliptic-lanceolate, 9 cm long, 3 cm wide, attenuate-acuminate apex, cuneate at base, margin entire, glabrous on both surfaces, thick coriaceous; petiole 12 mm long, flattened, glabrous. Flowers white. Fruit black, cylindrical, 15 mm long, 3 mm in diameter, apiculate, glabrous.

Distribution: Kwangtung, and Kwangsi.

12. **Symplocos** arisanensis Hayata

Bobua arisanensis (Hayata) Kaneh. et Sasak.

Tree 10 m high. Branchlets straight, dark brown, lenticellate, angular; leaves oblong-lanceolate, 8 cm long, 3 cm wide, long-acute apex, broad-cuneate at base, coarsely dentate-serrate margin, dark green, lustrous above, pale green, glabrous except somewhat brownish hairy along the midrib beneath, thick, coriaceous; petiole 2 mm long, grooved. Inflorescence in short, axillary racemes, sessile.

Distribution: Taiwan, at altitude 1330-2500 m.

13. **Symplocos botryantha** Franch.

Small tree 10 m high. Bark grayish, smooth. Branchlets thick, stout, glabrous. Leaves oblanceolate, 8-10 cm long, 2.5-3 cm wide, tapering into both ends, crenate-serrate margin, dark green lustrous above, paler glabrous beneath, thick, coriaceous. Fruit ovoid with calyx lobes attached to the apex, short-pedicellate, in axillary racemes.

Distribution: Kwangtung, Kweichow, Hupeh, Hunan, Yunnan, Tibet, Szechuan, and Fukien, at altitude 600-1300 m.

Var. 1. **Symplocos botryantha** var. **stenophylla** Franch.

This variety differs from its typical form in having oblong or lanceolate leaves and petiole 1.5 cm long; flowers yellow.

Distribution: Szechuan and Tibet, at altitude 3330 m.

14. **Symplocos cavaleiriei** Levl.

Small tree.

This species is related to *S. botryantha*, but is easily distinguished by the small
obovate-oblong, closely serrulate leaves, rather abruptly contracted into a short obtuse
acumen, and by the small fruit in short racemes.

Distribution: Kweichow.

15. **Symplocos caudata** Wall.

Small tree 8 m high. Branchlets stout, terete, dark brown, glabrous; leaves oblanceolate, 7 cm long, 3 cm wide, attenuate acuminate at apex, tapering toward the base,
coarsely crenate-serrulate, lustrous deep green above, light green glabrous beneath,
subcoriaceous; petiole 2 cm long glabrous. Flowers yellowish white, in short axillary
racemes. Fruits solitary, axillary, subglobular 1.5 cm long, 7 mm in diameter, openly
apiculated; pedicels 2 mm long.

Distribution: Kwangtung, Yunnan, Hupeh, Tibet, Hainan, Hunan, Kwangsi,
Szechuan and Taiwan, at altitude 1000-1300 m.

16. **Symplocos chinensis** (Lour.) Druce

Small shrub 1-2 m high. Branchlets very slender, whitish gray, glabrous. Leaves
obovate, 5 cm long, 3 cm wide, minutley acute with a sharp bristle at apex, broad-
cuneate at base, finely serrate margin, glabrous above, whitish hairy along the midrib
and veins beneath; petiole 1 mm long, hirsute. Flowers white in axillary long racemes,
densely pilose; stamens numerous. Fruit black, globular, 2 mm in diameter, apiculate,
3 or 4 in racemes.

Distribution: Kwangtung, Yunnan, Kwangsi, Szechuan, Hunan, Hupeh, Anhwei,
Fukien, Kiangsu, Kiangsi and Taiwan, at altitude 600-1400 m.

17. **Symplocos chunii** Merr.

Small tree 4 m high. Leaves oblanceolate, 12 cm long, 3.5 cm wide, acute apex,
tapering toward the base, incurved and remotely serrate margin, lustrous dark green
above, pale green glabrous beneath, thick, coriaceous; petiole 1 cm flattened, glabrous.
Flowers in short, dense, axillary racemes, white, pilose; stamens numerous, filaments
very slender; fruit purplish blue.

Distribution: Hainan.

18. **Symplocos cochinchinensis** (Lour.) Moore

Symplocos javanica (Blume) Moore

Shrub 4 m high. Leaves oblong, 15 cm long, 5 cm wide, small acuminate at apex,
acute at base, irregularly finely serrate margin, lustrous deep green above, light green
and whitish hairy on younger leaves along the midrib and veins beneath, coriaceous;
petiole 2-3 cm long, grooved and pubescent on younger leaves. Flowers in terminal and

axillary long racemes, brownish hairy, white.

Distribution: Hainan, Szechuan, Kwangtung, Kwangsi, Kiangsi, Fukien, and Taiwan, at altitude 300-1000 m.

19. **Symplocos confusa** Brand

Shrub or tree 4-8 m high. Bark gray, smooth, branchlets gray, rough, glabrous. Leaves oblong, 8 cm long, 3 cm wide, acute apex, cuneate at base, remotely, finely serrulate margin and incurved, lustrous dark green above, light green glabrous below, subcoriaceous; petiole 1-2 cm long, thick, reddish, glabrous. Flowers in short, clustered, axillary racemes, white. Wood brittle.

Distribution: Yunnan, Kwangtung, Kwangsi, Hainan, Chekiang, Kweichow, and Kiangsi, at altitude 700 m.

20. **Symplocos congesta** Benth.

Shrub 5 m high, fragrant. Leaves oblanceolate, 9 cm long, 3.5 cm wide, acute apex, cuneate at base, margin entire, incurved, lustrous dark green above, pale green glabrous except brownish pubescent along the midrib below, coriaceous. Petiole 5 mm long, flattened, grooved. Flowers white in very dense axillary clusters, racemes sessile.

Distribution: Kwangtung, Kwangsi, Fukien, Kweichow, Hainan, Tibet, Kiangsi, and Chekiang.

21. **Symplocos crassifolia** Benth.

Tree 5 m high. Bark gray, smooth. Leaves oblong, 8 cm long, 3.5 cm wide, short acuminate apex, obtuse cuneate at base incurved entire margin, lustrous olive-green above, paler olive-green, glabrous beneath; petiole 2-3 cm long, grooved, glabrous. Flowers in short axillary racemes, white. Fruit globose, 2 cm long, 8 mm in diameter, apiculate with calyx tube persistent on the top.

Distribution: Kwangtung, and Hongkong.

22. **Symplocos decora** Hance

Shrub of 3-4 m high, with brilliant white flowers in axillary and terminal racemes. Leaves obovate, 5 cm long, 3 cm wide, acute apex, broad cuneate at base, lustrous dark green above, pale green glabrous beneath, finely serrate or entire margin, thick, coriaceous; petiole 1-2 cm long, reddish, flattened.

Distribution: Hongkong.

23. **Symplocos dielsii** Levl.

Tree 7 m tall. Branchlets whitish gray, glabrous. Leaves oblanceolate, 9 cm long, 2.5 cm wide, acute apex, narrow-cuneate at base, incurved margin, bluish green above, glaucescent below, membranaceous; petiole 15 mm long, reddish brown, glabrous.

Distribution: Kwangsi, at altitude 1600 m.

24. **Symplocos divaricativenia** Hayata

Shrub with grayish slender branchlets. Leaves oblong, tapering toward both ends; petiole very slender, about 1-2 cm long, glabrous.

Distribution: Taiwan.

25. **Symplocos doii** Hayata

Small tree with dark gray smooth branchlets. Leaves elliptic-lanceolate, 5 cm long, 2 cm wide, long-acuminate apex, cuneate at base, irregularly finely serrate margin, dark green above, paler glabrous beneath, subcoriaceous; petiole 1 cm long, slender, glabrous. Fruit cylindrical, 1.5 cm long, 0.5 cm in diam. apiculate with persistent calyx on the top, brown, glabrous; pedicel slender, 1-2 mm long.

Distribution: Taiwan in lowland.

26. **Symplocos dolichotricha** Merr.

Tree 12 m tall. Leaves chartaceous, olive-green, elliptic or oblong-elliptic, 9-13 cm long, 4-5 cm wide, acuminate apex, rotundate at base, densely hirsute beneath and densely villose along the margin and midrib and veins below. Branchlet covered with dense yellowish villose, subcoriaceous. Inflorescence fascicled, 6-8-florous axillary and in axils after falling off the leaves. Flowers sessile, corolla tube 0.5 mm long, lobes 5; stamens 30; style 6 mm long. Fruit globose, viridis, glabrous, 6 mm in diam..

Distribution: Kwangtung, and Kwangsi.

27. **Symplocos crassilimba** Merr.

Tree 20 m tall, 1-1.5 m in diam. Bark whitish gray. Branchlets white, smooth, glabrous. Leaves oblong-obovate, 9 cm long, 5 cm wide, acute apex, rounded at base, incurved, crenate-serrate margin, lustrous green above, light green glabrous except brownish pubescent along the midrib below, coriaceous; petiole 3-4 cm long, flattened, glabrous. Flowers white, fragrant, interminal and axillary racemes. Fruit cylindrical, whitish green, 2 cm long, 1 cm in diameter, apiculate glabrous; pedicels 1 mm long, glabrous.

Distribution: Hainan.

28. **Symplocos delavayi** Franch.

Tree 8 m tall. Branchlets dark gray, smooth. Leaves oblong, 11 cm long, 5 cm wide, acute apex, obtuse cuneate at base, remotely bristlely serrate margin, lustrous shining green above, light glaucous glabrous beneath, thick, coriaceous; petioles 3 cm long, stout, grooved, brown, glabrous. Flowers in terminal and axillary racemes, white. Fruit small, globular, 1 mm in diameter, reddish black, mucronate apex.

Distribution: Yunnan, and Tibet, at altitude 3000 m.

29. **Symplocos discolor** Brand

Small tree 3-5 m tall. Branchlets gray, smooth, glabrous. Leaves elliptic-oblong, 9 cm long, 4 cm wide, short-acuminate at apex, cuneate at base, irregularly bristle-like serrate, incurved margin, olive green glabrous above, lighter olive-green, glabrous beneath, subcoriaceous; petiole 1.5 cm long, flattened, yellowish brown, glabrous. Flowers in axillary, clustered racemes, sessile, canary-white or yellow.

Distribution: Yunnan, at altitude 400-3330 m.

30. **Symplocos dryophilla** Clarke

Symplocos forrestii W. W. Smith

Tree with thick stout branchlets and clustered leaves on tops of branchlets. Leaves oblanceolate, 14 cm long, 3.5 cm wide, acute apex, cuneate at base, incurved margin, dark lustrous green above, pale green with prominent nerves below, subcoriaceous. Flowers in long terminal and axillary spikes, which are 6–8 cm long, 3 cm thick, slightly villose; Petals 5, imbricated, yellow.

Distribution: Yunnan, and Tibet, at altitude 1400–1850 m.

31. **Symplocos dung** Eberh. et Dub.

Shrub 4 m tall. Branchlets slender gray, glabrous. Leaves oblanceolate, 6 cm long, 3.5 cm wide, spathulate and broadest above the middle, acute apex, tapering down to the acututish base, coarsely serrate margin above the middle, subcoriaceous; petiole 1 cm long, glabrous. Flowers in terminal and axillary spikes. Fruits globular, 1 mm in diameter, apiculate, slightly villose.

Distribution: Kwangtung, and Hainan.

32. **Symplocos eriobotryaefolia** Hayata

Tree 8–12 m, 1 cm in diameter. Branchlets rough grayish, glabrous. Leaves oblong, 11 cm long, 3.5 cm wide, lustrous dark green above, pale brownish glabrous, with very prominently elevated midrib and veins and reticulations beneath, incurved margin, thick, coriaceous. Young branchlets and leaves covered with reddish dense villose; petiole 3 cm long, flattened and grooved when dry above, purplish red. Flowers in dense, sessile, axillary clusters, brownish villose.

Distribution: Taiwan.

33. **Symplocos ernesti** Dunn

Symplocos coronigera Levl.

Tree, with dark gray stout branchlets. Leaves broadlanceolate, 7 cm long, 2.5 cm wide, acute at apex, cuneate at base, lustrous dark green above, lighter green glabrous beneath, coriaceous; petiole 3–4 cm long, brown, grooved above. Fruit globular, 1 cm long, 6 mm in diameter, with persistent calyx on the top, pedicels 1 mm long, glabrous.

Distribution: Hupeh, Szechuan, Kweichow, Kwangsi, Hunan, and Yunnan, at altitude 1000–1200 m.

34. **Symplocos ferruginea** Roxb.

Tree, branchlets slender, densely covered with ferruginose hairs. Leaves oblanceolate, 15 cm long, 3 cm wide, acute apex, cuneate at base, incurved and remotely finely serrulate margin, lustrous deep green above, pale green with dense ferruginous hairs along the midrib and veins beneath, veins 10 pairs, prominently elevated, coriaceous; petiole 1–2 cm long, densely covered with ferruginous hairs. Flowers in short axillary racemes, ferruginous villose.

Distribution: Kwangtung, and Hainan, at altitude 1100 m.

35. **Symplocos ferruginifolia** Kanehira

Tree 5–7 m high. Branchlets, underside of leaves, petiole, and inflorescences ferruginous tomentose; branchlets reddish brown, terete. Leaves oblong-ovate to oblong-elliptic, coriaceous, 14–19 cm long, 4–8 cm wide, yellowish green when dry, shining, the apex distinctly and rather sharply acuminate, base, acute margins glandular-denticulate, the gland-like teeth small, black when dry, lateral veins 9 pairs, very prominent on the lower surface, anatomising, the reticulations lax; petiole 1.5–2.5 cm long, subterete. Spikes axillary, 1–5–branched, up to 6 cm long. Flowers arranged densely, sessile the subtended bracteoles ovate, obtuse, 3.5 mm long, pubescent.

Distribution: Taiwan, at altitude 100 m.

36. **Symplocos fordii** Hance

Shrub 3 m tall. Leaves obovate-lanceolate or lanceolate, oblique caudate-acuminate apex, margin revolute-denticulate, veins elevated reticulated. Flowers 5–10 aggregated on the peduncles, minutely ferruginous-pilose, bracts white ciliated, calyx membrana-ceous, lobes ovate, glabrous, corolla segments oblong. Fruit ovoid, glabrous.

Distribution: Hainan, at altitude 700 m.

37. **Symplocos formosana** Brand

Shrub 3 m tall. Branchlets slender, dark, smooth, glabrous. Leaves elliptic-oblong, 5 cm long, 2.5 cm wide, long attenuate-acuminate apex, cuneate at base, remotely finely serrate margin, subcoriaceous, lustrous deep green above, light green glabrous below; petiole slender, 5 mm long, glabrous, fruit globular, 1–2 mm in diameter apiculate, brown, glabrous, in axillary spikes.

Distribution: Taiwan, at altitude 2300 m.

38. **Symplocos fulvipes** (Clarke) Brand

Small tree 3 m high. Flowers white, fragrant, in long terminal and axillary spikes. Leaves oblong, 8 cm long, 3.5 cm wide, acuminate apex, cuneate at base, remotely crenate-serrate margin, subcoriaceous; petiole 1 mm long.

Distribution: Kwangtung, at altitude 1600 m.

39. **Symplocos glandulifera** Brand

Tree 6 m tall. Branchlets straight, stout, covered with densely ferruginous tomentose. Leaves oblanceolate, 12 cm long, 3 cm wide, acute at apex, cuneate at base, finely serrate margin, lustrous dark green above, pale green, ferruginous tomentose beneath, lateral veins 12 pairs, prominently elevated, reticulated, closed up on the margin of leaves beneath, coriaceous; petiole 2–3 cm long, densely reddish villose. Flower white, densely crowded in the axils of the fallen leaves; calyx 5–lobed, ridged yellowish toementose; stamens inserted on the corolla base; anther 2–celled.

Distribution: Kwangsi, Yunnan and Hunan, at altitude 300–1400 m.

40. **Symplocos grandis** Handel-Mazz.

Shrub 5–8 m tall. Leaves oblong, 15–20 cm long, 5–8 cm wide, short-acuminate apex, cuneate at base, incurved and sometimes with irregular bristle-like teethed lustrous olive-green above, pale green and glabrous below, thick, coriaceous; petiole 3 cm long, glabrous, brown, Flowers white, densely crowded in the axils of the fallen leaves. Fruit cylindrical, 1 cm long, 4 mm in diameter, apiculate, sessile, wrinkled glabrous.

Distribution: Yunnan, and Kwangsi, at altitude 1400 m.

41. **Symplocos glauca** Merr.

Tree 5-13 m tall. Branchlets dark gray, rough. Leaves lanceolate, 15 cm long, 3 cm wide, acuminate at apex, cuneate at base, entire, and finely bristle-like teethed on the top part of the leaf margin, dark green above, glaucous below, subcoriaceous; petiole 1 cm long, glabrous, grooved. Fruits cylindrical, 12 mm long, 3 mm in diameter, apiculate, in pairs on a short spur-like peduncle, with bracts persistent at base.

Distribution: Taiwan, Kwangtung, Hainan, Fukien and Chekiang, at low altitude.

42. **Symplocos glomerata** King

Shrub 2 m tall. Leaves oblanceolate, 15 cm long, 3.5 cm wide, attenuate-acuminate-acute apex, cuneate at base, glandular-serrate margin, dark green above, pale green glabrous beneath, coriaceous; petiole 15 mm long, glabrous, flowers yellow in axillary, clustered racemes. Fruit blue.

Distribution: Yunnan, at altitude 2800 m.

43. **Symplocos groffi** Merr.

Small tree 3-4 m tall.

A very characterized species allied to *Symplocos adenopus* Hance and *S. glandulifera* Brand, but differs from them by its axillary fascicled, crowded flowers its very densely villose branchlets and its villose leaves.

Distribution: Kwangtung and Kwangsi, at altitude 550 m.

44. **Symplocos hainanensis** Merr.

Tree 10-15 m high. Leaves chartaceous, distinctly petiolate, glabrous, oblong-elliptic, 8-11 cm long, 2.4-4 cm wide, acuminate apex, cuneate at base, margin crenate-serrulate; petiole 0.5-1 cm long, glabrous; Inflorescence in axillary spikes, 6 cm long, pubescent, multiflorae; flower sessile or subsessile, bracts broad-ovate; petals 4 or 5, white, ovate, stamens 25-30 filaments glabrous, 3-5 mm long; ovary 3 - locular, style 5 mm long; calyx persistent.

Distribution: Hainan, at altitude 430 m.

45. **Symplocos heishanensis** Hayata

Small tree with dark gray bark. Branchlets slender, dark gray, glabrous. Leaves elliptic-oblong, 6 cm long, 2.5 cm wide, long-acuminate at apex, narrow-cuneate at base, minutely serrate margin, dark green above, paler glaucous below, subcoriaceous; petiole 2 cm long, glabrous. Flowers in axillary spikes. Fruits cylindrical, 1 cm long, 2 mm in diam., black, glabrous, apiculate.

Distribution: Taiwan, at altitude 2300 m.

46. **Symplocos henryi** Brand

Shrub with oblong-lanceolate leaves, about 10 cm long, 6 cm wide, short acuminate at apex, broad-cuneate at base, irregularly crenate-serrate margin; petiole slender 2-3 cm long, glabrous

Distribution: Yunnan.

47. **Symplocos hookeri** C. B. Clarke

Tree 5 m tall. Branchlets slender, purplish brown, glabrous. Leaves obovate to rounded, 15 cm long, 10 cm wide, minutely acute at apex, cuneate at apex, cuneate at base, remotely dentate-serrate margin, lustrous dark green above, pale bluish green with prominently elevated midrib and veins and reticulations beneath, glabrous, coriaceous; petiole 2-3 cm long, brown, glabrous. Fruit cylindrical, 16 cm long, 6 cm in diameter, brown, glabrous, apiculate; pedicel 1 cm long, glabrous.

Distribution: Yunnan, at altitude 1100-1600 m.

48. **Symplocos howii** Merr. et Chun

Tree 18 m high. Branchlets slender, straight, brownish gray, smooth. Leaves oblanceolate, 10 cm long, 3 cm wide, acuminate apex, cuneate at base, crenate-serrate margin, lustrous pale green above, lighter green below, glabrous on both srufaces, coriaceous; petiole 2 cm long, brown, glabrous.

Distribution: Hainan.

49. **Symplocos illicifolia** Hayata

Bobua illicifolia (Hayata) Kan. et Sasak.

Shrub with brownish gray branchlets. Leaves elliptic, 3 cm long, 2 cm wide, acute to both ends, remotely crenate-serrate margin, subcoriaceous; petiole 1 cm long, glabrous, brown. Flowers in axillary small clusters.

Distribution: Taiwan.

50. **Symplocos javanica** Kurz

Tree with purplish brown branchlets, glabrous. Leaves oblong, 15-20 cm long, 6-7 cm wide, acute apex, cuneate at base, glandular-finely serrate margin, dark green lustrous above, glaucous brownish green below, midrib and veins prominently elevated and reticulated, densely covered with reddish villose. Flowers in axillary, purplish racemes, 6-8 cm long, purplish racemes, 6-8 cm long, purplish villose.

Distribution: Szechuan.

51. **Symplocos konishii** Hayata

Small tree with stout, dark gray, lenticelled branchlets. Leaves oblong, 15-20 cm long, 8 cm wide, minutely acute apex, obtuse cuneate at base, glandulary-serrate margin, dark green above, light green below, glabrous on both surfaces, coriaceous; petiole 3 cm long, grooved, glabrous. Flowers in short axillary racemes.

Distribution: Taiwan.

52. **Symplocos kotoensis** Hayata

Small tree with purplish lenticelled, stout branchlets. Leaves ovate or oblong, 14 cm long, 7 cm wide, aucte apex, ovate to broadly-cuneate at base, lustrous dark green above, pale green glabrous beneath, veins 6 pairs, prominent below, revolute margin, coriaceous; petiole thick, stout, 4-5 cm long, brown, glabrous. Fruit globular, 5mm in diameter, black, in axillary spikes, sessile, glabrous.

Distribution: Taiwan, in Botel, and Tobago.

53. **Symplocos koshunensis** Kanehira

A shrub, branchelts terete, glabrous. Leaves lanceolate to oblong–lanceolate chart – aceous, 22–27 cm long, 5–7 cm wide, apex acute to subacute, often caudate, base nar– rowed, obscured crenate, upper surface shining green, under surface glaucous, lateral nerves 11–13 on each side of the midrib, midrib and veins impressed above, pubescent underneath, petiole 2 cm long, subglabrous. Flowers fascicled above the leafscars, sessile, bracts and calyx tomentose; petals elliptic, 4 mm long, 3 mm wide.

A stricking species on acount of its large lanceolate leaves.

Distribution: Kaohsiung, Taiwan.

54. **Symplocos kwangsiensis** Merr.

Shrub 2 m tall. Branchlets balck, minutely pubescent. Leaves oblong–ovate or ovate–lanceolate, 2.5–4 cm long, 1–1.5 cm wide, long–acute or acuminate, base broadly acute or rotundate, margins glandulosous–serrulate; petiole 2 mm long, ciliate. Inflores– cence axillary, fascicled, subsessile; flowers sessile, bracts broad–ovate, densely pubescent; petals 5, white, oblong, 3.5 mm long, stamens 20–25, filaments free, glab– rous, disk annular, cinereo–pubescent; ovary 3–loculary; fruit ovoid, 6 mm long, 4.5 mm across, green.

Distribution: Kwangsi and Yunnan.

55. **Symplocos lotouchei** W. W. Sm.

Shrub 2 m tall. Leaves oblanceolate, 6 cm long, 2.5 cm wide, acute apex, cuneate at base, entire margin, subcoriaceous; petiole 1 mm long. Flowers white, fragrant, in axillary racemes.

Distribution: Kwangtung, and Kwangsi.

56. **Symplocos luntauensis** Merr.

Shrub 4 m tall, branchlets bluish villose. Leaves alternate, oblong, 6 cm long, 2.5 cm wide, acuminate apex, cuneate at base, revolved margin, stiff villose beneath, sub– coriaceous; petiole 1 mm long, densely villose. Fruit 1 cm long, 3 mm across, 5–ridged, densely prickly villose axillary, subsessile.

Distribution: Kwangtung.

57. **Symplocos lausifolia** S. et Z.

Symplocos aurea Levl.

Shrub 3 m tall. Branchlets slender, purplish, glabrous, smooth; leaves elliptic– lanceolate, 6 cm long, 2.5 cm wide, acuminte at apex, cuenate at base, finely serrate, margin, coriaceous, lustrous deep green above, purplish glabrous below; petiole 1 mm long, glabrous. Flowers white, fragrant; fruit black, globular, 2 mm long, 1.5 mm across, glabrous, sessile.

Distribution: Taiwan, Kwangtung, Fukien, Hainan, Kiangsi, Chekaign, Kwangsi, and Szechuan, at altitude 300–540 m.

Var. 1. **Symplocos lausifolia** var. **microcarpa** (Champ. et Benth.) Handel–Mazz.

Tree 8 m. Bark gray and smooth. Leaves elliptic-lanceolate, acute-acuminate apex, broadly-cuneate at base, entire incurved margin, lustrous dark green above, pale green glabrous beneath, thick, coriaceous, glabrous. Fruit ovoid, 2 mm long, 1 mm across, glabrous, subsessile, with persistent calyx, in axillary, stout spikes.

Distribution: Kwangsi, Kwangtung, Yunnan, Kiangsi, Fukien, Chekiang, and Taiwan, at altitude 660-800 m.

58. **Symplocos lancilimba** Merr.

Tree 3 m tall, branchlets slender, black, glabrous. Leaves elliptic-oblong, 5 cm long, 2.5 cm wide, long-acuminate at apex, cuneate at base, entire revolute at margin, lustrous dark green above, pale green, glabrous beneath, coriaceous; petiole 17 mm long, glabrous. Flowers in axillary small spikes; fruit subglobular, 18 mm long, 6 mm across, glabrous, black; pedicel 2 mm long, glabrous.

Distribution: Kwangtung, Hainan, Hunan, and Kiangsi, at altitude 330-800 m.

59. **Symplocos laurina** (Retz.) Wall.

Myrtus laurinus Retz.

Symplocos spicata Roxb.

Symplocos sublivacea W. R. Price

Shrub, leaves oblong, 10 cm long, 4.5 cm wide, acute apex, obtuse cuneate at base, crenate serrate margin, shining green above, pale green glabrous below, veins 6 pairs, rather prominently elevated below, coriaceous; petiole 2 cm long, glabrous, flattened. Flowers in axillary short spikes, 10-14-flowered.

Distribution: Kwangtung, Yunnan, Kwangsi, Kiangsi, Chekiang, Fukien and Szechuan, at altitude 300-600 m; In Hainan it reaches a large tree of about 16 m high.

Var. 1. **Symplocos laurina** var. **acuminata** Wilson

Tree 5-10 m tall. Branchlets dark gray, glabrous. Leaves oblong, 8-10 cm long, 4-6 cm wide, acuminate at apex, obtuse cuneate at base, revolute and incurved margin, lustrous dark green above, pale green, glabrous beneath, coriaceous. Flowers in axillary and terminal spikes, glabrous. Fruit globular 1 cm across, black, apiculate, sessile.

Distribution: Taiwan.

Var. 2. **Symplocos laurina** var. **bodinierei** (Brand) Handel-Mazz.

Tree 2 m tall. Leaves narrow lanceolate, 10 cm long, 2 cm wide, short acuminate at apex, cuneate at base, incurved margin subcoriaceous; Flowers greenish white; fruit dark blue.

Distribution: Kwangtung, Kwangsi, and Hainan.

Var. 3. **Symplocos laurina** var. **malasica** C. B. Clarke

Tree 3 m tall; flowers white, fragrant; fruit blue-black, globular, 5 mm across, glabrous, in axillary spikes, apiculate, subsessile, glabrous

Distribution: Kwangtung, Hainan, Szechuan, Hunan, Kwangsi, Yunnan, at altitude 1180–1200 m.

)。 Symplocos maclurei Merr.

Tree 10 m high. Leaves oblong, 6–9 cm long, 2–3 cm wide, subglaucescent beneath, acuminate apex, acute at base, margin subglandulous-crenulate, lateral nerves 5 ot 6 pairs; petiole 1 cm long, pilose. Inflorescence spikes 5–7 cm long. Fruit sessile, oblong, cylindrical, 10–12 mm long, 4 mm in diameter, densely villose. bracts densely villose.

Distribution: Hainan.

. Symplocos martini Levl.

This species is similar to *S. botryantha* Franch., but the leaves are broader, generally elliptic and the clayx-tube is silky strigose.

Distribution: Kweichow.

. Symplocos macrostroma Hayata

Shrub with dark gray branchlets. Leaves elliptic, 4 cm long, 2 cm wide, acute toward both ends, crenate-serrate margin, dark green rough above the surface, pale green glabrous below, coriaceous; petiole 1 cm long, grooved. Flowers in short terminal and lateral spikes.

Distribution: Taiwan, at altitude 1140 m.

3. Symplocos mairei Levl.

This species is very similar to *S. myriadenia* Merr. but the margin of leaves is rather closely and finely denticulated, nearly to the base with 3–4-teeth to 1 cm, almost reduced to a gland-like conical mucro, and the lateral veins and transverse veinlets are prominent beneath and impressed above; the not fully opened flowers are closely fascicled and smaller with broader and shorter petals and quite glabrous, not ciliate calyx-lobes.

Distribution: Yunnan, Kweichow and Kwangsi, at altitude 2000 m.

. Symplocos microcalyx Hayata

Shrub with very slender branchlets; leaves elliptic oblong, acute apex, broadly cuneate at base, crenate-serrate margin, subcoriaceous; petiole 2 mm long, glabrous. Calyx very small.

Distribution: Taiwan.

. Symplocos mollifolia Dunn

Shrub, Leaves oblong-ovate, 5.5–6.5 cm long, apex and base both acute, crenate-serrate margin, coriaceous, glabrous above, hirsute below; petiole 4 mm long. Spike axillary, 3–5 cm long; rachis dense ferruginous; Flowers subsessile, 5 mm long, 7 mm wide, bracts and bracteoles ovate, 1.5 mm long, tomentose, calyx free, glabrous, lobes rotundate, lobes connate and stamens adnated; stamens and corolla unequal in length.

Distribution: Kwangtung.

. Symplocos mollipila Li

Shrub or small tree, branchlets densely villose; leaves chartaceous, oblong, 5–10 cm

long, 2.5–4 cm wide, acuminate apex, broad–cuneate at base, margin entire, pubescen
below; petiole 2–3 mm long, pubescent; Inflorescence axillary, fascisled, subsessile
Fruit ellipsoid, 1 cm long, 7 mm across, sparsely pubescent.

This species is closely related to *S. glandulifera*. It differs in the shorter leaves
which are not glandular on the margins and which have broader sometimes rounded base
and the shorter fruits.

Distribution: Kwangsi.

67. Symplocos multipes Brand

Shrub 5 m tall. Leaves ovate or elliptic, 5.5–8.5 cm long, 3–4.5 cm wide, long
cuspidate apex, cuneate at base, sparsely serrate margin. Flowers spicate, greenisl
yellow, bracts glabrous, broad–ovate; calyx glabrous, lobes rotundate; stamens 25
ovary whitish villose.

Distribution: Kwangtung.

68. Symplocos myriantha Rehd.

Tree 5 m high.

This species is closely related to *S. stapfiana* Levl, but its leaves are proportionall
longer and narrower, and the lateral nerves are more deeply impressed on the uppe
surface and more distinct on the lower surface.

Distribution: Kwangtung, and Szechuan.

69. Symplocos microtricha Handel–Mazz.

Shrub or tree, 2–13 m tall; leaves oblong, or sublanceolate, rarely elliptic, 4–12 c
long, 2–5–parted angustitate integrate or obsolete undulate–serrate, small acuminate o
acute obtuse at apex, cuneate angustate at base, entire incurved margin, chartaceous
petiole 4–7 mm long. Bracts ovate, subacute, pilosulose; flowers white, fragrant
sessile, 4–5 mm in diameter. Fruit ovoid, apiculate, black or purplish when mature.

Distribution: Hainan, Kwangsi and Fukien, at altitude 660 m.

70. Symplocos modesta Brand

Shrub 3–4 m high. Brachlets slender, grayish, smooth. Leaves small, elliptic, 3 cr
long, 1.5 cm wide, long–acuminate apex, obtuse –cuneate at base, serrate margin, sub
coriaceous; petiole slender 1 mm long, glabrous. Flowers white, in axillary spikes
few–flowered. Fruit cylindrical, 1 cm long, 6 mm across, apiculate, glabrous; pedice
1 cm long, slender, glabrous.

Distribution: Taiwan, at altitude 2300 m.

71. Symplocos morrisonicola Hayata

Shrub with reddish tomentosed branchlets. Leaves elliptic, 2 cm long, 1.3 cm wdie
long–acute at apex, ovate at base, finely–crenate–serrate or entire incurved margin
dark green above, pale green, glabrous beneath, sub–chartaceous. Flowers white, i
small axillary spikes, few–flowered. Fruit cylindrical, 12 cm long, 5 mm broad, wit
persistent calyx on the tops, ciliated; pedicel 1 mm long, pubescent.

Distribution: Taiwan, at altitude 2100–2300 m.

2. **Symplocos nakaii** Hayata

Tree 7 m tall. Branchlets slender, straight, purplish gray, smooth, glabrous. Leaves oblong 6 cm long, 2.5 cm wide, acuminate-acute apex, cuneate at base, entire incurved margin, dark green above, pale green, light-glaucous beneath, chartaceous, lateral veins inconspicuous on both surfaces; petiole 1 cm long, glabrous; flowers in axillary short spikes, white, pubescent.

Distribution: Taiwan, at altitude 1000 m.

3. **Symplocos nokensis** (Hay.) Kaneh.

   Ilex nokensis Hayata

Shrubs with very short branchlets, bark deep gray. Leaves ovate or elliptic-ovate 2 cm long, 1.5 cm wide, acute apex, obtuse cuneate at base, coarse crenate-serrate above the middle, shining olive-green on both surfaces, glabrous, sub-sessile. Flowers in short, axillary spikes, very few-flowered, greenish.

Distribution: Taiwan, at altitude 666-3160 m.

4. **Symplocos ovalifolia** Handel-Mazz.

Shrub 3 m tall. Branchlets ferruginous-pilose. Leaves broad-ovate, or sub-elliptic, 6.5-10 cm long, acute to acuminate at apex, rotundate or cuneate at base, indistinctly glandular-undulate margin, chartaceous, dense ferruginous pilose beneath; calyx-lobe ovate, roundate, glabrous.

Distribution: Kwangsi.

5. **Symplocos pauciflora** Wight et Clarke

Shrub 4 m tall. Branchlets deep gray, rough, smooth. Leaves oblong-spathulate, 6 cm long, 3 cm wide and the broadest on the upper portion, rounded, slightly emarginate on the top, narrow-cuneate at base, incurved margin, lustrous deep green above, pale glaucous below, glabrous on both surfaces, subcoriaceous; petiole 1 cm long, glabrous. Flowers white, in short axillary spikes glabrous.

Distribution: Hainan, at altitude 1130 m.

6. **Symplocos permicophylla** Merr. et Chun

Shrub 2 m tall; branchlets dense-brown pubescent. Leaves oblong-ovate, 1.5-2.5 cm long, 0.5-1 cm wide, acuminate apex, attenuate at base, margin, glandulous - serrate; petiole 2-3 mm long, glabrous, glandulose. Flowers axillary, solitary, sessile or sub-sessile; bracts ovate, 1.5 mm long, densely brownish-pubescent; calyx-lobes 5 oblong, 1.5 mm long; petals 5, oblong, white, broad-ovate rotundate, 3.5 mm long, 2 mm wide; stamens 25-35, filaments 2.5-3.5 mm long; ovary 3-loculary, style 3.5 mm long. Fruit oblong, 6 mm long, sparsely brownish-pubescent.

Distribution: Hainan.

Symplocos phyllocalyx Clarke

Small tree, 7 m tall. Leaves oblong, 10 cm long, 3 cm wide, acute apex, cuneate at base, incurved at base, lustrous dark green above, pale glaucous below, glabrous on both surfaces, coriaceous; petiole 2-3 cm long, brownish glabrous. Flowers in axillary clusters of spikes, whitish green.

Distribution: Yunnan, at altitude 2600 m.

78. **Symplocos paniculata** (Thunberg) Miq.

Symplocos crataegoidcs Hance

Shrub 2 m tall. Flowers white. Fruit blue.

This species is variable, and with wide distribution ranging from the Himalayas through China to Korea and Japan. There seem to be no market geographical varieties, and the extremes in the shape and the pubescence of the leaves are so closely connected by intermediate forms that it seems to be useless to distinguish varieties or forms.

Distribution: Kwangtung, Szechuan, Kweichow, Yunnan, Chekiang, Fukien Taiwan, Anhwei, Shantung, Hopei to Manchuria, at altitude 1000 2300 m.

Var. 1. **Symplocos paniculata** var. **chinensis** Nakai

Shrub 12 m tall. Leaves elliptic-oblong, 6 cm long, 3.5–4 cm wide short-acuminate at base, ovate at base, finely serrate margin, dar green shining above, pale green whitish pubescent below, coriaceous petiole 1.5 cm long, pubescent. Flowers white, fragrant. Fruit glob ular, 2 mm across, black, in short axillary and terminal racemes glabrous.

Distribution: Chekiang, Fukien, Taiwan, Kwangtung, Kwan si and Yunnan, at altitude 1380 m.

Var. 2. **Symplocos paniculata** var. **biloba** (Lévl) Rehd.

This is a very interesting variety with all the leaves distinctly ob cordate and deeply emarginate at apex. The leaf of *S. paniculata* is nor mally elliptic or oval to oblong and acute or acuminate at the apex, b sometimes at least part of the leaves are rounded at the apex and o casionally slightly emarginate as in *Henry* 9948, *Rock* 3160, and *Scho* 50, and *H. H. Hu* 1958.

Distribution: Kweichow.

79. **Symplocos pilosa** Rehd.

Tree 3 m tall. Branchlets slender, densely pilose. Leaves oblong, 6–14 cm lon 3–6 cm wide, acute apex, broad-cuneate at base, irregularly doubly-serrate margi sometimes with remotely irregular teeth, or entire.

This species is distinctly distinguished by its densely pilose branches and pilo inflorescences which are racemose and branched at the base and by the nearly memb aous leaves, pilose beneath. It seems to be related to *S. javanica* Kurz and *S. laur* Wall., but differs considerably from these species in its dense pilose pubescence a in the thinner leaves rounded at the base. Like *S. myriantha* Rehd. most of the flowe are borne on the lower part of the branchlets below the foliage leaves.

Distribution: Yunnan, at altitude 2600 m.

80. **Symplocos pinfaensis** Levl.

This species resembles *S. terminalis* Brand, but the two inflorescences present are simple short racemes. The flowers have fewer stamens, about 20 and the leaves are chartaceous, with the veins above slightly raised, not impressed as in *S. terminalis*. It may also be compared with *S. lanceofolia* S. et Z. and *S. caudata* Wall. both of which have simple racemes, and smaller flowers partly stalked.

Distribution: Kweichow.

81. **Symplocos pittosporifolia** Handel-Mazz.

Tree 3-20 m tall. Leaves oblong or oblong-lanceolate, 6-13 cm long, caudate-acuminate apex, cuneate at base, undulate-denticulate margin, subcoriaceous, olivaceous-green above, lateral nerves 8-14 pairs; flowers 10-20 in simple racemes; calyx-tube glabrous, lobes free, semiorbicular, rotundate, sparsely and minutely pilose; stamens 40-50. Fruit cylindric 6-8 mm long, black.

Distribution: Hainan, Kwangsi, and Yunnan, at altitude 830 m.

82. **Symplocos poilanei** Guillaum

Symplocos fasciculiflora Merr.

Small tree 5 m tall. Leaves oblong or elliptic-oblong, 7 cm long, 3.5 cm wide, acute apex, cuneate at base, entire margin, shining light green on both surfaces, glabrous, olivaceous, thick subcoriaceous; petiole 2-3 cm long glabrous, flattened. Flowers in axillary tufted racemes, white, frgrant.

Distribution: Hainan.

83. **Symplocos psedubarberina** Goutsch.

Shrub 4 m tall. Branchlets greenish pubescent. Leaves elliptic-oblong, 5 cm long, 3 cm wide, acuminate apex, cuneate at base, entire margin, glabrous on both surfaces, subcoriaceous; petiole 1-2 cm long, glabrous. Flowers small, in axillary spikes; calyx in distinct 5-lobed. Fruit globose, 5 mm across, black, glabrous; pedicels short, 1 mm long.

Distribution: Kwangtung and Hainan.

84. **Symplocos pseudolancifolia** (Hatusima) Handel-Mazz.

Shrub 4 m tall. Branchlets stout purplish, glabrous. Leaves lanceolate, 8 cm long, 2.2 cm wide, acuminate at apex, cuneate at base, finely serrate margin, subcoriaceous; petiole 5 mm long. Flowers in simple axillary spikes, white.

Distribution: Kwangtung, Hunan, and Kiangsi.

85. **Symplocos propinqua** Hance

Scattered shrub 2 m tall. Leaves obovate, 6 cm long, 3 cm wide, blunt at apex, broad-cuneate at base, entire margin, dark green shining above, pale brownish slightly pubescent along the midrib below, coriaceous; petiole 1 cm long, grooved above. Flowers in axillary racesmes. Fruit globose, 1 cm long, 6 mm broad, reddish black, sepals 5 green; petals 7, white.

Distribution: Hainan, Kwangtung, and Kwangsi, at altitude 460 m.

86. Symplocos ramosissina Wall.

Tree 8–10 m tall. Branchlets dark gray slender, glabrous. Leaves oblong, 9 cm long, 3 cm wide, acuminate at apex, cuneate at base, finely serrate margin, dark shining green above, pale light green below, subcoriaceous; petiole 1 cm long, flat, glabrous. Flowers in lateral panicles, white, glabrous.

Distribution: Yunnan, Kwangtung, Kwangsi, and Tibet, at altitude 2400–2700 m.

87. Symplocos racemosa Roxb.

Shrub 2 m tall. Leaves oblong, 10 cm long, 4 cm wide, acute apex, cuneate at base, entire margin, lustrous dark green above, pale green, glabrous below, thick, coriaceous; petiole 15 mm long, brown, glabrous. Flowers white. Fruit in axillary racemes, cylindrical, 1 cm long, 4 mm in diameter, with persistent calyx on the top, blue color, glabrous.

Distribution: Yunnan, at altitude 1600 m.

88. Symplocos intermedia Brand

Shrub or small tree 6 m tall. Leaves obovate, 9 cm long, 5 cm wide, acute apex, rounded at base, slightly incurved margin, lustrous dark green above, pale green, glabrous below, coriaceous; petiole 1 cm long. Flowers in axillary spikes, white–cream color, pubescent, spikes 8 cm long, pubescent.

Distribution: Yunnan, at altitude 1400–1800 m.

89. Symplocos sasakii Hayata

Tree 5–6 m tall. Leaves elliptic oblong, 5 cm long, 3 cm wide, acute at apex, cuneate at base, undulate margin, semicoriaceous; petiole 1 cm long, flat, glabrous. Flowers in axillary clusters of racemes, white; stamens numerous.

Distribution: Taiwan, at altitude 2000 m.

90. Symplocos schefflerae Merr.

Tree 4–5 m tall. Leaves obovate or oblong-obovate, 4–6 cm long, 1.5–5.5 cm wide, abruptly acuminate at apex, acute at base, margin glandular-denticulate, lateral nerves 6 pairs, distantly distinct; petiole 5–8 mm long, Inflorescence axillary, spikes and racemose at base, 2.5–6 cm long; calyx elliptic – ovate lobed; petals elliptic ovate, rounded, 4 mm long, filaments 6 mm long.

Distribution: Kwangtung.

91. Symplocos seguini Levl.

Shrub with branchlets of lenticellate and rugose. Leaves oblong, glabrous, petiolate coriaceous, crenate margin, 5 cm long, 2 cm wide, Inflorescence spicate, pedicels and calyx rufous-tomentose, calyx-lobe obtuse, ovate; petals obtuse, venose.

Distribution: Kweichow.

92. Symplocos sinica Ker et Brand

Shrub with slender branchlets, pubescent when young. Leaves elliptic-ovate 5 cm long, 3 cm wide, acute apex, cuneate at base, finely serrate margin, glabrous above, densely pubescent below, membranous; petiole 1 mm long, pubescent. Flowers white, in axillary and terminal racemes, densely villose. Fruit globose, 3 mm long, 2 mm across, black, glabrous.

Distribution: Kwangtung, Fukien and Taiwan, at altitude 550 m.

93. Symplocos somai (Hayata) Sasaki

Shrub with dark gray branchlets, glabrous. Leaves elliptic-oblong, 4 cm long, 2 cm wide, acute apex, broad cuneate at base, finely serrate margin, coriaceous, petiole 2 mm long, glabrous. Flowers in small axillary spikes, glabrous.

Distribution: Taiwan.

94. Symplocos sozanensis Hayata

Small shrub with purplish branchlets, glabrous. Leaves elliptic-oblong, 3 cm long, 2 cm wide, acuminate apex, cuneate at base, entire revolute margin, subcoriaceous; petiole 1 cm long, glabrous. Fruit oblong, 6 mm long, 2 mm in diam., brown, in axillary racemes, pedicel slender, 1 mm long,

Distribution: Taiwan, 300 m altitude.

95. Symplocos spathulata Li

Shrub 4 m high. Leaves oblong spatulate, 8 cm long, 3.5 cm wide, blunt apex, cuneate at base, entire incurved margin, dark green above, pale green glabrous below; petiole 1 cm long, flat, glabrous. Flowers in axillary clusters of racemes.

Distribution: Kwangtung.

96. Symplocos szechuanensis Brand

Shrub 5 m tall. Branchlets stout, dark gray, smooth. Leaves oblong, 7 cm long, 3.5 cm wide, acute apex, obtuse cuneate at base, crenate-serrate margin, dark shining green above, light glaucous below, subcoriaceous; petiole 2 cm long, rounded, glabrous. Flowers in dense axillary clusters. Fruit cylindrical oblong, 1.5 cm long, 6 mm in diameter, apiculate, whitish tomentose, pedicels 1 mm long, white pubescent.

Distribution: Szechuan, Mt. Omei, at altitude 2000 m.

97. Symplocos sinuata Brand

Shrub 5 m tall. Leaves elliptic-oblong, 10 cm long, 3 cm wide, short-acuminate apex, cuneate at base, entire margin, lustrous dark green above, pale green glabrous below, coriaceous; petiole 2-3 cm long, glabrous. Flowers in dense axillary clustered spikes, white, glabrous. Fruit oblong, 2 cm long, 6 mm in diameter, black, glabrous.

Distribution: Kwangsi, and Yunnan, at altitude 1650 m.

98. Symplocos stenophylla Merr. et Chun

Symplocos angustifolia

Shrub 2 m tall. Leaves lanceolate, 8-10 cm long, 1.2-1.5 cm wide, long-acuminate at apex, base attenuate, margin serrulate and revolute. Inflorecence in simple spikes, axillary, sparsely pubescent; petals 5, oblong, 5 mm long, stamens 40, filaments, glabrous, 5-6 mm long; ovary 3-loculary.

This species is characterized by its lanceolate leaves, long-spicate inflorescences and somewhat conical fruit. It is most closely related to *S. laurina* Wall.

Distribution: Hainan, at altitude 400 m.

99. **Symplocos stenostachys** Hayata

Tree 12–26 m tall. Leaves oblanceolate, 7 cm long, 2.5 cm wide, long–acute at apex, cuneate at base revolute margin, lustrous deep green above pale green glabrous below, subcoriaceous; petiole 2 cm long, reddish brown. Flowers white, in terminal and axillary racemes, calyx 5–lobed, whitish pubescent. Fruit globose 6 mm long, 3 mm broad, glabrous.

Distribution: Taiwan, at altitude 1660 – 2160 m.

100. **Symplocos stewardii** Sleuma.

Tree 8–10 m high. Branchlets purplish gray, rough, lenticellate. Leaves elliptic–oblong, 6 cm long, 2.5 cm wide, long–acuminate apex, cuneate at base, incurved margin, dark shining green above, pale green, glabrous below, coriaceous petiole 12 cm long, glabrous. Fruit cylindrical, 1 cm long, 6 mm broad, black drupe–like, in an axillary spikes.

Distribution: Yunnan, and Kwangsi, at altitude 2900 m.

101. **Symplocos subconnata** Handel–Mazz.

Shrub 4 m tall. Leaves oblong–elliptic or oblong–lanceolate, 7–10.5 cm long, 3–4–parted angustitate, long–caudate–acuminate apex, cuneate–angustitate at base margin, undulate–serrulate, coriaceous; petiole 5–7 mm long, glabrous. Flowers white, glabrous; pedicel 3–5 mm long; calyx–tubes dense pilose, ciliate; stamens 30.

Distribution: Kwangsi.

102. **Symplocos suishariensis** Hayata

Shrub with slender branchlets. Leaves elliptic, 5 cm long, 3 cm wide, long–acuminate at apex, ovate or rounded at base, finely serrate margin; petiole 2 mm long, slender, glabrous. Flowers small, in terminal and axillary spikes, 6–8 cm long.

Distribution: Taiwan.

103. **Symplocos stapfiana** Levl.

Tree 10–15 m tall. Branchlets slender dark gray, glabrous. Leaves elliptic–oblong, 7 cm long, 3 cm wide, attenuate–acuminate apex, obtuse–cuneate at base coarsely serrate margin, lustrous shining green above, pale green below, glabrous; petiole 1–2 cm long, grooved. Flowers white, in axillary racemes, branched at base, globular, 1 mm in diameter, apiculate, glabrous, brown.

Distribution: Hunan, Kiangsi, Yunnan, Szechuan, Kwangtung and Kwangsi, a altitude 1300 m.

104. **Symplocos stellaris** Brand

Shrub 2 m tall. Leaves lanceolate, petiollate, glabrous, 15 cm long, 3 cm wide acute apex, cuneate at base revolute margin, thick, lustrous dark green above, pal brownish pubescent below, midrib deeply impressed above, prominently elevated beneath veins prominent above, inconspicuous beneath, coriaceous; petiole 2–3 cm long, groove above pubescent. Flowers in dense clusters in the axil of the fallen leaves, or on th old branchlets.

Distribution: Fukien, Kwangtung, Kweichow, Szechuan, Kiangsi, Chekiang, Anhwei, and Kwangsi, at altitude 855 m.

105. **Symplocos swinhoeana** Hance

Symplocos prunifolia Hance

Tree 13 m tall. Leaves elliptic-ovate, 4 cm long, 2.5 cm wide, attenuate-acuminate at apex, cuneate at base shallowly serrate above the middle, lustrous dark green above, olive-yellowish green below, coriaceous; petiole 1 - 2 cm long, grooved, glabrous. Flowers in short, axillary spikes, whitish yellow; calyx green ovate - lobed; petals oblong, fragrant, filaments numerous, 4 mm long, yellowish brown. Fruit cylindrical, 1.8 cm long, 6 mm broad, apiculate, green, glabrous, sessile.

Distribution: Kwangtung, Hainan, Hunan, Kiangsi, Kwangsi, Chekiang and Fukien, at altitude 100-240 m.

106. **Symplocos theaefolia** D. Don

Shrub 2-3 m tall. Leaves elliptic-oblong or elliptic-lanceolate, 8 cm long, 3 cm wide, short-acuminate apex, acute at base, crenate-serrate margin, olive-green glabrous on both surfaces, coriaceous; petiole 1 cm long, slightly yellowish pubescent, grooved. Flowers in dense, axillary racemes.

Distribution: Yunnan, and Tibet, at altitude 1800-2330 m.

107. **Symplocos theophrastaefolia** S. et Z.

Shrub 3 m tall. Leaves elliptic-oblong, 10 cm long, 3.5 cm wide, short-acuminate at apex, narrow-cuneate at base, incurved at margin, lustrous dark green above, pale-olivegreen glabrous beneath, coriaceous; petiole 1-2 cm long, glandular. Flowers in axillary racemes, branched at the base into spikes upward, glabrous. Fruit blue.

Distribution: Kwangsi, and Taiwan.

108. **Symplocos trichoclada** Hayata

Shrub with elliptic-oblong leaves, acute apex, obtuse cuneate at base, finely serrate margin, subcoriaceous; petiole 2 mm long, pubescent.

Distribution: Taiwan.

109. **Symplocos tythanta** Gontsch.

Shrub 1-2 m tall. Leaves oblanceolate, 4 cm long, 2 cm wide, long attenuate-acuminate apex, cuneate at base, revolute margin, dark green above, pale green glabrous except brownish pubescent along the midrib beneath, subcoriaceous; petiole 2 mm long, brownish pubescent. Flowers in axillary and terminal spikes, white, glabrous.

Distribution: Yunnan, Hainan, Kwangsi, and Fukien, at altitude 430 m.

110. **Symplocos viridissima** Brand

Shrub 3 m tall. Branchlets greenish pubescent, slender. Leaves oblanceolate, 11 cm long, 4.5 cm wide, acute apex, cuneate at the base, irregularly crenate-serrate margin, dark green, with deeply impressed midrib above, pale green with prominently elevated veins and midrib and reticulations beneath, whitish pubescent along the midrib below, subcoriaceous; petiole 1 cm long, pubescent, stout. Fruit oblong, 1 cm long, 5 mm broad, with persistent calyx on the top, glabrous, axillary, solitary.

Distribution: Yunnan and Hainan, at altitude 1500 m.

111. Symplocos wikstroemiifolia Hayata

Shrub with whitish gray branchlets, glabrous. Leaves lanceolate, 5 cm long, 1.5 cm wide, acute apex, and at base, revolute margin, clustered at the ends of the branchlets, lustrous shining green above, pale green, glabrous below, subcoriaceous; petiole 1 cm long, glabrous. Flowers in axillary clusters of racemes. Fruit oblong, 1 cm long, 3 mm in diameter, apiculate, glabrous, on short spikes on the older branchlets.

Distribution: Taiwan, at altitude 1700 m.

112. Symplocos wilsonii Hemsl.

Tree 7 m tall, evergreen, younger branches densely covered with short reddish brown indumentum. Leaves oblong-lanceolate, including petiole 10–12 cm long, 2–2.5 cm broad, acute, base cuneate, margin revolute, glabrous, coriaceous, shining above, paler below; lateral nerves alternate, distant, prominent on upper surface, obscure underneath; petiole angular, rather over 1 cm long, rusty pubescent when young. Flowers 1 cm across, greenish yellow, in nearly sessile cluster in the axils of fallen leaves or previous year's growth; pedicels very short, pilose; bracteoles 3, imbricate, broadly-obovate or orbicular, 2 mm long, ciliate sparsely pilose; calyx 1 mm long, up-shaped, lobes rounded; petals free, imbricate oblong-ovate or obovate, 6–8 mm long, rounded, ciliolate, concave; stamens about 20, slightly exceeding the petals; filaments flattened; disk annular; pistil a little longer than stamens; style persistent at least for a considerable time; ovary glabrous.

Distribution: Szechuan, at altitude 1200–1800 m.

113. Symplocos yunnanensis Brand

Shrub 3 m tall. Branchlets densely covered with reddish villose. Leaves oblong, 15 cm long, 4 cm wide, long-acuminate apex, obtuse – cuneate at base, sharply serrate margin, dark lustrous green above, brownish densely pubescent especially densely brownish villose along the midrib and veins beneath, prominently reticulated below, coriaceous; petiole 1 cm long, stout, densely villose. Flowers in dense clusterd on the older branchlets, white yellow, axillary on the fallen leaves. Fruit cylindrical 1.5 cm long, 2 mm broad, many-ridged, with persistent calyx on the top, brownish villose, subsessile; pedicels 2 cm long, densely villose.

Distribution: Yunnan, at altitude 1700–2200 m.

Family 60. Styracaceae DC.

Key to the genera of the family Styracaceae (See orig. text pages 894–895)

Genus (1) Pterostyrax S. et Z. (See orig. text page 895)

1. **Pterostyrax corymbosus** S. et Z. (See orig. text pages 895-896)

2. **Pterostyrax hispidium** S. et Z.

3. **Pterostyrax levillei** Chun

Tree 9 m tall. Leaves chartaceous, elliptic-oblong, 6-11 cm long, 3-6 cm wide, form variable, ovate or obovate-oblong, base cuneate, acute-acuminate apex, margin callous-denticulate, dense-pilose beneath, lateral veins 6-11 pairs; petiole 1-2 cm long, dense-stellate tomentose. Inflorescence paniculate, the panicle pyramidal, 12 cm long; calyx tomentose, articulate, bracts and bracteoles caducate; flowers 12-14 mm long, white, calyx tube 2 mm wide; petals 5, base free, densely white-pilose, elliptic spathulate, 6 mm long, 2 mm wide; stamens 10, exserted, unequal, 8-9 mm long, sparse pilose.

Distribution: Yunnan, Kweichow, and Kwangsi, at altitude 2200 m.

4. **Pterostyrax microcarpa** Diels (See orig. text page 897)

5. **Pterostyrax psilophyllus** Diels (See orig. text page 898)

6. **Pterostyrax trilobus** Hu

Tree 12 m tall. Branchlets gray, glabrous when old, brown pubescent when young. Leaves oblong-spathulate, 3-lobed on the top, cuneate at base, finely serrate margin, 6 cm long, 5 cm broad, dark green glabrous above, deep glaucous and bluish hairy beneath, subcoriaceous; petiole 2 cm long, flat, densely hairy.

Distribution: Kwangsi, at altitude 1330 m.

Genus (2) Sinojackia Hu (See orig. text pages 899-900)

1. **Sinojackia rehderiana** Hu

2. **Sinojackia xylocarpa** Hu (See orig. text pages 899-900)

Genus (3) Rehderodendron Hu (See orig. text pages 900-901)

1. **Rehderodendron macrocarpum** Hu

2. **Rehderodendron mapienense** Hu

3. **Rehderodendron kweichowense** Hu (See orig. text page 902)

4. **Rehderodendron hui** Chun

Shrub 3 m tall; wholly glabrous excepting the fruiting peduncles. Buds somewhat small, reddish brown, the outer scales glabrous, inner scales slightly ciliate along the margin, terminal narrow conical. Leaves alternate, chartaceous, elliptic-oblong, narrowly cuneate and shortly decurrent down the petiole at base, long-acuminate at apex 6-16 cm long, 3.5-5 cm wide, slightly crenate, entire or the upper margin very obscurely crenate-denticulate with obtusish calloused teeth, brighter green, concolorous on both sides, midrib chanelled above, elevated and yellowish beneath. Racemes 3-5-flowered, simple or slightly branched at base, excluding the flowers 4.5 cm long, covered with densely whitish stellate tomentose as well as the bracts, pedicels and the calyx; bracts ovate, obtuse at apex; pedicels 12 mm long; calyx broadly obconical, 4.5 mm high, 4 mm wide at the throat, obscurely 5-ridged, lobes triangular-lanceolate, with slender acumen; corolla tube 2 mm high, lobes slightly unequal, obovate or broadly elliptic, 20 mm long, 12 mm wide, thinly fasciculate tomentellous on both surfaces; stamens 20-25 mm long; anthers 5 mm long; style 28 mm long.

Distribution: Kwangtung.

5. **Rehderodendron kwangtungense** Chun

Tree 7 m tall. Branchlets brown or red brown, finally becoming yellow gray. Leaves alternate, chartaceous, oblong-elliptic, usually falcate-acuminate at apex, acute to obtuse or rounded at base, very unequal in size on the same branch, 7-16 cm long and 3-8 cm wide glabrous, green, concolorous, when dry sub-lustrous and brownish green, margin more or less crenulate very obscurely minutely callose-denticulate, midrib broadly chanelled above, sharply elevated beneath, lateral veins 8-11 pairs, sparse, slender, densely reticulate and equally prominent on both surfaces; petiole 1-1.5 cm long, reddish. Fruit solitary, on stout straight thinly stellate-pilose peduncles about 4 cm long and 3 cm in diameter on the previous year's growth, cylindric-oblong, 6.5-8 cm long, large, more or less 3.5 cm wide, brown or grayish brown, sparsely fasciculate pilose even when mature especially around the apex, base and ribs sharply 8-10 costate, base contracted, apex umbonate, with a broad short conical beak 6 mm wide at base, persistent calyx lobes narrowly triangular, exocarp hard, 1 mm thick, mesocarp 8-10 mm thick, spongy, chocolate brown; endocarp woody, 2-4-celled radiating outwards into about 16 woody, vertical dissepiments which extends to the exocarp; seed 2-4, cylindric-fusiform, 2.8-3 cm long, 3 mm thick.

Distribution: Kwangtung.

6. **Rehderodendron praeteritum** Sleumer

Tree 6 m tall. Leaves oblong-elliptic, 11-16 cm long, 5-7 cm wide, acuminate at apex, broad-cuneate at base, entire margin, membranaceous; petiole 2 cm long, glabrous. Fruit solitary oblong, 5-5.7 cm long, 3-3.5 cm wide, densely stellate-tomentose, 10 costate; seeds 2-4, cylindric-fusiform, 2 cm long, 5 mm across. Endosperm woody.

Distribution: South Kwangtung, at altitude 210 m.

7. **Rehderodendron tsangii** Hu et Cheng

Tree, young branchlets rusty stellate-pilosulose, those of second year brown, glabrescent. Leaves coriaceous, broad elliptic-oblong, acute broadcuneate at base, revolute and minutely denticulate along the margins, 18-20 cm long, 7.5-10 cm broad, upper surface stellate-pubescent along the midrib and veins and glabrous on the rest of surface, lower surface rusty stellate-tomentose along the midrib and veins, and stellate-pubescent on the rest of the surface, lateral veins 10-15 pairs, quite prominent with reticulate veinlets; petiole thick, 2 cm long, stellate-tomentose, grooved above. Fruit solitary, cylindric-oblong, 6-7 cm long, 3.5 cm broad, brown, many-ribbed, umbonate at apex; exocarp fragile, mesocarp spongy, 8 mm thick, endocarp thinly ligneous, extending outwards in vertical fibres; seed 1-2, linear, fleshy, 3 cm long.

Distribution: Yunnan, at altitude 1450-1550 m.

8. **Rehderodendron yunnanense** Hu

Tree 14 m tall. This years growth branchlets angular, sordid, brown-stellate-tomentulose, glabrous next year. Leaves membranaceous, broadly elliptic – oblong, acuminate rounded to broadly cuneate at base, shining, green and densely stellate-pilose along the midrib and veins and with scattered stellate hairs on the rest of the surface above, densely grey-stellate-tomentulose especially along the midrib and veins beneath, revolute and callose-denticulate along the margins, lateral veins 10–12 on each side, prominent beneath, 16–18 cm long, 7–8 cm wide; petiole 1 cm long, stellate-tomentulose. Panicle axillary, many-flowered, peduncle and pedicels slender, densely stellate-tomentose, pedicels 3–6 mm long, articulate; bracts subulate, grey-tomentose; calyx campanulate, 2 mm broad, adnate to the ovary, grey-stellate-tomentose, teeth 4–5, triangular, 1 mm long. Fruit 1–2, oblong, peduncles 3.5 cm long, 12-ribbed, conicalumbonate at apex. Aborted seeds 2 at the base of the fruit, 7–8 mm long.

Distribution: S. Yunnan, at altitude 1400 m.

Genus (4) Melliodendron Handel-Mazz. (See orig. text pages 902–904)

1. **Melliodendron xylocarpum** Handel-Mazz. (See orig. text page 904)

2. **Melliodendron wangianum** Hu

Tree 9 m tall. Branchlets brown or dark brown, with numerous conspicuous vate lenticels. Young branchlets quadrangular, purplish brown or yellowish brown, fasciate pilose. Leaves oblanceolate or obovate, acuminate at apex, cuneate at base, serrulate on the margin, 12–14 cm long, 4–6 cm broad, deep green above, light green below, sparsely puberulose; petiole 8–12 mm long, stellate-puberulous. Flowers solitary usually appearing before the development of leaves from the axillary buds; calyx turbinate, 4–5 mm long, whitish-pubescent outside, truncate or obsoletely 5-toothed, corolla white, pink flushed outside especially near the base, 20–40 mm long, base of the corolla united as a tube, 4–5 mm long; petals 5, conduplicate in buds, ovate or ovate-oblong, acute or obtuse, 19–22 mm long, 8–10 mm broad, sparingly villose on both surfaces; stamens 10, uniseriate, 20–22 mm long inserted on the calyx just inside the base of the corolla; ovary purplish, half or 2/3 inferior, 5-or 6-celled; 4–6-ovules in each cell; Fruit woody, ovoid pyriform, 3 cm long, 1.8–2 cm in diameter, contracted at the base, stellate-pubescent; peduncle erect, 1 cm long, stellate-pilose.

Distribution: Szechuan Mt. Omei, at altitude 800 m.

Genus (5) Styrax Linn. (See orig. text pages 904–906)

1. **Styrax argyi** Levl.

Small shrub, branchlets slender, whitish green glandulary-pubescent, gray. Leaves obovate, 4–7 cm long, 3–6 cm broad, acute to rounded at apex, obtuse cuneate to ovate at base, irregularly finely serrate margin, membranaceous; petiole 2 mm long, densely hairy. Flowers in terminal racemes, few-flowered; flowers white, pistils 2 cm long, petals imbricated; calyx green, tubular, 8 mm long, short lobed, lobes 5, whitish pubescent; pedicel 16 mm long, densely white hairy; calyx lobes triangular lanceolate. Fruit globose, striate, olivaceous.

Distribution: Kweichow, Yunnan, and Kiangsu.

2. **Styrax biaristatusm** W. W. Sm.

    Huodendron biaristatum (Sm.) Rehd.

    Shrub or trees 6–10 m high. Leaves chartaceous, oblong or elliptic-oblong, 9–11 cm long, 3–4 cm wide, apice acuminate, base broad asymmetrically cuneate, margin remotely and minutely denticulate, glabrous above, sparsely tomentose below; lateral nerves 7–9 pairs. Inflorescence paniculate, terminal or axillary, 6–10 cm long, multiflorous, axil densely stellate tomentose; calyx cupuliform, 2 mm long, lobes triangular subacute, densely adpressed white tomentose; corolla 5-parted lobes imbricate, 8–9 mm long, 2.5 mm wide, oblong, subobtuse; stamens 10, filaments free, 3 mm long, densely stellate-pilose; ovary ovoid, 3-loculary, many-celled; fruit ovoid, 4 mm long.

    Distribution: Yunnan, at altitude 2800 m.

3. **Styrax cavaleriei** Levl.

    Styrax macranthus Perk.

    Shrub 4 m tall.

    This species is closely allied to *Styrax grandiflorus* Griff., differing in the more glabrous pedicels and more deeply cut calyx.

    Distribution: Kweichow, and Yunnan, at altitude 1333 m.

4. **Styrax bodinieri** Levl.

    Shrub 3 m high. Leaves obovate, 4–6 cm long, 3–5 cm wide, acute at both ends, irregulary finely serrate margin, subcoriaceous; petiole 3 mm long.

    Distribution: Hunan, Hupeh, Kweichow and Kwangsi, Szechuan, at altitude 1180–1250 m.

5. **Styrax formosanum** Matsum.

    Tree 5–8 m high. Branchlets dark gray, densely pubescent. Leaves elliptic or elliptic-ovate, 5 cm long, 3.3 cm wide, acute apice, cuneate at base, irregularly finely to coarsely serrate margin, dark green above, pale glaucous green below, glabrous on both sides, membranaceous; petiole 2 mm long, pubescent. Flowers in terminal racemes, white, fragrant; calyx cupuliform, 2 mm long, white tomentose; petals 5, imbricate, free and adnate at the base, whitish tomentulose, pedicels 1–2 cm long, white villose. Fruit globose, 1 cm long, 5 mm in diameter, 3-valved, woody drupe, brown, glabrous, with persistent calyx, pedicels long, slender, 2–3 cm long, whitish villose.

    Distribution: Taiwan, at altitude 1000–2300 m.

6. **Styrax henryi** Perkins

    Small tree 5–8 m high. Branchlets dark gray, pubescent, slender. Leaves elliptic or elliptic-oblong, 4–8 cm long, 2–4 cm wide, acuminate at apex, cuneate to broad-cuneate at base, finely serrate to remotely crenate-dentate, sub-coriaceous, dark green above, pale green below; petiole 1–2 mm long, pubescent. Flowers white, in terminal and axillary racemes; calyx cupulary, 5-lobed, greenish pubescent, 1.5 mm long; petals 5, oblanceolate, acute apice, whitish pubescent outside, brownish pubescent inside; pedicels 2–3 cm long, slender pubescent.

Distribution: Taiwan, at altitude 600–1000 m.

7. **Styrax kotoensis** Hayata

Small tree with dark purplish slender branchlets. Leaves ovate or elliptic-obovate, 7 cm long, 4 cm wide, acute apice, obtuse cuneate at base, entire margin, shing deep green above, glaucous and glabrous beneath, membranaceous; petiole 2 mm long, flat, pubescent. Flowers white, in terminal racemes, calyx minutely cupulary, with whitish hairs, 2 mm long and broad; petals 5, oblong, 16 mm long, 10 cm wide, acute apice, whitish glandulary pubescent on both surfaces, pedicels 3–4 cm long, pubescent.

Distribution: Taiwan, Botel Tobago.

8. **Styrax leveillei** Fedde et Levl.

Shrub with leaves white beneath, lobed at the apex; stamens exserted.

Distribution: Kweichow.

9. **Styrax limprichtii** Lingsh.

Shrub 0.5 m tall. Leaves obovate, 4 cm long, 2.5 cm wide, acute apice, obovate at base, serrate margin, dark green above, white glaucous and pubescent below; petiole 1 mm long. Flowers white.

Distribution: Yunnan, Szechuan, and Kwangtung, at altitude 2100–2600 m.

10. **Styrax hypoglauca** Perk. (See orig. text page 906)

11. **Styrax japonicus** S. et Z.

Var. 1. Styrax japonicus var. calycothrix Gilg

This variety differs from the typical form in the densely stellate-pubescent calyx and in the obovate leaves, long-acuminate apice and at the base very gradually narrowed into the petiole.

Distribution: Shantung, Lau Shan.

12. **Styrax matsumurae** Perk.

Shrub with brownish pubescent branchlets, dark purple in color. Leaves obovate, 4 cm long, 2.8 cm wide, acute at apex, obtuse-cuneate at base, remotely, irregularly serrate or incurved margin, dark green above, densely pubescent and bluish glaucous beneath, subcoriaceous; petiole 2 mm long, densely bluish hairy. Flowers white, in short axillary racemes, brownish hairy.

Distribution: Taiwan.

13. **Styrax oligophlebius** Merr.

Shrub 2.5 m tall. Leaves oblong, 4–6 cm long, 1.5–2.5 cm wide, apice acuminate, base acute, densely stellate-tomentose beneath, glossy above; petiole 0.8–1.3 cm long, densely stellate-tomentose. Fruit globose, 1.2 cm in diameter, dense white tomentose, calyx persistent, cupulary, 6 mm long, irregular-lobed; pedicels 3 mm long.

Distribution: Kwangsi.

14. **Styrax pachyphyllus** Merr. et Chun

Tree 8 m tall; branchlets terete, glabrous. Leaves ovate, or elliptic-ovate, 7–9 cm long, 4–6 cm wide, acute-acuminate at apex, acute or sub-rotundate-acute at base, entire, lustrous dark green above, densely puberulent below; lateral nerves 5-6 pairs, coriaceous; petiole 1.5-2.5 cm long. Fruit sub-globose, 2 cm in diameter, with persistent calyx, densely ferruginous-pubescent, gray.

Distribution: Hainan, Kwangsi, and Yunnan, at altitude 900 m.

15. **Styrax perkinsiae** Rehd.

Shrub 2-3 m tall. branchlets purplish green, stellate-pilose. Leaves membranaceous, deciduous, ovate or ovate-oblong, 4.5-7.5 cm long, 2.3-3.7 cm wide, apex acuminate, cuneate at base, minutely denticulate margin, densely stellate-pilose beneath, lateral nerves 6-8 pairs, elevated. Inflorescence racemose, 2-3-flowered, solitary, axillary. Flowers white, corolla imbricate; calyx campanulate. Fruit ovoid, 8 mm long.

Distribution: Szechuan, at altitude 2000 m.

16. **Styrax obassia** S. et Z. (See orig. text page 908)

17. **Styrax rugosus** Kurz

Shrub 3-6 m tall; branchlets slender, brownish villose. Leaves obovate, 5 cm long, 3 cm wide, acute apex, rounded at base, distantly serrate, dark green above, bluish glaucous tomentose beneath, subcoriaceous; petiole 2 mm long, densely villose. Flowers white, in terminal racemes, whitish villose.

Distribution: Yunnan, at altitude 1330-1450 m.

18. **Styrax supaii** Chun et F. Chun

Shrub 2 m tall. Leaves few-nerved deeply lobed leaves. Flowered 3, in simple cymes, pedicels slender 15 mm long, calyx thin nearly translucent 12 mm long, half divided into long lanceolate lobes; stamens unequal, alternately 5 long and 5 short.

This species is related to *S. rugosus* Kurz. but evidently only remotely so. *S. shiraianus Makino* also has sinuate-lobate leaves but the flowers of that species have a corolla with lobes much shorter than the tube. It is altogether an outstanding species of this prolific genus.

Distribution: Kwangtung.

19. **Styrax subcrenatus** Handel-Mazz.

Small tree 5-8 m tall. Branchlets whitish gray, glabrous, and pubescent when young. Leaves oblong, 5-15 cm long, 3-6 cm wide, acute to short-acuminate at apex, cuneate to obtuse cuneate at base, finely serrate and incurved margin, dark shining green above, light green glabrous below; petiole 1 cm long, brown, slightly pubescent. Flowers greenish white, in terminal cymes; corolla 5, imbricate, tomentose, calyx green, tomentose, minutely teethed. Fruit globose, 2 cm long, 1 cm in diameter, whitish tomentose, short-beaked calyx persistent; pedicels 2 cm long, whitish tomentose.

Distribution: Hainan, at altitude 200-300 m.

29. Styrax suberifolius Hook. et Arn. (See orig. text pages 908-909)

Var. 1. **Styrax suberifolius** var. **caloneurus** Perk.

21. Styrax tibeticus Anth.

Styrax huodendron

Shrub 6–10 m tall. Leaves lanceolate, 7–10 cm long, 2–3 cm wide, entire margin, apice acuminate, base attenuate. Inflorescence in panicles of 3–5 cm long; pedicels glabrous; calyx cupulary, 1 mm long, 5–lobed, margin ciliate; corolla white, 7 mm long, exterior pubescent, interior glabrous; stamens and filaments 2 mm long; anthers 2 mm long; ovary 3–loculare, many–celled, style 3–fidus, 8 mm long. Fruit 3 mm long.

Distribution: Tibet.

22. **Styrax subniveus** Merr. et Chun

Small tree 5–7 m tall. Branchlets purplish, glabrous of densely ferruginous–pubescent. Leaves chartaceous, elliptic–ovate to ovate, entire, 5–9 cm long, 3–5.5 cm wide, base broadly rounded to acute, apex conspicuously and acutely acuminate, the upper surface glabrous, lustrous, greenish olivaceous, lower surface whitish, densely puberulent, lateral nerves usually 5, conspicuous on both surfaces, curved ascending, arched anastomising, the reticulations rather slender and lax; petiole 5–18 mm long. Inflorescence solitary, axillary, and terminal, few to rather many–flowered, racemose to narrowly paniculate, rather densely pubescent, 3–8 cm long. Flowers creamy white, 14 mm long; pedicels 4 mm long; calyx 5 mm long, densely stellate–pubescent, lobes 5, oblong, obtuse, minutely glandular on the margins; corolla stellate–pubescent outside, the tube 4 mm long, the lobes imbricate, 8 mm long, elliptic to oblong–elliptic; stamens 10, filaments 4 mm long, with scattered white–stellate hairs; ovary densely pubescent; style glabrous, 1 cm long.

Distribution: Kwangtung, and Kwangsi, at altitude 400 m.

23. **Styrax veitchiorum** Hemsl. et Wils. (See orig. text page 909)

24. **Styrax huanus** Rehd. (See orig. text pages 909–910)

25. – 39. (See orig. text pages 310–313)

40. **Styrax chrysocarpus** Li

Tree 7–20 m tall. Branchlets densely bluish–tomentose or glabrous. Leaves chartaceous, small, petiolate, scabrid stellate–tomentose, oblong–ovate 10–20 cm long, 5.5–11 cm wide, acuminate apex, base rotundate, margin integrate; nerves 5–10, subconspicuous, densely tomentose; petiole 5–8 mm long.

This species is characterized by its rather large, oblong–ovate leaves, more or less scabrid–hairy on both surfaces, the bright yellow tomentose fruits, and the membranaceous calyx.

Distribution: Yunnan, at altitude 1400 m.

41. **Styrax fukienensis** W. W. Sm.

Shrub 1 m high. Branchlets densely tomentose. Leaves ovate or oblong–ovate, 6–8 cm long, 2.5–3.5 cm wide, acuminate to acute at apex, subrotundate or cuneate at base, margins slightly denticulate, coriaceous, densely fulvotomentose beneath. Inflorescence racemose, 5–6–flowered, fulvo–stellate–tomentose. Petals 5 – parted; stamens 10, filaments free, 3 mm long; ovary ovoid, multi–ovulate, densely white pilose.

Distribution: Fukien.

42. Styrax hayataianum Perkins

Shrub 6 m tall. Branchlets slender, densely villose. Leaves oblong, 9 cm long, 3 cm wide, apex acuminate, cuneate at base, slightly crenate undulate margin, dark green above, whitish glaucescent and glabrous below. Flowers white, in axillary racemes, brownish villose. Fruit globose, gray.

Distribution: Kwangsi.

Genus (6) **Alniphyllum** Matsum.(See orig. text page 913)

1. Alniphyllum buddleifolium Hu et Cheng

Tree with dense flavo-stellate tomentose branchlets. Leaves persistent, chartaceous, elliptic or elliptic-oblong, rarely obovate, 6.5–16 cm long and 3.5–8 cm wide; apex acuminate, base cuneate or subrotundate, margin remote crenulate, sparsely stellate-pubescent or glabrous above, grayish stellate-pubescent and reticulate beneath, lateral nerves 10–15 pairs, impressed above, prominently elevated below, petiole 6–13 mm long, stello-pubescent, sulcate above, Inflorescence 1 cm long, dense white-stello-tomentose; style filiform, 17 mm long. Fruits in racemes, 2–2.5 cm long, oblong, pendulous, 18 cm long, epicarp deciduous, endocarp ligneous, 5–valved; seeds numerous, 4–5 mm long, 2 mm wide, irregularly broad.

This sepcies differs from *A. fauriei* Perkins of Taiwan chiefly in its elliptic, elliptic-oblong, rarely obovate leaves sparsely stellate-pubescent above, densely so beneath, with 10–15 pairs of lateral veins, and in its lanceolate calyx-lobes *A. pterospermum* Mats. differs from the present species in the deciduous habit, oblong-lanceolate leaves with acute apex, in the longer inflorescence, and in the much larger seeds.

Distribution: Yunnan, at altitude 1200 m.

2. Alniphyllum eberhardtii Guillaum

Small tree 7 m high. Branchlets purplish brown, glabrous and somewhat pubescent when young. Leaves oblong, 8 cm long, 3 cm wide, short acuminate apex, obtuse cuneate at base, revolute margin, lustrous dark green above, pale bluish glaucous beneath, lateral nerves 11–12 pairs, prominently elevated below, coriaceous; petiole 2 cm long, slightly pubescent. Flowers in axillary racemes. Fruit a woody capsule, 5–valved, ferruginous-pubescent, persistent calyx, densely brownish tomentose; pedicels 2 mm long, brownish tomentose.

Distribution: Yunnan, at altitude 1200 m.

3. Alniphyllum fauriei Perkins

Tree 8–10 m high. Branchlets sparsely stellate-pilose. Leaves alternate, petiolate, oblong-lanceolate or ovate-lanceolate, 6–12.5 cm long, 2.5–4.5 cm wide, acuminate apice, base cuneate, margin irregular, indistinctly, glandular, denticulated, membranaceous; petiole 0.5–1.3 cm long; lateral nerves 7–10. Inflorescence cymose, 2–3–flowered, forming a panicle; flowers white, 1.5 cm long, pedicels 2–5 mm long, articulated, fusco-tomentose, calyx lobes ovate-lanceolate, stellate tomentose outside, grayish pilose inside, corolla 5-parted, imbricate; stamens 10, unequal in length, style filiform, glabrous.

Distribution: Taiwan, Kee-Lung.

4. **Alniphyllum fortunei** (Hemsl.) Perkins   (See orig. text pages 913-914)

5. **Alniphyllum hainanense** Hayata

Tree 12 m high, 1 meter in diameter. Branchlets dark gray, rough, brownish pilose when young. Leaves obovate, 10 cm long, 6 cm wide, acute apex, rounded at base, irregularly remotely denticulate serrate, lustrous dark green above, bluish glaucous, tomentose along the midrib and veins below, subcoriaceous, lateral nerves 10-12 pairs, prominent on both surfaces; petiole 15 mm long, glandular-tomentose. Flowers pure white, in axillary racemes. Fruit a cylindrical woody capsule, brown, glabrous, 5 valved on persistent and 5-lobed calyx and brownish pubescent, about 2 cm long, 1 cm in diameter; seeds many, winged.

Distribution: Hainan, at altitude 830 m. Kwangtung, Yunnan, at altitude 1000-1500 m.

6. **Alniphyllum macranthum** Perkins

Shrub or small tree, 4-14 m tall. Branchlets gray and glabrous, brownish pubescent when young. Leaves oblong-obovate, 8-12 cm long, 3-6 cm wide, short acuminate at apex, obtuse cuneate at base, irregularly finely, glandular serrate margin, lustrous dark green above, light green, glabrous beneath, subcoriaceous; petiole 1 cm long, glabrous. Inflorescence in terminal racemes. Fruit oblong, 2 cm long, 1 cm broad brown, glabrous, a valved woody capsule, pedicels brownish glandulary pubescent; corolla 5-parts, petals oblong, 2 mm long, 1.5 mm broad, acute, white, glandular-tomentose.

Distribution: Kwangtung, Kwangsi, Yunnan, Szechuan, Kweichow, Hunan, and a large tree of 14 m tall in Kweichow, at altitude 1000-1150 m.

7. **Alniphyllum megaphyllum** Hemsl. et E. H. Wilson

Tree 7-40 m high. Branchlets brownish pubescent when young, angular. Leaves coriaceous, obovate or oblong, 14 cm long, 7-9 cm broad, acute apex, rounded at base, incurved or glandulary margins, lustrous dark green above, light green glandulary brownish pubescent along midrib and veins, and prominently elevated and reticulated beneath, lateral nerves 10 pairs, very highly elevated, petiole 2-3 cm long, stout, brown slightly angular, pubescent. Fruit in axillary racemes, 5-valved woody capsule, 2 cm long, 1 cm in diameter, oblong, beaked; pedicels 1 cm long, articulated, brown, glabrous.

Distribution: Kwangtung, and Kwangsi, at altitude 1130 m.

8. **Alniphyllum pterospermum** Matsum. (See orig. text page 914)

Order XXVI Rubiales

Family 61. Oleaceae Lindl.

Key to the arborescent genera of Oleaceae

Genus (1) Fraxinus Linn. (See orig. text page 916)

1. **Fraxinus bungeana** DC. (See orig. text pages 916-917)

> **form. 1.** Fraxinus bungeana f. macrophylla DC.
>
> > Small tree with odd-pinnate leaves; leaflets 3-5, obovate or oblong 6 cm long, 4 cm wide, long-attenuate-acuminate at apex, broad-cuneate at base, coarsely crenate - serrate margin, lustrous shining green above, light green beneath, subcoriaceous; rachis 8-10 cm long, grooved above; petiole 1-2 cm long, flattened, glabrous. Fruits in axillary panicles, winged; including seed, 3 cm long, 2 mm wide, narrow-lanceolate.
> >
> > Distribution: Hopei, and Honan.
>
> **form. 2.** Fraxinus bungeana f. rotunda DC.
>
> > Small shrub with odd-pinnate leaves; leaflets 5-7, small, rotundate, or elliptic-ovate, 2 cm long, 1.5 cm broad, acute apex, broad-cuneate at base, coarsely serrate above the middle margin, shining green on both sides, subcoriaceous; petiole 2 mm long, reddish green, glabrous.
> >
> > Distribution: Shansi.

2. **Fraxinus bracteata** Hemsl.

Shrub 8 m tall. Leaves odd-pinnate, leaflets 3, 5, or 7, obovate, or oblong, 8-12 cm long, 4.5-6.5 cm wide, acute at apex, rounded to ovate at base, entire margin, lustrous dark green above, pale brownish and glabrous except along the midrib and veins being slightly pubescent beneath, coriaceous; petiole 1-3 cm long, reddish and slightly pubescent. Inflorescence in large panicles, terminal, with bracts on the base of the rachis. Flowers small, white, 5-lobed. Fruit a samara, the wing, including the seed, 3 cm long, 3 mm broad, blunt at top, brown; peticels 2 mm long, very slender, reddish, glabrous.

Distribution: Hunan, and Hupeh, at altitude 300-1000 m.

3. **Fraxinus baroniana** Diels

Small tree 6-13 m tall. Leaves odd-pinnate, leaflets lanceolate or oblanceolate, 7 cm long, 2 cm wide, crenate-serrate margin, long-acuminate at apex, obtuse-cuneate at base, olive-green on both surfaces, nerves 4-5 pairs, inconspicuous above, prominent below; rachis slender, round, reddish, stout 10 cm long. Flowers in axillary and terminal panicles. Fruit small, with purplish wings, including the seed 12 mm long, 2 mm broad, emarginat at apex.

Distribution: Szechuan, Kansu, and Hupeh, at altitude 2800-3000 m.

4. Fraxinus cathayensis Rehd. et Wilson

Shrub 5 m tall. Branchlets gray, lenticelled, pubescent when young. Leaves odd-pinnate, leaflets 3-5, oblong, 6 cm long, 3 cm wide, acute apex, cuneate at base, dull green above, pale green, slightly brownish pubescent below.

This species is similar in general appearance to *F. chinensis* Roxb. and to *F. longicuspis* S. et Z. The young branchlets, the inflorescence, and the midrib and veins on the underside of the leaves are rather densely short-pilose, the upper side of the leaves is slightly puberulous and the under side sparingly pubescent between the veins, the minute calyx is deeply parted as in *F. longicuspis* or mostly fallen off, not campanulate as in *F. chinensis*. The fruit is oblong-spathulate, about 3 cm long and 6-7 mm broad.

Distribution: Anhwei, and Chekiang, at altitude 100 m.

5. Fraxinus chinensis Roxb. (See orig. text page 917)

Var. 1. **Fraxinus chinensis** var. **acuminata** Lingelsh

6. Fraxinus ferruginea Ling.

7. Fraxinus formosana Hayata

Tree 7 m tall. Branchlets purplish gray, lenticellate, glabrous but pubescent when young. Leaves odd-pinnate, leaflets, 3, 5, or 7, oblong or oblanceolate, 8 cm long, 3 cm wide, entire incurved margin, lustrous dark green above, light green glabrous except along the midrib slightly brownish pubescent below, acute at apex, broad-cuneate at base subcoriaceous; petiole 1 cm long, glabrous. Flowers in large terminal panicles, small, white, pubescent. Wing of fruit oblong, 3 cm long, spatulate, somewhat emarginate on the top, 3 mm broad, greenish yellow; pedicel very slender, 2 mm long, pubescent; rachis 15 cm long, with a lanceolate bracts at the base. Flowers white, pubescent all over.

Distribution: Taiwan, at altitude 1900-2000 m.

8. Fraxinus georgei S. Y. Hu

Shrub 2-4 m tall. Branchlets thick, stout, grayish brown, glabrous. Leaves odd-pinnate, leaflets usually 3, obovate, 8 cm long, 4 cm wide, apex acute, broad cuneate at base, irregularly coarsely dentate, olive-green shining above, brownish pubescent and prominently reticulated below; petiole 1 cm long, stout, glabrous. Fruit wing, including the seed, 3 cm long, 3 mm broad, acute at apex; pedicel very slender, 2-3 mm long, glabrous.

This species is affiliated to *F. trifoliolata* W. W. Sm. but differs from it in leaflets glabrous and acute samara.

Distribution: Yunnan, and Tibet, at altitude 2700 m.

9. Fraxinus griffithii C. B. Clarke (See orig. text page 920)

10. Fraxinus hopeiensis Tang

Tree 10 m high. Branchlets glabrous, lenticellate. Leaves 3-5-foliated; rachis glabrous; leaflets broad ovate or oblong-elliptic or suborbicular, crenate serrate or serrate-dentate, subincurved, long-acuminate at apex, base broad cuneate or sub-truncate; petiole 2-3 mm long, 7-12 cm long, 4-7.5 cm wide. Inflorescence in panicles terminal and lateral, glabrous, 12 cm long. Flowers hermaphrodite, pedicels glabrous, 4-7 mm long; calyx dentate, acute; petals linear, acute or subobtuse at apex, 3-6 mm long; stamens nearly as long as the petals with oblong-elliptic anthers; pistils much shorter than the stamens; ovary glabrous. Young fruit linear, attenuate downward, coronate with persistent stigmas or rounded at apex.

Distribution: Hopei, Miao Feng Shan near Peping.

11. **Fraxinus inopinata** Lingelsh. (See orig. text page 920)

12. **Fraxinus koehneana** Lingelsh.

Large tree 22 m high. Bark gray, smooth, somewhat fissured. Branchlets gray, pubescent, opposite. Leaves odd-pinnate, 3-5 leaflets, unequal in sizes. Leaflets oblong-lanceolate, 8 cm long, 3 cm wide, acuminate at apex, cuneate at base coarsely serrate margin, dark green above, light green glabrous except brownish pubescent along the midrib beneath, subcoriaceous; petiole 1-2 cm long, glabrous. Flowers in terminal and lateral panicles; fruits with lanceolate wings, about 3 cm long including seed, 7 mm broad, spathulate at tip, in opposite pairs.

Distribution: Chekiang, and Anhwei, at altitude 1000 m.

13. **Fraxinus lingelsheimii** Rehd. (See orig. text page 921)

14. **Fraxinus malacophylla** Hemsl.

15. **Fraxinus machurica** Rupr.

16. **Fraxinus micrantha** Lingelsh.

Shrub 2-6 m high. Branchlets gray, smooth, brownish pubescent when young, stout. Leaves 5-7, or 9-leaflets, rachis 14 cm long, grayish brown, minutely winged; leaflets oblong, 8 cm long, 4 cm wide, attenuate-acuminate at apex, unequally cuneate at base, coarsely serrate margin, shining light green on both surfaces, lateral veins 8-pairs, impressed above, prominently elevated below, coriaceous; petiole 5-10 mm long, glabrous. Flowers in dense terminal panicles, purplish, glabrescent. Fruits with lanceolate wing, 2.5 cm long, 2 mm broad, acute apex, pedicels very slender, 2 mm long.

Distribution: Yunnan, at altitude 3000-3300 m.

17. **Fraxinus paxiana** Ling. (See orig. text page 922)

18. **Fraxinus platypoda** Oliv. (See orig. text pages 922-923)

19. **Fraxinus rhynchophylla** Hance

F. chinensis var. *rhynchophylla* Hemsl.

Tree 2-10 m high. Branchlets gray smooth, glabrous. Leaves with 3, 5 or 7-foliates, rachis 10-25 cm long, slightly pubescent when young, slightly grooved above. Leaflets obovate oblong, or rounded, or elliptic-obovate, 8-10 cm long, 4-10 cm broad, acute to long-acuminate at apex, broad cuneate to rounded at base, crenate serrate or coarsely serrate margin, lustrous shining green above light green and glabrous below; petiole 1-3 cm long, glabrous. Flowers very small, in lateral and terminal panicles, with dense yellowish wools bracts at the base, purplish green, glabrous. Fruit including seed 2.5 cm long, 3 mm broad, lanceolate, acute apex, glabrous; pedicel very slender 3 mm long, reddish.

Distribution: Hopei, at altitude 200-900 m, Kiangsi and Hupeh, at altitude 1300 m.

20. **Fraxinus sikkimensis** (Lingelsh.) Handel-Mazz.

Tree 10-12 m high. Branchlets thick, stout, brownish gray, lenticelled. Leaves with 7-9 leaflets; rachis 10-25 cm long, brownish pubescent; leaflets oblanceolate 12 cm long, 4 cm broad, acuminate at apex, broadly cuneate, unequal at base, finely serrate margin, lustrous dark green above pale green and brownish pubescent along the midrib and veins beneath, coriaceous; petiole 1-2 mm long, densely pilose. Flowers small, whitish green, in dense terminal and lateral panicles, glabrous; peduncles 15 cm long, purplish, glabrous. Fruit including wing 2.5 cm long, 2 mm broad, slightly emarginate at apex; pedicels slender, 2 mm long.

Distribution: Yunnan, at altitude 2250-2900 m.

21. **Fraxinus retusa** Champ. ex Benth. (See orig. text page 924)

Var. 1. **Fraxinus retusa** var. **henryana** Oliv.

22. **Fraxinus sargentiana** Lingelsh.

23. **Fraxinus sureaveolens** Smith

24. **Fraxinus mariesi** Hook. (See orig. text pages 925-926)

25. **Fraxinus trifoliata** Smith

Genus (2) Forsythia Vahl (Golden-bell)

Deciduous shrub, glabrous, rarely leaves pubescent; winter-buds with several outer scales, superposed and often laterally branched; branches hollow or with lamellate pith. Leaves opposite, petioled serrate or entire, occasionally 3-parted or 3-foliate, thickish. Flowers 1-6, axillary, heterostylous, before the leaves; calyx deeply 4-lobed, persistent; corolla yellow, with 4 oblong lobes, longer than the campanualate tube usually striped orange within; stamens 2, inserted at the base of corolla, not or slightly exserted; style slender, with 2 lobed stigma, in the macrostyle form longer, in the microstyle shorter than the stamens; fruit a 2-celled dehiscent capsule, with many winged seeds.

A genus with 6 or 7 species occurred in Eastern Asia (After Wm. Forsyth prominent English horticulturist, 1737-1800)

1. **Forsythia giraldiana** Lingelsh.

Shrub 2 m high. Bark whitish gray. Leaves oblong, 8 cm long, 3.5 cm wide, acuminate apex, cuneate at base entire margin, dark green above, pale green glabrous beneath, coriaceous; petiole 1 cm flattened.

Distribution: Yunnan, and Kansu.

2. **Forsythia suspensa** Vahl

Small tree. Leaves obovate-oblong, 4-8 cm long, 2.5-4 cm wide, acute apex, broad cuneate at base, coarsely serrate above the middle, light green on both surfaces, glabrous; petiole 2-3 cm long, flattened, glabrous, purplish. Flowers whitish yellow, 4-parted; petals obovate, rounded at apex; calyx 4-lobed. Fruit an olive-shaped capsule, 2 cm long, 1.5 cm broad, tapering toward both ends, 2 - parted dehiscent, lenticelled, brown; pedicel 3 cm long, glabrous.

Distribution: Shantung, Shansi, Shensi, and Hupeh, at altitude 750 m.

3. Forsythia viridissima Lindl.

A branching shrub 1-2 m tall. Branches erect, angular, darkish brown. Leaves oblong or ovate-lanceolate, or altogether lanceolate, acute, serrated in the upper part, tapering into the petiole, penninerved. Peduncles short, axillary, solitary or in pairs from the sides of the branches, each araising from a bud-scale; calyx deeply cut into 4 oval, concave, membranaceous, green lobes; corolla large, yellow, rotate rather than campanulate, the tube very short, limb of 4 spreading, oblong, obtuse segments, every-where glabrous; stamens 2, inserted at the base of the corolla, shortly included; anther oblong; ovary nearly globose; style longer than the tube of corolla; stigma bifid.

Distribution: Kiangsu, Chekiang, Hupeh, Anhwei, and Hunan, at altitude 1000 m.

Genus (3) Syringa Linn.

Deciduous shrub or small trees; winter-buds ovoid, with several outer scales, the terminal bud often wanting; leaves opposite, petioled, entire or sometimes lobed or pinnate; flowers perfect, in terminal or lateral panicles on the branches of the previous season; calyx small, campanulate, 4-toothed, irregularly dentate or nearly truncate, small, persistent; corolla salver-shaped, with cylindric tube and 4 spreading valvate lobes; stamens 2, included or exserted; style with 2-lobed stigma, not exceeding the stamens; ovary 2-celled. Fruit an oblong, leathery loculicidal capsule, with 2 - winged seeds in each cell.

About 28 species in Asia and Southeast Europe. Ornamental shrubs with large and showly panicles of often fragrant flowers in spring and early summer.

1. Syringa emode Wall. et D. Don.

Shrub or small 1-6 m tall. Leaves obovate, 6 cm long, 3.5 cm wide, acute apex, obtuse-cuneate at base, entire margin; petiole 2 cm long, glabrous. Flowers purplish white in terminal panicles. Fruit a purplish cylindric capsule, 2-valved dehiscent.

Distribution: Yunnan, at altitude 4000 m.

2. Syringa giraldiana C. Schneider

Small shrub. Leaves ovate to rounded, 4 cm long, 2.5 cm wide, blunt-acute apex, broadly cuneate at base, entire margin, thin papery, dark green above, light green glabrous beneath; petiole 1 cm long, glabrous, purplish. Flowers in long terminal racemes; corolla pink, tubular, with 4-lobes.

Distribution: Kansu, Shensi, at altitude 2000 m.

3. Syringa julianae C. Schneider

Shrub 1-2 m high, densely branched, branchlets rather pubescent, finally becoming glabrous and blackish. Leaves ovate-elliptic, acute and cuneate, entire, shortly pubes-cent. Inflorescence, in small cymose, pedicel short; hairy; bracts linear, shorter than the calyx; flowers white-lilac-purple, calyx violet, glabrous; teeth rather distinct, wide-triangular, anthers violet, inserted little below the corolla-throat.

Distribution: Western Hupeh, at altitude 3300 m.

4. **Syringa komarowii** Schneid.

Shrub 3 m tall. Branchlets slender, purplish, lenticelled. Leaves oblong, 12 cm long, 5 cm wide, acuminate at apex, broad-cuneate at base, undulate entire margin, dark green above, pale glaucous and glabrous beneath, membranaceous; petiole 2 cm long, grooved, glabrous. Flowers in terminal cymes, long tubed with 4 small acute lobes, purplish. Stamens much longer than the corolla.

Distribution: Szechuan, at altitude 2400-2500 m.

5. **Syringa mairei** (Levl.) Rehd.

Shrub 4-6 m tall. Flower is rose-violet.

This speices is closely related to *S. potaninii* Schneid. which differs in the not dis-tinctly rugulose leaves, less densely pubescent branchlets and inflorescences, in the longer and narrower corolla-lobes and in the stamens inserted much below the mouth.

Distribution: Yunnan, at altitude 2600 m.

6. **Syringa microphylla** Diels

Shrub 2-3 m tall. Leaves very small, obovate, 2.5 cm long, 2 cm wide, acute apex, broad cuneate at base, entire margin. Flowers in terminal panicles, lavender color.

Distribution: Southern Kansu, at altitude 2780 m.

7. **Syringa oblata** Lindl.

Shrub 3 m tall. Leaves opposite, obovate, 5 cm long, 5.5 cm broad, acute apex, rounded or truncate at base, entire margin. Flowers in terminal panicle, white-pink long tubular, with 4 spreading lobes, glabrous. Fruit 2-valved woody capsule oblong, tapering toward both ends, 2.5 cm long, 6 mm broad; pedicel 1 cm long., glabrous.

Distribution: Shantung, Shansi, Hopei, Manchuria, and Kansu, at altitude 1300 m

Var. 1. **Syringa oblata** var. **alba** Rehd.

Shrub 6 m tall. Flowers white, fragrant, flower tubes much shorter and fruit smaller than that of the type.

Distribution: Kansu, at altitude 1375-2400 m.

Var. 2. **Syringa oblata** var. **hupehensis** Pamp.

Shrub with leaves much smaller than that of the type.

Distribution: Shensi, Hupeh, at altitude 1750 m.

Var. 3. **Syringa oblata** var. **giraldii** Rehd.

This variety differs from the type chiefly in its slendered and loose habit, less compact inflorescence, longer more acuminate capsules and smaller usually narrower and ovate leaves, truncate at base and finely soft-pubescent on sterile branchlets particularly on those near the base of the shrub and on young plants.

Distribution: Kansu, at altitude 1500–2000 m.

8. **Syringa pinnatifolia** Hemsl.

This species differs from other groups of the genus in its pinnate leaves and also in the terminal bud of the flowering branchlets developing into a leafy shoot. It is closely related to *S. vulgaris* and particularly to *S. persica* L. of that series, which has leaves partly entire and partly lobed or pinnatified with 3–7 lobes, but the flowering branches have no terminal bud.

Distribution: Szechuan, at altitude 2200–2400 m.

9. **Syringa potaninii** C. Schneider

Shrub 4 m high, with delicately slender branchlets. Leaf-blade varying from ovate to lanceolate from a rounded to a pointed base, acutely acuminate, 4–5.5 cm long, 1–2.5 cm broad, dark green above, finally glaucous beneath and more or less downy on the back particularly along the nerves, nerves 3 or 4 very slanting. Flower sweet scented, almost sessile in whorls of 5 to 10; corolla white, lobes linear, 4–5 mm long, recurved at length more or less twisted; anthers purplish or yellow or whitish, or the connective orange, inserted high up in the tube; ovary hairy on the top.

Distribution: Southwest Kansu, Tibet, and Szechuan, at altitude 2100–2700 m.

10. **Syringa pekinensis** Rupr.

Tree up to 12 m high. Bark gray; leaves obovate, 5 cm long, 3.5 cm broad, acute apex, broad-cuneate at base entire margin, deep green above, pale whitish beneath, membranaceous; petiole 3–4 cm long, purplish, glabrous. Flowers in terminal panicles, creamy white. Fruit cylindrical capsule, 2-valevd, 2 cm long, 3 mm broad, glabrous; pedicels 2 mm long.

Distribution: Kansu, at altitude 2600–3000 m.; Hopei, Shansi, and Hunan, at altitude 900–1500 m.

11. **Syringa reflexa** C. K. Schneider

Shrub 6 m tall. Leaves elliptic-oblong or obovate, 7–15 cm long, 3.5–8 cm wide, acute apex, cuneate to rotundate at base. Flowers fascicled forming a raceme; corolla purplish red, lobes white, 1 cm long. Fruit cylindrical, curved or subfusiform, apiculatous, 12–15 mm long, 2–3.5 mm across.

Distribution: Hupeh, at altitude 2000–2700 m.

12. **Syringa rugulosa** McKelvy

Shrub 2 m tall. Leaves ovate or elliptic, 3–7 cm long, 1.5–4 cm wide, acute or acuminate apex, cuneate at base, irregularly undulate margin, densely villose beneath; petiole 2–5 mm long, densely villose. Flowers fascicled in panicles, lateral and terminal, rachis densely villose; corolla tube 5–7 mm lcng, acute cupulary.

Distribution: Yunnan, at altitude 2600–3000 m.

13. **Syringa trichophylla** Tang

Small tree 1–2 m tall. Branchlets smooth, hirtellous, lenticellate. Leaves orbicular-ovate, ovate, acute or obutse apex, base rotundate.

This species is closely related to *S. microphylla* Diels in respect of small leaves and lateral inflorescences with similar flowers, but differs from the lateral species in the densely hirtellous branchlets, rachis of the inflorescence, petiole and leaves with inconspicuous nerves on both surfaces, except the basal nerves being sometimes conspicuous beneath. The insertion of stamens to the corolla-tube is a little higher than that of *S. microphylla.*

Distribution: Southern Shansi, at altitude 1200-1250 m.

14. **Syringa wardii** W. W. Sm.

Small tree or shrub, 3-5 m tall; branchlets dense incano-pubescent. Leaves suborbicular, or ovate, 1-2 cm long, and wide, rotundate or obtuse at apex, rotundate at base; petiole 2-3 mm long, minutely pubescent. Inflorescences 10 cm long, 7 cm broad, sublaxflorous, whitish pubescent or glabrescent.

Distribution: Yunnan, at altitude 3300 m.

15. **Syringa tomentella** Bureau et Franch.

Shrub 2-7 m tall. Branchlets whitish lenticelled. Leaves elliptic - lanceolate or elliptic-ovate, 6-12 cm long, 2-5.5 cm wide, rotundate acuminate apex, base cuneate, entire undulate margin, membranaceous. Inflorescence terminal, 15 cm long, 10 cm wide, glabrous, flowers white lilac-color, calyx glabrous, sparsely pilose at base.

Distribution: Szechuan, at altitude 2500-3300 m.

Var. 1. **Syringa tomentella** var. **glabricuscula** Rehd.

Shrub with straight, glabrous, lenticelled branchlets. Leaves obovate, 6 cm long, 3 cm wide, long acute apex, broad cuneate at base, undulate margin. Inflorescence in terminal panicles. Fruit cylindrical 2 cm long, 3 mm broad, glabrous, purplish, with persistent bracts.

Distribution: Szechuan, at altitude 2700-3000 m.

Var. 2. **Syringa tomentella** var. **rehderiana** Schneider

This variety differs from the type chiefly in the tomentulous branchlets, the densely large short-pilose inflorescence and in the leaves being slightly pubescent above and more densely so beneath particular on the veins.

Distribution: Szechuan, at altitude 3600-4000 m.

6. **Syringa sweginzowii** Koehne et Lingelsheim

Shrub 4 m high.

This species is distinguished from all the others by having extreme long lobes of the corolla, minutely puberulous inflorescence and in the nearly truncate calyx.

Distribution: Szechuan, at altitude 3600-4000 m.

7. **Syringa villosa** Vahl

Shrub, all glabrous except the leaves beneath. Leaves broad elliptic-ovate, obtuse at apex, base cuneate, rarely rotundate margins toward the base obscurely ciliate.

Flowers sessile, rose-lilac-color; corolla - tube variable in length, lobes oblong, obtuse, margin thick reflexed; stigma narrowly oblong, notched; ovary globose or cylindrical.

Distribution: Hopei, and Shansi, at altitude 1600-3000 m.

18. **Syringa yunnanensis** Franch.

Small tree 3 m high. Branchlets angulate and lenticelled; leaves oblong, 4 cm long, 2 cm wide, acute apex, cuneate at base, dark green above, glaucous below, finely serrate margin, membranaceous; petiole 15 mm long, purplish, glabrous. Flowers in dense large terminal panicles; white glabrous. Fruit cylindrical, 2 cm long, 4 mm in diameter, glabrous, 2-valved, brown; rachis angular purplish, glabrous.

Distribution: Yunnan, at altitude 4000 m.

Genus (4) Ligustrum Linn. (Privet)

Deciduous or evergreen shrubs or rarely trees; winter-buds ovoid, with about 2 outer scales. Leaves opposite, short-petioled, entire. Flowers perfect, white, small, in terminal panicles, rarely from lateral leafless buds; calyx campanulate, 4-toothed corolla salver-shaped, with usually short or sometimes elongated tube and with spreading lobes; stamens 2; enclosed or exserted; style cylindrical, not exceeding the stamens ovary 2-celled, the cells 2-ovuled. Fruit a 1-4-seeded berry-like drupe, normally black or bluish black; endocarp in one species dehiscent.

About 50 species chiefly in East Asia, ornamental shrubs or small trees mostly grown for their handsome foliage or for their often profusely produced white fragrant flowers the fruit of *L. lucidum* Aiton (女 貞) used in Chinese medicine.

1. **Ligustrum brachystachyum** Decne.

Small shrub with yellowish brown and lenticellate branchlets. Inflorescence in terminal and lateral racemes, light purple; rachis short, 2-3 cm long, brownish pubescent flowers white.

Distribution: Yunnan, Kinkiang.

2. **Ligustrum coryanum** W. W. Sm.

Shrub; branchlets densely rugolous. Leaves ovate or elliptic-lanceolate, 7 cm long 2.5 cm wide, obtuse attenuate and mucronate at the apex, base rotundate or subrotundate papery. Inflorescence terminal, panicles, 6 cm long, 4 cm broad; calyx cupulary, 1. mm long; corolla white, glabrous, 4-4.5 mm long, lobes oblong.

This species is affiliated to *L. rugosulo* Sm.

Distribution: Yunnan

3. **Ligustrum expansum** Rehder

Shrub 3 m high. Branchlets terete, sparsely pilose, lenticellate. Leaves elliptic oblong or lanceolate-oblong, 6-12 cm long, 2-3.5 cm wide, acuminate at apex, cuneate at base, minutely villose beneath. Inflorescence paniculate, 10-18 cm long, 12-16 cm wide, Flowers solitary, in axils, 2-3-fascicled, sessile.

Distribution: Hupeh, at altitude 1300 m.

4. **Ligustrum acutissimum** Koehne

Shrub 3 m tall. Branchlets dark gray, smooth, pubescent when young. Leaves elliptic-lanceolate, 5 cm long, 1.5 cm wide, acute apex, broad cuneate at base, slightly incurved margin, shining green above, glabrous except densely villose along the midrib below, lateral veins inconspicuous on both surfaces. Inflorescence small, in terminal racemes, purplish white, rachis 5-8 cm long, densely whitish villose. Fruit a globular berrylike drupe, 1 cm long, 6 mm in diameter, black.

Distribution: Kiangsu, Chekiang, Kiangsi, Fukien, Hupeh, Szechuan and Anhwei at altitude 1300 m.

5. **Ligustrum compactum** Hook. f.

Small tree 3-7 m tall. Leaves oblong or oblong-ovate, 9 cm long, 4.5 cm wide, blunt-acute at apex, obtuse cuneate at base, finely incurved margin, membranaceous; petiole 2-3 cm long flattened above, glabrous. Flowers white; fruit blue - black, globose, 1 cm long, 6 mm in diameter; peticels 6 mm long, pubescent.

Distribution: Hupeh, and Yunnan, Sikang, at altitude 1800-2000 m.

6. **Ligustrum delavayanum** Hariot

Shrub 2-3 m tall. Leaves elliptic-obovate, 4 cm long, 2 cm wide, blunt-acute apex, cuneate at base, entire subcoriaceous, olive-green on both sides, glabrous; petiole slender, 6 mm long, glabrous. Flowers in lateral panicles, creamy white, fragrant, glabrous.

Distribution: Szechuan, Yunnan and Tibet, at altitude 3300 m.

7. **Ligustrum formosanum** Rehder

Shrub, 4 m tall; branchlets dark gray, pubescent. Leaves obovate, 3.5 cm long, 2 cm wide, short acute at apex, broad-cuneate at base, entire margin, papery, glabrous on both surfaces; petiole 3 mm long, pubescent. Inflorescence in lateral and terminal panicles, white, rachis 7-9 cm long, densely pubescent.

Distribution: National Taiwan University, Taipei.

8. **Ligustrum henryi** Hemsl.

Tree 4 m high. Bark blackish.

This speices is closely related to *L. delavayanum* Kariot but differs in usually suborbicular or orbicular-ovate shining leaves, with usually rounded base, peduncled inflorescences and oblong often curved fruit.

Distribution: Hupeh, Szechuan, and Yunnan, at altitude, 300-1000 m.

9. **Ligustrum medium** Franch.

Shrub with slender branchlets. Leaves obovate, acute at apex, cuneate at base, entire margin. Flowers in terminal panicles. Fruit a berry-like drupe, blue-black.

Distribution: Taiwan.

10. **Ligustrum japonicum** Thunberg

Small tree 3 m tall; branchlets smooth gray, glabrous. Leaves obovate, 6 cm long, 4 cm wide, acute at apex, obovate to rounded at base, entire margin, thick coriaceous, dark green above, pale green glabrous below; petiole 2 cm long, flatened, brown, glabrous. Flowers in large terminal panicles, glabrous; pedicels 6 mm long, slightly pubescemt. Fruit globose 5 mm across.

Distribution: Kwangtung, and Kiangsi, at altitude 700 m.

Var. 1. Ligustrum japonicum var. **pubescens** Koidzumi

Small tree; branchlets dark gray lenticellate, pubescent when young. Leaves elliptic-ovate, 4 cm long, 2.8 cm wide, blunt-acute at apex, cuneate to obtuse at base, revolute margin, lustrous shining green above, pale green, glabrous beneath, subcoriaceous; petiole 12 mm long, reddish brown, glabrous. Flowers in terminal panicles; rachis angular, pubescent. Fruit immature brownish.

Distribution: Taiwan, Tsu-Tze* Lake, at altitude 800 m.

11. Ligustrum lucidium Aiton

Small tree 10 m to 18 m high; bark gray. Leaves ovate, 6-9 cm long, 3-4 cm wide, long-acute at apex, broad cuneate at base, margin revolute, glabrescent, coriaceous, lateral nerves 7-8, distantly arranged, inconspicuous on both surfaces. Flowers fragrant, in terminal panicles, white, glabrous, 20 cm long and broad; calyx cupulariform, inconspicuously denticulate; corolla-lobes ovate.

Distribution: Kiangsu, Chekiang, Anhwei, Hunan, Hupeh, Szechuan, Kweichow Yunnan, Kwangtung, Kwangsi, Fukien and Taiwan, at altitude 300-600 m; a common hedge plant; ripe fruit used in Chinese medicine.

12. Ligustrum mellosum Decaisne

Shrub 1-3 m tall. Branchlets brownish gray, lenticelled. Leaves elliptic-ovate 3 cm long, 2.5 cm wide, acute apex, broad cuneate or rotundate at base, margin enter, glabrous on both surfaces, coriaceous; petiole 3 mm long. Flowers in terminal panicles, white, glabrous. Fruit solitary, globose, 1 cm in diameter, black, with persistent calyx; pedicel 2 mm long, slender, brownish pubescent.

Distribution: Szechuan, at altitude 1000-1700 m.

13. Ligustrum myrsinites Dcne.

Shrub 1-2 m tall. Branchlets slender, dark gray, pubescent. Leaves small, elliptic, 1.5 cm long, 1 cm wide, acute apex, cuneate at base, entire margin; petiole 1 mm long, glabrous. Flowers in terminal panicles whitish creamy-color; fruit globose, 5 mm in diameter, reddish-brown.

Distribution: Yunnan, and Szechuan, at altitude 3400 m.

14. Ligustrum molliculum Hance

Shrub 3 m tall. Leaves oblanceolate, 5 cm long, 2 cm wide, acute apex, cuneate at base, entire margin, subsessile, subcoriaceous. Flowers in terminal racemes, white, glabrous.

Distribution: Hupeh, Kiangsi, and Anhwei, at altitude 1800 m.

15. Ligustrum pricei Hayata

Small tree 8 m tall. Leaves obovate or oblong, 4 cm long, 2 cm wide, acute apex, obtuse cuneate at base, margin revolute, glabrous on both surfaces, subcoriaceous. Fruits in terminal panicle, globose, 2 mm across, with persistent calyx.

Distribution: Taiwan, 2330-2930 m.

16. **Ligustrum quihoui** Carriere

Shrub 2 or 3 m tall. Branchlets gray smooth, lenticelled. Leaves lanceolate, 4 cm long, 1.5 cm wide, blunt at apex, narrow cuneate at base, entire. Flowers in terminal, panicles and in axillary racemes on the branchlets. Fruits small, globular, 2 mm long 1 mm in diameter, black with bluish blooms.

Distribution: Shensi, Hupeh, Kiangsu, and Anhwei, at altitude 1000-1330 m.

17. **Ligustrum sempervirens** Franch.

Shrub 2 m tall. Leaves elliptic, 3.5 cm long, 2.5 cm wide, acute toward both ends, entire, dark green above, pale green pubescent below, thick, coriaceous, nerves inconspicuous on both surfaces; petiole 2 mm long, glabrous. Fruits in terminal panicles, globular 5 mm in diameter, black.

Distribution: Yunnan, at altitude 2600-2800 m.

18. **Ligustrum sinense** Lour.

Shrub 2 m tall; branches densely pubescent. Leaves evergreen, chartaceous, obtuse at apex, dark green above, light green beneath, flowers white, fragrant.

Distribution: Kwangtung.

19. **Ligustrum myrianthum** Diels

Shrub 2-3 m tall. Leaves oblong, 4 cm long, 2 cm wide, acute apex, cuneate at base, margin revolute, coriaceous; petiole 2 mm long, pubescent. Flowers white. Fruit blue-black.

This species differs from all others in the inflorescences, which spring directly from the axils of the leaves of the previous year without leaves at their base or are borne, if the subpersistent leaves have fallen, on perfect leafless branches, is possibly only an abnormal form of *L. sinense* Lour.

Distribution: Kwangtung, Szechuan, Kwangsi, and Hupeh, at altitude 1700-2000 m

Var. 1. **Ligustrum myrianthum** var. **latifolium** S. Y. Hu

Shrub 7 m tall. Branchlets slender greenish gray, densely lenticelled, glabrous, pubescent when young. Leaves oblong-obovate, 7 cm long, 3.5 cm wide, acute apex, cuneate at base or obtuse obovate at base entire margin, glabrous on both surfaces; petiole 2 mm long, glabrous. Flowers in terminal panicles. Fruits black, berrylike, globose, 5 mm in diameter, pedicel 1 cm long, pubescent.

Distribution: Kwangsi, 1500 m.

20. **Ligustrum groffiae** Merr.

Shrub 3 m tall. Branchlets yellowish densely pubescent. Leaves elliptic-ovate 5 cm long, 2.5 cm wide, acute at apex, broad-cuneate at base, dark green above, yellowish pubescent below, margin entire, subcoriaceous; petiole 1 cm long, densely yellowish pubescent. Fruits in lateral panicles, globose 3 mm in diameter black, glabrous.

Distribution: Kwangtung and Fukien, at altitude 200–400 m.

21. **Ligustrum sinense** Lour.

Shrub 3 m tall. Bark grey. Leaves ellipitc or elliptic-oblong, 5 cm long, 2 cm wide, acute apex, broad-cuneate at base, entire margin, thick, coriaceous; petiole 2 mm long, pubescent. Flowers white, corolla-lobes longer than the tube. Fruits in terminal panicles, black, globose 2 mm in diameter.

Distribution: Kwangtung.

Var. 1. **Ligustrum sinense** var. **nitidum** Rehd.

Shrub 2–4 m tall; branchlets slender, gray, lenticelled. Leaves ovate-oblong, or oblong-lanceolate, 6 cm long, 3 cm wide. Flowers in axillary panicles, rachis pubescent. Fruits black, globose, 6 mm in diameter, glabrous, pedicel 2 mm long, pubescent.

Distribution: Hupeh, at altitude 1000–1900 m.

22. **Ligustrum rugosulum** W. W. Sm.

Shrub 2 m tall; branchlets gray, densely pubescent. Leaves oblong, 6 cm long, 2.5 cm wide, acute apex, broad cuneate at base, margin revolute, dark green above, pale green, brownish pubescent beneath, coriaceous; petiole 1 cm long, densely villose. Fruits in terminal panicles, globose, 2 mm in diameter.

Distribution: Szechuan, at altitude 1330 m. Kweichow and Yunnan, at altitude 2000 m.

23. **Ligustrum tibeticum** Decaisne

Shrub 3 m tall; branchlets grayish brown, lenticelled. Leaves oblong, 6 cm long, 3 cm wide, acuminate apex, broad cuneate at base, entire margin, dark green above, pale green glabrous beneath. Flowers in terminal panicles, white.

Distribution: Szechuan, and Tibet, at altitude 1000–1700 m.

Genus (5) Chionanthus Linn.(See orig. text page 926)

1. **Chionanthus retusus** Lindl. (See orig. text pages 926–927)

Var. 1. **Chionanthus retusus** var. **serrulatus** (Hay.) Koidz.

Order XXV Polemoniales

Family 62. Boraginaceae Lindl.

(See orig. text page 928)

Genus (1) Ehretia Linn. (See orig. text pages 928–929)

1. **Ehretia acuminata** R. Brown.

Ehretia thyrsiflora Nakai

Ehretia taiwaniana Nakai

Ehretia acuminata Hemsl.

Ehretia serrata Franch.

Tree 12 m tall, 30 cm in diameter; bark dark gray, rough. Leaves obovate or obovate-elliptic, 9 cm long, 6 cm wide, acuminate at apex, rounded or broad cuneate at base, margin serrate, usually red, lustrous dark green above, light green, glabrous beneath, subcoriaceous; petiole 2-3 cm long, flattened above, glabrous. Flowers small, in terminal panicles, rachis 10 cm long, 8 cm broad, pubescent. Fruits small, round, 1 mm in diameter, brownish yellow, glabrous.

Distribution: Kwangsi, Chekiang, Fukien, Taiwan, Shantung, Hunan, Hupeh, Kiangsi, Yunnan, Kiangsu, Kwangtung, Anhwei, Hainan and Ryukyu, at altitude 200-1500 m.

2. **Ehretia hanceana** Hemsley

Ehretia asperula

Small shrub or a climber on trees. Leaves ovate-oblong, 7 cm long, 4.5 cm wide, acute apex, broad-cuneate or rounded at base, entire margin, thick, lustrous shining green above, pale green, reticulated and with prominently elevated midrib and veins beneath, coriaceous; petiole 3 cm long, roughly glandular, brown. Flowers in terminal panicles, small, white, pubescent, rachis 10 cm long, brownish villose. Fruit red.

This species resembles *E. ovalifolia* Hance, but is readily distinguished by its muriculate branches and petioles and the strong venation of the leaves.

Distribution: Hainan.

3. **Ehretia wallichiana** Hook. f.

Shrub or small tree, 6-10 m tall. Leaves oblong, 9 cm long, 4.5 cm wide, acuminate apex, broad cuneate at base, finely serrate margin, membranaceous; petiole 12 mm long, glabrous. Flowers dull creamy yellow, in dense terminal panicles. Fruits globose, 6 mm long, 3 mm broad, somewhat ridged and pitted, black, glabrous.

Distribution: Yunnan, at altitude 2100 m.

4. **Ehretia corylifolia** Wright   (See orig. text page 929)

5. **Ehretia dicksonii** Hance (See orig. text pages 929-930)

Vars. 1. - 2. (See orig. text page 931)

. **Ehretia dunniana** Levl.

Shrub or small tree 3-10 m tall, branchlets slender, dark gray, pubescent. Leaves oblong, 12 cm long, 7 cm wide, acute apex, broad cuneate at base, entire revolute margin, lustrous dark green above, pale green, glabrous, except brownish pubescent along the midrib and veins beneath, subcoriaceous; petiole thick, round, 3-4 cm long, dark brown pubescent. Flowers white, small, in terminal panicles; calyx cupular, 4-lobed; corolla tubular, 4-lobed, glabrous; stamens longer than corolla. Fruit globose 1 cm long, 7 mm broad, slightly ridged, black, glabrous.

Distribution: Kwangsi, at altitude 1300-1700 m.

. **Ehretia longifolia** Champ. et Benth.

. **Ehretia laevis** Roxb.

Var. 1. **Ehretia laevis** var. **canarensis** C. B. Clarke

This variety differs from the type in having sessile flowers.

Distribution: Hainan.

Var. 2. **Ehretia laevis** var. **platyphylla** Merr.

Tree 8 m high. Branchlets thick, creamy-whitish color, smooth, glabrous, lenticelled. Leaves oblong, 8 cm long, 4.5 cm wide, rounded and spatulate at apex, tapering down from the lower half of the leaf to a narrow cuneate base, incurved margin, subcoriaceous; petiole 3 cm long, stout, thick, purplish brown. Flowers in terminal and lateral panicles, white.

Distribution: Hainan, at altitude 1650 m.

9. **Ehretia formosana** Hemsl.

Ehretia resinosa Hance

Tree with pubescent branchlets. Leaves obovate, 10 cm long, 7 cm wide, acute apex, rounded at base, entire margin, dark green above, pale green, with dense brownish villose along the midrib and veins and prominently elevated reticulation beneath, coriaceous; petiole 3 cm long, brownish pubescent, round thick, stout. Flowers in terminal panicles, white; rachis 8 cm long, densely whitish villose.

Distribution: Taiwan, Kao-Hsiung.

10. **Ehretia microphylla** Lamark   (See orig. text page 932)

11. **Ehretia volubilis** Handel-Mazz. (See orig. text page 934)

Family 63. Scrophulariaceae Lindl.

(See orig. text page 934)

Key to closely related woody genera

A. Stamens surpassing the top of corolla; calyx entire, tight-fitting --- (2) *Wightia* Wallich

AA. Stamens not surpassing the top of corolla; calyx with 5 outstanding lobes.

B. Flower buds oblong and slender, with stigma appearing bilamellate at this stage of immaturity; corolla not longer than 3 cm ----- (3) *Shiuyinghua* J. Paclt.

BB. Flower buds broadly ovate and robust, with stigma appearing punctiform at this stage of immaturity; corolla at least 3 cm long, mostly much longer. --- (1) *Paulownia* Sieb. et Zucc.

Genus (1) Paulownia Sieb. et Zucc. (See orig. text pages 934-935)

1. **Paulownia elongata** S. Y. Hu

Tree 8-10 m tall; branchlets reddish-gray, glabrous, lenticelled, brownish pubescent when young. Leaves simple, opposite, obovate with elongated tip, 18-22 cm long, 12-1 cm wide at the broadest portion below the middle. (The largest leaves 30 cm long broad) acute at the apex, cordate or auriculate and 7-nerved at base, undulate margin, membranaceous, dark green above, light green glabrous except brownish pubescent along the midrib and primary veins below; petiole 10-20 cm long, rounded, somewhat grooved above, pubescent. Flowers lavender-purple, in large terminal panicles; calyx tubular, 5-lobed, covered with yellowish hairs; corolla funnel-shaped, 7 cm long, 2 cm broad, 4-unequal-lobed, covered with long branched yellowish hairs outside, black dotted inside; stamens 4, filaments 2-3 cm long, shorter than the pistil. Fruit a woody capsule, 3 cm long, 2 cm in diameter, 2-parted dehiscent, olive-shaped, with tapering points towards both ends, brown, glabrous, set on the persistent, 5-lobed thick and yellowish hairy calyx; pedicels 3 cm long, yellowish pubescent; seeds numerous, oblong, 1 mm across, samara-like, winged.

Distribution: Honan, Shantung and Hupeh, at altitude 300 m.

. **Paulownia fargsii** Franch. (See orig. text pages 935-937)

. **Paulownia fortunei** Hemsl.

. **Paulownia glabrata** Rehder

A deciduous sparsely branched tree, about 15 m high; young shoots borne in the axils of the fallen leaves on the old branches below the inflorescences, pale green, slightly viscid, clothed with short stellate hairs and both short and gland-tipped ones. Leaves opposite, petiolate, blade ovate from a sub-truncate or more or less deeply cordate base, acutely acuminate, 12.5-30.5 cm long, 7.5-17.5 cm broad, dull green, viscid pubescent above with hairs of 3 kinds, medium sized stellate hairs being mixed with smaller pointed or gland-tipped simple ones, more coarsely viscid pubescent beneath; petiole 3.5-9 cm long, viscid pubescent. Inflorescence terminal pyramidal panicle, 22.5-37.5 cm long, about 2/3 as broad, lateral branches all distinctly pedunculates, the upper ones 3-flowered, the lower ones rising at a rather higher angle, once or twice branched, 7-many-flowered; pedicels thickened upwards into the base of the calyx and tomentose with the buff-colored stellate hairs in the upper part; calyx at first cupshaped and finally becoming campanulate by the lobes curving outwards, 1.2 cm long, finely buff-tomentose outside; corolla descending funnel-shaped, with wide-spreading limb, pale lilac with yellow throat, glandular hirsute with spreading hairs outside, tube 4.5 cm long, bent forwards somewhat flattened from the back and front, stamens didynamous, the front pair longer, ovary ovoid, conical, about 6 mm long, white and glabrous in the lower third, densely glandular pubescent in the upper 2/3, bilocular, with a thick planoconvex axile placenta in each locule, narrowly ovate in outline, with a narrow line of attachment, and covered with numerous ovules; style lilac, 2.5 cm long, glandular, the uppermost 1.5 mm enlarged and bent forwards, minutely bifid, with lobes almost touching.

This species is closely related to *P. tomentosa* (Thunb.) Steud. but it differs by having leaves sparsely pubescent, calyx minutely tomentose, lobes obtuse and acute, corolla lilac-colored, bignoide-bilabiate.

Distribution: Western China.

5. Paulownia shensiensis Y. Y. Pai

Tree 15 m tall, with spreading branches; branchlets shortly pubescent, densely s
when young. Leaves rather large, ovate to ovate-oblong, 11–29 cm long, 10–21 c
broad, acuminate, cordate, entire or sometimes 3–5-lobed, pilose sparsely glandula
above, densely pilose along the veins towards the margin, stellate pubescent and glan
ular beneath; petiole short-pubescent, 3–13 cm long, panicle pyramidal, 16–28 cm long
rachis yellow-tomentose, calyx densely yellow-tomentose on both sides, 12–14 mm lon
divided to 2/3, lobes oblong-ovate, acute; corolla funnel-form-campanulate, glandula
pilose outside, glabrous inside, light purple, limb 5-lobed, 5 cm in diameter, tube 3
cn long, 1.5 cm in diameter, slightly narrow at the base, lobes rounded, 2 cm in dia
meter, spreading, glandular-pilose on both surfaces, stamens didynamous, shorter th
the tube; anthers divergent; style longer than the filaments, glandulose at the bas
stigma clavate; ovary ovoid, glandulose. Capsule ovoid, beaked, 3 cm long, 2.5
broad, locucidally dehiscent; seeds oblong, 2 mm long, with hyline wings, notched
both ends, 4 mm long, 2 mm broad.

Distribution: Shensi, at altitude 1200 m.

6. Paulownia thyrsoidea Rehder

Paulownia kawakamii T. Ito   (See orig. text page 938)

7. Paulownia tomentosa (Thunb.) Steudel   (See orig. text pages 939–940)

Var. 1. Paulownia tomentosa var. lenata Schneid.

Genus (2) Wightia Wallich (See orig. text page 940)

Deciduous trees, hemi-epiphytic pseudo-lianas, or epiphytic shrubs, twigs with pi
Leaves opposite, entire, coriaceous, glabrous or sparsely to densely clothed w
stellate indumentum, at least the lower surface with conspicuous glands mostly near
nerve-axils; midrib sulcate above, thyrses or racemes lateral (sometimes termina
showy; flowers rarely solitary axillary. Large, purple, mauve to pale ros
pubescent or tomentose; calyx campanulate, truncate-entire or lobed, corolla spars
hairy to tomentose; tube curved; upper lip erect, 2-lobed, lower spreading, 3-lob
stamen didynamous, exserted, with hairy base; staminode absent, anthers bisifix
oblong, sagittate; cells parallel, splitting length-wise, introrse, style long, with
curved tip; stigma seemingly simple, slightly knob-shaped, consisting of 2 appres
lobes, ovary 2-celled, each cell with one axile length-wise (line-wise) fastened, th
placenta, broadened in the middle and covered with ovules, in the central part (in cro
section) appearing parted. Capsule ovoid to lanceolate, septicidal numerous-seed
valves separating from the persistent, placentiferous axis, winged by 1/4 sept
seeds oblong, winged, all round, without a sinus; albumen 0; embryo straight.

About 6 species distributed from the Himalayan Region to South China and West
Malaysia.

1. Wightia elliptica Merr.

Tree 7 or 8 m high; branchlets thick, stout, rough, dark gray, lenticelled. Leaves oblong-obovate, 20-25 cm long, 12-14 cm broad, blunt-obtuse at apex, obtuse or rounded, pseudo-5-nerved at the base, entire, lustrous dark green above, pale green, glaucous and bluish-pubescent beneath, lateral nerves 2-3 pairs, alternatively winding up in 45 degrees towards the margin, prominently elevated and with bluish hairs along the midrib and veins beneath, coriaceous; petiole 2-4 cm long, flattened and grooved when dry, glabrous. Flowers in terminal racemes, purplish pink, calyx campanulate, 5-lobed, pubescent.

Distribution: Yunnan, at altitude 1550 m.

2. **Wightia speciosissima** (D. Don) Merr.

Wightia gigantea Wall.

Tree 7-10 m high. Branchlets dark gray, rough, prominently lenticelled. Leaves oblong, 18-23 cm long, 9-12 cm wide, blunt-acute at apex, obtuse-cuneate at base, entire margin, dark green above, pale green, glabrous beneath, coriaceous; petiole 3 cm long, grooved, purplish-pubescent. Inflorescences in terminal cyme-racemes, darkish pink; calyx campanulate, 5-lobed, purplish-pubescent; corolla tube 2.2 cm long, 1 cm broad, purplish hairy outside, pistil 4 cm long, curved. Fruit oblong, 2 cm long, 7 mm broad, brownish pubescent, mucronate pointed, pedicel 1 cm long, brownish pubescent.

Distribution: Yunnan, at altitude 1250-2100 m.

nus (3) **Shiuyinghua** J. Paclt.

Leaves simple opposite. Inflorescences in axillary cymose; calyx lobes 5, membranaceous or chartaceous; corolla gamo-petalous quinquefidal tubular, lobes sub-unequal in length; stamens didynamous, inserted in the tubes; stigma bilamellatous.

The only species of this genus has charaters which do not permit one to classify this plant as a member of the genus *Catalpa*. This may be summarized as follows:

1. The conspicuous dimorphic shape of leaves, which are broadly ovate (cordate) in the axil position and elliptically lanceolate in the abaxial position on flowering branches.

2. The flowering branches which bear both leaves and almost laterally situated (axillary) loose cymes of flowers, as in *Paulownia fortunei* (Seem.) Hemsl. and substantially all other species of *Paulownia*. In *Catalpa*, the inflorescences are formed terminally and correspond to racemes or true panicles (Thyrses).

3. The calyx which is 5-lobed and patelliform, as in *Paulonia* but not *Catalpa* in which the calyx is gamosepalous, splitting into two strongly convex lobes at anthesis. Also the lower buds are generally oblong in *Paulownia silvestrii*, instead of showing the typically subglobular shape of the bud of Catalpa.

Shiuyinghua silvestrii (Pamp. et Bonati) J. Paclt.

Paulownia silvestrii Pamp. et Bonati (See orig. text pages 940-941)

Catalpa silvetsrii (Pamp. et Bonati) S. Y. Hu

A tree with simple opposite obovate or oblong leaves. Inflorescences in axillary cymes; calyx 5-lobed, corolla gamo-petalous; stamens didynamous, inserted on th

corolla tube, not surpassing the top of the corolla, which is not longer than 3 cm.

Distribution: Hupeh, near Han-Kiang at altitude 700 meters.

Family 64. Bignoniaceae Pers.

(See orig. text page 941)

Genus (1) Catalpa Linn. (See orig. text pages 941-942)

1. **Catalpa bungei** C. A. Mey (See orig. text page 942)

Var. 1. Catalpa bungei var. intermedia Pamp.

Small tree, differs from the type in its leaves being much small

and more triangular shaped, with broad-acute leaf-base instead of co

date or rounded.

Distribution: Hupeh, at altitude 700 m.

2. **Catalpa duxclouxii** Dode

3. **Catalpa fargesii** Bureau (See orig. text pages 943-945)

form 1. Catalpa fargesii f. ducolouxii (Dode) Gilmour

Tree 10 m tall. Branchlets slender, brownish pubescent. Leav

obovate triangular, truncate at base. Flowers in terminal racemes, r

color or purple color

Distribution: Yunnan, at altitude 1800-2000 m.

4. **Catalpa ovata** D. Don (See orig. text page 945)

5. **Catalpa vestita** Diels (See orig. text pages 945-946)

6. **Catalpa bignonioides** Walt. (See orig. text pages 946-947)

7. **Catalpa tibetica** G. Forrest

Shrub. Leaves ovate, glabrous above, pubescent beneath. Flowers creamy-yello

calyx 8-9 mm long, lobes rotundate; corolla 2.5 cm long. Fruit 13-18 cm long, 1.2-

cm broad, cylindrical, slightly curved.

Distribution: South-East Tibet.

Order XXIV Gentianales

Family 65. Rubiaceae Juss.

Key to the tree genera of the family Rubiaceae (See orig. text page 947)

Genus (1) Adina Salisbury (See orig. text page 948)

1. **Adina asperula** Handel-Mazz. (See orig. text page 948)

2. **Adina globiflora** Salisbury

Shrub 3 m tall. Branchlets gray to dark gray, slender, smooth, lenticellate, gl

rous. Leaves oblanceolate, 5 cm long, 2 cm wide, acute-acuminate at apex, cuneat

base, dark shining glabrous green above, pale green, glabrous below, subcoriace petiole 6 mm long, glabrous. Flowers solitary, axillary of leaves, a globular head, 1 cm in diameter, yellowish white, stamens 5 inserted at the corolla of the male flowers, corolla tubular-funnel-form, glabrous, filaments filiform, 8 mm long; pedicels 2-3 cm long, glabrous, set on the top of the peduncle of the same thickness and enclosed by 4 bracteoles, 2 of them oblong-lanceolate and 2 of them linear, sitting opposite in alternations, peduncles of almost the same length of the pedicels.

Distribution: Kwangtung, and Fukien, at altitude 730 m.

3. **Adina metcalfii** Merr.

Shrub 2 m tall. Leaves chartaceous, petiolate, glabrous, oblong, or obovate-oblong, 8-13.5 cm long, 3-5 cm wide, acuminate at apex, long-attenuate at base, olive-viridis green and minutely impressed above, pale green, with elevated 8-10 lateral nerves beneath, margin anastomsing; petiole 1.5-2.5 cm long. Inflorescences terminal, 8 cm long, glabrous, flower-head 1.5 cm in diameter, peduncles terete, 2.5-5.5 cm long, glabrous; flowers yellow, fragrant, corolla lobes 5, ovate, glabrous, 1 mm long; stamens inserted on the corollas; anthers apiculate; style exserted, 8 mm long, stigma subglobose.

Distribution: Kwangsi.

4. **Adina mollifolia** Hutchinson (See orig. text page 949)

5. **Adina pilulifera** (Lam.) Franch.

Var. 1. Adina pilulifera var. tonkinensis (Pit.) Merr.

Small tree 1-2 m tall. Branchlets dark - brownish gray, smooth, glabrous, lenticellate. Leaves lanceolate or oblanceolate, 7-13 cm long, 2-4 cm wide, attenuate-acuminate at apex, acute-cuneate at base, undulate margin, dark shining green above, pale yellowish green, reticulated and prominently elevated midrib and veins, glabrous beneath, nerves 4 pairs on each side of the midrib, subcoriaceous; petiole 1 cm long, glabrous. Inflorescence in terminal panicles of yellowish globular heads, 1 cm in diameter; pedicels 3-4 cm long, set on the tops of the peduncles, enclosed at the base by the reduced leaves; pedicels and peduncles of the same length and slightly brownish pubescent. Flowers white, or yellow fragrant.

Distribution: Kwangtung, Hainan, Kwangsi and Yunnan, at altitude 2000 m.

6. **Adina racemosa** Miq. (See orig. text page 950)

7. **Adina rubella** Hance

Genus (2) Emmenopterys Oliv. (See orig. text pages 951-952)

1. **Emmenopterys henryi** Oliv. (See orig. text page 952)

Index to Families and Genera

中華民國六十二年十一月出版

中國森林植物學續篇

定價新台幣５００元

著作者　李　　　順　　　卿

出版兼
發行者　中　華　林　學　會

印刷者　金　剛　工　藝　社

Forest Botany of China
Supplement

by
Shun-ching Lee

November 30, 1973

Published by the Chinese Forestry Association

Taipei (100), Taiwan, China

Price : US $ 15.00